W9-AYF-917

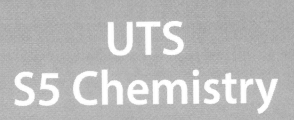

UTS
S5 Chemistry

Development Team

Authors

Cheri Smith
Yale Secondary
School District 34 Abbotsford

Gary Davidson
School District 22 Vernon

Megan Ryan
Walnut Grove Secondary
School District 35 Langley

Chris Toth
St. Thomas More Collegiate
Burnaby, British Columbia

Program Consultant

Lionel Sandner
Edvantage Interactive

Customization by

Jennifer Howell
UTS, Toronto

EDVANTAGE
● ●● INTERACTIVE

COPIES OF THIS BOOK MAY BE
OBTAINED BY CONTACTING:

Edvantage Interactive

E-MAIL:
info@edvantageinteractive.com

TOLL-FREE FAX:
866.275.0564

TOLL-FREE CALL:
866.422.7310

UTS S5 Chemistry
Copyright © 2016, Edvantage Interactive

All rights reserved. No part of this publication may be reproduced or transmitted in any form or by any means, or stored in a database or retrieval system, without the prior written permission of Edvantage Interactive.

ISBN 978-1-77249-176-0
University of Toronto Schools – 2017 Version

Care has been taken to trace ownership of copyright material contained in this text. The publishers will gladly accept any information that will enable them to rectify any reference or credit in subsequent printings.

Vice-President of Marketing: *Don Franklin*
Director of Publishing: *Yvonne Van Ruskenveld*
Design and Production: *Donna Lindenberg*
Proofreading: *Eva van Emden*
Editorial Assistance: *Rhys Sandner*
Index: *Noeline Bridge*
Photos: *p. 33, K. Jung; p. 34, Bureau international des poids et mesures (BIPM)*

The AP Big Ideas at the beginning of each chapter are quoted from AP Chemistry: Course and Exam Description, revised edition, effective Fall 2013, published by the College Board, New York, NY. Advanced Placement, AP and College Board are registered trademarks of the College Board.

QR Code — What Is This?

The image to the right is called a QR code. It's similar to bar codes on various products and contains information that can be useful to you. Each QR code in this book provides you with online support to help you learn the course material. For example, find a question with a QR code beside it. If you scan that code, you'll see the answer to the question explained in a video created by an author of this book.

You can scan a QR code using an Internet-enabled mobile device. The program to scan QR codes is free and available at your phone's app store. Scanning the QR code above will give you a short overview of how to use the codes in the book to help you study.

Note: We recommend that you scan QR codes only when your phone is connected to a WiFi network. Depending on your mobile data plan, charges may apply if you access the information over the cellular network. If you are not sure how to do this, please contact your phone provider or us at info@edvantageinteractive.com

Contents

1 Thermodynamics

By the end of this chapter, you should be able to do the following:

- Use representations and models to predict the sign and relative magnitude of the entropy change associated with chemical or physical processes
- Predict, either quantitatively or qualitatively, whether or not a physical or chemical process is thermodynamically favored by determination of the signs of both $\Delta H°$ and $\Delta S°$, and calculation or estimation of $\Delta G°$ when needed
- Determine whether a chemical or physical process is thermodynamically favorable by calculating the change in standard Gibbs free energy
- Explain why a thermodynamically favored chemical reaction may not produce large amounts of product based on consideration of both initial conditions and kinetic effects, or why a thermodynamically unfavored chemical reaction can produce large amounts of product for certain sets of initial conditions

By the end of this chapter, you should know the meaning of these **key terms**:

- endergonic
- exergonic
- Gibbs free energy
- microstates
- positional disorder
- second law of thermodynamics
- thermal disorder
- thermodynamically favorable
- third law of thermodynamics

Thermodynamics is the study of heat and temperature and their relation to energy and work. It includes concepts such as entropy and pressure.

Chapter 1 Prep Questions

1. Indicate whether each of the following changes is endothermic or exothermic:
   (a) Barbecuing a steak

   (b) Freezing a tray full of water to make ice

   (c) Neutralizing an acid spill with baking soda

   (d) Making a grilled cheese sandwich

   (e) Lighting a barbecue igniter

   (f) Condensing water on a mirror

2. Convert the following ΔH notation equations into thermochemical equations using the smallest whole number coefficients possible:
   (a) $\frac{1}{2}\,C_3H_8(g) \rightarrow \frac{1}{2}\,C_3H_8(l)$ $\Delta H = -175$ kJ/mol

   (b) $Li(s) + \frac{1}{2}\,CaCl_2(aq) \rightarrow LiCl(aq) + \frac{1}{2}\,Ca(s)$ $\Delta H = -362$ kJ/mol

   (c) $2\,B(s) + 3\,H_2O(g) \rightarrow B_2H_6(g) + 3/2\,O_2(g)$ $\Delta H = 762$ kJ/mol

   (d) $\frac{1}{2}\,P_4(s) + 3\,Cl_2(g) \rightarrow 2\,PCl_3(s)$ $\Delta H = -613$ kJ/mol

   (e) $NH_3(g) + 3/2\,N_2O(g) \rightarrow 2\,N_2(g) + 3/2\,H_2O(l)$ $\Delta H = -505$ kJ/mol

   (f) $\frac{1}{2}\,Fe_3O_4(s) + \frac{1}{2}\,CO(g) \rightarrow 3/2\,FeO(s) + \frac{1}{2}\,CO_2(g)$ $\Delta H = 9$ kJ/mol

3. Convert the following thermochemical equations into ΔH notation using the smallest whole number coefficients possible.
   (a) $C(s) + 2\,H_2(g) + \frac{1}{2}\,O_2(g) \rightarrow CH_3OH(l) + 201$ kJ/mol

   (b) $\frac{1}{2}\,Cu(s) + \frac{1}{2}\,H_2(g) + \frac{1}{2}\,O_2(g) \rightarrow \frac{1}{2}\,Cu(OH)_2(s) + 225$ kJ/mol

   (c) 389 kJ/mol $+ \frac{1}{2}\,Sb_4O_6(s) + 3\,C(s) \rightarrow 2\,Sb(s) + 3\,CO(g)$

   (d) 56 kJ/mol $+ NO_2(g) \rightarrow NO(g) + \frac{1}{2}\,O_2(g)$

        © Edvantage Interactive 2016

(e) $PCl_3(g) + \frac{1}{2}O_2(g) \rightarrow Cl_3PO(g) + 286$ kJ/mol

(f) $F_2(s) + \frac{1}{2}O_2(g) \rightarrow OF_2(g) + 22$ kJ/mol

4. Use the equations in question 3 to answer the following questions:
   (a) How much energy would be released during the formation of 4 mol of methanol?

   (b) How many moles of nitrogen dioxide could be decomposed through the use of 168 kJ of energy?

   (c) Is more energy absorbed or released during the formation of Cl_3PO gas from PCl_3 and O_2 gas?

   (d) What is the ΔH value for the decomposition of OF_2 gas into its elements?

   (e) How much energy is required to decompose 1 mol of copper(II) hydroxide?

5. Does the following potential energy diagram represent an endothermic or an exothermic reaction? What is ΔH for this reaction?

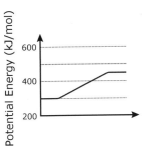

Progress of the reaction

6. What is ΔH for this reaction?

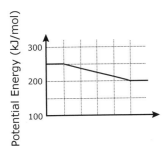

Progress of the reaction

1.1 Law of Thermodynamics and Calorimetry

Warm Up: Calorimetry – The Measurement of Heat Transfer

The apparatus shown here is used to collect data that produces the graph shown. The hot plate supplies kinetic energy to the water sample the entire time. As heat is absorbed, the temperature rises. What is that energy being used for in each labeled region on the graph? Approximately how much energy was used for each change to the water? (Region A is completed as a sample.)

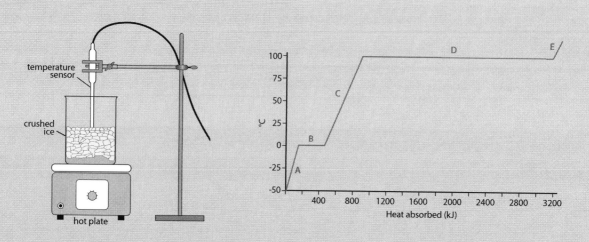

Region	Energy is used to...	Energy required
A	Heat solid water from –50 to 0°C	Approximately 180 kJ of energy
B		
C		
D		
E		

Study regions A, C, and E. What three things might cause the energy required to differ?
1.
2.
3.

Study regions B and D. What two things might cause the energy required to differ?
1.

2.

© Edvantage Interactive 2016

Internal Energy, State Functions, and Conventions of Thermochemistry

Chemical energy is one of our most important energy sources. It can be converted into the heat, mechanical, and electrical energy we all use to operate a myriad of devices every day. The origin of this chemical energy lies in the position and motion of atoms, molecules, and subatomic particles. The various types of energies that combine to give the total **internal energy, E**, of a sample of matter include the following:

- *electronic* — kinetic energy of moving electrons and most significantly, potential energy due to electron-nuclei interactions
- *rotational* — kinetic energy due to rotation of a molecule about its center of mass
- *vibrational* — kinetic energy due to vibrations of atoms within the molecule
- *translational* — kinetic energy associated with gas molecules as they move linearly from one place to another

Many physics textbooks use the symbol U for internal energy.

Thermodynamics is the study of energy changes and the laws governing the conversion of heat into other forms of energy. Thermodynamics is primarily concerned with *macroscopic properties*, those you can see or measure such as temperature, pressure and volume, so a detailed analysis of the of the sources of internal energy is not necessary in this discussion. The mathematical study required is better covered in a university physical chemistry course. The reaction or physical system we are studying will be called the **system** and the rest of the universe will be called the **surroundings**. Additionally, we will refer to certain quantities as *state properties or functions*.

A **state function** or *state variable* is a property that depends on the current "state" of a system. These are conditions such as its volume, temperature, pressure and composition. State functions are independent of the pathway taken to reach the state. Common state functions include internal energy and enthalpy changes. ΔE does not depend on how a change in internal energy takes place, but on the difference between the initial and final internal energy of the system.

Functions that do depend on the pathway taken to reach the current state may be referred to as **pathway dependent functions** or *process quantities*. Conditions such as work and heat are examples.

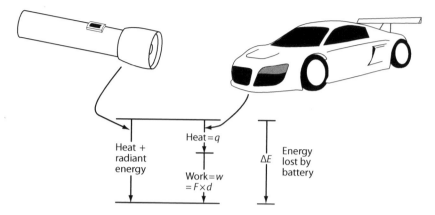

Figure 1.1.1 *A flashlight (left) and a remote control car (right) are operated using the same two D-cell batteries. The total change in internal energy is the same. However, the work done and heat and radiant energy released differ. This indicates that ΔE (internal energy equal to q + w) is a state function while q (heat) and w (work) are not.*

Sign conventions apply to most state functions. Energy leaving or produced by the system has a negative sign. Energy entering the system from the surroundings has a positive sign. If the volume of a system decreases, ΔV will be negative. If the volume of a system increases or expands, ΔV will be positive. When work involves gases being formed or consumed in a chemical reaction, the change in the number of moles of gas, Δn, should be shown as negative if the total number of moles of gas decrease and positive if they increase.

The **First Law of Thermodynamics** is really as far as we'll go in thermochemistry. The first Law is really just a restatement of our old friend, Antoine Lavoisier's **Law of Conservation of Mass**.

Energy cannot be created or destroyed. It can be converted from one form to another.

$$\Delta E_{universe} = \Delta E_{system} + \Delta E_{surroundings} = 0$$

Two common methods for transferring energy between a system and its surroundings are heat, q, and work, w. The first law is sometimes expressed by defining internal energy as the sum of heat and work.

Although there are many different types of work, we will discuss primarily electrical work in our unit on electrochemistry and the work done by expanding gases. Work done by expanding gases is called, **pressure-volume work** and is equal to the product of the constant external pressure, P, exerted on the expanding gas and the change in volume, ΔV. Work can be converted to the familiar unit of energy, the joule, with the conversion factor 101.3 J equivalent to 1 litre-atmosphere.

$$\Delta E = q + w \text{ and } w = -P\Delta V$$

© Edvantage Interactive 2016

Sample Problem — Internal Energy, Heat, and Work Relationships

A potato cannon propels a piece of potato using the energy from a combusted fuel. The fuel performs 948 J of work on the potato and heats the cannon with 1355 J of heat. Calculate ΔE for the combustion process.

What to Think about	How to Do It
1. Determine the q and w values. 2. Assign the appropriate signs.	The cannon gets hot; therefore the reaction is exothermic. So $q = -1355\,J$ Work is done BY the system; therefore the reaction is exergonic. So $w = -948\,J$
3. Use $\Delta E = q + w$ to determine the answer.	$\Delta E = -1355\,J + (-)948\,J = -2303\,J$

Practice Problems — Internal Energy, Heat, and Work Relationships

1. A system absorbs 392 J of heat while the surroundings do 234 J of work on the system. What is the change in internal energy for the system?

2. A system releases 475 J of heat as it performs 524 J of work on the surroundings. Calculate ΔE for the system.

3. A system released 64 kJ of energy as its internal energy increased by 43 kJ. Did the system do work on the surroundings or was work done on the system? How much work was involved?

The ideal gas law, $PV = nRT$, can be rearranged to show that the ratio of the product of a gas sample's pressure and volume to the product of the gas sample's number of moles, n, and Kelvin temperature, is a constant. That ratio, R, only changes with the units of pressure selected. It may be 0.0821 L·atm/mol·K or 62.4 L·mmHg/mol·K for example. Multiplication of the first value by 101.3 J/L·atm gives 8.31 J/L·atm. The ideal gas law will be used extensively in the chapter on gases. It can also be used in the following derivation for pressure-volume work situations.

$$\Delta E = q - P\Delta V \text{ and since } PV = nRT \text{ then } \Delta E = q - \Delta nRT$$

When heat is absorbed or released from a chemical system and the external pressure is constant, the heat released or absorbed is equal to the enthalpy change of the process, $q_p = \Delta H$. For reactions that do not involve gases or a change in the number of moles of gas, the pressure-volume work done is zero, the $P\Delta V$ term becomes zero and $\Delta H = \Delta E$.

Sample Problem — Enthalpy vs. Internal Energy at Constant Pressure

Consider the following reaction occurring in an open container.

$$CaCO_3(s) \rightarrow CaO(s) + CO_2(g) \quad \Delta H° = 571 \text{ kJ/mol}_{rxn}$$

(i)   How do q and ΔH compare under these conditions?
(ii) Calculate the change in internal energy.
(iii) How would ΔE and ΔH compare if both values were given to two significant figures?

What to Think About	How to Do It
1. Consider external pressure conditions. In this case, external pressure is constant and is equal to atmospheric pressure.	Under these conditions, $q_p = \Delta H$
2. $\Delta E = q + w$ where $q_p = \Delta H$ and $w = -P\Delta V = -\Delta nRT$ $\Delta E = \Delta H - \Delta nRT$ where $\Delta n = +1$ mole of gas	$\Delta E = 571 \text{ kJ/mol}_{rxn} -$ $\left(\dfrac{1 \text{ mol}}{\text{mol}_{rxn}}\right)\left(\dfrac{0.00831 \text{ kJ}}{\text{mol·K}}\right)(298 \text{ K})$ $= 571 \text{ kJ/mol}_{rxn} - 2.48 \text{ kJ/mol}_{rxn}$ $= 569 \text{ kJ/mol}_{rxn}$
3. Round the given ΔH and calculate ΔE to two significant figures.	$\Delta E = \Delta H = 570 \text{ kJ/mol}_{rxn}$ Note: There is only 2.48 kJ difference per mole of gas formed (or consumed). To two significant figures, the values are virtually the same.

Practice Problems — Enthalpy vs. Internal Energy at Constant Pressure

1. Consider the imaginary reaction: $A(s) + 2 B_2C_3(aq) \rightarrow 4 D(g) + 3 EF_4(g)$
    The reaction's ΔE value is measured as 442.26 kJ/mol$_{rxn}$. What is $\Delta H°$?

2. A cylinder equipped with a piston expands against an external pressure of 1.04 atm. A combusted fuel causes an expansion from 0.243 L to 1.650 L with the emission of 1.553 kJ of heat. What is ΔE for this process? Note: Be sure to include the conversion factor 101.3 J/L•atm where necessary.

3. To inflate a weather balloon you must increase its volume from 0.58 L (nearly empty for a weather balloon) to a full volume against an external pressure of 1 atm exactly. The process requires 22.632 kJ of work. What is the volume of the balloon?

© Edvantage Interactive 2016

Specific Heat, Heat Capacity, Heat of Fusion, and Heat of Vaporization

Recall that heat is the exchange of thermal energy between a system and its surroundings. This exchange is caused by a temperature difference and the energy always moves from a region of high temperature to a region of lower temperature.

Temperature is a measure of the average *thermal energy* in a sample of matter.

Heat is the energy *transferred* from one body to another because of a difference in temperature.

The quantity of energy required to change the temperature of a particular sample of material is the sample's **heat capacity**. It is symbolized by an upper case letter **C**. Heat capacity is generally measured in units of **J/°C**. For the most part in chemistry, it is much more useful to consider a material's **specific heat capacity**, sometimes simply referred to as **specific heat.** This is represented by a lower case letter **c**.

Specific heat capacity, *c*, is the quantity of *heat* required to raise the temperature of a *specific quantity* of a substance by *one degree celsius*.

For water, $c = 4.180$ J/g°C $= 1$ cal/g °C

Substance	J/g°C
Elemental Solids	
Aluminum	0.900
Beryllium	1.830
Cadmium	0.230
Copper	0.387
Germanium	0.322
Gold	0.129
Iron	0.448
Lead	0.128
Silicon	0.703
Silver	0.234
Other Solids	
Brass	0.380
Glass	0.837
Ice (–5°C)	2.090
Marble	0.860
Wood	1.700

Substance	J/g°C
Liquids	
Alcohol (ethyl)	2.400
Mercury	0.140
Water (15°C)	4.180
Gas	
Steam (100°C)	2.010

Table 1.1.1 *Specific heat capacity values for common substances*

Quick Check

Examine Table 1.1.1.

1. How do the specific heat capacities of metals compare to that of liquid water?

2. If equal masses of water and iron were exposed to the same heat source, which one would reach the temperature of 100°C first?

3. Consider equal masses of iron and water at 100°C. Which would cool to room temperature more quickly?

Regions A, C, and E of the Warm Up graph indicate that not only does the identity of a substance influence its specific heat capacity, but so does the state. Comparing regions A and C of the graph in the Warm Up, we can see that for a 50°C increase in temperature, ice required about 100 kJ but liquid water required about 200 kJ over the same temperature increment. Liquid water took two times the energy required to warm the same amount of ice. As indicated in Table 3.1.1, liquid water's specific heat capacity c = 4.18 J/g °C, while solid water, or **ice has c = 2.09 J/g°C**. Interestingly, gaseous water or **steam has c = 2.01 J/g°C,** which is close to that of ice. The high heat capacity of liquid water is responsible for the relatively constant temperatures of coastal and island cities such as Vancouver, San Francisco, Honolulu, and Shanghai.

Changes of State

Frozen water molecules vibrate but can't change places.

Water molecules in a liquid state slide over each other.

Water molecules in a gaseous state move randomly throughout their container.

Figure 1.1.2 *The states of matter*

Regions B and D of the Warm Up graph indicate the significant amount of energy required to change the state of matter without raising its temperature. This energy is required to overcome the attractive forces holding the substance's molecules together in the solid or liquid state. These attractive forces are generally referred to as **intermolecular forces (IMFs)**. There are three types, increasing in strength for a particular substance:

- **London dispersion forces** — a weak force that involves instantaneous induced poles of opposite charge on the molecules
- **dipole-dipole forces** — a slightly stronger force caused by permanent poles of opposite charge produced by differences in atoms' electronegativity at the opposite ends of bonds in a molecule
- **hydrogen bonds** — the strongest IMF is due to very strong dipoles produced by bonds where hydrogen is attached to one of the three smallest diameter, largest electronegativity elements – N, O, or F

As water melts and evaporates (or boils), its weak London dispersions forces and its strong dipole-dipole/hydrogen bonds must be overcome to allow freedom of motion as the water changes state.

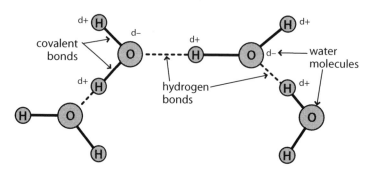

Figure 1.1.3 *Hydrogen bonds form between the slightly negative partial charges on oxygen atoms on one water molecule and the slightly positive partial charges on hydrogen atoms on another water molecule. The partial charges, indicated with a lower case delta (δ), are due to the higher electron density on the side of the covalent bond closest to the more electronegative oxygen atom and the lower electron density on the hydrogen side of the bond in the water molecule. Note the difference between intermolecular H-bonds and intramolecular covalent bonds.*

The energy required to overcome these intermolecular forces is called the **heat of fusion** or **heat of vaporization** depending on whether the substance is undergoing melting or evaporation.

The **heat of fusion** is the quantity of *heat* required to change a particular *quantity* of a pure solid *at its melting point* into a *liquid*.

$$H_{fusion} \text{ of water} = 334 \text{ J/g}$$

© Edvantage Interactive 2016

The **heat of vaporization** is the quantity of *heat* required to change a particular *quantity* of a pure liquid *at its boiling point* into a gas.

$$H_{vaporization} \text{ of water} = 2250 \text{ J/g}$$

Note that regions B and D in the Warm Up graph indicate the difference between H_{fusion} and H_{vap} for water. The heats of fusion and vaporization are independent of the temperature change as there is no temperature change. The temperature remains constant during a change of state. This is because all energy is being used to overcome the intermolecular forces between the particles. During cooling, heat is released as intermolecular forces are formed. The magnitude of energy needed for the change is the same, but the value of the energy is given a negative number to indicate that energy is released. The energy required for the phase change from gas to liquid is called **heat of condensation** and energy required for the phase change from liquid to gas is **the heat of solidification**. A heat change that occurs at constant temperature is referred to as **latent heat**.

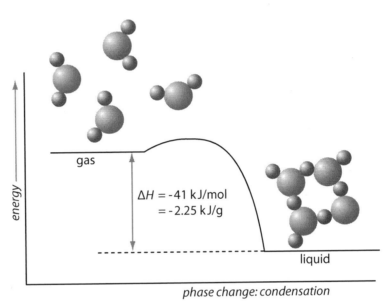

phase change: condensation

Figure 1.1.4 *Hydrogen bonds form as gaseous water condenses to become liquid. Note that $H_{vap} = -H_{cond}$ and the magnitude of the energy is the same, but the sign is reversed and the value may be expressed in units of kJ/mol or kJ/g. There will be a difference of 18.01 times when comparing the value in kJ/mol to that in kJ/g as this is the mass of one mole of water.*

The amount of heat absorbed or released during a cooling or heating process can be calculated by considering the specific heat capacity, the mass, and the temperature change. Where a state change is included, only the mass and the heat of vaporization and/or fusion need be considered. Heat is represented by q.

For a temperature change: $q = mc\Delta T$

For a state change: $q = H_{fus}m$ or $q = H_{vap}m$

For these calculations, the system is assumed to be entirely insulated from the surroundings so that no heat can enter or leave the system from or to any outside heat source or sink.

Sample Problem — Calculation of Heat Changes

Calculate the heat required to change 50.0 g of water at 25.0°C into steam at 120.0°C.

What to Think About	How To Do It

What to Think About

1. It is helpful to represent the energy changes with a sketch.

2. Apply the appropriate equations to each portion of the problem.

3. Calculate the heat required to accomplish each change. *Take care* with substitution into the equations. It is easy to confuse the *c* values for different states and the *H* values for fusion and vaporization.

4. Sum the *q* values for each portion. Take care with significant figures and units, rounding only at the end and ensuring all of the energy values have the same units before adding them together

5. Remember that when summing or subtracting the final answer is rounded to the *least precise place value*.

How To Do It

25.0°C ———————— 100.0°C 120.0°C

q_{water} q_{vap} q_{steam}

$q_{water} = mc_{water}\Delta T$
$q_{vap} = H_{vap}m$
$q_{steam} = mc_{steam}\Delta T$

$q_{water} = 50.0\ g \times \dfrac{4.18\ J}{g\cdot°C} \times 75.0°C$

$q_{water} = 15\ 675\ J$ (3 sig figs)

$q_{vap} = \dfrac{2250\ J}{g} \times 50.0\ g = 112\ 500\ J$ (3 sf)

$q_{steam} = 50.0\ g \times \dfrac{2.01\ J}{g\cdot°C} \times 20.0°C = 2010\ J$ (3 sf)

Note: All ΔT values are treated as (+).

$15\ 675\ J + 112\ 500\ J + 2010\ J$
$130\ 185\ J = 1.30 \times 10^5\ J = 130.\ kJ$

(In this case, the thousands place is the least precise.)

Practice Problems — Calculation of Heat Changes

1. Aluminum metal is commonly used to determine the temperature of different portions of a Bunsen burner flame. Calculate the heat required to completely melt a 0.325 g piece of aluminum wire beginning at a room temperature of 22.5°C. The melting point of aluminum is 660.3°C and its heat of fusion is 398 J/g. Refer to Table 1.1.1 for the specific heat capacity.

2. A piece of iron metal initially at a room temperature of 21.5°C is left on the window ledge in the lab on a sunny day. It absorbs 862.4 J of heat and warms to 32.5°C. What is the mass of the iron? See Table 1.1.1.

3. A 75.45 g sample of silicon initially at 20.5°C absorbs 1326 J of heat. What is the final temperature of the sample? See Table 1.1.1.

4. Calculate the heat required to change a 55.00 g ice cube at –15.0°C into steam at 125.0°C. (Hint: There should be five different *q* values in your calculation.)

The First Law of Thermodynamics – Energy is Always Conserved

Heat calculations involving physical processes which consider the system and the surroundings, for example, where something hot is added to something cold, require a generalized version of the First Law of Thermodynamics expressed simply as the Law of Conservation of Energy.

$$\text{heat lost} + \text{heat gained} = 0$$
$$\text{or}$$
$$(-)\,\text{heat lost} = \text{heat gained}$$

Where *heat lost* is the *total* heat lost by the hotter substance and *heat gained* is the *total* heat gained by the colder substance.

As with the previous calculations, we are assuming the interacting systems are thermally insulated from the rest of the universe.

Sample Problem — Calculating Heat Changes in Systems Combining Hot and Cold

If 50.0 g of water at 15.0°C is added to 40.0 g of water at 85.0°C, what is the final temperature of the system?

What to Think About

1. A sketch along the lines of the one shown in the previous sample problem is helpful; however, the final temperature is represented by a variable such as *T*. Again, *remember* to consider all ΔT values to be positive.

2. Apply the appropriate equations to each portion of the problem. Note that for simplification, we are working with the absolute values of q_{hot} and q_{cold}.

3. Calculate the heat required to cause each change. *Take care* with substitution into the equations. In addition to different temperature values, there are different masses to keep track of.

4. A bit of algebra, involving first, distribution through the brackets…then collection of like terms…and finally solving for *T*…provides an answer.

5. Notice the answer *makes sense* as it is between the two initial temperatures and closer to the cold one as the cold mass was greater.

How To Do It

15.0°C   *T*°C   85.0°C

50.0 g q_{cold} q_{hot} 40.0 g

Since $q_{cold} = q_{hot}$,
then $mc\Delta T_{cold} = mc\Delta T_{hot}$

and $m_{cold}c_{water}(T - 15.0)$
$= m_{hot}c_{water}(85.0 - T)$

$50.0\ g \times 4.18\ J/g°C \times (T - 15.0) =$

    $40.0\ g \times 4.18\ J/g°C \times (85.0 - T)$

So,

$= 209T - 3135 = 14\,212 - 167.2T$

$\therefore\ 376.2T = 17\,347$

$\therefore\ T = 17\,347/376.2 = 46.1°C$

Note: The significant figures in the final answer are based on the original problem rather than each step in the algebra. Sig figs apply to measurements, not algebra.

Practice Problems — Calculating Heat Changes in Systems Combining Hot and Cold

1. A 29.65 g solid gold earring at 33.5°C falls from your ear into a thermally isolated 245.0 mL cup of 65.5°C coffee. Use information from the Table 1.1.1 to determine the final temperature of the earring and the coffee when they reach the same temperature (*thermal equilibrium*). Assume the specific heat capacity and the density of the coffee is the same as those of water and that the final temperature will be between the initial temperatures.

2. A brass ball bearing with an initial temperature of 95.55°C is placed in a thermally insulated beaker containing 125.0 mL of water (assume d_{water} = 1 g/mL exactly) at 20.50°C. When the two substances reach thermal equilibrium, their final temperature is 26.55°C. What is the mass of the brass ball bearing?

3. What is the final temperature when a 348.00 g block of ice at −44.5°C is added to 95.00 g of steam at 125.5°C in an insulated system? Assume the final result will be liquid water.

Coffee Cup Calorimetry

Most people are familiar with the Calorie unit of heat measurement in the context of the labels of virtually all prepared foods we purchase in supermarkets today. Government regulations have required nutrition facts labels on all prepared foods since 1994 in the United States and since 2003 in Canada (see Fig 1.1.7).

The caloric content on these labels is in Calories (Cal) or "big C" calories. A food calorie reported on Nutrition Facts labels is actually equivalent to 1000 cal or 1 kcal.

1 Cal = 1000 cal = 1 kcal = 4.184 kJ
= the energy to warm 1 g of water by 1 Celsius degree
(or 1 Kelvin degree as the *change* is the same)

Where does the information on the caloric content of foods values come from? How is it measured? The caloric content is measured with a device called a **calorimeter**. The first calorimeter was designed and used by Antoine Lavoisier and Pierre Laplace in the early 1780s. They used the mass of ice melted by a chemical change as a measure of the amount of heat produced during the change. In laboratories everywhere, we now use the temperature change produced in a given mass of water as a measure of the amount of heat produced or absorbed during a physical or chemical change occurring in the calorimeter. If the change is exothermic, energy is released and the temperature increases; if it is endothermic, energy is absorbed from the water and the temperature decreases.

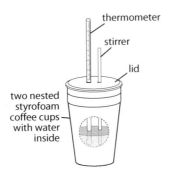
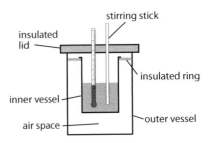

Figure 1.1.5 *Calorimeters. The nesting of two cups, one inside the other, provides reasonable insulation in a coffee cup calorimeter. A thermos with a sealed thermometer and stirrer is similar but slightly more sophisticated. A layer of air provides excellent insulation.*

The principle behind the calorimeter is once again, the law of conservation of energy, a simplified expression of the first law of thermodynamics.

> heat lost + heat gained = 0
>
> Hence, heat lost, or gained, by the physical or chemical change in the calorimeter *equals* heat gained, or lost, by the system—usually an aqueous solution—inside the calorimeter.

Simple calorimeters may be used to collect data for the situations in the practice problems in the first half of this section. Additionally, they may be used to determine heats of reaction and heats of solution.

Sample Problem — Determining the Enthalpy Change of an Aqueous Solution

A neutralization reaction between 50.0 mL of 1.00 mol/L HCl and 50.0 mL of 1.00 mol/L NaOH is performed with constant stirring at a room temperature of 20.50°C. The temperature rises to 27.13°C. Assume the solution volumes are additive and that the density and specific heat capacity of the final solution is the same as those values for water. Assume also that only a negligible amount of heat is absorbed or released from or to the surroundings. Calculate the molar enthalpy change (ΔH_{neut}) for this reaction.

What to Think About	How To Do It
1. Determine a balanced chemical equation for the process. As the reactants are present in "equimolar" quantities, neither is in excess, so we can assume both will be consumed completely.	$HCl(aq) + NaOH(aq) \rightarrow NaCl(aq) + H_2O(l)$ $50.0 \ \text{mL} \times \dfrac{1.00 \ \text{mol}}{1000 \ \text{mL}} = 0.0500 \ \text{mol each of HCl and}$ NaOH will be completely converted to 0.0500 mol of NaCl dissolved in water.
2. Calculate the heat absorbed by the 100.0 mL of resulting solution. Remember to treat all temperature changes as positive values.	Since $q = mc\Delta T$, $q = \left(100.0 \ \text{mL} \times \dfrac{1 \ g}{\text{mL}}\right) \times \dfrac{4.18 \ J}{°C} \times (27.13°C - 20.50°C)$
3. Since *heat lost = heat gained*, the heat absorbed by the solution must equal the heat released by the neutralization reaction.	$= 100.0 \ g \times \dfrac{4.18 \ J}{g·°C} \times 6.63°C$ $= 2770 \ J$

Continued on next page

Sample Problem — *Continued*

What to Think About

4. Finally, relate the heat released to the quantity of reactant neutralized. Since the reaction takes place at constant pressure, $q = \Delta H$.

5. Once the magnitude has been calculated, check the *sign*. In this case, heat was *released* from the neutralization to the solution, thus the reaction must be *exothermic* and so a *negative* sign is appropriate.

How To Do It

$q_{solution} = q_{neutralization} = 2770 \text{ J}$

$\Delta H = \dfrac{2770 \text{ J}}{0.0500 \text{ mol}} \times \dfrac{1 \text{ kJ}}{1000 \text{ J}} = 55.4 \text{ kJ/mol}$

$\Delta H_{neutralization} = -55.4 \text{ kJ/mol}$

Practice Problems — Determining the Enthalpy Change of an Aqueous Solution

1. When 500.0 mL of 2.00 mol/L $Ba(NO_3)_2$ solution at 22.50°C is combined in a coffee cup calorimeter with 500.0 mL of 2.00 mol/L Na_2SO_4 solution also at 22.50°C, a white precipitate forms and the temperature of the mixture rises to 25.60°C. Assume the calorimeter materials absorb only a negligible quantity of heat and the final solution's density and specific heat capacity are identical to those of water. Calculate the molar enthalpy of precipitation of $BaSO_4(s)$.

2. A coffee cup calorimeter contains 50.00 g of water at 20.73°C. When 2.13 g of NH_4NO_3 pellets are stirred into the water, the temperature falls to 17.41°C. Assume the heat capacity of the resulting solution is the same as that of water and that no energy is absorbed or released from or to the surroundings. Calculate the molar enthalpy of dissolution of ammonium nitrate, a chemical commonly used in the production of cold packs.

3. Given: $2 HCl(aq) + Ba(OH)_2(aq) \rightarrow BaCl_2(aq) + 2 H_2O(l) + 118 \text{ kJ/mol}_{rxn}$. Calculate the heat released when 300.0 mL of 0.500 mol/L hydrochloric acid is combined with 100.0 mL of 1.00 mol/L of barium hydroxide. Assume that the temperature of both solutions is initially 21.55°C. The final mixture has a mass of 400.0 g and a heat capacity the same as that of water with negligible heat "leakage" to or from the system. What is the final temperature of the mixture?

Constant Volume Calorimetry — The Bomb Calorimeter

A bomb calorimeter is more sophisticated than a coffee cup or even a thermos-type calorimeter. It is often used to determine the heat change involved in a chemical reaction, including reactions that do not occur in solution such as combustion reactions. The reaction chamber is surrounded by a metal jacket that sits inside a known mass of water at a known temperature. The prototype bomb calorimeters had extremely precise thermometers extended from inside the bomb with a sliding magnifying lens to assist in reading the temperature to the third decimal place. Modern calorimeters provide the temperature as a digital read out.

A known quantity of reacting substance is placed into the bomb and the bomb is sealed inside the calorimeter. A spark or electric current from a DC source supplies the activation energy to initiate the reaction. The maximum temperature of the system is recorded. As in the coffee cup or thermos calorimeter, it is assumed that no energy is lost or gained by the system apart from the energy produced or required by the reaction.

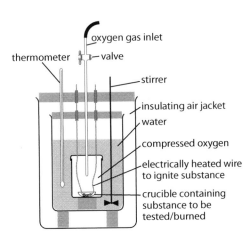

thermometer
oxygen gas inlet
valve
stirrer
insulating air jacket
water
compressed oxygen
electrically heated wire to ignite substance
crucible containing substance to be tested/burned

Figure 1.1.6 *A bomb calorimeter measures the heat released at constant volume, q_v or ΔE, which is extremely close to ΔH.*

Sometimes calculations involving bomb calorimeters require an overall q or ΔH value to be determined by calculating a value for the water inside the calorimeter *and* a value for the metal jacket using the specific heat capacities and the masses of each. These may be added together.

Other times, an overall *heat capacity* in units of J/°C may simply be used for the entire calorimeter and all of its components. Some references call this value a **calorimeter constant**. It indicates the number of joules the entire calorimeter must absorb or release in order to change its temperature by one Celsius (or one Kelvin since it is a *change*) degree.

Nutrition Facts

Serving Size 1 piece (219g)
Servings per container 6

Amount per serving	
Calories 520	Calories from Fat 240

	% Daily Value *
Total Fat 27g	41%
Saturated Fat 12g	61%
Cholesterol 255mg	86%
Sodium 1110mg	46%
Total Carbohydrates 29g	10%
Dietary Fiber 1g	5%
Sugars 1g	
Protein 39g	

Vitamin A 20%	•	Vitamin C 4%
Calcium 15%	•	Iron 25%

* Percent Daily Values are based on a 2,000 calorie diet. Your daily values may be higher or lower depending on your calorie needs:

	Calories	2,000	2,500
Total Fat	Less than	65g	80g
Saturated Fat	Less than	20g	25g
Cholesterol	Less than	300mg	300mg
Sodium	Less than	2,400mg	2,400mg
Total Carbohydrates		300g	375g
Dietary Fiber		25g	30g

Calories per gram:
Fat 9 • Carbohydrates 4 • Protein 4

Figure 1.1.7 *Nutrition Facts label for half a dozen "breakfast muffins" — not exactly a healthy way to start the day.*

Sample Problem — Calculating the Heat of a Combustion Reaction with a Bomb

Anthracene is a unique aromatic compound composed of three fused benzene rings. It is a component of coal tar and can be used to make several different anthroquinone dyes. A 5.12 g sample of anthracene, $C_{14}H_{10}$, was burned in an iron "bomb" having a mass of 1896 g. The bomb was immersed in 2.900 L of water inside a calorimeter. The initial temperature of all parts of the system was 20.80°C and the final temperature was 36.60°C. Calculate the molar heat of combustion of anthracene.

What To Think About	How To Do It
1. First find the heat absorbed by the calorimeter bomb *and* the water. Specific heat capacities of iron and water may be found in Table 1.1.1. Since water has a density of 1 g/mL, 2.900 L has a mass of 2.900 kg or 2900. g.	$q_{Fe\,Bomb} = mc_{Fe}\Delta T =$ $1896\ \cancel{g} \times \dfrac{0.448\ J}{\cancel{g}\text{°C}} \times (36.60\text{°C} - 20.80\text{°C})$ $= 13\ 421\ J = 13.4\ kJ$
2. Assuming no heat loss to the surroundings, the total heat given off by the combustion must equal the sum of the heat absorbed by the water and the heat absorbed by the calorimeter jacket.	$q_{water} = mc_{water}\Delta T =$ $2900.\ \cancel{g} \times \dfrac{4.18\ J}{\cancel{g}\text{°C}} \times (36.60\text{°C} - 20.80\text{°C})$ $= 191\ 528\ J = 192\ kJ$
3. Since $q_{lost} = -q_{gained}$, a negative sign is required.	$q_{total} = q_{calorimeter} + q_{water}$
4. The molar heat of combustion is q/n as dictated by unit analysis.	$q_{gained\ by\ calorimeter\ +\ water} = 192 + 13.4 = 205\ kJ$ $q_{combustion} = q_{lost\ by\ reaction\ system} = -q_{gained}$
5. The negative value is consistent with a combustion reaction.	$= -205\ kJ$ $\dfrac{205\ kJ}{5.12\ \cancel{g}} \times \dfrac{178.0\ \cancel{g}}{1\ mol} = 7130\ kJ/mol$

Sample Problem — Using the Calorimeter Constant

The brand new treat Chemical Candies contains only 12.0 Calories per serving according to the Nutrition Facts label. The Chemical Candies are tested by placing one serving in a bomb calorimeter like the one in Figure 1.1.6 and burning them in $O_2(g)$. The temperature rises from 21.431°C to 27.079°C. The heat capacity of the calorimeter is 8.808 kJ/°C. What is the actual caloric content?

What To Think About	How To Do It
1. Determine the amount of energy required to increase the temperature of the calorimeter by the stated amount.	$(27.079\cancel{\text{°C}} - 21.431\cancel{\text{°C}}) \times \dfrac{8.808\ kJ}{\cancel{\text{°C}}}$ $= 49.75\ kJ$
2. Convert the energy unit from kJ to Calories where 1 Cal = 1 kcal = 4.184 kJ.	$49.75\ \cancel{kJ} \times \dfrac{1\ Cal}{4.184\ \cancel{kJ}} = 11.89\ Cal$

© Edvantage Interactive 2016

Practice Problems — Calculating the Heat of a Combustion Reaction

1. A 3.00 g chunk of coal, C(s), was burned entirely to produce $CO_2(g)$ in a copper bomb. The mass of the bomb was 2.000 kg and the mass of water in which the copper bomb was immersed was 2.778 kg. The initial temperature of the system was 21.00°C and the final temperature was 29.30°C. Calculate the heat of formation of $CO_2(g)$. See Table 1.1.1 for the specific heat capacity of copper.

2. Toluene, C_7H_8 may be tri-substituted with nitro groups, $-NO_2$, to form the explosive, trinitrotoluene or TNT. A 750.0 mg sample of toluene liquid was placed in a bomb calorimeter with excess oxygen. The heat capacity of the calorimeter was 22.53 kJ/°C. When the calorimeter was fired, the combustion of the toluene caused the temperature to increase from 23.002°C to 24.415°C. Calculate ΔH for the reaction:

   $C_7H_8(l) + 9\ O_2(g) \rightarrow 7\ CO_2(g) + 4\ H_2O(l)$.

3. (a) A standard calibration reaction is used to determine the heat capacity, C, of a bomb calorimeter. The temperature increases 1.275°C because of the input of 14 580 J of energy. What is the heat capacity of the calorimeter?

   (b) Use the data in the table of Standard Enthalpy of Formation (in section 3.2) to calculate the $\Delta H_{combustion}$ of methane, CH_4 (g).

   (c) A sample of 1.754 g of methane is combusted in the calorimeter calibrated in part (b). If the initial temperature of the calorimeter is 20.754°C, what final temperature should be attained?

Energy, Our Environment, and the Future

Fossil fuels have many advantages as an energy source. They are convenient to use, are found in many countries in the world, and are reasonably portable to areas that need them. On the other hand, they are non-renewable and they produce pollution. Despite the problems associated with fossil fuels, we show little inclination to give them up or reduce their use any time soon.

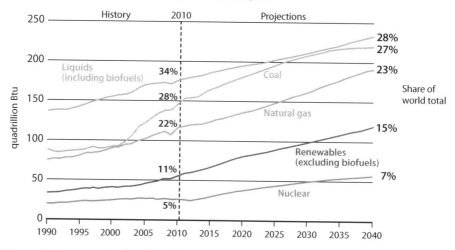

World energy consumption by fuel

Figure 1.1.8 *Past and projected world energy consumption by fuel type*

Nuclear energy has shown promise, but comes, of course, with many dangers of its own. The 2011 event in Fukushima, Japan, is only the most recent of several major nuclear accidents that have occurred in the past few decades (Figure 3.1.9). Even when nuclear reactors function successfully, there is still the problem of storage for radioactive by-products. The fallout from nuclear accidents can be long lasting and widespread.

Figure 1.1.9 *Map of distribution of nuclear fallout from the Fukushima, Japan, reactor accident in March of 2011.*

Renewable energy sources and biofuels show some of the best promise for the future. Wind power, hydro, and solar energy are some of the least polluting forms of energy production. Later we will spend an entire chapter studying the application of electrochemical reactions to the production of energy in batteries and fuel cells.

As we move further into the 21st century the chemistry students of today may be responsible for changing the shape of the graph in Figure 3.1.8 completely. Maybe you will be responsible for some of the changes!

© Edvantage Interactive 2016

1.1 Review Questions

1. Complete the following table about symbols and sign conventions in the equation, $\Delta E = q + w$.

Symbol	Description	Sign	Meaning	Sign	Meaning
			System gains thermal energy		
	Work				Done by the system
ΔE		+			

2. Indicate whether each of the following is a state function or is pathway dependent:
   (a) A plane's total mileage meter

   (b) A plane's altimeter (indicates altitude)

   (c) Work

   (d) ΔH

   (e) Your monthly cell phone bill

3. Calculate the change in internal energy for a gas that absorbs 28.5 J of heat and then performs 16.4 J of work.

4. A gas expands from a volume of 1.4 L to 6.7 L against an external pressure of 1.00 atm. During this process, 565 J of heat is transferred from the surroundings to the gas.
   (a) How much work has been done?

   (b) What is the change in internal energy of the system?

5. Though we are unaware of it at rest, breathing requires work. A 70 kg man likely has an "empty" lung volume of 2210 mL.
   (a) If 50.7 J of work is required to take a single breath against a constant external atmospheric pressure of 1.00 atm, what is the man's "full" lung volume?

   (b) During exercise, the elastic lungs expand to a "full" volume of 5250 mL. How much work is required to take a single breath during exercise?

6. The following is a molecular representation of a state change occurring inside a piston-cylinder assembly against a constant external pressure of 1.05 atm.

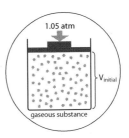
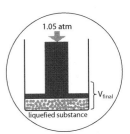

Indicate whether each of the following is (+), (–), 0 or impossible to determine.
Justify your answer in each case.
(a) w_{system}

(b) q_{system}

(c) ΔE_{system}

7. The diagram shows one mole each of the metals copper, iron, zinc, and aluminum. The quarter is included for size comparison only.

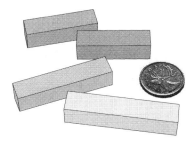

(a) Use the pictures and a table of molar masses to rank the samples from heaviest to lightest.

(b) Each bar is placed in boiling water for half an hour and then removed. Given the data in Table 1.1.1 and the heat capacity of zinc is 390. J/kg°C, rank the bars in order from most to least time required to cool to room temperature.

8. What mass of glass can be heated from room temperature (20.0°C) to 75.5°C if 1550 J of heat is added? See data in Table 3.1.1.

9. A restaurant worker places a 1 kg plastic jug full of water into the industrial fridge in the kitchen. At the same time, he places an empty 1 kg aluminum jug into the same fridge. One hour later one of the objects is much colder than the other. Which is colder and why?

10. In biology class, students sometimes hear of "high energy phosphate bonds." In general, how do phosphate bonds produce energy?

11. Copper can just be melted at the tip of the outer blue cone in a Bunsen burner flame where the temperature is 1085°C. How much energy is required to completely melt a 250.0 mg piece of copper wire? Assume the initial temperature of the wire was 22.5°C and the heat of fusion of copper is 205 J/g.

12. When combusted, 5.00 g of anthracite coal gives off 153 kJ of energy. What mass of coal is needed to heat a cauldron of 50.0 L water from 26.5°C until it just boils away, so that all the water vaporizes, but none of the steam is heated above 100.0°C?

© Edvantage Interactive 2016

13. Determine the final temperature when 145.0 g of ice at –17.5°C is placed into 335.0 g of water at 72.5°C in an insulated system. Assume everything is liquid water when the final temperature is reached.

14. A 45.05 g sample of a metal of unknown identity at 96.5°C is placed into 81.5 mL of water in an insulated container at a room temperature of 19.5°C. If the final temperature of the system is 34.5°C, what is the specific heat capacity of the metal? Use Table 1.1.1 to identify the metal.

15. A 45.0 g piece of silver metal at 15.5°C was placed into an insulated 0.345 g sample of steam at 106.0°C. The steam immediately condensed and coated the piece of silver metal with water. What is the final equilibrium temperature of the system?

16. (a) The following samples, both at 21.00°C, are mixed in a coffee cup calorimeter: 100.0 mL of 2.00 mol/L sodium hydroxide and 100.0 mL of 3.00 mol/L hydrochloric acid. After the reaction, the final solution's temperature rises to 34.40°C. Assuming no loss of heat to the surroundings and/or the calorimeter and a density and specific heat capacity for the final solution equal to those of water, calculate the molar enthalpy of neutralization for the reaction. (Hint: The acid and base are *not* in equimolar quantities.)

(b) Suppose the process in (a) were repeated with double the molarity of sodium hydroxide used.
(i) How would this affect the change in temperature (be specific)?

(ii) How would this affect the amount of heat, q, produced? Explain.

(iii) How would this affect the molar enthalpy of neutralization for the reaction? Explain your answer.

17. The enthalpy of dissolution of cesium hydroxide may be communicated as follows:

$CsOH(s) \rightarrow Cs^+(aq) + OH^-(aq)$ $\Delta H = -71.55$ kJ/mol. A 15.00 g sample of CsOH is dissolved in 110.0 g of water with both substances at 21.50°C. Calculate the final temperature of the solution, assuming the system is perfectly insulated and has a heat capacity equal to that of water.

18. A combustion experiment performed in a bomb calorimeter produced the following data:

heat capacity of bomb calorimeter = 9.35 kJ/°C
mass of methyl propane burned = 751 mg
initial temperature of calorimeter = 20.415°C
final temperature of calorimeter = 24.435°C

Calculate the molar enthalpy of combustion of methylpropane, which is used as lighter fluid.

19. Octane produces a tremendous amount of energy when combusted in gasoline. The following data were collected from a combustion experiment performed in a bomb calorimeter:

$\Delta H_{combustion} = -5074$ kJ/mol C_8H_{18}
heat capacity of bomb calorimeter = 10.45 kJ/°C
initial temperature of calorimeter = 21.002°C
final temperature of calorimeter = 27.014°C

Determine the mass of the sample of octane combusted in the calorimeter.

20. (a) Use the data in the table of Standard Enthalpy of Formation to calculate ΔH_{rxn} for the combustion of methanol, $CH_3OH(l)$.

(b) A 525.0 mg sample of methanol was used to calibrate a calorimeter. Combustion of the sample caused the calorimeter's temperature to rise from 21.057°C to 22.425°C. What is the heat capacity of the calorimeter? (Express C in units of kJ/°C.)

© Edvantage Interactive 2016

1.2 Enthalpy

Warm Up

Examine the following series of reactions and their associated enthalpy changes.

$$CH_4(g) + 2\,O_2(g) \rightarrow CO_2(g) + 2\,H_2O(l) \qquad \Delta H^o_{combustion} = -891 \text{ kJ/mol}$$

$$C(s) + O_2(g) \rightarrow CO_2(g) \qquad \Delta H^o_f = -394 \text{ kJ/mol}$$

$$H_2(g) + \tfrac{1}{2}\,O_2(g) \rightarrow H_2O(l) \qquad \Delta H^o_f = -286 \text{ kJ/mol}$$

Using the principles developed in Section 4.4, rearrange the reactions and combine them to give this overall reaction.

Rx 1:

Rx 2:

Rx 3:

$$C(s) + 2\,H_2(g) \rightarrow CH_4(g)$$

Determine the enthalpy change associated with the overall reaction.

The Use of Bond Energy

A third way to calculate enthalpy changes is to use bond energy values. Bond energy is the *energy required to break a bond*. Bond energy values are frequently presented in tables. Most AP Chemistry texts list bond energies as positive values in units of kJ/mole. Such values represent the amount of energy that must be input into the system to break the bond. To represent the value of the energy released when product bonds form, a negative sign must precede the value given in Table 1.2.1.

Bond energy is the *enthalpy change* required to *break* a *given bond* in *one mole* of *gaseous molecules*. Bond energy is *always positive* and is expressed in units of kJ/mole.

The bond energy of a particular bond between two atoms, for example C-C, will vary depending on the "chemical environment" the bond is in, what other bonds are adjacent to it, and what lone pairs and bonding pairs of electrons are nearby. The bond energy for H-Cl, determined from hydrogen chloride gas, HCl, will differ from that determined within the PVC precursor, C_2H_5Cl, even when it is gasified. This means the bond energies typically reported in tables are really *average bond energies* gathered for each bond in a large variety of different compounds.

Table 1.2.1 *Average Bond Energy (KJ/mol)*

Bond	Energy	Bond	Energy	Bond	Energy	Bond	Energy
Single Bonds							
H–H	432	N–H	391	Si–H	323	S–H	347
H–F	565	N–N	160	Si–Si	226	S–S	266
H–Cl	427	N–P	209	Si–O	368	S–F	327
H–Br	363	N–O	201	Si–S	226	S–Cl	271
H–I	295	N–F	272	Si–F	565	S–Br	218
		N–Cl	200	Si–Cl	381	S–I	~170
C–H	413	N–Br	243	Si–Br	310		
C–C	347	N–I	159	Si–I	234	F–F	159
C–Si	301					F–Cl	193
C–N	305	O–H	467	P–H	320	F–Br	212
C–O	358	O–P	351	P–Si	213	F–I	263
C–P	264	O–O	204	P–P	200	Cl–Cl	243
C–S	259	O–S	265	P–F	490	Cl–Br	215
C–F	453	O–F	190	P–Cl	331	Cl–I	208
C–Cl	339	O–Cl	203	P–Br	272	Br–Br	193
C–Br	276	O–Br	234	P–I	184	Br–I	175
C–I	216	O–I	234			I–I	151
Multiple Bonds							
C=C	614	N=N	418	C≡C	839	N≡N	945
C=N	615	N=O	607	C≡N	891		
C=O	745	O_2	498	C≡O	1070		
	(799 in CO_2)						

When you examine a number of different average bond energies, such as those represented in this table, several patterns are noticeable. Consider the bond between hydrogen and members of the halogen family, for example. Because the highest energy bond is more difficult to break, HF behaves as a weak acid, while HCl through HI release their hydrogen ions more easily and so are strong acids.

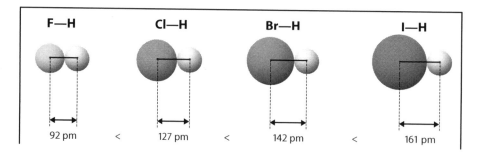

Figure 1.2.1 *Bond length increases with the atomic radius of each atom involved in the bond. Greater bond lengths result in less energetic and thus weaker bonds.*

A second pattern that is obvious is that bond energies depend not only on the elements involved in the bond, but also on whether the bond is single, double, or triple. Triple bonds are the most energetic and hence the strongest, while single bonds are the weakest and least energetic.

© Edvantage Interactive 2016

Bond energy and strength also relate to bond length. Triple bonds involve more electron energy-level overlap and hence are shorter.

Because bond energies are *averages*, the answer to an enthalpy problem determined using bond energies might not be exactly the same as one calculated using Standard Enthalpy of Formation, but it will closely approximate it. Since bond energy is a state function, there is a simple algorithm available for calculating enthalpy changes using bond energies. It is similar to the one described for the calculation of enthalpy changes.

$$\Delta H_{reaction} = \sum nB.E._{(bonds\ broken)} - \sum nB.E._{(bonds\ formed)}$$

Because the reactants and products appear in the opposite order in this equation compared to calculation of enthalpy from Standard Enthalpy of Formation students frequently make errors in the calculation of enthalpy changes using bond energies. The most common incorrect result has the correct magnitude, but the wrong sign. The easiest way to ensure you fully understand how to determine the overall bond energy change is to always remember that:

Bond *breaking requires energy* while bond *forming releases energy*!

Once the structural formulas of all species in a balanced equation are written down, the bonds that are broken and the bonds that are formed can be determined. The broken bonds are assigned *positive* bond energy values and each newly formed bond is assigned a *negative* one. Then the sum of the bond energies is calculated. For example, in the sample problem from the law of Hess,

$$CH_4(g) + 2\ O_2(g) \rightarrow CO_2(g) + 2\ H_2O(g) \qquad \Delta H^\circ_{comb} = -802.7\ kJ/mol_{rxn}$$

Four C-H bonds and two O=O bonds are broken while two C=O bonds and four O-H bonds are formed. Using tabular bond energy values, we would calculate:

$$\left[\frac{4\ mol\ C\text{-}H}{mol_{rxn}} \left(\frac{413\ kJ}{mol\ C\text{-}H} \right) - \frac{2\ mol\ O\text{=}O}{mol_{rxn}} \left(\frac{498\ kJ}{mol\ O\text{=}O} \right) \right] +$$

$$\left[\frac{2\ mol\ C\text{=}O}{mol_{rxn}} \left(\frac{799\ kJ}{mol\ C\text{=}O} \right) - \frac{4\ mol\ O\text{-}H}{mol_{rxn}} \left(\frac{467\ kJ}{mol\ O\text{-}H} \right) \right] = -818\ kJ/mol_{rxn}$$

While these two values are not exactly the same, they are both exothermic and are within 2% of each other. For reactions occurring in the gas state, bond energies give very close approximations to the enthalpy changes calculated with standard ΔH°_f values.

Sample Problem — Enthalpy Changes from Average Bond Energy Values

Use Table 1.2.1 to determine the enthalpy change for the Haber process for the production of ammonia:

$$N_2(g) + 3\ H_2(g) \rightarrow 2\ NH_3(g)$$

What to Think About	How To Do It
1. Consider the bonding arrangement of the reactants and products. Structural formulas are very useful.	:N≡N: + 3 H-H → 2 H-N-H (with H below) Continued on next page

---

© Edvantage Interactive 2016

Chapter 1 Thermodynamics 27

Sample Problem — *Continued*

What to Think About

2. Multiply the bond energies by the appropriate coefficients and apply the correct mathematical symbols to the convention: (+) for bonds breaking and (−) for bonds forming. Count the number of bonds carefully.

   Note: Should a bond remain intact, there is no need to break and reform it. Simply ignore it in the calculation.

3. Do the math!

4. It's always a good idea to consider the feasibility of your answer.

How To Do It

$$\frac{1 \text{ mol } N \equiv N}{mol_{rxn}}\left(\frac{945 \text{ kJ}}{mol_{N \equiv N}}\right) + \frac{3 \text{ mol } H-H}{mol_{rxn}}\left(\frac{432 \text{ kJ}}{mol_{H-H}}\right)$$

$$- \frac{6 \text{ mol } N-H}{mol_{rxn}}\left(\frac{391 \text{ kJ}}{mol_{N-H}}\right)$$

$$= -105 \text{ kJ}/mol_{rxn}$$

As we are forming ammonia, an exothermic answer makes sense. The enthalpies of formation table give a ΔH_f as −45.9 kJ/mol of NH_3. The reaction forms two moles of ammonia, so our answer is close enough to be reasonable.

Practice Problems — Enthalpy Changes from Average Bond Energy Values

Use Table 1.2.1 to produce a full *thermochemical equation* for each of the molecular representations below.

1.

$$H-\underset{\underset{H}{|}}{\overset{\overset{H}{|}}{C}}-\underset{\underset{H}{|}}{\overset{\overset{H}{|}}{C}}-\underset{\underset{H}{|}}{\overset{\overset{H}{|}}{C}}-H + 5\ O=O \longrightarrow 3\ O=C=O + 4\ H-O-H$$

2.

$$H-\underset{\underset{H}{|}}{\overset{\overset{H}{|}}{C}}-O-H_{(g)} + 1\tfrac{1}{2}\ O=O_{(g)} \longrightarrow O=C=O_{(g)} + \begin{matrix} H \overset{O}{} H \\ H \overset{O}{} H_{(g)} \end{matrix}$$

It is comforting to know that there are multiple ways to use tabular data to solve a problem in thermochemistry. But for most chemists, the real joy lies in working in the laboratory to determine the values of the bond energy through calorimetry.

© Edvantage Interactive 2016

The value of the Enthalpy of Formation for each of the compounds involved in a chemical change may be rearranged to calculate the overall enthalpy change for a process. Using the enthalpies of formation for methane, carbon dioxide, and liquid water we can determine the overall enthalpy change for the combustion of methane as follows:

$$CH_4(g) \rightarrow C(s) + 2\,H_2(g) \qquad \Delta H^\circ = +75 \text{ kJ/mol}_{rxn}$$

$$C(s) + O_2(g) \rightarrow CO_2(g) \qquad \Delta H^\circ_f = -394 \text{ kJ/mol}_{rxn}$$

$$2\,H_2(g) + O_2(g) \rightarrow 2\,H_2O(l) \qquad \Delta H^\circ_f = -572 \text{ kJ/mol}_{rxn}$$

$$\overline{CH_4(g) + 2\,O_2(g) \rightarrow CO_2(g) + 2\,H_2O(l) \qquad \Delta H^\circ_{comb} = -891 \text{ kJ/mol}_{rxn}}$$

The overall enthalpy of a reaction can also be calculated using the formula:

$$\Delta H^\circ_{(overall)} = \sum n H^\circ_{f(products)} - \sum n H^\circ_{f(reactants)}$$

The symbol Σ means "sum of" and n is the coefficient of each species in a balanced equation. It is critical to keep in mind that:

The H°_f for a *pure element* in its standard state is always equal to *zero*.

Observe the state of the species in a balanced chemical equation carefully when using enthalpy values from a table of standard enthalpies of formation , as the state of a substance affects its enthalpy of formation value. The formula above can be used to calculate the overall enthalpy change for the combustion of methane as follows:

$$\Delta H^\circ_{comb} = [1 \times H_{f\,CO_2}(g) + 2 \times H_{fH_2O}(l)] - [1 \times H_{fCH_4}(g) + 2 \times H_{fO_2}(g)]$$

$$\text{thus: } \Delta H^\circ_{comb} = \left[\frac{1 \text{ mol } CO_2}{\text{mol}_{rxn}}\left(\frac{-394 \text{ kJ/}}{\text{mol } CO_2}\right) + \frac{2 \text{ mol } H_2O}{\text{mol}_{rxn}}\left(\frac{-286 \text{ kJ/}}{\text{mol } H_2O}\right) \right] -$$

$$\left[\frac{1 \text{ mol } CH_4}{\text{mol}_{rxn}}\left(\frac{-75 \text{ kJ}}{\text{mol } CH_4}\right) + \frac{2 \text{ mol } O_2}{\text{mol}_{rxn}}\left(\frac{0 \text{ kJ}}{\text{mol } O_2}\right) \right] = -891 \text{ kJ/mol}_{rxn}$$

As demonstrated, calculating the enthalpy of a reaction using enthalpy values from a table of standard enthalpies of formation will be equivalent to calculating the enthalpy of a reaction using Hess's Law which we will study later.

Table 1.2.2 *Examples of Standard Enthalpy of Formation*

$NH_3(g)$	–45.9 kJ/mol	$NO(g)$	90.3 kJ/mol
C(s) [diamond]	1.896	$NO_2(g)$	33.2
$N_2O_5(g)$	11.0	$C_3H_8(g)$	–105.0
$CO_2(g)$	–393.5	$PF_5(g)$	–1594.4
$C_2H_4Cl_2(g)$	–166.8	$NaHCO_3(s)$	–947.4
$C_2H_5Cl(g)$	–112.2	$Na_2SO_4(aq)$	–1387.1
$C_2H_6(g)$	–84.7	$SO_2(g)$	–296.8
$C_2H_4(g)$	52.5	$SO_3(g)$	–396.0
$HCl(g)$	–92.3	$H_2SO_4(aq)$	–907.5
$H_2S(g)$	–20.2	$H_2O(g)$	–241.8
$CH_4(g)$	–74.9	$H_2O(l)$	–285.8
$CH_3OH(g)$	–238.6	ZnO(s)	–348.0

Sample Problem — Standard Enthalpy of Formation

Given the following Standard Enthalpy of Formation, ΔH_f° of $SO_2(g)$ = –296.8 kJ/mol$_f$ and ΔH_f° of $SO_3(g)$ = –396.0 kJ/mol$_f$, what is the enthalpy change for the following reaction: $2\ SO_2(g) + O_2(g) \rightarrow 2\ SO_3(g)$?

What To Think about

1. Determine the ΔH_f° (Standard Enthalpy of Formation) values for each of the species involved in the reaction from a table of standard enthalpies of formation. Remember that the enthalpy of formation for an element in its standard state is zero.

   Note: Generally these values will be found in a *table of standard enthalpies of formation.*

2. Multiply products and reactants by their coefficients and subtract the sum of the products from the sum of the reactants.

How To Do It

ΔH_f° of $SO_2(g)$ = –296.8 kJ/mol and
ΔH_f° of $SO_3(g)$ = –396.0 kJ/mol and
ΔH_f° of O_2 = 0 kJ/mol (pure element)

$$\frac{2\ mol\ SO_3}{mol_{rxn}}\left(\frac{-396.0\ kJ}{mol\ SO_3}\right) -$$

$$\left[\frac{2\ mol\ SO_2}{mol_{rxn}}\left(\frac{-296.8\ kJ}{mol\ SO_2}\right) + \frac{1\ mol\ O_2}{mol_{rxn}}\left(\frac{0\ kJ}{mol\ O_2}\right)\right]$$

$$= -198.4\ kJ/mol$$

© Edvantage Interactive 2016

Practice Problems— Standard Enthalpy of Formation

Use the values in Table 1.2.1 to solve the practice problems below (values are listed alphabetically *by name* in this table):

1. Determine the enthalpy change for each of the following reactions:
   (a) $C_3H_8(g) + H_2(g) \rightarrow C_2H_6(g) + CH_4(g)$

   (b) $2 H_2S(g) + 3 O_2(g) \rightarrow 2 SO_2(g) + 2 H_2O(l)$

2. Use the following information along with the tabular data to calculate the *molar* enthalpy of $ZnS(s)$.
   $2 ZnS(s) + 3 O_2(g) \rightarrow 2 ZnO(s) + 2 SO_2(g)$ $\Delta H_f^\circ = -878.2 \text{ kJ/mol}_{rxn}$

Hess's Law

Enthalpy changes involving an overall *decrease* in potential energy are *exothermic*. The ΔH value for an exothermic change is always a *negative* value as the system is releasing energy. Changes involving an overall *increase* in potential energy are *endothermic* and the ΔH value for such a change is *positive*. Placement of the correct sign in front of ΔH values is an important accounting convention, and the signs must be applied consistently throughout all thermodynamic calculations.

As enthalpy is an *extensive property*, the *magnitude* of an enthalpy change for a chemical reaction *depends on the quantity of material* that reacts. This means if the amount of reacting material in an exothermic reaction is doubled, twice the quantity of heat will be released. Thus for the oxidation of sulfur dioxide gas:

$$SO_2(g) + \tfrac{1}{2}O_2(g) \rightarrow SO_3(g) \qquad \Delta H^\circ = -99 \text{ kJ/mol}_{rxn}$$

Doubling the reaction results in:

$$2\,SO_2(g) + O_2(g) \rightarrow 2\,SO_3(g) \qquad \Delta H^\circ = -198 \text{ kJ/mol}_{rxn}$$

A comparison of the absolute enthalpy content of the reactants and products of a reversible reaction makes it evident that the *magnitude* of ΔH for an exothermic reaction *remains the same when it is reversed*. There is merely a *sign change* and the reaction becomes endothermic. Hence if the above reaction were reversed:

$$2\,SO_3(g) \rightarrow 2\,SO_2(g) + O_2(g) \qquad \Delta H^\circ = +198 \text{ kJ/mol}_{rxn}$$

In addition to being an extensive property, enthalpy is also a *state function*. As we just learned, this means an enthalpy change is *completely independent of the pathway followed* to accomplish it. These concepts may be applied to determine the overall enthalpy change for any reaction by manipulation of a series of other reactions. The process is known as **Hess's Law of Heat Summation**. Simply stated:

> The *enthalpy change* of a *reaction* is expressed as the *algebraic sum* of the *enthalpy changes* of a series of other reactions that have been manipulated to produce the overall reaction.

Hess's Law of Heat Summation

In Grade 11, we learned that the enthalpy of a reaction is the result of the chemical potential energy in the bonds of the reactants which is converted into heat absorbed or released as the reactant bonds break and form product bonds.

There are a number of methods for calculating overall enthalpy changes that a chemistry student should be familiar with. The three most common are Hess's Law, the use of tabular Standard Enthalpy of Formation and the use of bond energies.

In addition to being an extensive property, enthalpy is also a state function. Enthalpy change is completely independent of the pathway followed to convert reactants into products. The conversion of reactants into products is often achieved through a series of chemical processes. The overall enthalpy change for any overall reaction is usually calculated by manipulation of a series of reactions that lead to the overall process. The process is known as Hess's Law of heat summation and is defined as:

> The algebraic sum of the enthalpy changes of a series of reactions that produce the overall reaction will equal the overall enthalpy of the reaction.

As indicated in the Warm Up, given the following reactions and their enthalpy changes, it is possible to determine the heat of formation for methane:

$$CH_4(g) + 2\,O_2(g) \rightarrow CO_2(g) + 2\,H_2O(l) \qquad \Delta H^o_{comb} = -891 \text{ kJ/mol}_{rxn}$$

$$C(s) + O_2(g) \rightarrow CO_2(g) \qquad\qquad\qquad \Delta H^o_f = -394 \text{ kJ/mol}_{rxn}$$

$$H_2(g) + \tfrac{1}{2}\,O_2(g) \rightarrow H_2O(l) \qquad\qquad \Delta H^o_f = -286 \text{ kJ/mol}_{rxn}$$

The reaction we are attempting to come up with is:

$$C(s) + 2\,H_2(g) \rightarrow CH_4(g)$$

Begin by *looking for species that appear as reactants and products in the overall reaction*. This will provide a clue as to whether a reaction needs to be reversed or not. Second, *consider the coefficients of species that appear in the overall reaction*. This will help determine whether a reaction needs to be multiplied before the overall summation. Leaving the formation of carbon dioxide reaction as is and doubling the formation of water reaction appears to be a good start in that this will provide the reactants desired. The combustion of methane reaction will need to be reversed to provide the desired number of moles of product. Reorganization of the three equations as described with the accompanying change in their ΔH^o values results in:

$$C(s) + \cancel{O_2(g)} \rightarrow \cancel{CO_2(g)} \qquad\qquad \Delta H^o_f = -394 \text{ kJ/mol}_{rxn}$$

$$2\,H_2(g) + \cancel{O_2(g)} \rightarrow \cancel{2\,H_2O(l)} \qquad\qquad \Delta H^o_f = -572 \text{ kJ/mol}_{rxn}$$

$$\cancel{CO_2(g)} + \cancel{2\,H_2O(l)} \rightarrow CH_4(g) + \cancel{2\,O_2(g)} \qquad \Delta H^o_{rxn} = +891 \text{ kJ/mol}_{rxn}$$

$$\overline{C(s) + 2\,H_2(g) \rightarrow CH_4(g) \qquad\qquad\qquad \Delta H^o_f = -75 \text{ kJ/mol}_{rxn}}$$

Sample Problem — Hess's Law

As an alternative to burning coal, the following process, called *methanation*, can be used to produce energy from carbon monoxide, a product of coal combustion. The carbon monoxide is only one component of a mixture called "coal gas." Not only does this reaction produce energy, it also produces methane, itself a valuable component of natural gas that may be further combusted to produce energy.

$$3\,H_2(g) + CO(g) \rightarrow CH_4(g) + H_2O(g)$$

Determine the standard enthalpy change for the methanation reaction using the following series of reactions and their enthalpy changes:

$$2\,H_2(g) + O_2(g) \rightarrow 2\,H_2O(g) \qquad\qquad \Delta H^o_f = -483.6 \text{ kJ/mol}_{rxn}$$

$$2\,C(s) + O_2(g) \rightarrow 2\,CO(g) \qquad\qquad\quad \Delta H^o_f = -221.0 \text{ kJ/mol}_{rxn}$$

$$CH_4(g) + 2\,O_2(g) \rightarrow CO_2(g) + 2\,H_2O(g) \qquad \Delta H^o_{comb} = -802.7 \text{ kJ/mol}_{rxn}$$

$$C(s) + O_2(g) \rightarrow CO_2(g) \qquad\qquad\qquad \Delta H^o_f = -393.5 \text{ kJ/mol}_{rxn}$$

Continued

What To Think About *continued*	**How To Do It**
1. Hydrogen gas only appears as a reactant in one reaction. So this reaction must be multiplied by 1.5 to give three reactant H_2 molecules.	$(2\ H_2(g)\ +\ O_2(g)\ \rightarrow\ 2\ H_2O(g)\quad -483.6\ kJ/mol_{rxn})\ \times 1.5$
2. To make CO a reactant requires reversal of the second reaction. It must be divided by two to give one CO_2 and the sign must be changed.	$(2\ CO(g)\ \rightarrow\ 2\ C(s)\ +\ O_2(g)\quad +221.0\ kJ/mol_{rxn})\ \times -0.5$
3. To make methane a product, the third reaction must be reversed and the sign changed.	
4. This leaves one CO_2 to be cancelled, as it does not appear anywhere in the overall reaction. So the last reaction may remain as is.	$(CO_2(g)\ +\ 2\ H_2O(g)\ \rightarrow\ CH_4(g)\ +\ 2\ O_2(g)$ $+802.7\ kJ/mol_{rxn})\ \times -1$
5. Changing coefficients and altering the enthalpy changes values accordingly.	$(C(s)\ +\ O_2(g)\ \rightarrow\ CO_2(g)\quad -393.5\ kJ/mol_{rxn})\ \times 1$
6. Summing the four equations with appropriate algebraic cancelling gives the correct overall equation with the correct ΔH_{rxn} value for the equation as written.	$3\ H_2(g)\ +\ \cancel{1.5}\ O_2(g)\ \rightarrow\ 3\ H_2O(g)\quad -725.4\ kJ/mol_{rxn}$ $1\ CO(g)\ \rightarrow\ \cancel{1\ C(s)}\ +\ \cancel{0.5\ O_2(g)}\quad +110.5$ $\cancel{CO_2(g)}\ +\ \cancel{2\ H_2O(g)}\ \rightarrow\ CH_4(g)\ +\ \cancel{2\ O_2(g)}\ +\ 802.7$ $\cancel{C(s)}\ +\ \cancel{O_2(g)}\ \rightarrow\ \cancel{CO_2(g)}\quad -393.5$ ===================================== $3\ H_2(g)\ +\ CO(g)\ \rightarrow\ CH_4(g)\ +\ H_2O(g)$ $\Delta H_{rxn}\ =\ -205.7\ kJ/mol_{rxn}$

Practice Problems — Hess's Law

1. The complete decomposition of NOCl gas into its elements occurs by the following reaction:

$$2\ NOCl(g)\ \rightarrow\ N_2(g)\ +\ O_2(g)\ +\ Cl_2(g)$$

Use the following two reactions and their enthalpy changes to determine the enthalpy change for the decomposition reaction.

$$\tfrac{1}{2}\ N_2(g)\ +\ \tfrac{1}{2}\ O_2(g)\ \rightarrow\ NO(g)\qquad \Delta H_f = 90.3\ kJ/mol_f$$

$$NO(g)\ +\ \tfrac{1}{2}\ Cl_2(g)\ \rightarrow\ NOCl(g)\qquad \Delta H_{rxn} = -38.6\ kJ/mol_{rxn}$$

Continued

© Edvantage Interactive 2016

Practice Problems — *Continued*

2. Polyvinyl chloride is commonly referred to as PVC. It is a polymer produced from a monomer formed by the addition of ethylene and chlorine gas. Use the following reactions and their enthalpy changes to determine the overall enthalpy change for the PVC monomer reaction:

$$H_2(g) + Cl_2(g) \rightarrow 2\,HCl(g) \qquad \Delta H_f = -184.6\ \text{kJ/mol}_{rxn}$$

$$C_2H_4(g) + HCl(g) \rightarrow C_2H_5Cl(l) \qquad \Delta H_{rxn} = -65.0\ \text{kJ/mol}_{rxn}$$

$$C_2H_3Cl(g) + H_2(g) \rightarrow C_2H_5Cl(l) \qquad \Delta H_{rxn} = -138.9\ \text{kJ/mol}_{rxn}$$

$$C_2H_4(g) + Cl_2(g) \rightarrow C_2H_3Cl(l) + HCl(g) \qquad \Delta H_{rxn} = \ \textbf{(?)}$$

3. Given the following data (all species are gases):

$$2\,O_3 \rightarrow 3\,O_2 \qquad \Delta H_{diss} = -427\ \text{kJ/mol}_{rxn}$$

$$O_2 \rightarrow 2\,O \qquad \Delta H_{diss} = 495\ \text{kJ/mol}_{rxn}$$

$$NO + O_3 \rightarrow NO_2 + O_2 \qquad \Delta H_{rxn} = -199\ \text{kJ/mol}_{rxn}$$

Calculate the enthalpy change for the following reaction: $NO + O \rightarrow NO_2$

1.2 Review Questions

1. In the 1970s, scientists became concerned about the depletion of the ozone layer due to the affects of aerosol propellants such as chlorofluorocarbons. Chlorofluorocarbons are now known to absorb high-energy radiation, producing free radical chlorine atoms. These chlorine atoms have a catalytic effect on the removal of ozone from our atmosphere.

   Use the following two reactions and their enthalpy changes to calculate the enthalpy change for the removal of ozone by free radical oxygen. (This is the net equation involved in ozone destruction in the atmosphere.) O atoms (free radicals) are present due to O_2 dissociation by high-energy radiation. All species are gaseous.

   $O_3 + Cl \rightarrow O_2 + ClO$ $\Delta H° = -126$ kJ/mol$_{rxn}$

   $ClO + O \rightarrow Cl + O_2$ $\Delta H° = -268$ kJ/mol$_{rxn}$
   ==

2. Determine the enthalpy change for the following reaction:
   $CH_4(g) + 4\,Cl_2(g) \rightarrow CCl_4(l) + 4\,HCl(g)$
   Using the following information:

   $C(s) + 2\,H_2(g) \rightarrow CH_4(g)$ $\Delta H°_f = -74.6$ kJ/mol$_{rxn}$

   $C(s) + 2\,Cl_2(g) \rightarrow CCl_4(g)$ $\Delta H°_f = -95.7$ kJ/mol$_{rxn}$

   $H_2(g) + 2\,Cl_2(g) \rightarrow 2\,HCl(g)$ $\Delta H°_f = -92.3$ kJ/mol$_{rxn}$

3. The **Born-Haber cycle** is a hypothetical series of steps that represent the formation of an ionic compound from its constituent elements. According to Hess's Law, the sum of the enthalpy changes for each step in the series should sum to give the overall enthalpy change for the formation of the ionic compound from its elements in their standard states. The enthalpy change for the formation of an ionic compound from its ions in the gas state is called the **lattice energy** of the compound. Here is the Born-Haber cycle for cesium fluoride.

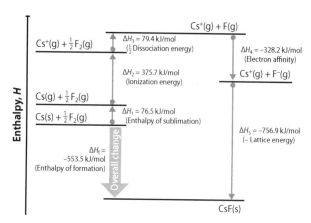

   Use the Born-Haber cycle to show how five equations may be added together using Hess's Law to give the overall enthalpy of formation for cesium fluoride from the following equation: $Cs(s) + ½ F_2(g) \rightarrow CsF(s)$. Label each of the processes involved. Be sure to use *five steps*. The first step is done for you as an example.

Step 1: $Cs(s) \rightarrow Cs(g)$ $\Delta H_{sub} = 76.5 \text{ kJ/mol}_{Cs}$ sublimation of Cs

Step 2:

Step 3:

Step 4:

Step 5:

Overall Rxn: $Cs(s) + ½ F_2(g) \rightarrow CsF(s)$ $\Delta H_f = ?$ formation of CsF(s)

4. The Ostwald process for making nitric acid involves multiple steps, beginning with ammonia reacting with oxygen, forming nitrogen monoxide and water. Determine the $\Delta H^°_{rxn}$ for this *first step* in the Ostwald process. Begin by writing a *balanced chemical reaction*. Then use the standard enthalpy of formation values.

6. Consider the following *unbalanced* molecular representation of an oxidation-reduction reaction. Translate this molecular representation to a balanced formula equation. Then use the table of standard enthalpy of formation values to determine the overall enthalpy change for the balanced molecular equation.

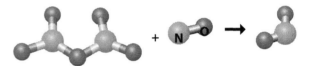

5. Use the standard enthalpy of formation values to determine the overall enthalpy change for the reaction depicted by the complete combustion of methane depicted below.

7. Solid baking soda (sodium bicarbonate or sodium hydrogen carbonate) neutralizes sulfuric acid solution spills, producing sodium sulfate, water, and carbon dioxide. Write a complete, balanced *thermochemical* equation for this process.

8. Hess's Law Practice Problem 2 on page 214 involves steps in the production of polyvinylchloride (PVC) plastic. The addition of hydrogen chloride gas, HCl, to ethene, C_2H_4, forms the monomer, $C_2H_5Cl(l)$ which is used to make the polymer, PVC. Given the overall enthalpy change of –65.0 kJ/mol$_{rxn}$ determine the enthalpy of formation for the monomer, $C_2H_5Cl(l)$.

9. Chlorine gas can react in a substitution reaction with the gaseous monomer mentioned in question 14 as follows: $C_2H_5Cl(g) + Cl_2(g) \rightarrow C_2H_4Cl_2(g) + HCl(g)$

   (a) Calculate the $\Delta H°$ for the reaction above.

   (b) Repeat the calculation done in part (a) using $\Delta H_f^°$ values.

   (c) Compare the answer to part (a) with part (b). Comment on the comparison.

10. (a) Use a highlighter or some other method to indicate the bonds that break on the reactant side and form on the product side of this reaction. Remember the note in the sample problem about enthalpy changes from average bond energy values in Table 1.2.2 — if a bond remains intact there is no need to break and reform it. Calculate the enthalpy change using the bond energy values.

(b) Repeat for this reaction.

(c) Considering bond energy is a state function, combine steps (a) and (b) into one reaction and calculate the overall enthalpy change.

11. The following shows the structural formulas for the reaction:

$2 CH_2CHCH_3(g) + 2 NH_3(g) + 3 O_2(g) \rightarrow 2 CH_2CHCN(g) + 6 H_2O(g)$

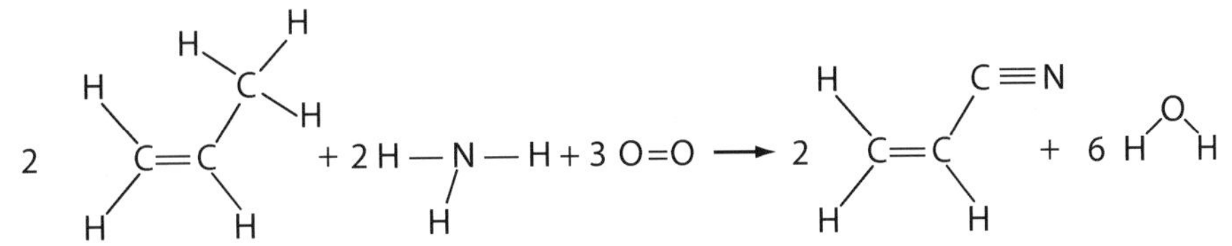

Use the bond energy in Table 1.2.1 to calculate ΔH_{rxn} for the given reaction.

1.3 Potential Energy Diagrams

Warm Up

Complete the following table by placing a checkmark in the appropriate energy change column for each chemical change classification listed.

Reaction Type	Endothermic	Exothermic
Most synthesis (combination) reactions		
Most decomposition reactions		
Neutralization reactions		
Combustion reactions		

Sources of Energy

Fuels such as natural gas, wood, coal, and gasoline provide us with energy. In Grade 11, you learned that most of this energy is stored as chemical potential energy that can be converted into heat. The amount of potential energy available depends upon the position of the subatomic particles making up a chemical sample and the composition of the sample. While the absolute potential energy content of a system is not really important, a change in potential energy content often is. We use conversions of chemical energy to other energy forms to do work for us, such as heating our homes and moving our vehicles. Because chemical energy is most commonly converted to heat, we use the symbol, ΔH to symbolize a change in energy available as heat. The symbol is sometimes read as "delta H" or an enthalpy change.

Enthalpy is potential energy that may be evolved (given off) or absorbed as heat.

All sorts of processes, both physical and chemical, have an enthalpy change associated with them. A general change in enthalpy is symbolized as ΔH. Combustion reactions have a large enthalpy change and are frequently used for energy production:

$$C_3H_8(g) + 5\,O_2(g) \rightarrow 3\,CO_2(g) + 4\,H_2O(l) \qquad \Delta H_{combustion} = -2221 \text{ kJ/mol}$$

What causes the enthalpy stored in reactants to differ from that in the products of a physical or chemical change? What exactly is responsible for producing the ΔH value? The answer is the chemical bonds.

The Energy of Chemical Bonds

Suppose your textbook has fallen off your desk to the floor. When you lift it back to the desktop, you give the text potential energy. The gravitational potential energy your text now has in its position on the desktop could easily be converted into mechanical and sound energy should it happen to fall again.

In a similar way, the electrons in the atoms of the molecules of any substance have potential energy. Think of the negative electrons as being pulled away from the positive nucleus of their atom. If it were not for their high velocity, they would certainly rush toward and smash directly into the nucleus of their atom, much like your textbook falling to the floor. By virtue of the position of the negative electrons in an atom relative to the positive nucleus and the other nuclei nearby in a molecule, the electrons (and the protons in the nuclei) have potential energy. This is the chemical potential energy called **bond energy.**

Bond *breaking* requires energy *input*, while bond *forming* results in energy *release*.

It's fairly intuitive that breaking something requires energy. For a karate master to break a board, he must certainly apply energy. Similarly, breaking chemical bonds requires energy. This energy is used to overcome the electrostatic forces that bind atoms or ions together. It should follow from this that bond formation must result in a more stable situation in which energy is released.

If more energy is absorbed as bonds break than is released as bonds form during a chemical change, there will always be a net absorption of energy. As energy is required to break bonds, there will be a gain in enthalpy. Reactions such as these will have a positive ΔH value and are called **endothermic** reactions.

Figure 1.3.1 *Energy is required to break bonds.*

The energy absorbed to break bonds is greater than the energy released during bond formation in an *endothermic* reaction. Therefore, they have *positive ΔH values*.

If, on the other hand, more energy is released as bonds are formed than is absorbed as they are broken during a chemical change, there will always be a net release of energy. Hence, there will be a decrease in enthalpy content. Reactions such as these will have a negative ΔH value and are called **exothermic reactions**.

More energy is released during bond formation than is absorbed during bond breaking in an *exothermic* reaction. Therefore, they have *negative ΔH values*.

You may recall from Grade 11 there are two ways to express the ΔH value associated with a chemical reaction.

A *thermochemical equation* includes the energy change as an integral part of the chemical equation, while *ΔH notation* requires the energy change to be written after the equation following a "$\Delta H =$" symbol.

Quick Check

Given the following ΔH values, write a balanced thermochemical equation and an equation using ΔH notation with the smallest possible whole number coefficients for each of the following chemical changes. Note: These units imply that the energy released or absorbed is for *1 mol* of the reacting species. The first one is done as an example.

1. $\Delta H_{synthesis}$ of $NH_3(g) = -46.1$ kJ/molNH_3

   Thermochemical equation: $N_2(g) + 3\,H_2(g) \rightarrow 2\,NH_3(g) + 92.2$ kJ/mol$_{rxn}$

   ΔH notation: $N_2(g) + 3\,H_2(g) \rightarrow 2\,NH_3(g)$ $\Delta H = -92.2$ kJ/mol$_{rxn}$

2. $\Delta H_{combustion}$ of $C_2H_6(g) = -1428.5$ kJ/molC_2H_6

3. $\Delta H_{decomposition}$ of HBr$(g) = 36.1$ kJ/molHBr

Transition State Theory

If we could examine reacting molecules coming together in a collision at a molecular level, we would see them slow down as their electron clouds repel one another. At some point, they would collide and then fly apart. If a reaction occurs during a collision, the particles that separate are chemically different from those that collide. When collision geometry is favorable and the colliding molecules have a kinetic energy at least equal to E_a, they interact to a form a high-energy, unstable, transitory configuration of atoms called an **activated complex**. This unstable complex will decompose and form new, lower-energy, more stable products.

As the reacting molecules collide, their electron cloud repulsions cause the reactant bonds to stretch and weaken. As reactant bonds break, kinetic energy is transformed into potential energy. At the same time, new bonds are forming between the atoms of the product. This process evolves energy as the newly formed bonds shorten and strengthen. The activated complex forms when potential energy is at a maximum and kinetic energy is minimized. The energy conversions and mechanics of bond breaking and forming are very complex and occur extremely rapidly (in less than a nanosecond or 10^{-9} s). The easiest way to follow these changes is to use a visual profile of the energy changes that occur during a collision. Figure 1.3.2 shows how the following reactions proceeds:

$$H_2(g) + I_2(g) \rightleftharpoons 2\,HI(g)$$

$$
\begin{array}{ccccc}
\text{H} & \text{I} & & \text{H} \cdots \text{I} & & \text{H} \!-\! \text{I} \\
| \ + \ | & \rightleftharpoons & \begin{array}{cc} | & | \\ | & | \end{array} & \rightleftharpoons & + \\
\text{H} & \text{I} & & \text{H} \cdots \text{I} & & \text{H} \!-\! \text{I}
\end{array}
$$

Figure 1.3.2 H_2 and I_2 bonds break ($KE \rightarrow PE$) as HI bonds form ($PE \rightarrow KE$). The activated complex H_2I_2 exists for less than a nanosecond between these two processes

Potential Energy Profiles

A **potential energy diagram** is a graphical representation of the energy changes that take place during a chemical reaction. The enthalpy changes can be followed along the vertical axis, which measures potential energy in kJ/mol. The horizontal axis is called by a variety of names such as the "reaction coordinate" or the "progress of reaction." It is critical to remember it is *not* a time axis. We are simply following the energy profile as the reaction proceeds from reactants to activated complex formation to products. Increasing the rate of the reaction will *not* change the length of this axis.

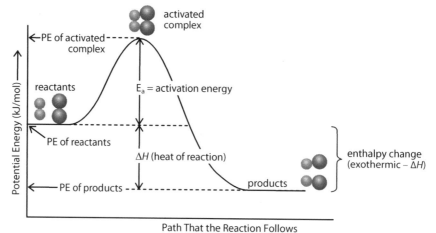

Figure 1.3.3 A potential energy diagram. The reactants are diatomic elements combining to form an activated complex, which decomposes to form two product molecules.

The activation energy, E_a, is the difference between the potential energy of the activated complex and the total potential energy of the separated reactant molecules. It represents the amount of energy the reactant molecules must gain to form an activated complex. Thus $E_a = PE_{activated\ complex} - PE_{reactants}$

© Edvantage Interactive 2016

It is important to be aware that the net energy evolved or absorbed during the reaction is independent of the activation energy. If the potential energy (enthalpy) of the products is less than that of the reactants, the reaction is exothermic. Such is the case in Figure 1.3.3 above. On the other hand, if the products have more potential energy than the reactants, the reaction must be endothermic.

The enthalpy change (ΔH) is the difference between the total potential energy of the products and the total potential energy of the reactants.

Thus $\Delta H = PE_{products} - PE_{reactants}$

While altering factors such as concentration, surface area, or temperature will affect the rate of a chemical reaction, they will *not* affect the appearance of a potential energy diagram. This should make sense if we think of the diagram as a profile of potential bond energies (or enthalpies) per mole. While increasing the concentration of a reactant supplies more bonds, and consequently more bond energy, it also supplies more moles, so the energy *per mole* does not change. Changing temperature changes reaction rate, but it has no effect on the potential energy of the reactant or product bonds.

Sample Problem — Reading an Energy Profile

Read the following potential energy diagram and answer the questions.

1. Is the reaction endothermic or exothermic?
2. What is the activation energy of the reaction?
3. What is the potential energy of the activated complex?
4. What is the ΔH for this reaction?

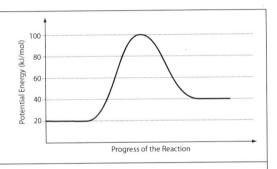

What to Think About

1. Check if the products or the reactants have more PE.

2. Consider the activation energy. The activation energy is the difference between the PE of the activated complex and the reactants.

3. Do not confuse the potential energy of the activated complex with the E_a. Activation energy is *always positive*.

4. Note endothermicity or exothermicity to ensure the sign is correct. This is an essential step.

How to Do It

The products have more PE than the reactants. The reaction must be endothermic.

$E_a = PE_{AC} - PE_{react}$
$\quad = 100 - 20 = 80 \text{ kJ/mol}$

$PE_{AC} = 100 \text{ kJ/mol}$

$\Delta H = PE_{prod} - PE_{react}$
$\quad = 40 - 20 = +20 \text{ kJ/mol}$

Reversible Reactions

Many chemical reactions are reversible under certain conditions. This should be easy to accept if you think about a simple combination reaction being reversed to cause decomposition. The potential energy diagrams for a reaction pair such as these are simply mirror images of one another. Consider the combination of diatomic molecules A_2 and B_2 to form two AB molecules and the decomposition of two AB molecules to form diatomic A_2 and B_2. The potential energy profiles for these reactions would appear as shown in Figure 1.3.4.

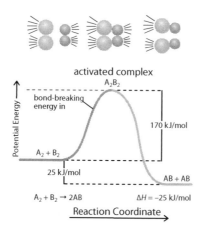
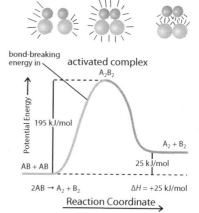

Figure 1.3.4 *The exothermic combination reaction's profile is simply the reverse of that for the endothermic decomposition reaction.*

Notice that the first potential energy diagram could be read in reverse to give the same measurements provided by the second diagram. Whether A_2 and B_2 are reactants or products, their potential bond energy or enthalpy is the same. The same could be said for two AB molecules. As a consequence, the decomposition reaction's ΔH value can be read as +25 kJ/mol from either Figure 1.3.4 or by reading Figure 1.3.3 in reverse (from right to left).

Sample Problem — Reading a Reversible Energy Profile

Read the potential energy diagram for a reversible reaction and answer the questions.

1. Which reaction, forward or reverse, is exothermic?
2. Give ΔH for the forward reaction and the reverse reaction.
3. Give E_a for the forward reaction and the reverse reaction.
4. Give the potential energy for the activated complex. How does this value compare for the forward and reverse reactions? Explain

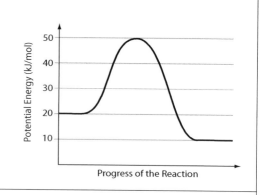

What to Think About

1. Check if the products or the reactants have more PE. Exothermic reactions have $PE_{prod} < PE_{reactants}$.

2. Identify the sign of the ΔH. We know the forward ΔH is $-\Delta H$ because this is an exothermic reaction. The reverse ΔH must be $+\Delta H$ as the reactants become products and vice versa.

3. Recall the definition of E_a. Do not confuse it with the PE of the activated complex. When determining E_a for the reverse reaction, the reactants become the products.

4. Remember that the complex is the same aggregation (collection and arrangement) of atoms whether formed by the reactants or the products.

How to Do It

The forward reaction is exothermic.

$$\Delta H_{forward} = PE_{prod} - PE_{react} = 10 - 20 = -10 \text{ kJ/mol}$$

$$\Delta H_{reverse} = PE_{prod} - PE_{react} = 20 - 10 = +10 \text{ kJ/mol}$$

$$E_{a(forward)} = PE_{AC} - PE_{react} = 50 - 20 = 30 \text{ kJ/mol}$$

$$E_{a(reverse)} = PE_{AC} - PE_{react} = 50 - 10 = 40 \text{ kJ/mol}$$

$PE_{AC} = 50$ kJ/mol for forward and reverse reaction as the same atoms are assembled in the same way and hence have the same potential bond energy (enthalpy) in both cases.

© Edvantage Interactive 2016

Practice Problems — Reading a Reversible Energy Profile

1. Answer the following questions about this potential energy diagram:

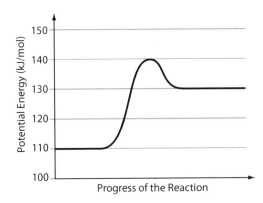

(a) Is the forward reaction exothermic or endothermic?

(b) Indicate the following values for the forward reaction:

(i) activation energy

(ii) enthalpy change

(iii) potential energy of the products

(iv) potential energy of the activated complex

2. Indicate the meaning of each of the measured values, I through IV, on the following potential energy diagram.

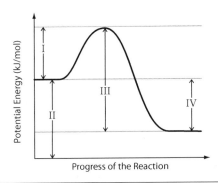

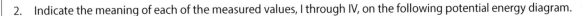

Summary for Reversible Diagrams

In summary, we see that for a reversible potential energy diagram the following points are always true:

- ΔH for the forward and reverse reactions have the *same magnitude* and *opposite signs*.
- E_a is always smaller for the exothermic reaction.
- Altering temperature, pressure, concentration, or surface area will have *no effect* on a potential energy diagram. There is only one thing that will alter a diagram and that is discussed below.

An increase in temperature or concentration allows many more collisions to attain activation energy and hence react successfully. Increasing temperature may, in some situations, cause the decomposition of reactants before they can react. Increased temperature may also cause the formation of unwanted side products. Fortunately, since the great Swedish chemist Berzelius, scientists have been aware of catalysts that may increase the rate of a reaction without raising the temperature.

In general, catalysts provide an alternate reaction pathway in which a different, lower-energy activated complex can form. Reaction pathways are called *mechanisms*.

Catalysts provide an *additional reaction mechanism* with a *lower activation energy*, which results in an *increased reaction rate*. The catalyst is *neither consumed nor changed* following the reaction.

Catalysts reduce the activation energy to the same extent for both the forward and the reverse reaction in a reversible reaction. Consequently both forward and reverse reaction rates are increased by the same amount.

Catalysts must be consumed in one step of a reaction mechanism and be regenerated in a later step. This is why they are neither consumed, nor changed as a chemical reaction occurs. A consequence of this is that more than one activated complex is formed. This leads to more than one "peak" in the potential energy diagram for most catalyzed reactions. Occasionally textbooks show a single peak in the catalyzed pathway on a potential energy diagram. In those cases, the diagram is simply showing a *net* or *overall* reduced energy pathway produced by the use of the catalyst.

Potential energy profiles for catalyzed reactions will usually involve the formation of more than one activated complex and hence more than one "peak" in the diagram.

The calculation of the activation energy for a multiple peak diagram such as Figure 1.3.5 is simply the difference between the highest energy activated complex and the reactants.

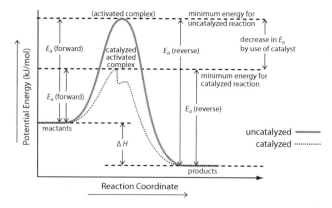

Figure 1.3.5 *The presence of a catalyst actually changes the energy profile to a lower activation energy pathway.*

© Edvantage Interactive 2016

Quick Check

Study the following potential energy diagrams for two independent reactions.

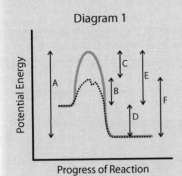

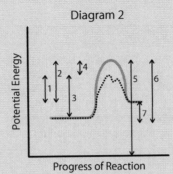

1. For diagram 1, indicate what each of the measurements shown by the lettered arrows represents. A is completed for you as an example.
2. From diagram 2, indicate the number that *represents* the same measurement in diagram 1. A is completed for you as an example.

A. Reverse uncatalyzed activation energy. $E_{a(\text{reverse uncatalyzed})}$ is #2 in diagram 2.

B.

C.

D.

E.

F.

1.3 Activity: Comparing and Contrasting Concepts in Kinetics

Question

How can you compare and contrast endothermic and exothermic processes?

Procedure

1. Use the outline provided below to organize what you've learned about endothermic and exothermic reactions.
2. The first row has been completed as an example of what is expected. Note that there may be many other comparisons and contrasts (or similarities and differences) that you can add to your table. Don't feel limited to only those lines where clues have been provided.

Characteristic	Endothermic	Exothermic
Sensation	Feels cold	Feels hot
Sign of ΔH		
Change in enthalpy		
PE $\leftarrow \rightarrow$ KE transformation		
Sample thermochemical equation		
Sample equation using ΔH		
Bond energy comparisons		
Energy involved in breaking vs. forming bonds		
Sample PE diagram		

Results and Discussion

You will find it very helpful to produce similar charts to help you summarize material for study in the remaining sections of this course. Add these to the dedicated section of your notebook for summary notes and refer to them from time to time to help you in preparing for your unit and final examinations.

1.3 Review Questions

1. Given the following ΔH values, write a balanced thermochemical equation and an equation using ΔH notation with the smallest possible whole number coefficients for each of the chemical changes given below.

   (a) The replacement of iron in thermite, $Fe_2O_3(s)$, by aluminum $\Delta H = -852$ kJ/molFe_2O_3

   (b) The formation of $Ca(OH)_2(s)$ from its elements $\Delta H = -986$ kJ/mol$Ca(OH)_2$

   (c) The decomposition of $H_2O(l)$ into its elements $\Delta H = +286$ kJ/molH_2O

2. Study the graphs shown below.

   (a) Draw a vertical line on the first graph to represent E_a. Place the line so that about 10% of the particles in the reacting sample have enough energy to react.

   (b) Rotate the first graph in such a way that the energy axes of the two graphs are both oriented up and down. Redraw the graph(s) in this orientation.

   (c) Explain what these graphs indicate about the reacting particles.

   (d) Repeat part (b) on the right side of the second graph.

   (e) What does this say about an endothermic reaction compared to an exothermic one?

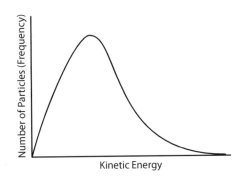

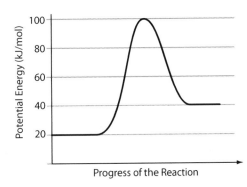

3. For a hypothetical reaction, $XY(g) \rightleftharpoons X(g) + Y(g)$ $\Delta H = 35$ kJ/mol. For the reverse reaction, $E_a = 25$ kJ/mol.
    (a) Sketch a potential energy diagram for this reaction (label general values as given).

    (b) What is the activation energy for the forward reaction?

    (c) What is ΔH for the reverse reaction?

4. Study the potential energy diagram shown below.

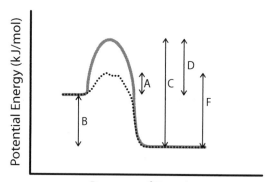

    (a) Indicate what each of the letters (A through E) represents.

        A.

        B.

        C.

        D.

        E.

    (b) Is this reaction endothermic or exothermic?

(c) How would the diagram be affected if the reacting system were heated?

5. Examine the following potential energy diagram for this reaction:

$Q + S \rightarrow T$

(a) Determine ΔH for the reaction.

(b) Write the thermochemical equation for the reaction.

(c) Rewrite the equation in ΔH notation.

(d) Classify the reaction as exothermic or endothermic.

(e) Determine the E_a of the reaction.

6. Why are exothermic reactions usually self-sustaining. In other words, why do they continue once supplied with activation energy? Use the burning of a pile of driftwood as an example.

7. Fill in the blanks for an EXOthermic reaction: The energy released during bond forming is _____ than the energy required for bond _____. As a result, there is a net _____ of energy. The bonds formed have _____ potential energy than the _____ bonds did.

8. How would a PE diagram for a *fast* reaction compare to a PE diagram for a *slow* reaction? Explain.

9. (a) As two reactant particles approach one another for a collision, what happens to their kinetic energy? Why?

   (b) What happens to their potential energy? Why?

   (c) What happens to their total energy (sum of potential and kinetic)?

   (e) Complete the following graph:

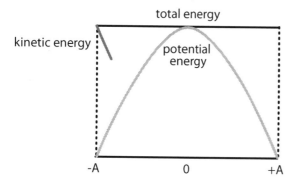

© **Edvantage Interactive 2016**

10. Study the following potential energy diagram.

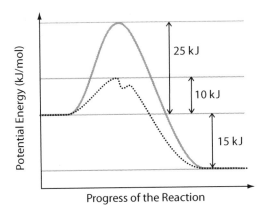

(a) Is this reaction endothermic or exothermic?

(b) What is E_a for the catalyzed pathway?

(c) What is E_a for the uncatalyzed pathway?

(d) What is ΔH for this reaction? How does this value change with a catalyst?

(e) How much lower is the potential energy of the activated complex with a catalyst?

(f) How does this affect the reaction rate?

1.4 Entropy Change versus Enthalpy Change

Warm Up

Everything around you can be perceived as being in a relative state of organization or disorganization. For each picture below, check the box that applies.

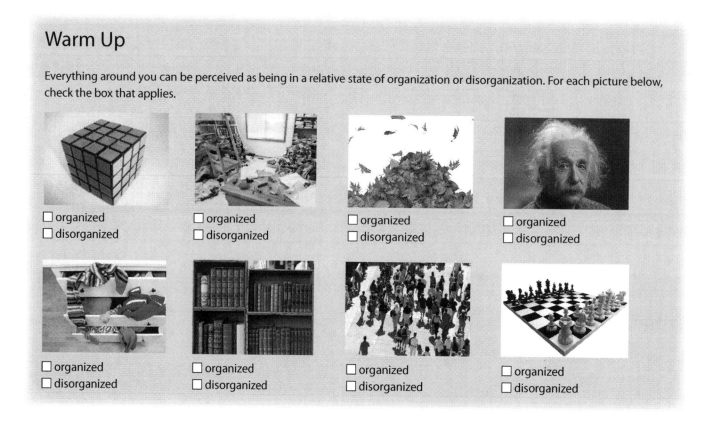

☐ organized
☐ disorganized

☐ organized
☐ disorganized

☐ organized
☐ disorganized

☐ organized
☐ disorganized

☐ organized
☐ disorganized

☐ organized
☐ disorganized

☐ organized
☐ disorganized

☐ organized
☐ disorganized

What Is Entropy?

Entropy is the amount of thermal energy in a closed system that is not available to do work. An analogy used to explain entropy in simple terms is that the entropy of a substance or a system correlates with its state of disorganization or energy dispersal.. The analogy of randomness or energy dispersal refers to the number of ways in which the energy of a system can be arranged. The possible ways in which energy can be distributed in a system are called microstates. . Every form of matter and every particle, except a fundamental particle, has a degree of energy dispersal which can be measured. Scientists use the letter S as the symbol for entropy. Standard molar entropies are expressed in joules per mole per kelvin (J/K • mol). Scientists view a more organized — lower entropy — system as one with fewer available variations or fewer microstates. In other words, a more organized state is a more "fixed" state with few possible ways in which energy can be distributed. Simpler things have lower entropies because they have fewer possible configurations or microstates.. What follows is a somewhat non-scientific example to help understand the concept of entropy. There are few microstates, or arrangements in which your bedroom is "neat", a neat bedroom is a system with a low entropy. However, there are a vast number of arrangements in which your bedroom can be "messy", a messy bedroom can be used as a simple analogy of a system with a high entropy. This example falls short for many reasons, not the least of which is that your bedroom is one system so both the neat and the messy microstates are actually part of the same system.

In a chemical system with a low entropy there are few species and few way of arranging the species that are present. A solid has a lower entropy than a liquid which, in turn, has a lower entropy than a gas. Entropy increases in a chemical system where one reactant species decomposes into two product species and decreases where two reactant species are synthesized into one product species.

Atoms are organizations of subatomic particles; molecules are organizations of atoms; and molecular substances are organizations of molecules. A molecular substance's entropy is a function of its intramolecular (within molecules) relationships and its intermolecular (between molecules) relationships. The third law of thermodynamics states that a perfect crystal at 0 kelvin has 0 entropy.

For elements of the same state within a family, the higher the element's atomic number is, the greater its entropy. More electrons provide more variability in positions. For example, the entropies of the noble gases increase as you move down the periodic table (Table 1.4.1).

Table 1.4.1 *Standard Entropies (S°) of the Noble Gases*

Noble Gas	He	Ne	Ar	Kr	Xe
S° (J/mol·K)	126	147	155	164	170

Likewise, the heavier and more complex a molecule is, the greater its compound's entropy. As well as having more atoms (each with its own variability), more complex molecules have more possible rotational and vibrational orientations. This is exemplified by the entropies of nitrogen oxides (Table 1.4.2).

Table 1.4.2 *Standard Entropies (S°) of Some Nitrogen Oxides*

Substance	$NO(g)$	$N_2O(g)$	$N_2O_4(g)$	$N_2O_5(g)$
S° (J/mol·K)	211	220	304	356

The entropy of a substance is strongly dependent on its temperature. As particles gain kinetic energy, their motion becomes increasingly chaotic. The physical state or phase of a substance affects its entropy as illustrated by the standard entropies of different phases of molecular iodine shown in Table 1.4.3. Entropy increases from solid to liquid to gas. Particle motion (whether individual atoms or molecules) in the gas state is almost completely random. Particle motion in the liquid state is limited to within the body of the liquid but the particles can still slip past one another thereby allowing many different permutations (orders) of the same particles. The order of the particles is fixed in the solid state, thereby leaving only vibrational motion to provide for different possible inter-particle configurations.

Table 1.4.3 *Standard Entropies (S°) of Different Phases of Molecular Iodine*

Substance	$I_2(s)$	$I_2(aq)$	$I_2(g)$
S° (J/mol·K)	116	137	261

Quick Check

1. Define "entropy"?

   _____

2. Which of these two elements has greater entropy: Ag(s) or Cu(s)? Explain.

   _____

3. Which of these two compounds has greater entropy: water, $H_2O(l)$, or hydrogen peroxide, $H_2O_2(l)$? Explain.

   _____

Chemical Reactions and Entropy Change

A chemical equation alone does not contain enough information for you to reliably determine whether entropy increases or decreases during the reaction. This can only be determined with certainty by comparing the standard entropies of the reactants and products. The standard entropies are included in the examples below to verify each example's claim regarding entropy change. Thermodynamic data for compounds can be found in a CRC Handbook or other reliable Chemical Handbook.

1. Entropy Changes in Reactions Involving Gases

Combining particles reduces their number but increases their complexity. The reduced number of particles usually decreases entropy more than the increased complexity increases it.

> Entropy usually decreases when gas particles combine into fewer particles.

The entropy of gases is considerably greater than the entropy of solids or liquids. For this reason, the entropy change in reactions involving gases is usually dominated by the increasing or decreasing moles of gas.

In the synthesis of water from its elements, entropy decreases as three gas molecules are organized into two.

$$2\,H_2(g) + O_2(g) \rightarrow 2\,H_2O(g)$$
$$2(131) + 205 \;>\; 2(189) \quad J/K \cdot mol$$

Solids typically decompose by releasing a gas. Entropy increases in the following example as zero gas molecules are converted into one. The standard entropies show that entropy increases mainly because a gas is produced.

$$CaCO_3(s) \rightarrow CaO(s) + CO_2(g)$$
$$93 \;<\; 40 + 214 \quad J/K \cdot mol$$

Despite the following reaction being a synthesis reaction, entropy increases because one gas molecule becomes two.

$$2\,C(s) + O_2(g) \rightarrow 2\,CO(g)$$
$$2(5.7) + 205 \;<\; 2(197.6) \quad J/K \cdot mol$$

If the number of gas molecules doesn't change during the reaction then count the number of atoms that are part of gas molecules. Entropy decreases in the following example as there are 9 atoms (3 CO_2) in reactant gas molecules and only 6 atoms (3 CO) in product gas molecules.

$$2\,Fe(s) + 3\,CO_2(g) \rightarrow Fe_2O_3(s) + 3\,CO(g)$$
$$2(27.3) + 3(213.6) \quad > \quad 87.4 \quad + 3(197.6) \qquad J/K \cdot mol$$

Recall the caution given in the opening paragraph of this subsection. The standard entropies show that entropy increases in the following synthesis reaction despite six gas molecules combining into four. The phosphorus atoms changing from the solid state to the gas state in a compound with hydrogen has a greater influence on the entropy than the reduced number of gas particles.

$$P_4(s) + 6\,H_2(g) \rightarrow 4\,PH_3(g)$$
$$44 + 6(131) \quad < \quad 4(210) \quad J/K \cdot mol$$

2. The Reorganization of Atoms of the Same Element

What if a reaction the number of gas molecules does not change during a reaction and neither does the number of atoms that are part of gas molecules? If reactant molecules change from a solid phase to a liquid phase, entropy is usually increasing. If atoms of the same type, such as those found in a diatomic element, are rearranged into heterogeneous combinations of atoms, entropy is usually increasing.

(a) Phase Changes

Entropy decreases in the reaction below as three of the oxygen atoms go from being part of a gaseous compound (CO_2) to being part of a solid compound (Fe_2O_3). All the other atoms go from reactants to products of the same phase.

$$2\,Fe(s) + 3CO_2(g) \rightarrow Fe_2O_3(s) + 3\,CO(g)$$
$$2(27.3) + 3(213.6) \quad > \quad 87.4 \quad + 3(197.6) \ J/K \cdot mol$$

(b) Chemical Changes

A group of items has less entropy when the common items are grouped together. In the example below, nitrogen and oxygen atoms have less entropy when the "like" atoms are combined together than when the "unlike" atoms are combined.

$$N_2(g) + O_2(g) \rightarrow 2\,NO(g)$$
$$191.5 + 205 \quad < \quad 2(210.7) \quad J/K \cdot mol$$

Recall that a state's entropy increases with the number of ways it can be achieved or expressed. There is only one way to combine two nitrogen atoms ($^aN^bN$) where the superscripts "a" and "b" tag or distinguish the two atoms. Likewise, there is also only one way to combine two oxygen atoms ($^aO^bO$). On the other hand, there are two ways of combining the two nitrogen atoms with the two oxygen atoms to form NO ($^aN^aO$ & $^bN^bO$ or $^aN^bO$ & $^bN^aO$). Since the product condition has more variations (more microstates), it represents the less ordered system and therefore the one with greater entropy.

Entropy increases when common items split up to form or be part of more groups. In the example below, entropy increases as the oxygen atoms go from being in the same molecule (CO_2) to being in two molecules (CO and H_2O).

$$CO_2(g) + H_2(g) \rightarrow CO(g) + H_2O(g)$$
$$213.6 + 130.6 < 197.6 \quad + \quad 188.7 \quad J/K \cdot mol$$

Sample Problems — Predicting by Inspection Whether Entropy Increases or Decreases

Predict whether entropy increases or decreases in each of the following and provide your reasoning:

(a) $PCl_3(g) + Cl_2(g) \rightarrow PCl_5(g)$

(b) $Fe_2O_3(s) + 3\,H_2(g) \rightarrow 2\,Fe(s) + 3\,H_2O(g)$

What to Think About	How to Do It
For both problems, consider (in usual order of importance) the following: 1. Changes in the number of gas particles 2. Reorganization of atoms of the same element	(a) Entropy <u>decreases</u> because two gas molecules combine into one. (b) Entropy <u>increases</u> because there are only six atoms in the reactant gas molecules and there are nine atoms in the product gas molecules..

Practice Problems — Predicting by Inspection Whether Entropy Increases or Decreases

Predict whether entropy increases or decreases in each of the following and provide your reasoning

1. $2\,FeO(s) \rightarrow 2\,Fe(s) + O_2(g)$

2. $S_8(s) + 8\,O_2(g) \rightarrow 8\,SO_2(g)$

3. $H_2O(s) \rightarrow H_2O(l)$

Natural Thermodynamic Drives

Two thermodynamic "drives" influence an equilibrium's position:
1. the drive toward decreasing enthalpy
2. the drive toward increasing entropy or disorder

1. The Drive Toward Decreasing Enthalpy

Objects naturally adopt the lowest energy state available to them. This is illustrated by placing a book on its edge in the trunk of a car. Nobody would expect the book to remain in this position after the car had moved. A slight jostle causes the book to adopt a more stable orientation as it falls onto its face. The book lowers its gravitational potential energy as its center of mass moves closer to Earth. The jostle plays the role of the activation energy in this analogy. This principle applies to all objects including molecules, atoms, and subatomic particles. It is responsible for atoms forming stronger bonding associations with lower potential energy. In other words, chemical reactions tend to proceed in the exothermic direction.

For example, consider this reaction: $N_2(g) + 2\,O_2(g) + 68\ kJ/mol \rightarrow 2\,NO_2(g)$

The tendency toward decreasing enthalpy (energy) pushes this reaction in the exothermic direction toward reactants (Figure 1.4.1).

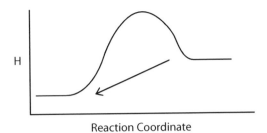

Reaction Coordinate

Figure 1.4.1 *Chemical reactions tend to proceed in the exothermic direction.*

2. The Drive Toward Increasing Entropy

Randomly moving objects such as liquid and gas molecules become disorganized when left on their own. It takes work to collect such objects and to keep them organized. Diffusion is an example of the tendency of objects toward disorder. Diffusion is the self-movement of chemicals from an area of greater concentration to an area of lesser concentration. If you open a bottle of perfume, its molecules will rapidly diffuse throughout the room. This tendency toward increasing entropy applies to chemical changes as well as to physical processes.

Enthalpy, Entropy, and Equilibrium

Chemical reactions are driven toward minimum or decreasing enthalpy and maximum or increasing entropy. If both drives are toward products then the reaction, having no opposition, will achieve an equilibrium position far to the right. If both drives are toward reactants, the forward reaction barely gets going before establishing equilibrium with a position far to the left. From a thermodynamic perspective, equilibria with a "reasonable" proportion of both reactants and products develop as a compromise between the two drives when they oppose each other.

> If the drive toward increasing entropy opposes the drive toward decreasing enthalpy, an equilibrium will develop with a "reasonable" proportion of both reactants and products.

Consider the following two examples:

$2\ CO_2(g) + 566\ kJ/mol \rightarrow 2\ CO(g) + O_2(g)$

Decreasing enthalpy favors reactants.

←――――――――――――

――――――――――――→
Increasing entropy favors products.

$2\ H_2(g) + O_2(g) \rightarrow 2\ H_2O(g) + 483.6\ kJ/mol$

Decreasing enthalpy favors products.

――――――――――――→

←――――――――――――
Increasing entropy favors reactants.

The movement of rainwater is a good thermodynamic model of equilibrium. Water flows downhill and also seeps outward. Consider how rain distributes itself on a street. Some water covers the street but some also collects in the gutters and into puddles (Figure 1.4.2). The puddles and gutters are the low enthalpy–low entropy option while the street surface is the high enthalpy–high entropy option.

Figure 1.4.3 shows the four possible enthalpy-entropy combinations that could occur in a chemical reaction. Both the enthalpy and entropy could increase, they could both decrease, or one could increase and one could decrease. Although Figure 1.4.3 nicely lays out every possible thermodynamic scenario for reactions, there is absolutely no benefit to memorizing it. The thermodynamic drives themselves can easily be applied to any reaction rather than applying a table derived from them.

Figure 1.4.2 *The low enthalpy–low entropy option for water's movement*

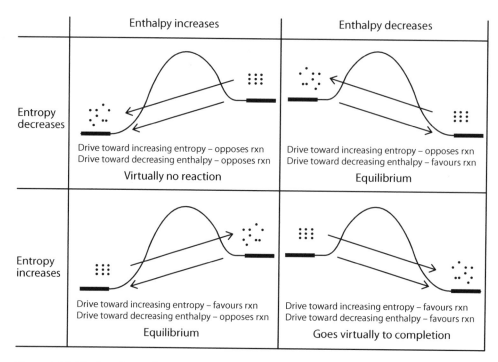

Enthalpy increases	Enthalpy decreases
Entropy decreases Drive toward increasing entropy – opposes rxn Drive toward decreasing enthalpy – opposes rxn **Virtually no reaction**	Drive toward increasing entropy – opposes rxn Drive toward decreasing enthalpy – favours rxn **Equilibrium**
Entropy increases Drive toward increasing entropy – favours rxn Drive toward decreasing enthalpy – opposes rxn **Equilibrium**	Drive toward increasing entropy – favours rxn Drive toward decreasing enthalpy – favours rxn **Goes virtually to completion**

Figure 1.4.3 *The four thermodynamic categories of chemical reactions*

Why does a reaction not go entirely to completion when both drives are toward products? Maximum entropy is achieved just short of the completed reaction because even if the entropy of the products is much greater than the entropy of the reactants, a mixture containing a very small proportion of reactants will have a greater entropy than products alone. Chemists may say that such a reaction "goes to completion" because the equilibrium mixture consists of very nearly pure products.

Likewise, even if both drives are toward reactants, a mixture containing a very small proportion of products will still have greater entropy than the reactants alone. Chemists may say that such a reaction "does not occur" because the equilibrium mixture consists of very nearly pure reactants.

The relationship between enthalpy, entropy, and equilibrium facilitates a popular series of questions where students are directly or indirectly provided with two of these features of a reaction and asked for the third.

Sample Problem — Predicting an Equilibrium's Position from Its Thermodynamics

State whether the following reaction will achieve *equilibrium* (with a reasonable proportion of reactants and products), go nearly to *completion*, or virtually *not occur*.

$$N_2(g) + 3\,H_2(g) \rightarrow 2\,NH_3(g) \qquad \Delta H = -92 \text{ kJ/mol}$$

What to Think About	**How to Do It**

1. Consider the two thermodynamic drives:
  • The drive toward increasing entropy is toward reactants.
  • The drive toward decreasing enthalpy is toward products.
	Since the two drives are opposing each other, the reaction will achieve equilibrium with a reasonable proportion of reactants and products.

© Edvantage Interactive 2016

Sample Problem — Predicting an Equilibrium's Thermodynamics from Its Position

The following equilibrium has a reasonable proportion of reactants and products. State whether the forward reaction is endothermic or exothermic.

$$C(s) + H_2O(g) \rightleftharpoons H_2(g) + CO(g)$$

What to Think About	How to Do It
1. Determine from the equilibrium position whether the drives are opposed, both toward reactants, or both toward products.	The two thermodynamic drives are opposed because the reaction establishes equilibrium with a reasonable proportion of reactants and products.
2. By inspection, determine whether entropy is increasing or decreasing.	Entropy is increasing as one gas molecule reacts to produce two gas molecules.
3. Decide whether the reaction is endothermic or exothermic from steps 1 and 2.	The drives are opposed and the drive toward increasing entropy is toward products. Therefore the drive toward decreasing enthalpy must be toward reactants: the reaction is endothermic.

Practice Problems — Predicting an Equilibrium's Position from Its Thermodynamics or Vice Versa

1. State whether the following reaction will achieve *equilibrium* (with a reasonable proportion of reactants and products), go nearly to *completion*, or almost *not occur*. $\quad 3\,O_2(g) \rightleftharpoons 2\,O_3(g) \quad \Delta H = +285$ kJ/mol

2. The following reaction establishes equilibrium with a reasonable proportion of reactants and products. State whether this reaction is endothermic or exothermic. $\quad CO(g) + H_2O(g) \rightleftharpoons CO_2(g) + H_2(g)$

3. The following equilibrium has a reasonable proportion of reactants and products. State whether entropy increases or decreases during the forward reaction. $\quad CH_2O(g) + O_2(g) \rightleftharpoons CO_2(g) + H_2O(g) \quad \Delta H = -518$ kJ/mol

Enthalpy, Entropy, and Spontaneity

The spontaneity of a reaction is frequently a concern for chemists. A **spontaneous process** is one that happens "on its own" with no outside intervention.

Chemical systems move spontaneously toward equilibrium.

The system's entropy change and enthalpy change both play a role in determining whether or not a reaction is spontaneous. You will learn much more about this in later chemistry courses. Do not confuse whether it's going to happen (spontaneity) with when it's going to happen (how quickly the final condition will be achieved). A spontaneous reaction can occur at a tediously slow rate. Nails spontaneously rust, and diamond spontaneously turns into graphite. Spontaneity is a thermodynamic function and depends only on the conditions at the start and end of the process. Rate is a kinetic function and depends on the path taken between the two. The situation is loosely analogous to children telling their parents that they will take out the kitchen garbage but when this will occur is an entirely different matter.

1.4 Activity: Imitating Disorder

Question

Can you place some black dots in a matrix so that they appear to your classmates to be randomly distributed?

Background

When people attempt to randomize objects in space or time, they tend to err toward an even distribution.
Let's see if you and your classmates can identify which of each other's two matrices contains the set of dots that are actually randomly distributed.

Procedure

1. Attempt to randomly distribute 12 dots within the squares of one of the two matrices below. You may place more than one dot within a square.

2. Randomly place a single dot *in the other matrix* by rolling a dice twice to determine the row and column to place the dot in (e.g., a 1-1 roll would place the dot in the upper left hand corner of the matrix). Repeat this technique 11 more times to produce a matrix that actually contains 12 randomly distributed dots.

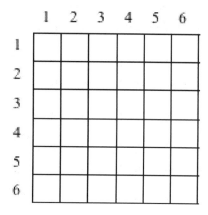

3. Exchange books with 10 classmates. Each time, attempt to identify which of your classmate's two matrices contains the set of dots that are actually randomly distributed.

Continued on next page

© Edvantage Interactive 2016

1.4 Activity: *Continued*

Results and Discussion

1. Keep a record (IIII) in the table below of how many of your classmates chose correctly and how many times you chose correctly.

Your Guesses	
Correct	Incorrect

Your Classmates' Guesses	
Correct	Incorrect

If a person can't tell the difference between the two matrices then there is still a 50% chance that the person will choose the correct matrix. There is only a 17% probability that 7 or more of the 10 people could pick the correct (random) matrix by chance. If this happens, we'll declare your fake "busted." Likewise, if you can correctly identify the random distribution 7 out of 10 times then we'll declare you "randomly gifted."

Each trial tests two things: a person's ability to fake a random distribution and another person's ability to spot the fake. Correctly spotting the random distribution could indicate a "poor" fake or a "good" spotter.

2. Look around the room at your classmates' results and comment on whether there is a relationship between people who are good at faking random patterns and people who are good at recognizing random patterns.

1.4 Review Questions

1. Which substance in each of the following pairs would likely have the greater entropy? Explain.
    (a) $Br_2(l)$ or $Br_2(g)$

    (b) $SO_3(g)$ or $SO_2(g)$

    (c) $Sn(s)$ or $Pb(s)$

2. For each of the following state whether entropy is increasing or decreasing and briefly state your reasoning.
    (a) $2 NH_3(g) \rightarrow N_2(g) + 3 H_2(g)$

    (b) $NOCl_2(g) + NO(g) \rightarrow 2 NOCl(g)$

    (c) $4 Fe(s) + 3 O_2(g) \rightarrow 2 Fe_2O_3(s)$

    (d) $H_2(g) + Cl_2(g) \rightarrow 2 HCl(g)$

    (e) $WO_3(s) + 3 H_2(g) \rightarrow W(s) + 3 H_2O(g)$

3. State whether each of the following reactions will achieve equilibrium with a reasonable amount of reactants and products, go almost to completion, or virtually not occur.

(a) $4\,NH_3(g) + 5\,O_2(g) \rightarrow 4\,NO(g) + 6\,H_2O(g)$ $\Delta H = -907.2$ kJ/mol

(b) $N_2(g) + 2\,O_2(g) \rightarrow 2\,NO_2(g)$ $\Delta H = +68$ kJ/mol

(c) $PCl_3(g) + Cl_2(g) \rightarrow PCl_5(g)$ $\Delta H = -92.5$ kJ/mol

(d) $S(s) + O_2(g) \rightarrow SO_2(g)$ $\Delta H = -297$ kJ/mol

4. For the following reaction, state whether the forward reaction is endothermic or exothermic, given that the two thermodynamic drives are opposed to each other. Explain your reasoning.
$$CaCO_3(s) \rightleftharpoons CaO(s) + CO_2(g)$$

5. Describe the thermodynamics of a reaction that establishes equilibrium so far toward reactants that it is said to virtually not occur.

6. The following equilibrium has a reasonable proportion of reactants and products. State whether entropy is increasing or decreasing during the forward reaction. Explain your reasoning.
$$CO_2(g) + NO(g) \rightleftharpoons NO_2(g) + CO(g) \quad \Delta H = +82 \text{ kJ/mol}$$

7. Given that equilibrium is established with a reasonable proportion of reactants and products, in what direction will the system shift when the temperature is decreased? Explain your reasoning.
$$2\,SO_2(g) + O_2(g) \rightleftharpoons 2\,SO_3(g)$$

8. Why does a reaction that has both thermodynamic drives toward products (the drive toward increasing entropy and the drive toward decreasing enthalpy) not go entirely to completion?

© Edvantage Interactive 2015

1.5 Entropy — A Quantitative Treatment

Warm Up

In Grade 11, you learned that heat flows from a region of high energy to a region of low energy. This might lead to the conclusion that
spontaneous change must be exothermic.

1. Consider the following change occurring at room temperature:

ice cube
(crystal structure)

time →

puddle of water
(no organized structure)

    (a) Is this change spontaneous (did it occur without outside intervention)? _____

    (b) Is this process endothermic or exothermic? _____

    (c) What is the sign of ΔH? _____

2. Consider the change at a molecular level:

      Order   Disorder

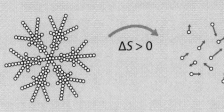

$\Delta S > 0$

      ice   water

    (a) What is the sign for ΔS? _____

    (b) Is this process enthalpy driven or entropy driven? _____

Explain. _____

_____

The First Law of Thermodynamics

Energy is conserved — never created or destroyed. When energy is released by an exothermic change, the potential energy stored in chemical bonds is converted to kinetic energy, which is the energy of motion of atoms and molecules. As the kinetic energy of the atoms and molecules in the system and the surroundings increases, the temperature rises. A system releases heat during an exothermic change. Heat is the energy transferred between a system and its surroundings. By convention, we indicate that the system is releasing heat by placing a negative sign in front of the enthalpy value.

Spontaneous Change

When thermodynamicists say that a reaction is spontaneous, they mean that the reaction will occur without any outside intervention. They do not mean the reaction occurs rapidly.

    In contrast, a non-spontaneous event can continue only as long as it receives some sort of outside assistance. All non-spontaneous events occur at the expense of spontaneous ones. They can occur only when some spontaneous change occurs first.

Enthalpy and Spontaneity

When a change lowers the potential energy of a system, it tends to occur spontaneously. Fuels evolve heat as they combust to form H_2O and CO_2 and convert the potential energy in the bonds of the reactants to heat. Since a change that lowers the potential energy of a system is exothermic, we can say that exothermic changes have a tendency to occur spontaneously.

While many spontaneous changes are indeed exothermic, there are common examples of spontaneous endothermic changes including the melting of ice, the vaporization of water, and the dissolving of most salts in water to form aqueous solutions. Since each of these events is both endothermic AND spontaneous, they must have some other factor in common that allows them to overcome the unfavorable energy change. Careful examination shows that in each of these events, there is an increase in the randomness or disorder of the system. These observations led to the development of the **Second Law of Thermodynamics**.

Figure 1.5.1 *Every spontaneous process increases the entropy of the universe.*

Second Law of Thermodynamics: The entropy of the universe increases with every spontaneous process.

Quick Check

1. Use qualitative reasoning to decide which of the two options in each of these examples will occur spontaneously:

   (a) A mole of ice at 0°C *or* a mole of liquid water at the same temperature

   _____

   (b) Solid sodium chloride in the bottom of a bucket of water *or* a solution of the salt in water

   _____

   (c) A collection of jigsaw pieces *or* the completed puzzle

   _____

   (d) One kilogram of raw rubber *or* 1 kg of vulcanized rubber (Vulcanized rubber is rubber that is polymerized into long chains; vulcanized rubber is used to make tires.)

   _____

   (e) A pack of cards arranged in suits *or* a pack of cards that is randomly shuffled

   _____

The Boltzmann Equation

Ludwig Boltzmann, a famous physicist, studied fluid mechanics in the late 1800s. During this time, Boltzmann determined the probability that a group of particles might occupy a particular set of positions in space at any particular time. These sets of positions are referred to as **microstates**. It has been suggested that this term, microstates (states), may have led to the symbol **S** being selected to represent entropy. Boltzmann noted that entropy is directly proportional to the natural log of the number of microstates available. In 1872, Boltzmann derived his famous equation to represent entropy:

$$S = k_B \ln W$$

where S = entropy

k_B = Boltzmann's constant = R/N_A = $\dfrac{8.314 \text{ L·kPa/mol·K}}{6.02 \times 10^{23} \text{ mol}^{-1}}$ = 1.38×10^{-23} J/K

W = number of microstates

© Edvantage Interactive 2016

In a pure crystal at absolute zero (0 K), the particles orient themselves in only one possible microstate. At absolute zero, the entropy is $S = 1.38 \times 10^{-23}$ J/K (ln 1). Since the natural log of 1 = 0, the *entropy of a pure crystal at 0 K equals zero*. This is the **Third Law of Thermodynamics**.

> **Third Law of Thermodynamics:** The entropy of a *pure crystal* at absolute zero is zero ($S = 1.38 \times 10^{-23}$ J/K $\times$ ln (1) = 0).

Increasing the number of electrons in an element or increasing the number of atoms in a molecule leads to an increase in entropy. More electrons or atoms mean more possible microstates and therefore a higher entropy according to the Boltzmann equation.

The Second Law of Thermodynamics states "the entropy of the universe increases with every spontaneous change." The "universe" is the *system* plus the *surroundings* and the entropy of a system is a quantitative measure of the disorder or randomness within a system. There are two kinds of disorder in a system: **positional disorder**, depending on the arrangement of particles (molecules and atoms) in space, and **thermal disorder**, depending on how the total energy is distributed among all the particles. The more random the distribution of particles in space, the higher the entropy. The more randomly energy is distributed among the particles, the greater the entropy.

Table 1.5.1 shows all possible arrangements for two identical particles among three relative energy levels. The most likely total energy is 2 kJ. Maximizing positional disorder does not necessarily lead to maximum overall energy.

Table 1.5.1 *All possible two-particle arrangements among three relative energy levels*

Energy Level	Particle Arrangements					
2 kJ			X		X	XX
1 kJ		X		XX	X	
0 kJ	XX	X	X			
Total energy	0 kJ	1 kJ	2 kJ	2 kJ	3 kJ	4 kJ

Adding heat to a system results in greater disorder and, therefore, greater entropy. The entropy increase is directly proportional to the amount of heat added. However, the increase in entropy is more significant when we add heat to a system at a lower temperature where little disorder exists, rather than at high temperature where there is already substantial disorder. For a given quantity of heat, the entropy change is inversely proportional to the temperature at which we add the heat. Thus entropy can be determined as:

$$S_{surroundings} = \frac{q}{T} = \frac{-\Delta H}{T}$$

The equation above shows that entropy has units of energy divided by temperature (J/K). If an entropy change is being calculated for a particular quantity of material undergoing a physical or chemical change, the units may be J/K·mol.

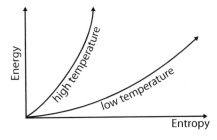

Figure 1.5.2 *The change in entropy (ΔS) is most noticeable at a low temperature.*

Quick Check

1. When 1.0 mole of steam condenses to form 1.0 mole of liquid water at 100.0°C, 40.7 kJ of heat is released. What is ΔS for the surroundings?

2. Select the example with greater entropy in each case.

    (a) $F_2(g)$ or $Cl_2(g)$

    (b) $CO_2(g)$ or $CO(g)$

    (c)

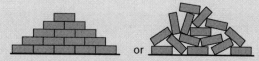
    or

Entropy Is a State Function

We know the Third Law of Thermodynamics states that at absolute zero, the entropy of a pure crystal is equal to zero joules. Mathematically, we can state:

$$S = 0 \text{ J when } W = 1 \text{ at } T = 0 \text{ K}$$

Entropy has a value of 0 J at absolute zero and it is therefore possible to determine the amount of entropy that a substance possesses at temperatures above 0 K. If we determine the entropy of 1 mole of a substance at a temperature of 298 K (25°C) and a pressure of 1 atm, we call it the standard entropy or $S°$. Standard entropy values at STP for several species are listed in the appropriate table. (Notice that the standard entropy values of pure elements in their standard states are *not* equal to zero because standard entropy values are not recorded at 0 K.) Once we know the entropies of a variety of substances we can calculate the standard entropy change, or $\Delta S°$, for chemical reactions in the same way as we calculated $\Delta H°$ earlier.

Entropy is a state function — it is not pathway dependent. Therefore, we can use the same logic as that of a Hess's Law type of calculation to determine the entropy change for a given chemical reaction. It is important to note that like enthalpy, entropy is an extensive property — it depends on the amount of substance present. This means that the number of moles of all species in the reaction must be taken into account. Hence:

$$\Delta S°_{reaction} = \sum nS°_{products} - \sum nS°_{reactants}$$

For a process to be spontaneous, there must be an overall increase in the entropy of the universe. If the entropy change of the universe is negative, the process is non-spontaneous. For an individual reaction, which would be the system, the change may be spontaneous, even if the entropy change for the reaction is negative. However the overall change in entropy of the universe (system + surroundings) as a result of the reaction would be positive .

© Edvantage Interactive 2016

Sample Problem — Quantifying Entropy Change

Urea (from urine) hydrolyzes slowly in the presence of water to produce ammonia and carbon dioxide.

$$CO(NH_2)_2(aq) + H_2O(l) \rightarrow CO_2(g) + 2 NH_3(g)$$

What is the standard entropy change, for this reaction when 1 mol of urea reacts with water? Is the process spontaneous? The standard entropies for reactants and products are:

Substance	$S°$ (J mol^{-1} K^{-1})	Substance	$S°$ (J mol^{-1} K^{-1})
$CO(NH_2)_2(aq)$	173.7	$CO_2(g)$	213.8
$H_2O(l)$	70.0	$NH_3(g)$	192.8

What to Think About

1. Calculate the change in entropy using the equation:

$$\Delta S°_{rxn} = \sum n S°_{products} - \sum n S°_{reactants}$$

2. After determining the stoichiometrically correct entropy values, substitute and solve.

3. Does the answer make sense?
   One mole of aqueous substance and 1 mole of liquid form *3 moles of gas*.

4. What does the answer mean?

How to Do It

Determine $S°$ values for all reactants and products. These are listed in the table given above in this example.

$$\left[\frac{1 \text{ mol } CO_2}{\text{mol rxn}} \times \frac{213.8 \text{ J}}{\text{mol K}} + \frac{2 \text{ mol } NH_3}{\text{mol rxn}} \times \frac{192.8 \text{ J}}{\text{mol K}} \right] -$$

$$\left[\frac{1 \text{ mol } CO(NH_2)_2}{\text{mol rxn}} \times \frac{173.7 \text{ J}}{\text{mol K}} + \frac{1 \text{ mol } H_2O}{\text{mol rxn}} \times \frac{70.0 \text{ J}}{\text{mol K}} \right]$$

$$= 599.4 - 243.7 = 355.7 \text{ J/mol}_{rxn} \cdot K$$

The number of microstates (W) has increased. So we expect a positive ΔS value. ✓

A positive ΔS value is indicative of a spontaneous change

Practice Problems — Quantifying Entropy Change

1. Use qualitative reasoning (no calculations are necessary) to predict whether the entropy change in each of the following processes is positive or negative. Does the entropy change of the system favor spontaneous change or not?
   (a) The evaporation of 1 mole of rubbing alcohol

   (b) $2 Ca(s) + O_2(g) \rightarrow 2 CaO(s)$

   (c) $XeF_4(g) \rightarrow Xe(g) + 2 F_2(g)$

   (d) The dilution of an aqueous solution of lime Kool-Aid

2. Use a standard entropy table to calculate the standard entropy change for each of the following reactions. Is the reaction thermodynamically favorable (spontaneous) based on the $\Delta S°$ value?
   (a) $CaO(s) + 2 HCl(g) \rightarrow CaCl_2(s) + H_2O(l)$

   (b) $C_2H_4(g) + H_2(g) \rightarrow C_2H_6(g)$

1.5 Review Questions

1. Predict the sign you would expect for $\Delta S°$ in each of the following processes. Give a short explanation of why you think it is (+) or (−). Do NOT do any calculations.

   (a) Blowing up a building

   (b) Organizing a stack of files in alphabetical order

   (c) $AgCl(s) \rightarrow Ag^+(aq) + Cl^-(aq)$

   (d) $2\,H_2(g) + O_2(g) \rightarrow 2\,H_2O(l)$

   (e) $Na(s) + \frac{1}{2}\,Cl_2(g) \rightarrow NaCl(s)$

   (f) Removing medication from bottles and organizing the pills by the day in "blister packs"

2. Predict the sign of $\Delta S°$ you would expect for each of the following changes. Give a short explanation of why you think it is (+) or (−). Do NOT do any calculations.

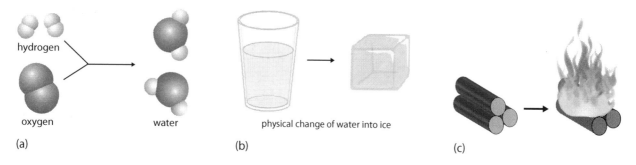

hydrogen

oxygen   water

(a)

physical change of water into ice

(b)

(c)

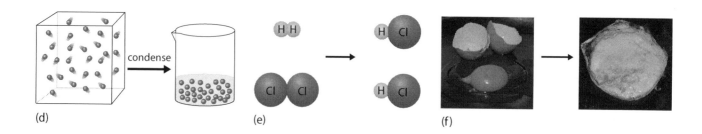

condense

(d)

H H

Cl Cl

H Cl

H Cl

(e)

(f)

© Edvantage Interactive 2016

3. The boiling point of chloroform ($CHCl_3$) is 61.7°C. The enthalpy of vaporization is 31.4 kJ/mol. Calculate the entropy of vaporization. Does the sign for entropy of vaporization make sense? Explain.

4. (a) What is the normal boiling point for formic acid, HCOOH?
   Given: $\Delta H_f^\circ = -424.72$ kJ/mol for liquid HCOOH and -379.1 kJ/mol for gaseous HCOOH
   $S^\circ = 128.95$ J/mol K for liquid HCOOH and 251.0 J/mol K for gaseous HCOOH

   (b) Based on the calculated boiling point, in what state does formic acid exist at room temperature? Explain.

5. The normal boiling point of water is 100.0°C, and its molar enthalpy of vaporization is 40.7 kJ/mol. What is the change in entropy in the system in J/K when 39.3 g of steam at 1 atm condenses to a liquid at the normal boiling point? Does the sign for the value you calculate make sense? Explain.

6. Iodine is an unusual element that sublimes under standard conditions. If the ΔS_{subl}° of iodine is 145 J/mol K and the ΔH_{subl}° of iodine is 62 kJ/mol, what is the standard sublimation temperature for iodine?

7. Consider the following addition reaction: $C_2H_2(g) + 2\ H_2(g) \rightarrow C_2H_6(g)$
   The following data is known for this reaction:

Substance	S° (J/mol K)	ΔH_f (kJ/mol)
$C_2H_2(g)$	200.9	226.7
$H_2(g)$	130.7	0
$C_2H_6(g)$	????	−84.7

   (a) If the value of ΔS° for the reaction is −232.7 J/mol K, calculate the value of S° for C_2H_6 gas.

   (b) Calculate the enthalpy change ΔH° for the reaction.

(c) Assume that Boltzmann's equation (page 183) applies when the system is in equilibrium. What is the temperature at this point (use the non-SI unit of °C)?

8. Consider the following reaction: $2 H_2S(g) + SO_2(g) \rightarrow 3 S(s) + 2 H_2O(g)$
   (a) Predict the sign of $\Delta S°$ for the reaction at 298 K. Explain the basis of your prediction.

   (b) Calculate the actual value of $\Delta S°$ for the reaction. Assume the sulfur produced is the *rhombic* form. Does your calculation justify your prediction? Explain.

   (c) Assume that Boltzmann's equation (page 183) applies when the system is in equilibrium. What is the temperature at this point (use the non-SI unit of °C)?

9. The combustion of methanol is described by the following equation:

$$2 CH_3OH(l) + 3 O_2(g) \rightarrow 4 H_2O(l) + 2 CO_2(g)$$

The value of $\Delta S°$ for this reaction is –38.6 cal/mol K at 25°C. One calorie is the energy required to warm 1 g of water by 1°C. One calorie is equivalent to 4.18 J.
Data collected for this reaction:

Reaction Species	$\Delta H_f°$ (kcal/mol) at SATP	$S°$ (cal/mol K) at SATP
$CH_3OH(l)$	–57.0	30.3
$H_2O(l)$	–68.3	16.7
$CO_2(g)$	–94.0	51.1

Calculate the standard absolute entropy $S°$ per mole of $O_2(g)$. Convert this value to units of J/mol K.

© Edvantage Interactive 2016

10. Use a standard entropy table to calculate $\Delta S°$ for each of the following equations. (It is important to refer to a recommended source for reference values to ensure consistency in answers.)

(a) $H_2(g) + \frac{1}{2} O_2(g) \rightarrow H_2O(g)$

(b) $3 O_2(g) \rightarrow 2 O_3(g)$

(c) $CH_4(g) + 2 O_2(g) \rightarrow CO_2(g) + 2 H_2O(g)$

(d) $P_4O_{10}(s) + 6 H_2O(l) \rightarrow 4 H_3PO_4(s)$
(Given $S°$ for solid phosphoric acid = 110.54 J/mol K.)

(e) The complete combustion of octane in gasoline

1.6 Gibbs Free Energy

Warm Up

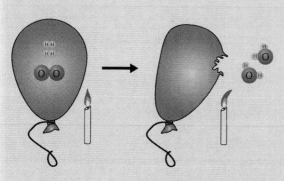

1. Write a balanced chemical equation (including phase subscripts) for the reaction shown in the diagram.

2. Use a standard enthalpy table to calculate ΔH_{rxn} and ΔS_{rxn} for the reaction.

3. What is the function of the candle in this process?

_____

4. Is this spontaneous process *enthalpy driven* or *entropy driven*? Explain.

_____

_____

_____

Free Energy — Enthalpy and Entropy Combine

We have now seen that two factors — enthalpy and entropy — determine whether or not a physical or chemical event is spontaneous or thermodynamically favorable. Sometimes these two factors work together. For example, when a stone wall crumbles, its enthalpy decreases and its entropy increases. Since a decrease in enthalpy and an increase in entropy both favor a spontaneous change, the two factors complement one another. In other situations, the effects of enthalpy and entropy are in opposition. Such is the case in the melting of ice, the vaporization of water and even the formation of water from its elements as in the Warm Up.

When enthalpy and entropy effects oppose one another, the overall reaction spontaneity is less obvious. We can determine the net effect of the two factors through another thermodynamic quantity called **Gibbs free energy, G**, named after Josiah Willard Gibbs (1839–1903), a U.S. scientist (Figure 1.6.1). Gibbs free energy is defined as: $G = H - TS$. For a chemical or physical *change* at constant temperature and pressure, the equation becomes:

$$\Delta G = \Delta H - T\Delta S$$

A change is spontaneous only if it is accompanied by a decrease in free energy. In other words, ΔG must be negative for a spontaneous change. A spontaneous change is also termed a **thermodynamically favorable** change.

Spontaneous change must be accompanied by a decrease in free energy. That is, ΔG must be *NEGATIVE* for a spontaneous change.

Table 1.6.1 shows the effects of positive and negative values of ΔH and ΔS on ΔG. The table shows the importance of the absolute temperature in determining whether a change will occur spontaneously. Temperature is important in cases where ΔH and ΔS have the same signs.

Table 1.6.1 *Impact of ΔH and ΔS at various temperatures on the thermodynamic favorability (spontaneity) of chemical reactions*

ΔH	ΔS	ΔG	Reaction Characteristics	Examples
−	+	Always negative	Reaction is spontaneous at all temperatures; reverse reaction is always non-spontaneous.	$2\,O_3(g) \rightarrow 3\,O_2(g)$
+	−	Always positive	Reaction is non-spontaneous at all temperatures; reverse reaction occurs spontaneously.	$3\,O_2(g) \rightarrow 2\,O_3(g)$
−	−	Negative at low temps; positive at high temps	Reaction is spontaneous at low temperatures and becomes non-spontaneous as temperature is raised.	$CaO(s) + CO_2(g) \rightarrow CaCO_3(s)$
+	+	Positive at low temps; negative at high temps	Reaction is non-spontaneous at low temperatures but becomes spontaneous as temperature is raised.	$CaCO_3(s) \rightarrow CaO(s) + CO_2(g)$

Reactions that occur with a free energy decrease in the system are **exergonic**. Those that occur with a free energy increase are **endergonic**.

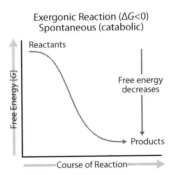
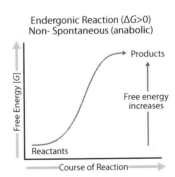

Figure 1.6.2 *Exergonic (left) and endergonic reactions*

The terms *exergonic* and *endergonic* are most commonly applied in biological contexts (Figure 1.6.2). Catabolic processes break down large proteins and lipids into amino and fatty acids producing many small molecules, each resulting in a large number of bond formations. These catabolic processes are exergonic. Anabolic processes form biological macromolecules following a multitude of bond breakages. Anabolic processes are endergonic. Essentially, *anabolic processes* are "powered" by *catabolic processes* during the metabolic processes that occur in our bodies. When one reaction is "powered" by another, the reactions are said to be **coupled**.

Figure 1.6.1 *American scientist Josiah Willard Gibbs*

Free Energy and Maximum Work

Spontaneous chemical reactions perform useful work. The burning of fuels in heat engines, chemical reactions in batteries, and the catabolic portion of metabolism within our bodies are all spontaneous processes that produce useful work. We cannot harness all of the energy released when spontaneous chemical reactions occur. Some energy is lost as heat. Engineers seek to maximize the efficiency of converting chemical energy to work and to minimize the amount of energy transferred unproductively to the environment as heat.

Is there a limit to the amount of energy in a reaction that can be harnessed as useful work? The maximum amount of energy we can harness from a reaction, as work is equal to ΔG. This is the energy that is not lost as heat and is *therefore free* (or available) to be used for work. By determining the value of ΔG, we can find out whether or not a given reaction will be an effective source of energy. By comparing the actual work derived from a given system with the ΔG value for the reactions involved, we can measure the efficiency of the system.

Free Energy and Equilibrium

Reactions with a negative free energy change are spontaneous (thermodynamically favorable), while those with a positive free energy change are non-spontaneous. The negative sign in front of the Free Energy value indicates that the energy is released in the process. A positive sign in front of the Free Energy value indicates that Free Energy from the surrounding is required to drive the process All reactions proceed spontaneously until they reach equilibrium. When the value of ΔG is equal to zero, the reaction is at equilibrium. We will learn later that at equilibrium the forward and reverse reactions occur at equal rates.

For the state change, $H_2O(l) \rightleftharpoons H_2O(s)$, equilibrium exists at 0°C and atmospheric pressure. Above 0°C, only liquid water can exist, and below 0°C, all the liquid will freeze to form ice. This gives us an interesting relationship between ΔH and ΔS.

$$\Delta G = 0 = \Delta H - T\Delta S$$

Therefore at equilibrium, $\Delta H = T\Delta S$; and

$$\Delta S_{system} = \frac{\Delta H}{T}$$

Thus, if we know ΔH and ΔS, we can calculate the temperature at which equilibrium will occur. This is the temperature at which a state change occurs.

Quick Check

1. For the process $Br_2(l) \rightleftharpoons Br_2(g)$, $\Delta H = +31.0$ kJ/mol and $\Delta S = 92.9$ J/mol K.

   (a) Explain why a (+) value for the enthalpy change is reasonable for this process.

   _____

   _____

   (b) Why would we expect the entropy change to be (+) for this process?

   _____

   (c) Assuming that ΔH and ΔS are temperature independent, calculate the temperature at which $Br_2(l)$ will be in equilibrium with $Br_2(g)$. Give the answer in °C.

   _____

   (d) What property does this temperature represent for bromine?

   _____

About the same time the American Josiah Gibbs derived the free energy equation, German physicist Hermann von Helmholtz deduced the same thing. For this reason, the Gibbs-Helmholtz equation is a common name for $\Delta G = \Delta H - T\Delta S$. The equation is valid under all temperature, pressure, and concentration conditions. We will begin by restricting all of our calculations to standard conditions of pressure (1 atm) and concentration (1 M, where it applies). In other words, we will use the equation in the form:

$$\Delta G° = \Delta H° - T\Delta S$$

Where $\Delta G°$ is the standard free energy change (determined at 1 atm, 1 M), $\Delta H°$ is the standard enthalpy change calculated from reference values, $\Delta S°$ is the standard entropy change calculated from reference values, and T is the Kelvin temperature.

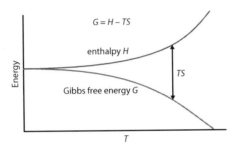

Figure 1.6.3 *This graph of energy vs. temperature shows that the difference between enthalpy (H) and free energy (G) is equal to TS. The graph shows that as the temperature increases, the difference between these two forms of energy becomes larger.*

Since enthalpy and entropy are state functions, it follows that Gibbs free energy is also a state function. We can use Hess's law and we can calculate standard free energies of formation as follows:

$$\Delta G° = \sum n\Delta G°_{prod} - \sum n\Delta G°_{react}$$

Note: $\Delta G°_f = 0$ for an element in its normal state at 25°C and 1 atm.

Sample Problem — Using the Gibbs-Helmholtz Equation to Calculate a Free Energy Change at Standard Temperature

For the process $NaCl(s) \rightarrow Na^+(aq) + Cl^-(aq)$, use tables to calculate:

(a) $\Delta H°$

(b) $\Delta S°$

(c) Use the values from (a) and (b) to calculate $\Delta G°$.

(d) According to your results, is this a spontaneous process?

What to Think About

1. As $\Delta H°$ is a state function, calculate it. The $\Delta H_f°$ values are listed in the appropriate table.

   Notice that while *elements in their standard states have $\Delta H_f°$ values of 0 kJ/mol*, this is *not* the case for ions in solution.

2. We use a similar process to determine $\Delta S°$. Absolute entropy values of formation $S_f°$ are in the appropriate table.

3. Instructions indicate that you should calculate $\Delta G°$ using the answers to (a) and (b). Use the Gibbs- Helmholtz equation.

   *It is important to ensure that the **units are consistent** throughout the equation.* In other words, you must convert $\Delta S°$ to kJ/K mol before substituting the values into the Gibbs equation.

   *In general, if a question requiring the Gibbs Equation does not provide a specific temperature, assume **SATP conditions (or $T = 25°C = 298$ K) apply**.* The presence of the ° symbol, however, does **not** restrict all calculations to a temperature of 25°C.

4. A (–) ΔG value indicates spontaneity (also called **thermodynamic favorability**) though the magnitude is not very large.

How to Do It

a) $\Delta H°_{(overall)} = \Sigma n \Delta H°_{f(prod)} - \Sigma n \Delta H°_{f(react)}$

$\Delta H_f°$ for $Na^+(aq) = -240.12$ kJ/mol

$\Delta H_f°$ for $Cl^-(aq) = -167.16$ kJ/mol

$\Delta H_f°$ for $NaCl(s) = -411.15$ kJ/mol

$\Delta H° = \left[\dfrac{1 \; mol \; Na^+}{mol \; rxn}\left(\dfrac{-240.12 \; kJ}{mol \; Na^+}\right) + \dfrac{1 \; mol \; Cl^-}{mol \; rxn}\left(\dfrac{-167.16 \; kJ}{mol \; Cl^-}\right)\right]$

$\left[-\dfrac{1 \; mol \; NaCl}{mol \; rxn}\left(\dfrac{-411.15 \; kJ}{mol \; NaCl}\right)\right] = 3.87$ kJ/mol rxn

(b) $\Delta S° = \Sigma n S°_{prod} - \Sigma n S°_{react}$

$S_f°$ for $Na^+(aq) = 59.0$ J/K mol

$S_f°$ for $Cl^-(aq) = 56.5$ J/K mol

$S_f°$ for $NaCl(s) = 72.13$ J/K mol

$\Delta S° = \left[\dfrac{1 \; mol \; Na^+}{mol \; rxn}\left(\dfrac{0.0590 \; kJ}{K \; mol \; Na^+}\right) + \dfrac{1 \; mol \; Cl^-}{mol \; rxn}\left(\dfrac{0.0565 \; kJ}{K \; mol \; Cl^-}\right)\right]$

$-\left[\dfrac{1 \; mol \; NaCl}{mol \; rxn}\left(\dfrac{0.07213 \; kJ}{K \; mol \; NaCl}\right)\right] = 0.04337$ kJ/K mol rxn

(c) $\Delta G° = \Delta H° - T\Delta S°$

$\Delta G° = 3.87 \dfrac{kJ}{mol_{rxn}} - 298 \; K \left(\dfrac{0.04337 \; kJ}{K \; mol_{rxn}}\right)$

$= -9.05$ kJ/mol$_{rxn}$

(d) The dissolving of the salt has a (–) ΔG value meaning it is spontaneous as would be expected for dissolving a salt at room temperature.

In fact, endothermicity and an increased number of microstates also make sense for the dissolving process. This process is entropy driven.

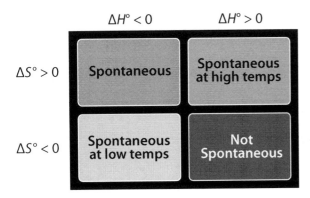

	$\Delta H° < 0$	$\Delta H° > 0$
$\Delta S° > 0$	Spontaneous	Spontaneous at high temps
$\Delta S° < 0$	Spontaneous at low temps	Not Spontaneous

Figure 1.6.4 *Examination of the equation, $\Delta G° = \Delta H° - T\Delta S°$, shows that if $\Delta H°$ and $\Delta S°$ share the same sign, temperature will determine spontaneity. The temperature at which $\Delta H°$ and the term $T\Delta S°$ are equal is the temperature at which equilibrium will occur. "High" and "low" temperatures are relative and refer to temperatures above or below the equilibrium T value.*

It is significant that $\Delta S°$ values are usually very small compared to $\Delta H°$. Only multiplication by T causes subtraction of the $T\Delta S°$ term from $\Delta H°$ to have a significant impact on the value of $\Delta G°$. In an example such as the dissolving of table salt, both $\Delta H°$ and $\Delta S°$ are positive. This dissolution process is spontaneous only when the temperature is large enough to allow subtraction of the $T\Delta S°$ term from $\Delta H°$ to result in a negative $\Delta G°$.

The values of standard free energies of formation of pure compounds and elements and aqueous ions are listed in the appropriate table. As is the case for the $S°$ and $\Delta H_f°$ values in the appendix, standard conditions for $\Delta G_f°$ are 25°C and 1 atm.

Sample Problem — Using Free Energies of Formation to Calculate a Free Energy Change at Standard Temperature

For the process $NaCl(s) \rightarrow Na^+(aq) + Cl^-(aq)$, use tables to calculate:

(a) $\Delta G°$

(b) According to your results in (a), is this a spontaneous process?

What to Think About

1. As $\Delta G°$ is a state function, calculate the value using the equation introduced earlier in this section. The $\Delta G_f°$ values are listed in the provided table.

   As with $\Delta H°_f$ values, **elements in their standard states have $\Delta G_f°$ values of 0 kJ/mol**. This is *not* the case for ions in solution.

   The value calculated for $\Delta G°$ using reference values and the state function equation is very close to the value calculated using the Gibbs-Helmholtz equation. Using the state function algorithm to calculate $\Delta H°$ and $\Delta S°$ values introduces further approximations due to rounding to appropriate significant figures. This leads to differences between the two calculated values.

2. A (−) ΔG value indicates spontaneity even though the magnitude is not very large.

How to Do It

(a) $\Delta G° = \Sigma n \Delta G°_{(prod)} - \Sigma n \Delta G°_{(react)}$

$\Delta G_f°$ for $Na^+(aq) = -261.91$ kJ/mol

$\Delta G_f°$ for $Cl^-(aq) = -131.23$ kJ/mol

$\Delta G_f°$ for $NaCl(s) = -384.12$ kJ/mol

$\Delta G° = \left[\dfrac{1 \text{ mol } Na^+}{\text{mol rxn}} \left(\dfrac{-261.91 \text{ kJ}}{\text{mol } Na^+} \right) + \dfrac{1 \text{ mol } Cl^-}{\text{mol rxn}} \left(\dfrac{-131.23 \text{ kJ}}{\text{mol } Cl^-} \right) \right]$

$\left[\dfrac{1 \text{ mol } NaCl}{\text{mol rxn}} \left(\dfrac{-384.12 \text{ kJ}}{\text{mol } NaCl} \right) \right] = -9.02$ kJ/mol rxn

b) This is a spontaneous process. This makes sense for the dissolving of a salt at room temperature. We know that virtually all salts dissolve spontaneously at room temperature. This is generally entropy driven. It is interesting that the dissolving of NaCl is very nearly at equilibrium under SATP conditions.

© Edvantage Interactive 2016

Practice Problems — Using the Gibbs-Helmholtz Equation and Free Energies of Formation to Calculate a Free Energy Change at Standard Temperature

1. Use the ΔG_f° values to calculate ΔG_{comb}° for the combustion of ethanol under SATP conditions.

2. Calculate the maximum work available from the oxidation of 1 mole of octane at 25°C and 1 atm. Use the ΔH_f° and the S_f° values from a standard enthalpy table along with the Gibbs-Helmholtz equation.

3. Calculate ΔG_{rxn}° for the reaction of $N_2(g) + O_2(g) \rightarrow 2\,NO(g)$. Do the calculation *two* ways. First by determining ΔH_f°, then ΔS_f° followed by the Gibbs-Helmholtz equation. Then use the ΔG_f° values and see how the values compare.

Calculation of Free Energy at Non-Standard Temperatures

ΔG° *is the most temperature dependent* of the thermodynamic functions. We can use the Gibbs-Helmholtz equation to calculate ΔG° at temperatures other than 25°C. To do this, we neglect the variations of ΔH° and ΔS° with temperature because they are relatively temperature independent quantities compared to ΔG°.

ΔH° is essentially independent of temperature and the variations of ΔS° with temperature are ordinarily very small — entropy is most dependent on temperature near absolute zero. Near room temperature, variations in ΔS° are negligible.

In other words, we take the values of ΔH° and ΔS° from the tables and simply insert them into the Gibbs-Helmholtz equation using the appropriate value of T (in Kelvin degrees) to calculate ΔG°.

© Edvantage Interactive 2016

Sample Problem — Using the the Gibbs-Helmholtz Equation to Calculate a Free Energy Change at Non-Standard Temperatures

Calculate $\Delta G°$ for the reaction $Cu(s) + H_2O(g) \rightarrow CuO(s) + H_2(g)$ at a temperature of 227.0°C.

What to Think About	**How to Do It**
1. As the temperature is non-standard, you must use the Gibbs-Helmholtz equation to solve the problem.	$\Delta H°_{(overall)} = \Sigma n\Delta H°_{f(prod)} - \Sigma n\Delta H°_{f(react)}$
2. Use reference tables to determine the $\Delta H°$ and $\Delta S°$ values of each compound or element in the reaction first.	$\Delta H°_f$ for CuO (s) $= -157.3$ kJ/mol $\Delta H°_f$ for H_2 (g) $= 0$ kJ/mol $\Delta H°_f$ for Cu (s) $= 0$ kJ/mol $\Delta H°_f$ for H_2O (g) $= -241.82$ kJ/mol
3. Calculate the overall enthalpy change for the reaction.	$\Delta H° = \left[\dfrac{1 \text{ mol CuO}}{\text{mol rxn}}\left(\dfrac{-157.3 \text{ kJ}}{\text{mol CuO}}\right) + \dfrac{1 \text{ mol } H_2}{\text{mol rxn}}\left(\dfrac{0 \text{ kJ}}{\text{mol } H_2}\right)\right]$ $- \left[\dfrac{1 \text{ mol Cu}}{\text{mol rxn}}\left(\dfrac{0 \text{ kJ}}{\text{mol Cu}}\right) + \dfrac{1 \text{ mol } H_2O}{\text{mol rxn}}\left(\dfrac{-241.82 \text{ kJ}}{1 \text{ mol rxn}}\right)\right]$ $= 84.5 \text{ kJ/mol}_{rxn}$
4. Evaluate the sign of the enthalpy value and its significance.	A slightly endothermic process
5. Calculate the overall entropy change for the reaction	$\Delta S° = \Sigma n S°_{(prod)} - \Sigma n S°_{(react)}$ $S°_f$ for CuO (s) $= 42.63$ J/K mol $S°_f$ for H_2 (g) $= 130.68$ J/K mol $S°_f$ for Cu (s) $= 33.15$ J/K mol $S°_f$ for H_2O (g) $= 188.83$ J/K mol $\Delta S° = \left[\dfrac{1 \text{ mol CuO}}{\text{mol rxn}}\left(\dfrac{42.63 \text{ kJ}}{K \text{ mol CuO}}\right) + \dfrac{1 \text{ mol } H_2}{\text{mol rxn}}\left(\dfrac{130.68 \text{ kJ}}{K \text{ mol } H_2}\right)\right]$ $- \left[\dfrac{1 \text{ mol Cu}}{\text{mol rxn}}\left(\dfrac{33.15 \text{ kJ}}{K \text{ mol Cu}}\right) + \dfrac{1 \text{ mol } H_2O}{\text{mol rxn}}\left(\dfrac{188.83 \text{ kJ}}{K \text{ mol rxn}}\right)\right]$ $= -48.67 \text{ kJ/mol}_{rxn} K$
6. Consider the sign of the overall entropy change of the reaction and its significance.	A (−) value for ΔS makes sense as the O atoms have moved from a gaseous compound to a solid compound. Additionally the H has moved from gaseous water where it was combined with oxygen to pure gaseous hydrogen.
7. Finally, use the Gibbs-Helmholtz equation to calculate $\Delta G°$ at a temperature of 227.0 °C, but first convert the temperature to Kelvin degrees.	$227 °C\left(\dfrac{1 K}{1 °C}\right) + 273 K = 500. K$ $\Delta G° = \Delta H° - T\Delta S°$ $\Delta G° = 84.5 \dfrac{\text{kJ}}{\text{mol}_{rxn}} - 500. K\left(\dfrac{-0.04867 \text{ kJ}}{K \text{ mol}_{rxn}}\right)$ $= 108.8 \text{ kJ/mol}_{rxn}$ Note that the (+) $\Delta G°$ value indicates a non-spontaneous reaction. The (+) $\Delta H°$ and the (−) $\Delta S°$ both favor a non-spontaneous reaction. Hence this reaction would be non-spontaneous under any temperature conditions.

Practice Problems — Using the Gibbs-Helmholtz Equation to Calculate a Free Energy Change at Non-Standard Temperatures

1. The mineral calcite decomposes according to the following reaction:

    $CaCO_3(s) \rightarrow CaO(s) + CO_2(g)$ in which $\Delta H° = 178.3$ kJ/mol$_{rxn}$ and $\Delta S° = 160.6$ J/mol$_{rxn}$ K.

    (a) Calculate $\Delta G°$ at 750.0°C.

    (b) Calculate $\Delta G°$ at 950.0°C.

    (c) Does the reaction become more or less spontaneous (thermodynamically favorable) as temperature increases?

Experimental Manipulation of the Gibbs-Helmholtz Free Energy Equation

We can arrange the equation, $G = H – TS$ to the form $G = –ST + H$. A plot of G vs. T will be a straight line with a slope of $–S$ and a y-intercept of H. Various experiments may be set up to study the variables in the Gibbs-Helmholtz equation. These experiments produce graphs such as those shown in Figure 1.6.5.

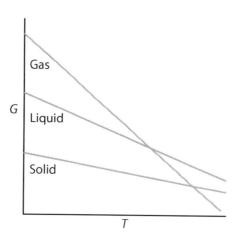

Figure 1.6.5 *The graph above shows that free energy (G) varies with temperature (T).*

Since all chemical species have a positive value for entropy, G decreases with an increase in temperature (at constant pressure and state). Gases have far greater entropy than liquids, which have greater entropy than solids. Figure 1.6.5 shows the free energies of gases are more temperature dependent than liquids, which are more temperature sensitive than solids.

The direct measurement of free energy is not easily accomplished. In the next section, we will apply our understanding of equilibrium to a more detailed investigation of free energy and how it varies with temperature.

1.6 Review Questions

1. (a) What two factors, other than temperature, influence the spontaneity of a process?

    (b) Describe each factor.

    (c) What sign is associated with spontaneity for each factor?

2. Complete the following table for the equation: $\Delta G° = \Delta H° - T\Delta S°$.

Sign of $\Delta H°$	Sign of $\Delta S°$	Temperature	Sign of $\Delta G°$	Spontaneous /Non-Spontaneous
–	+	low		
–	+	high		
+	–	low		
+	–	high		
–	–		–	
+	+			spontaneous
–	–	high		
+	+		+	

3. Examine the representation of ice melting and water condensing on a glass of ice water. Consider circled areas A and B.
    Circle A:
    (i) What are the signs of $\Delta H°$ and $\Delta S°$ for this process? Explain your answers.

    (ii) Is this process spontaneous at all temperatures, only low temperatures, only high temperatures or never? Explain.

    Circle B:
    (i) What are the signs of $\Delta H°$ and $\Delta S°$ for this process? Explain your answers.

    (ii) Is this process spontaneous at all temperatures, only low temperatures, only high temperatures or never? Explain.

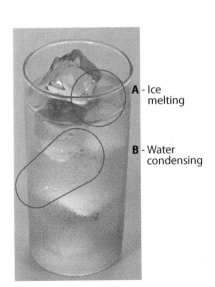

A - Ice melting

B - Water condensing

4. $\Delta H°$ is -196.1 kJ/mol$_{rxn}$ for the following representation of a reaction of $H_2O_2(l)$.

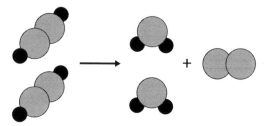

(a) What are the signs of $\Delta S°$ and $\Delta G°$ for the reaction? Explain.

(b) Is the process spontaneous at all temperatures, only low temperatures, only high temperatures or never? Explain.

5. (a) Use the representation below to produce a balanced chemical equation. Use the lowest possible whole number coefficients in your equation.

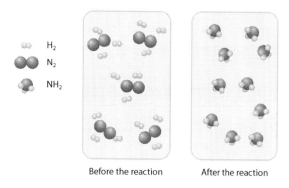

H$_2$

N$_2$

NH$_2$

Before the reaction   After the reaction

(b) Use the appropriate table to calculate $\Delta H°_{rxn}$ for the reaction. Show your work.

(c) Predict the *sign* of $\Delta S°_{rxn}$ for the reaction (do not calculate).

(d) Is this process spontaneous at all temperatures, only low temperatures, only high temperatures or never? Explain.

(e) Determine the temperature (in °C) at which the spontaneity of this reaction changes.

6. Shiny silver iodine crystals are deposited on the surface of ice placed into a test tube filled with purple iodine vapor.

    (a) Write a balanced chemical equation to describe the process pictured here.

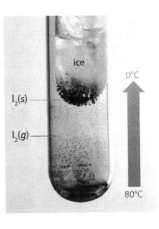

ice

0°C

$I_2(s)$

$I_2(g)$

80°C

    (b) Calculate the sublimation temperature (same as the deposition temperature) for iodine.

7. Consider the following reaction: $2 O_3(g) \rightarrow 3 O_2(g)$. $\Delta H° = -285.4$ kJ/mol$_{rxn}$.
    (a) Predict the signs for $\Delta S°_{rxn}$ and $\Delta G°_{rxn}$ and the spontaneity of the reaction (no calculations required).

    (b) Calculate $\Delta S°_{rxn}$ and $\Delta G°_{rxn}$ and to determine the accuracy of your prediction.

8. Calculate $\Delta G°_{rxn}$ for each of the following reactions.
    (a) $NH_3(g) + HCl(g) \rightarrow NH_4Cl(s)$

    (b) $AgNO_3(aq) + NaI(aq) \rightarrow AgI(s) + NaNO_3(aq)$ (Hint: Use the net ionic equation.)

    (c) $P_4O_{10}(s) + H_2O(l) \rightarrow H_3PO_4(l)$ (Hint: The reaction is unbalanced.)

9. Government requirements in the United States and Canada state that fuels should contain a "renewable" component. Fermentation of glucose isolated from a variety of garden products such as sugar cane, beets, and corn produces ethanol. Producers can add ethanol to gasoline to fulfill the renewable fuel requirement. Here is the fermentation reaction for glucose:
    $C_6H_{12}O_6(s) \rightarrow 2 C_2H_5OH(l) + 2 CO_2(g)$

Calculate:

(a) $\Delta H°$

(b) $\Delta S°$

(c) $\Delta G°$

(d) Under what temperature conditions does this reaction occur spontaneously? Justify.

(e) How might this impact the economic feasibility of producing renewable fuels in this way?

10. In low concentrations, phosgene is a colorless to pale yellow cloud with the pleasant odor of freshly cut hay. In higher concentrations, phosgene becomes a choking agent toxic to the pulmonary system. Armies used phosgene to kill hundreds of people during the World War 1. Carbon monoxide and chlorine combine to form phosgene, $COCl_2(g)$.

(a) Calculate $\Delta S°_{rxn}$ given that $\Delta H° = -220.$ kJ/mol$_{rxn}$ and $\Delta G° = -206$ kJ/mol$_{rxn}$ at 25 °C.

(b) The $(-)\Delta G°$ value means the production of the war gas is spontaneous under SATP conditions. Considering the signs of $\Delta S°$ and $\Delta H°$, what temperature conditions should further favor the spontaneous production of phosgene?

(c) Assuming the temperature effects on $\Delta S°$ and $\Delta H°$ are negligible, calculate $\Delta G°$ at 435°C. Is the reaction spontaneous at this higher temperature?

© Edvantage Interactive 2016

2 Reaction Kinetics

By the end of this chapter, you should be able to do the following:

- Demonstrate awareness that reactions occur at differing rates
- Experimentally determine rate of a reaction
- Demonstrate knowledge of collision theory
- Describe the energies associated with reactants becoming products
- Apply collision theory to explain how reaction rates can be changed
- Analyze the reaction mechanism for a reacting system
- Represent graphically the energy changes associated with catalyzed and uncatalyzed reactions
- Describe the uses of specific catalysts in a variety of situations

By the end of this chapter, you should know the meaning of these **key terms**:

- activated complex
- activation energy
- bimolecular
- catalyst
- catalytic converter
- collision theory
- ΔH notation
- elementary processes
- endothermic
- enthalpy
- enzymes
- exothermic
- heterogeneous catalysts
- homogeneous catalysts
- initial rate
- integrated rate law
- KE distribution curve
- kinetic energy (KE),
- metalloenzymes
- molecularity
- overall order
- potential energy (PE)
- product
- rate-determining step
- reactant
- reaction intermediate
- reaction mechanism
- reaction rate
- successful collision
- termolecular
- thermochemical equation

External tanks of liquid oxygen and hydrogen fuel react to create the energy needed to launch a rocket carrying the space shuttle.

2.1 Measuring the Rate of Chemical Reactions

Warm Up

In previous years, you were introduced to the concept of rate of change in the position of an object as it moves. You learned that this is the object's velocity. If we don't consider the object's direction, we might use the more general terms, "speed" or "rate." Velocity is a vector quantity while speed is a scalar quantity. When dealing with chemical reactions, we need not concern ourselves with vectors.

Assume a vehicle moves the following distances over the stated periods of time as it travels from the eastern Fraser Valley into Vancouver:

What is the average velocity (rate) of the car (over the entire time period)?

(a) in km/min _____

(b) in km/h _____

(c) Why do we refer to this as an *average* rate?

_____

_____

(d) A unit of _____ is always placed in the denominator when calculating rate.

Distance Travelled (km)	Time (min)
0	0
22	20.0
62	50.0
117	90.0
125	100.0

Measuring Reaction Rate

Chemical reactions involve the conversion of reactants with a particular set of properties into products with a whole new set of properties.

Chemical kinetics is the investigation of the rate at which these reactions occur and the factors that affect them.

If you consider familiar reactions like the explosion of a firecracker, the metabolism of the lunch you ate today and the rusting of your bicycle, it is evident that chemical reactions occur at a wide variety of rates (Figure 2.1.1).

Time for reaction: < 1 s   several hours   weeks to many months

Figure 2.1.1 *An explosion, food digestion, and rusting metal all involve chemical reactions but at very different rates.*

Reaction rates may be determined by observing either the disappearance of a reactant or the appearance of a product. Deciding exactly what to measure can be a tricky business. There are several things the chemist needs to consider:

• Is there a measurable property associated with the change in quantity of a reactant or product you might use to determine the rate?

- Exactly how might you measure the quantity of reactant or product in the laboratory?
- Finally, what units would be associated with the quantity you measure and consequently, what units will represent the reaction rate?

Once these questions have been answered, it is simply a matter of determining the rate using the following equation:

$$\text{average reaction rate} = \frac{\text{change in a measurable quantity of a chemical species}}{\text{change in time}}$$

Experimentally, it turns out that, for most reactions, the rate is greatest at the beginning of the reaction and decreases as the reaction continues. Because the rate changes as a reaction proceeds, reaction rates are generally expressed as averages over a particular time period. As reactants are being consumed during a reaction, the forward rate might be thought of as having a negative value. However, we generally report the rate as an absolute or positive value.

Quick Check

Thionyl chloride is a reactive compound used in a variety of organic synthesis reactions. Due to its potential to release dangerous gases explosively on contact with water, it is controlled under the Chemical Weapons Convention in the United States. It can be decomposed in solution with an organic solvent according to the reaction:

$SO_2Cl_2(soln) \rightarrow SO_2(g) + Cl_2(g)$

Removal of small samples called aliquots and titration of these samples as the reaction proceeds produces the data given in the table on the next page.

Note: Ideally, a reaction should be *monitored* as it proceeds without interference. In a technique such as this, it is critical to remove as small an aliquot as possible so that the sampling's interference with the subject reaction is minimal. It is also important to complete the titration as quickly as possible because the reaction, of course, continues to occur within the sample. Nonetheless, removal and sampling of small aliquots is one technique for monitoring the rate of a chemical reaction.

Use the grid provided on the next page to produce a graph of concentration of thionyl chloride versus time.

[SO$_2$Cl$_2$] (mol/L)	Time (seconds)
0.200	0
0.160	100.
0.127	200.
0.100	300.
0.080	400.
0.067	500.
0.060	600.

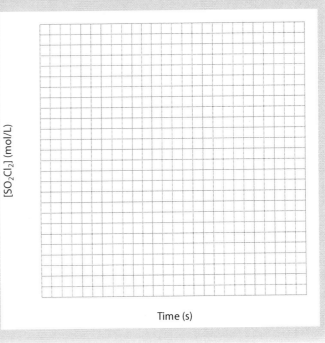

(Quick Check continued on next page)

Quick Check (continued)

1. What would the slope of this graph ($\Delta[SO_2Cl_2]/\Delta$time) represent?

    _____

2. How does the slope of the graph change as time passes?

    _____

3. What does this indicate about the reaction rate?

    _____

4. What is the average rate of decomposition of thionyl choride?

    _____

5. How does the rate at 500 s compare to the rate at 300 s?

    _____

6. Suggest a way to determine the rate at the particular times mentioned in question 5. The rates at those particular instants are called **instantaneous rates**.

    _____

    _____

7. Calculate the instantaneous rates of reaction at 500 s and 300 s (if you're unsure of how to do this, ask a classmate or your teacher).

Reaction Measuring Techniques

The technique used to measure the change in the quantity of reactant or product varies greatly depending on the reaction involved and the available apparatus. In many cases, the reactant or product involved in a reaction may be measured directly. As in the Quick Check above, the concentration of a reactant in solution may be determined from time to time as the reaction proceeds by the titration of an aliquot of the reacting species. If a gas is being formed or consumed in a closed system, a manometer may be used to measure the change in pressure (Figure 2.1.2(a)). Gas production might also be measured using a pneumatic trough and a gas volume measuring tube called a eudiometer (Figure 2.1.2(b)). Of course, if a gas is leaving an open system, there will be a change in mass that could easily be measured using a balance.

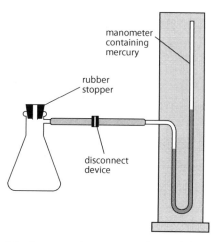

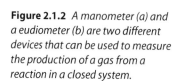

Figure 2.1.2 *A manometer (a) and a eudiometer (b) are two different devices that can be used to measure the production of a gas from a reaction in a closed system.*

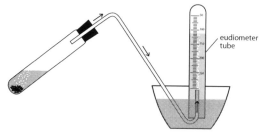

(a) A manometer measures the partial pressure of a gas formed in a reaction

(b) A eudiometer measures the volume of gas produced during a reaction.

© Edvantage Interactive 2016

If the amount of a reactant or a product can't be monitored directly, a chemist can monitor some property of the reacting mixture that correlates in a known manner with the quantity of a reactant or a product. If a reaction is occurring in aqueous solution, the solution's color and pH (acidity) are properties that might indicate the quantity of reactant or product present.

A pH electrode is one type of ion selective electrode (ISE) that can be used to measure acidity. The concentrations of many types of ions can be measured with different ISEs. The ion's concentration correlates with the charge that builds up as the ion diffuses across the ISE's membrane. It is simplest if only one chemical involved in the reaction affects the monitored property. If the property is influenced by more than one chemical, then their relative influences must be known. Reactions involving color changes may be colorimetrically analyzed using a spectrophotometer.

Sample Problem — Determining the Rate of a Reaction in the Laboratory State

five different methods for measuring the rate of the reaction of an iron nail in concentrated hydrochloric acid.

What to Think About

1. Begin by writing a balanced chemical equation. It is very important to consider the states (and any colors) of all species.

2. Decide if there is a property associated with the quantity of reactant consumed or product produced that you might measure to monitor the reaction rate.

3. Decide exactly how you might measure this property and what unit would be associated with it.

How to Do It

$$Fe(s) + 2 HCl(aq) \rightarrow FeCl_2(aq) + H_2(g)$$

colorless   yellow-orange color (like rust)

The first species, Fe(s) is a solid that will be consumed during the reaction.

A balance could be used to determine the mass of the iron before and after the reaction was completed. The time would also need to be recorded.

The resulting rate of reaction would be recorded in units of g Fe used/unit of time.

4. A repeat of the same steps would reveal more than five different ways to determine the rate of this particular reaction. Other answers might include:

$\dfrac{\Delta[HCl]}{time}$	$\dfrac{\Delta pH}{time}$	$\dfrac{\Delta Vol\ H_2}{time}$	$\dfrac{\Delta P_{(H_2)}}{time}$	$\dfrac{\Delta mass_{H_2}}{time}$
titrate	pH meter	eudiometer	manometer	balance (open system)
M/s	pH units/s	mL/s	kPa/s	g/s

Practice Problems — Determining the Rate of a Reaction in the Laboratory

1. Indicate two methods for determining the rate of each of the following reactions:

   (a) $Cu(s) + 2\,AgNO_3(aq) \rightarrow Cu(NO_3)_2(aq) + 2\,Ag(s)$ (Cu^{2+} ions are blue.)

   (b) $PCl_5(g) \rightarrow PCl_3(g) + Cl_2(g)$

   (c) $CaCO_3(s) \rightarrow CaO(s) + CO_2(g)$

   (d) $H_2SO_4(aq) + Ba(OH)_2(aq) \rightarrow BaSO_4(s) + 2\,H_2O(l)$

2. Why would volume of water **not** be an acceptable answer for question 1(d) above?

3. Why would concentration of copper metal, $[Cu(s)]$, **not** be an acceptable answer for question 1(a) above?

Calculating Reaction Rate

Once the chemist has decided what quantity of a particular chemical species to measure, he or she may begin to gather data. These data may be used to calculate the rate of the chemical reaction. Data may be presented graphically to monitor the rate throughout the entire reaction, or initial and final data may be used to determine the reaction's average rate as indicated earlier.

$$\text{average reaction rate} = \frac{\Delta \text{ measurable quantity of a chemical species}}{\Delta \text{ time}}$$

As chemistry often involves the application of a balanced chemical equation, it is possible to convert from the rate of one reacting species to another by the simple application of a **mole ratio**.

Sample Problem — Calculating Average Rate from Laboratory Data

A paraffin candle ($C_{28}H_{58}$) is placed in a petri dish on an electronic balance and combusted for a period of 15.0 min. The accompanying data is collected.

(a) Calculate the average rate of combustion of the paraffin over the entire 15 min period.

(b) Calculate the average rate of formation of water vapor for the same period.

(c) Note the mass loss in each 3.0 min time increment. Comment on the rate of combustion of the candle during the entire trial. Suggest a reason why the rate of this reaction isn't greatest at the beginning, with a steady decrease as time passes.

(d) Why don't the mass values drop in a completely constant fashion?

Time (min)	Mass (g)
0	180.00
3.0	178.00
6.0	175.98
9.0	173.99
12.0	172.00
15.0	170.01

Continued opposite

© Edvantage Interactive 2016

Sample Problem (Continued)

What to Think About

1. Write a balanced chemical equation. Hydrocarbon combustion always involves reaction with oxygen to form water vapor and carbon dioxide.

2. Think about the system carefully. Consider the balanced equation. What is causing the loss of mass?

Question (a)

3. Apply the equation with appropriate significant figures to calculate the rate.
   Note that the rate is a negative value as paraffin is lost. To simplify things, reactant and product rates are often expressed as absolute values. Consequently they appear positive.

Question (b)

4. Now apply appropriate molar masses along with the mole ratio to convert the rate of consumption of paraffin to the rate of formation of water vapor as follows:

   mass paraffin (per minute)
   → moles paraffin
   → moles water vapor
   → mass water vapor (per min)

Question (c)

5. Notice the mass loss in each 3.0 min time increment recorded in the table.

Question (d)

6. Explain why the mass values do not drop in a completely constant fashion.

How to Do It

$$2\,C_{28}H_{58}(s) + 85\,O_2(g) \rightarrow$$
$$56\,CO_2(g) + 58\,H_2O(g)$$

In this case, all mass loss is due to the combusted paraffin. This paraffin is converted into two different gases: carbon dioxide and water vapor.

$$\frac{170.01\ g - 180.00\ g}{15.0\ min - 0\ min} = -0.666\ g/min$$

$$\frac{0.666\ g\ C_{28}H_{58}}{min} \times \frac{1\ mol\ C_{28}H_{58}}{394.0\ g\ C_{28}H_{58}}$$

$$\times \frac{58\ mol\ H_2O}{2\ mol\ C_{28}H_{58}} \times \frac{18.0\ g\ H_2O}{1\ mol\ H_2O}$$

$$= 0.882\ g\ H_2O/min$$

The rate of consumption of paraffin seems to be nearly constant. This may be due to the $[O_2]$ being very plentiful and so essentially constant. As well, the quantity of molten paraffin at the reacting surface stays constant through the entire reaction. As this reaction proceeds, there is no decrease in [reactants] to lead to a decrease in reaction rate.

There is some variation in rate. This is due to the expected uncertainty associated with all measuring devices (in this case, the balance).

Practice Problems — Calculating Average Rate

1. A piece of zinc metal is placed into a beaker containing an aqueous solution of hydrochloric acid. The volume of hydrogen gas formed is measured by water displacement in a eudiometer every 30.0 s. The volume is converted to STP conditions and recorded.

   (a) Determine the average rate of consumption of zinc metal over the entire 150.0 s in units of g/min.

Volume H_2 (STP) (mL)	0	15.0	21.0	24.0	25.0	25.0
Time (seconds)	0	30.0	60.0	90.0	120.0	150.0

   (b) When is the reaction rate the greatest?

   (c) What is the rate from 120.0 to 150.0 s?

   (d) Assuming there is still a small bit of zinc left in the beaker, how would you explain the rate at this point?

2. A 3.45 g piece of marble ($CaCO_3$) is weighed and dropped into a beaker containing 1.00 L of hydrochloric acid. The marble is completely gone 4.50 min later. Calculate the average rate of reaction of HCl in mol/L/s. Note that the volume of the system remains at 1.00 L through the entire reaction.

Using Rate as a Conversion Factor

In Grade 11, you may have learned about **derived units**. A derived unit is a unit that consists of two or more other units. A quantity expressed with a derived unit may be used to convert a unit that measures one thing into a unit that measures something else completely. One of the most common examples is the use of a rate to convert between distance and time.

The keys to this type of problem are:
- determining which form of the conversion factor to use, and
- deciding where to start.

Sample Problem — Using Rate as a Conversion Factor

A popular organic chemistry demonstration is the dehydration of sucrose, $C_{12}H_{22}O_{11}$, using sulfuric acid to catalyze the dehydration. The acid is required for the reaction, but it is still present once the reaction is complete, primarily in its intact form and partially as dissolved sulfur oxides in the water formed. Because of this, it does not appear at all in the reaction. The product is a large carbon cylinder standing in a small puddle of water as follows: $C_{12}H_{22}O_{11}(s) \rightarrow 1\,H_2O(g) + 12\,C(s)$. Due to the exothermicity of the reaction, much of the water is released as steam, some of which contains dissolved oxides of sulfur. Ask your teacher to perform the demonstration for you, ideally in a fume hood.

Given a rate of decomposition of sucrose of 0.825 mol/min, how many grams of C(s) could be formed in 30.0 s?

Continued opposite

© Edvantage Interactive 2016

Sample Problem (Continued)

What to Think About

1. In this problem, you want to determine the mass of carbon in grams. Essentially, the question is: Do you use the rate as is or do you take the reciprocal? As time needs to be cancelled, use the rate as is. Once you have determined the need to convert time into mass, consider which form of the conversion factor to use.

2. Now design a "plan" for the "conversion route," using the rate, the mole ratio, and the molar mass.

How to Do It

As your answer contains one unit, begin with a number having one unit, in this case the time.

time → moles sucrose → moles carbon → mass of carbon

$$30.0 \text{ s} \times \frac{1 \text{ min}}{60 \text{ s}} \times \frac{0.825 \text{ mol } C_{12}H_{22}O_{11}}{1 \text{ min}}$$

$$\times \frac{12 \text{ mol C}}{1 \text{ mol } C_{12}H_{22}O_{11}} \times \frac{12.0 \text{ g C}}{1 \text{ mol C}}$$

$$= 59.4 \text{ g C}$$

Practice Problems — Using Rate as a Conversion Factor

1. Ozone is an important component of the atmosphere that protects us from the ultraviolet rays of the Sun. Certain pollutants encourage the following decomposition of ozone: $2 O_3(g) \rightarrow 3 O_2(g)$, at a rate of $6.5 \times 10^{-4} \text{ M } O_3/\text{s}$. How many molecules of O_2 gas are formed in each liter of atmosphere every day by this process? (As this problem provides a rate in units of mol/L/s and requires molecules/L as an answer, we can simply leave the unit "L" in the denominator the entire time.)

2. Propane gas combusts in camp stoves to produce energy to heat your dinner. How long would it take to produce 6.75 L of CO_2 gas measured at STP? Assume the gas is combusted at a rate of 1.10 g C_3H_8/min. Begin by writing a balanced equation for the combustion of C_3H_8.

3. A 2.65 g sample of calcium metal is placed into water. The metal is completely consumed in 25.0 s. Assuming the density of water is 1.00 g/mL at the reaction temperature, how long would it take to consume 5.00 mL of water as it converts into calcium hydroxide and hydrogen gas?

2.1 Review Questions

1. Give three reasons why the distance-time data in the Warm Up at the beginning of this section is so different from the property-time data collected for a typical chemical reaction.

2. Consider the following reaction, which could be done in either flask, using any of the equipment shown:

$$6 \, Cu(s) + 8 \, HNO_3(aq) + O_2(g) \rightarrow 6 \, CuNO_3(aq) + 4 \, H_2O(l) + 2 \, NO_2(g)$$

(a) If 5.00 g of copper solid is completely reacted in 250.0 mL of excess nitric acid in 7.00 min at STP, calculate the rate of the reaction in:

(i) g Cu/min

(ii) g NO_2/min

(iii) mol HNO_3/min

(b) Assume the reaction continues at this average rate for 10.0 min total time. Determine the final:

(i) mL NO_2 formed at STP

(ii) molarity of $CuNO_3$

(c) Describe SIX ways you might measure the reaction rate. Include the equipment required, measurements made and units for the rate. You may use a labeled diagram.

© Edvantage Interactive 2016

3. Consider the graph for the following reaction:
   $CaCO_3(s) + 2 HCl(aq) \rightarrow CaCl_2(aq) + CO_2(g) + H_2O(l)$

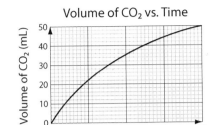

Volume of CO_2 vs. Time

Recall the discussion of the *instantaneous rate* earlier in this section.

(a) Determine the instantaneous rate at the following times:
   (i) an instant after 0 min (This is the *initial rate.*)

   (ii) 1 min

   (iv) 4 min

(b) How do these rates compare? What do you suppose causes this pattern?

4. Here is a table indicating the volume of gas collected as a disk of strontium metal reacts in a solution of hydrochloric acid for 1 min.
   $Sr(s) + 2 HCl(aq) \rightarrow SrCl_2(aq) + H_2(g)$

Time (seconds)	Volume of Hydrogen at STP (mL)
0	0
10.0	22.0
20.0	40.0
30.0	55.0
40.0	65.0
50.0	72.0
60.0	72.0

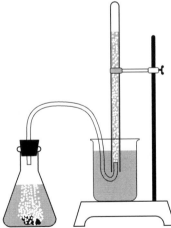

(a) Calculate the average rate of reaction in moles of HCl consumed/second over the first 50.0 s.

(b) Calculate the mass of strontium consumed in this 50.0 s period.

(c) Why did the volume of gas collected decrease in each increment until 50.0 s?

(d) Why did the volume of gas remain unchanged from 50.0 s to 60.0 s?

5. The spectrophotometer works by shining a single wavelength of light through a sample of a colored solution. A photocell detects the amount of light that passes through the solution as **% transmittance** and the amount of light that does not pass through as the **absorbance**. The more concentrated the solution, the darker the color. Dark color leads to a lower percentage of light transmitted and thus a higher absorbance. There is a direct relationship between absorbance and the concentration of a colored solution. The "calibration curve" (actually a straight line) below was created using solutions of *known* $Cu(NO_3)_2$ concentration.

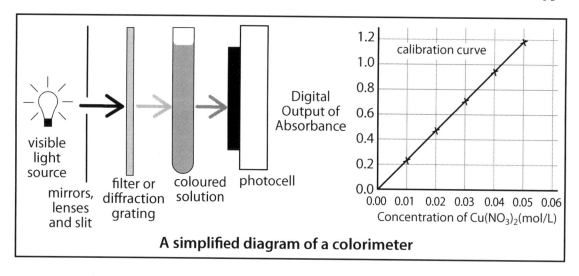

A simplified diagram of a colorimeter

A copper sample was reacted with 250 mL of nitric acid by the following reaction:

$$3\ Cu(s) + 8\ HNO_3(aq) \rightarrow 3\ Cu(NO_3)_2(aq) + 2\ NO(g) + 4\ H_2O(l)$$

As the reaction proceeded, small aliquots were removed and placed in a cuvette (the special test tube used to hold a sample in the spectrophotometer). The cuvettes were then placed in the instrument and the absorbances were recorded as follows:

Time (seconds)	Absorbances (no unit)	Concentration of Copper(II) Ion (mol/L)
0	0	0 mol/L
20.	0.40	
40.	0.70	
60.	0.90	
80.	1.00	

Find the absorbances on the standard graph and record the corresponding concentrations of the copper(II) ions (equal to the concentration of $Cu(NO_3)_2$) in the table.

(a) Calculate the average rate of the reaction from time 0 s to 80. s in units of $ML^{-1}s^{-1}$ of $HNO_3(aq)$.

(b) What mass of $Cu(s)$ will be consumed during the 80. s trial?

(c) What will you observe in the main reaction flask as the reaction proceeds?

2.2 Factors Affecting Rates of Reaction

Factors Affecting Reaction Rate

In section 2.1, we discovered that reactions tend to slow down as they proceed. What might cause this phenomenon? What is true about a reacting system when it contains lots of reactants? Consideration of this question leads us to recognize there are more particles available to react when a reaction first starts. Intuition tells us in order for a reaction to occur, the reacting particles must contact each other. If this is so, anything that results in an increased frequency of particle contact must make a reaction occur faster.

The three factors of surface area, concentration, and temperature may all be manipulated to increase the frequency with which particles come together. Different chemicals inherently react at different rates so the nature of the reactants affects reaction rate. Finally, you may recall from previous years that a chemical species called a *catalyst* may be used to increase the rate of a reaction. We will consider each of these five factors in turn.

Surface Area

Most reactions in the lab are carried out in solution or in the gas phase. In these states, the reactants are able to intermingle on the molecular or atomic level and contact each other easily. When reactants are present in different states in a reacting system, we say the reaction is **heterogeneous.** Most heterogeneous systems involve the reaction of a *solid* with a solution or a gas. In a heterogeneous reaction, the reactants are able to come into contact with each other only where they meet at the interface between the two phases. The size of the area of contact determines the rate of the reaction. Decreasing the size of the pieces of solid reactant will increase the area of contact (Figure 2.2.1).

Increasing the surface area of a solid will increase the rate of a heterogeneous reaction.

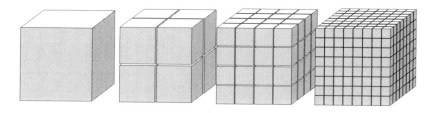

Figure 2.2.1 *Increasing the number of pieces leads to a significant increase in the surface area.*

Concentration (Pressure)

The rates of all reactions are affected by the concentrations of the dissolved or gaseous reactants. When more solute is placed in the same volume of solvent, the solution's concentration is increased (Figure 2.2.2).

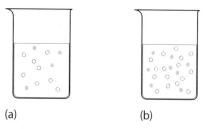

(a)   (b)

Figure 2.2.2 *Solution (b) contains twice the number of solute particles in the same volume as solution (a). The opportunity for particle contact is doubled in solution (b).*

When more gas particles are placed in the same volume of a container, the **partial pressure** of the gas has increased. In Figure 2.2.3, container (b) has twice as many gas particles in the same volume as container (a). This, of course, means the concentration has been doubled. We might also say the *partial pressure* of the gas has doubled. In container (c), the piston has been lowered to half the volume. The result is another doubling of concentration (and pressure).

© Edvantage Interactive 2016

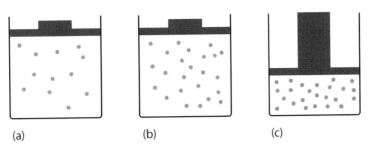

Figure 2.2.3 *The partial pressure in (b) is greater than in (a) because of the increased concentration of particles. In (c, decreasing the volume increases the concentration and the pressure.*

Increasing the concentration (or partial pressure of a gas) will increase the rate of a chemical reaction.

Always remember the concentration of pure solids and liquids cannot be increased because adding more substance increases both the moles and the liters, so the molarity or moles per liter remains constant. Also remember that crushing or breaking a solid will increase its surface area. However it is impossible to cut a piece of liquid or gas into smaller bits. The surface area of liquids can be increased by spreading them over a larger area.

Temperature

There is a qualitative relationship between temperature and kinetic energy. Mathematically speaking, $KE = 3/2RT$ where R is a constant having the value 8.31 J/mol K, and T is the Kelvin temperature. From this relationship, we see that temperature and kinetic energy are directly related to one another. If the temperature is doubled, the kinetic energy is doubled (as long as the temperature is expressed in units of Kelvin degrees).

An increase in temperature will lead to particles striking one another more frequently. However, we now see that it will also result in the particles striking one another with more energy. In other words, an increase in temperature means that the same particles are travelling faster. As a consequence, they hit each other more frequently and more forcefully. As a result, *temperature is the most significant factor* that affects reaction rate.

Another thing you may have learned in previous years is within any substance there is a "normal" distribution of kinetic energies among the particles that make up the system due to their random collisions. Such a distribution might be graphed as shown in Figure 2.2.4.

Fraction of Particles vs. Kinetic Energy

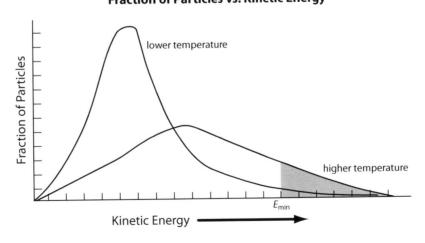

Figure 2.2.4 *Kinetic energy shows a "normal" distribution at both lower and higher temperatures.*

Note that some of the particles have very little energy and others have a lot. The *x*-axis value associated with the peak of the curve indicates the kinetic energy of most of the particles. The second curve indicates how the distribution would change if the temperature were increased. The area under the curves represents the total number of particles and therefore should be the same for both curves. The gray area represents the particles that have sufficient energy to *collide successfully* and produce a product. Notice that this has increased with an increase in temperature. A common generalization is that an increase of 10°C will double reaction rate. This is true for some reactions around room temperature.

Increasing temperature will increase the rate of a reaction for *two* reasons: *more frequent* and *more forceful* collisions.

The Nature of Reactants

Fundamental differences in chemical reactivity are a major factor in determining the rate of a chemical reaction. For instance, zinc metal oxidizes quickly when exposed to air and moisture, while iron reacts much more slowly under the same conditions. For this reason, zinc is used to protect the integrity of the iron beneath it in galvanized nails.

Generally reactions between simple monoatomic ions such as Ag^+ and Cl^- are almost instantaneous. This is due to ions being extremely mobile, in close proximity to one another, having opposite charges, and requiring no bond rearrangement to react. However, more complicated ionic species such as CH_3COO^- react more slowly than those that are monoatomic.

In general, differences in chemical reactivity can be attributed to factors that affect the breaking and forming of chemical bonds. Ionization energy, electronegativity, ionic and molecular polarity, size, and complexity of structure are some of these factors. The state of the reacting species may also play a role.

In general, at room temperature the rate of (*aq*) reactants > (*g*) > (*l*) > (*s*).

Precipitation occurs quickly between ions in solution. In Figure 2.2.5(a), the AgCl forms as a heavy, white precipitate the instant the silver ions contact the chloride in solution. In (b), the $AgCH_3COO$ precipitate is less heavy and forms over a period of 10 s to 20 s. The complex structure of the acetate ion makes it more difficult to achieve the correct orientation to bond successfully.

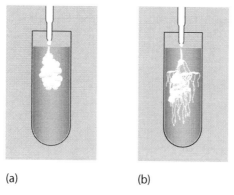

(a)   (b)

Figure 2.2.5 *(a) AgCl quickly forms a precipitate. (b) AgCH$_3$COO forms a precipitate more slowly.*

© Edvantage Interactive 2016

Presence of a Catalyst

Catalysts are substances that increase the rates of chemical reactions without being used up. Because they remain in the same quantity and form when a reaction is completed, the formulas of catalysts are not included in the chemical reaction. Sometimes the formula is shown above the arrow between the reactants and products like this:

$$2\,H_2O_2(l) \xrightarrow{MnO_2} 2\,H_2O(l) + O_2(g)$$

What actually happens is that catalysts are consumed during an intermediate step in a reaction and regenerated in a later step. The catalysts most familiar to you are probably the enzymes produced by living organisms as they catalyze digestive and other biochemical processes in our bodies. We will discuss catalysts in more detail later in this chapter.

The reaction depicted in graduated cylinders in Figure 2.2.6 is the catalyzed decomposition of hydrogen peroxide as shown in the equation above. In addition to the H_2O_2, there is a bit of dish soap and some dye in the cylinders so the oxygen gas bubbles through the soap solution and produces foam. This demonstration is often called "elephant toothpaste." Note that the cylinder in (b) contained 30% hydrogen peroxide while the cylinder in (a) was only 6%, so the effect of concentration was demonstrated in addition to the catalytic effect.

> A catalyst increases reaction rate without itself being consumed or altered.

An **inhibitor** is a species that reduces the rate of a chemical reaction by combining with a reactant to stop it from reacting in its usual way. A number of pharmaceuticals are inhibitors. Drugs that act through inhibition are called *antagonists*.

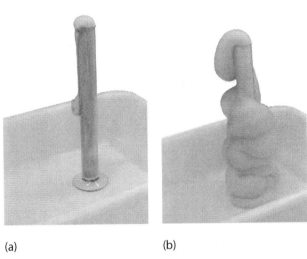

(a)   (b)

Figure 2.2.6 *"Elephant toothpaste" is produced through a catalytic reaction. The concentration of H_2O_2 is greater in (b) than in (a)*

Sample Problem — Factors Affecting Reaction Rate

Which of the following reactions is faster at room temperature?

(a) $H_2(g) + I_2(s) \rightarrow 2\,HI(g)$ (b) $Ba^{2+}(aq) + SO_4^{2-}(aq) \rightarrow BaSO_4(s)$

List two ways to increase the rate of each reaction.

What to Think About	**How to Do It**
1. First consider the nature of the reactants.	The reactant states lead us to believe that reaction (b) involving aqueous species would be the fastest.
2. To increase the rate of reaction (a), start by recognizing this is a heterogeneous reaction. This means that, in addition to the usual factors, surface area can be considered.	• Increase surface area of iodine solid. • Increase temperature. • Increase concentration of hydrogen gas. • Increase partial pressure of hydrogen gas (decrease container volume). • Add an appropriate catalyst.
3. To increase the rate of reaction of the homogeneous reaction in (b), apply all the usual factors except surface area. *Note that you must be specific when mentioning the factors.* For example, what species' concentration will be increased?	• Increase temperature. • Increase concentration of either or both reactant ions (Ba^{2+} and/or SO_4^{2-}). • Add an appropriate catalyst.

2.2 Activity: Graphic Depiction of Factors Affecting Reaction Rates

Question

How do concentration, surface area, and temperature affect reaction rate?

Background

Four trials were carried out in which a chunk of zinc was reacted with hydrochloric acid under four different sets of conditions. In all four trials, the chunk of zinc was of equal mass. The data collected indicate that varying factors have a significant impact on reaction rate. These data can be represented in tabular and graphical form.

The reaction was allowed to proceed for the same time period in each trial. In all four trials, the gas was collected in a eudiometer using the apparatus shown below.

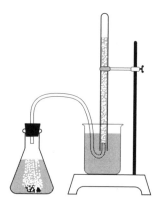

Time (s)	Trial 1 25°C, 1 M HCl (mL)	Trial 2 50°C, 1 M HCl (mL)	Trial 3 25°C, 2 M HCl (mL)	Trial 4 25°C, 1 M HCl, zinc powder (mL)
0	0	0	0	0
30.	12	34	20	26
60.	19	56	34	44
90.	24	65	44	57
120.	27	65	51	65
150.	29	65	54	65

Procedure

1. Use the following grid to graph all four sets of data. Vary colors for each trial line.

Results and Discussion

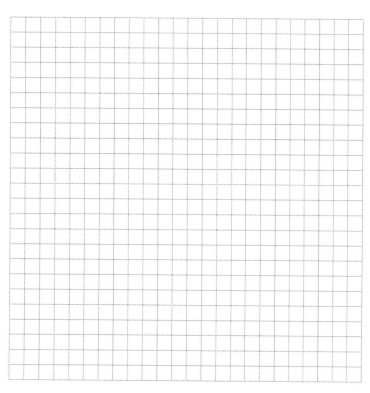

© Edvantage Interactive 2016

1. Write a balanced equation for the reaction that was studied.

2. Rank the conditions from those producing the fastest to slowest reaction rates. What factor influences reaction rate the most? Which factor is second most effective? Which factor has the least influence on the rate?

3. Calculate the average reaction rate in mL H_2/min for each trial. Use the time required to collect the maximum amount of hydrogen gas formed (e.g., the time for trial 2 will be 90. s). Place the rates on the graphed lines.

4. How many milligrams of zinc were used in 1.50 min for each trial? Assume a molar volume for $H_2(g)$ of 24.5 L/mol. (This is for SATP conditions or 25°C and 101.3 kPa or the pressure at sea level.) For the 50°C trial, use 26.5 L/mol.

5. What error is introduced by the assumption in question 4? Would the actual mass of Zn be larger or smaller than that calculated? Explain.

2.2 Review Questions

1. Identify the four factors that affect the rate of any reaction. Give a brief explanation as to how each one applies. Which of these factors can be altered to change the rate of a particular chemical reaction?

2. Identify the one factor that affects only the rate of heterogeneous reactions. Explain why it does not affect homogeneous reaction rates.

3. Use the Internet to find examples of catalysts that do the following:
   (a) Convert oxides of nitrogen into harmless nitrogen gas in the catalytic converter of an automobile.

   (b) Increase the rate of the Haber process to make ammonia.

   (c) Found on disinfectant discs to clean contact lenses.

   (d) Found in green plants to assist in photosynthesis.

4. How would each of the following changes affect the rate of decomposition of a marble statue due to acid rain? Begin by writing the equation for the reaction between marble (calcium carbonate) and nitric acid below.

   (a) The concentration of the acid is increased.

   (b) Erosion due to wind and weathering increases the surface area on the surface of the statue.

   (c) The statue is cooled in cold winter weather.

   (d) The partial pressure of carbon dioxide gas in the atmosphere is increased due to greenhouse gases.

5. (a) At room temperature, catalyzed decomposition of methanoic acid, HCOOH, produced 80.0 mL of carbon monoxide gas in 1.00 min once the volume was adjusted to STP conditions. The other product was water. Calculate the average rate of decomposition of methanoic acid in moles per minute.

© Edvantage Interactive 2016

(b) Give general (approximate) answers for the following:
  (i)   How long would you expect the production of 40.0 mL of gas to take?

  (ii) How long would you expect the production of 80.0 mL to take without a catalyst?

  (iii) How long would you expect the production of 80.0 mL of gas to take at 10°C above the experimental conditions?

6. Answer the questions below for each of the following reactions:
  (i) $C(s) + O_2(g) \rightarrow CO_2(g)$

  (ii) $Pb^{2+}(aq) + 2\,I^-(aq) \rightarrow PbI_2(s)$

  (iii) $Mg(s) + CuCl_2(aq) \rightarrow MgCl_2(aq) + Cu(s)$

  (a) Indicate whether you think it would be fast or slow if performed at room temperature. Then rank the three reactions from fastest to slowest.

  (b) List which of the five factors could be used to increase the rate of each reaction.

7. Rank the diagrams below in order of expected reaction rate for this reaction:
  $G(g) + B(g) \rightarrow GB(g)$
  where G = gray, B = black and GB is the product. Explain your ranking. Assume the same temperature in all three reacting systems.

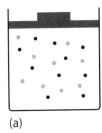
(a)

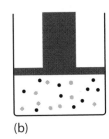
(b)

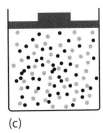
(c)

2.3 Collision Theory

Warm Up

Consider a hypothetical reaction between two gas particles, A and B, to form AB according to the reaction, A(g) + B(g) → AB(g). Determine the total number of possible distinct collisions that could occur between the A particles and the B particles in each situation shown in the diagram below. Let ☐ represent A and ● represent B. Draw arrows from each A particle to each B particle in turn to help you track each possible collision. The third case is done as an example for you.

Total possible collisions: _____   _____   __6__   _____

What is the relationship between the number of A and B particles and the total number of distinct collisions possible?

_____

What might this relationship indicate regarding the rate of a reaction between A and B?

_____

Collisions and Concentrations

From our study of the factors affecting reaction rates, it seems obvious that a successful reaction requires the reacting particles to collide with one another. The series of diagrams in the Warm Up above show that the more particles of reactant species present in a reacting system, the more collisions can occur between them in a particular period of time. Careful examination of the situations described in the Warm Up reveals that the number of possible collisions between the reactant molecules, A and B, is simply equal to the product of the number of molecules of each type present. That is:

number of A × number of B = total possible collisions between A and B

The number of particles per unit volume may be expressed as a concentration. In the example, all of the particles are in the same volume so we can think of the number of particles of each type as representing their concentrations. From this, we can infer that the concentration of the particles colliding must be related to the rate. These two statements allow us to represent the relationship discovered in the Warm Up as follows.

The rate of a reaction is directly proportional to the product of the concentrations of the reactants.

When two variables are directly proportional to one another there is a constant that relates the two. In other words, multiplying one variable by a constant value will always give you the other variable. We call this multiplier a *proportionality constant*. In science, proportionality constants are commonly represented by the letter k.

The slope of any straight-line graph is a proportionality constant. A quick review of this concept can be found in your M4 Chemistry textbook. Applying this concept to the relationship discovered in the Warm Up results in the following.

$$\text{reaction rate} = k[A]^x[B]^y$$

© Edvantage Interactive 2016

The relationship above is called a **rate law**. The proportionality constant in this case is called a **rate constant**. Every reaction has its own unique rate law and its own unique rate constant. For many reactions, the exponents, x and y, are each equal to 1. The values of x and y are called **reactant orders**. In this section, we will focus on reactions that are first order with respect to all reactants. In other words, both $x = 1$ and $y = 1$. Be aware, however, that there are reactions involving second and even third order reactants. Clearly, the higher the order of a particular reactant, the more a change in the concentration of that reactant affects the reaction rate.

Quick Check

1. Write the general form for a rate law in which two reactants, C and D, react together. Assume the reaction is first order for each reactant. Explain what the rate law means.

   _____

   _____

   _____

2. Assume a reaction occurs by this rate law: rate = $k[A]$. How would the rate be affected by each of the following changes in concentration?
   (a) [A] is doubled.

   _____

   (b) [A] is halved.

   _____

3. Assume a gaseous reaction occurs by this rate law: rate = $k[A][B]$. How would the rate be affected if the volume of the container were halved?

   _____

4. How is the rate of a reaction affected by increasing the temperature? What part of the rate law must be affected by changing temperature?

   _____

   _____

A Distribution of Collisions

When reacting particles collide with one another, each collision is unique in its energy and direction. If you've ever played a game of billiards, snooker, or 8-ball, you're familiar with the transfer of energy from the shooter's arm to the pool stick to the cue ball to the ball being shot. Only when the shooter sends the cue ball directly into the ball being shot with a controlled amount of strength are the momentum and direction of the ball easily predictable.

This control is required in a "direct shot" or in a classic "bank shot" where, much like a beam of reflected light, the angle of incidence equals the angle of reflection (Figure 2.3.1(a)). Bank shots may be necessary when an opponent's balls are blocking a clear shot. In most cases, however, collisions between the cue ball, the ball being shot, and other balls on the table are different in direction and amount of energy transferred (Figure 2.3.1(b)). Skillful players may intentionally play "shape" or put "English" on the ball to manipulate the direction and the amount of energy transfer involved in collisions.

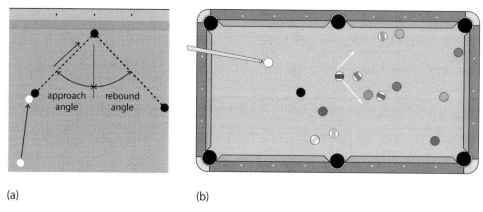

(a)   (b)

Figure 2.3.1 *(a) A bank shot involves predictable collisions. (b) Skilled players determine exactly what type of collision is required for the shot they need to make.*

The break at the start of the game is probably the best model of the distribution of collision energies involved between the reacting particles in a chemical reaction (Figure 2.3.2). Some of the particles move quickly and collide directly with others to transfer a great deal of energy. Others barely move at all or collide with a glancing angle that transfers very little energy. In addition, we must remember that real reactant collisions occur in three dimensions, while our pool table model is good for two dimensions only (Figure 2.3.3).

Figure 2.3.2 *The break at the start of a game provides a large distribution of collision energies.*

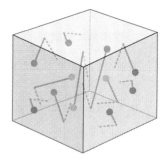

Figure 2.3.3 *The collisions occurring between species in a chemical reaction occur in three dimensions.*

Collision Theory

Regardless of the fact that the energy of particle collisions is distributed in a regular way, the rate of a reaction actually depends on *two* considerations.

> **Collision theory** states that reaction rates depend upon:
> - the number of collisions per unit time, and
> - the fraction of these collisions that succeed in producing products.

Requirements for Effective Collisions

A mixture of hydrogen and oxygen gas may sit indefinitely inside a balloon at room temperature without undergoing any apparent reaction regardless of concentrations. Addition of a small amount of energy such as a spark to the system, however, causes the gases to react violently and exothermically. How can this phenomenon be explained?

In 1 mol of gas under standard conditions, there are more than 10^{32} collisions occurring each second. If the rate of collisions per second were equal to the rate of reaction, every reaction would be extremely rapid. Since most gaseous reactions are slow, it is evident that only a small fraction of the total collisions effectively result in the conversion of reactants to products.

As discussed earlier, the tremendous number of collisions in a reacting sample results in a wide

Quick Check

Consider the factors affecting reaction rate that you studied in section 2.2.

1. Which of these factors do you think increase reaction rate by increasing the number of collisions per unit time?

   _____

2. Which of the factors do you think increase reaction rate by increasing the fraction of collisions that succeed in producing products?

   _____

3. Do you think any of the factors increase *both* the number of collisions per unit time and the fraction of successful collisions? If so, which one(s)?

   _____

range of velocities and kinetic energies. Only a small percentage of the molecules in a given sample have sufficient kinetic energy to react.

> The minimum kinetic energy that the reacting species must have in order to react is called the **activation energy** or E_a of the reaction.

Only collisions between particles having the threshold energy of E_a are energetic enough to overcome the repulsive forces between the electron clouds of the reacting molecules and to weaken or break bonds, resulting in a reaction. Most gaseous reactions have relatively high E_a values; hence reactions like the one between hydrogen and oxygen gas do not occur at room temperature.

The activation energy of a reaction depends on a comparison of the energy released during the formation of new chemical bonds and the energy required to break existing bonds. As bond energies are a characteristic of a particular chemical species, the only thing that can change the activation energy of a reaction is to change the pathway between reactant and product species. This is precisely what occurs when a reaction is catalyzed.

In section 2.2, a kinetic energy distribution diagram was shown for a sample of matter at two different temperatures. Figure 2.3.4 shows a similar pair of energy distributions at two different temperatures. It also shows two different activation energies. E_{a2} represents the activation energy without a catalyst present. E_{a1} represents a lowered activation energy that results in the presence of a catalyst. Note that in both cases, with and without a catalyst, the number of particles capable of colliding effectively (as represented by the shaded area under the curve) increases at the higher temperature.

Number of Molecules vs. Kinetic Energy

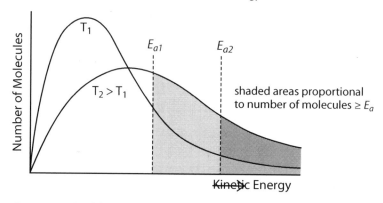

Figure 2.3.4 *With higher temperatures, the number of particles capable of colliding effectively increases.*

It turns out there is one further factor that complicates collision theory even more. Particles having the activation energy associated with a given reaction don't always react when they undergo a collision. Even very high-energy collisions may not be effective unless the molecules are properly oriented toward one another.

In addition to attaining E_a, the *geometric shape* and the *molecular orientation* of reacting particles must also be favorable for a successful collision to occur.

Consider the reaction $CO(g) + NO_2(g) \rightarrow CO_2(g) + NO(g)$

Figure 2.3.5 shows two different ways the reactants CO and NO_2 could collide. Here we see a successful collision followed by an unsuccessful collision between carbon monoxide and nitrogen dioxide in an attempt to form carbon dioxide and nitrogen monoxide. No matter how energetic the collision, it will succeed only when the carbon and oxygen atoms in the respective molecules are oriented properly. For the CO molecule to become CO_2, the oxygen from the NO_2 molecule must collide with the carbon atom in the CO molecule so that a bond can form.

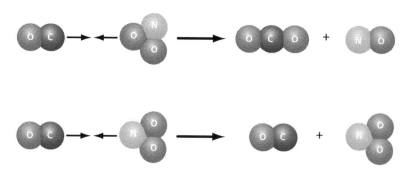

Figure 2.3.5 *The top collision is successful because the molecules are oriented so that the carbon and oxygen atoms can bond to form CO_2.*

Collision Theory and Factors Affecting Reaction Rate

Increased temperature, concentration, and surface area all increase the frequency of collisions leading to an increase in reaction rate. The presence of a catalyst and temperature both increase the fraction of collisions that are successful.

© Edvantage Interactive 2016

Sample Problem — Collision Theory

Study the following data for 1 mol of reactants at two different temperatures. $T_1 < T_2$.

	Temperature 1	Temperature 2
Frequency of collisions:	1.5×10^{32} s^{-1}	3.0×10^{32} s^{-1}
% of collisions $> E_a$:	10%	30%

(a) How many collisions exceed activation energy per second at each temperature?

(b) How many times greater is the reaction rate at temperature 2 than temperature 1? (Assume the percent of collisions with correct geometry is the same at both temperatures.)

(c) If the frequency of collisions was only doubled by increasing the temperature from T_1 to T_2, why is the rate increased by a factor of six?

What to Think About	How to Do It
1. Multiply the percentage by the frequency at each temperature.	$0.10\,(1.5 \times 10^{32}$ s$^{-1}) = 1.5 \times 10^{31}$ s^{-1} at T_1 $0.30\,(3.0 \times 10^{32}$ s$^{-1}) = 9.0 \times 10^{31}$ s^{-1} at T_2
2. Divide the result for T_2 by the result for T_1.	$\dfrac{9.0 \times 10^{31}\ s^{-1}}{1.5 \times 10^{31}\ s^{-1}} = 6.0 \times$ greater
3. Decide what, in addition to collision frequency, must be influenced by reaction temperature.	Increasing reaction temperature increases the energy of collisions as well as collision frequency.

Practice Problems — Collision Theory

1. For slow reactions, at temperatures near 25°C, an increase of 10°C will approximately double the number of particles that have enough energy to react. At temperatures much higher than that, increasing temperature leads to smaller and smaller increases in the number of successful collisions. In the graph below, the area under the kinetic energy distribution curve represents the total number of particles.

   (a) Assume the curve shown represents the kinetic energy distribution for a sample of reacting particles at room temperature. Add a curve to represent the kinetic energy distribution for a sample of reacting particles at 10°C above room temperature.

   (b) Add a second curve to represent the kinetic energy distribution for a sample of reacting particles at a temperature 100°C above curve (a).

   (c) Add a third curve for a temperature 10°C above curve (b).

Number of Particles vs. Energy

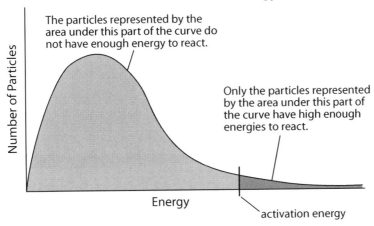

The particles represented by the area under this part of the curve do not have enough energy to react.

Only the particles represented by the area under this part of the curve have high enough energies to react.

Continued on the next page

Practice Problems (Continued)

2. At higher temperature ranges, that is, for reactions already occurring at a high rate, most of the collisions already possess E_a. Hence, an increase in temperature increases the rate primarily because of the increased frequency of collisions. Although the particles hit each other harder and with more energy, this is not really relevant because they have already achieved E_a. Complete the following table for a reacting particle sample.

Temperature	100°C	300°C
Frequency of collisions	2.00×10^{15} s^{-1}	3.00×10^{15} s^{-1}
Force of collisions (% possessing E_a)	95.0%	97.0%
Frequency of collisions possessing activation energy		

(a) Calculate the fraction by which the percentage of particles possessing E_a increases with an increase of 200°C. Divide the percentage for 300°C by the percentage for 100°C.

(b) Calculate the fraction by which the frequency of collisions increases with an increase of 200°C.

(c) Calculate the fraction by which the frequency of collisions possessing E_a increases with an increase of 200°C.

(d) The data in the table shows that at higher temperatures the increase in rate is almost entirely due to what?

(e) Why might increasing the force of collisions eventually produce less successful reactions?

© Edvantage Interactive 2016

2.3 Review Questions

1. List the two things that affect the rates of all chemical reactions according to collision theory.

2. What are the two requirements for a collision to be successful?

3. One chunk of zinc is left whole and another is cut into pieces as shown. Both samples of zinc are reacted in an equal volume of 6.0 mol/L aqueous hydrochloric acid.

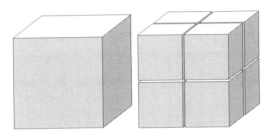

   (a) Assuming the surface area of the first zinc sample is 6.00 cm², what is the surface area of the second sample of zinc?

   (b) Compare the frequency of collisions between the hydrochloric acid and the single piece of zinc with those between the acid and the cut sample of zinc.

   (c) Assuming the average rate of reaction for the single piece of zinc with the acid is 1.20×10^{-3} mol Zn/min, calculate the rate of reaction for the cut sample of zinc.

   (d) Assuming this rate is maintained for a period of 4.50 min, how many milliliters of hydrogen gas would be collected at STP?

4. A reaction between ammonium ions and nitrite ions has the following rate law:

$$\text{rate} = k[NH_4^+][NO_2^-]$$

Assume the rate of formation of the salt is 3.10×10^{-3} mol $L^{-1}s^{-1}$. Note that the units may also be expressed as mol/(L s). The reaction is performed in aqueous solution at room temperature.

(a) What rate of reaction would result if the $[NH_4^+]$ was tripled and the $[NO_2^-]$ was halved?

(b) Determine the reaction rate if the $[NH_4^+]$ was unchanged and the $[NO_2^-]$ was increased by a factor of four?

(c) If the $[NH_4^+]$ and the $[NO_2^-]$ were unchanged, but the rate increased to 6.40×10^{-3} mol/(L s), what must have happened to the reacting system?

(d) What would the new reaction rate be if enough water were added to double the overall volume?

5. A student reacts ground marble chips, $CaCO_3(s)$, with hydrochloric acid, $HCl(aq)$, in an open beaker at constant temperature.
   (a) In terms of collision theory, explain what will happen to the rate of the reaction as it proceeds from the beginning to completion.

   (b) Sketch a graph of volume of $CO_2(g)$ vs. time to show the formation of product with time as the reaction proceeds.

© Edvantage Interactive 2016

6. Consider the following three experiments, each involving the same mass of zinc and the same volume of acid at the same temperature. Rank the three in order from fastest to slowest, and explain your ranking using collision theory.

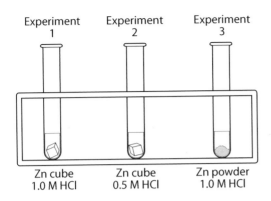

Experiment 1	Experiment 2	Experiment 3
Zn cube 1.0 M HCl	Zn cube 0.5 M HCl	Zn powder 1.0 M HCl

7. Is the following collision likely to produce Cl_2 and NO_2 assuming the collision occurs with sufficient energy? If not, redraw the particles in such a way that a successful collision would be likely.

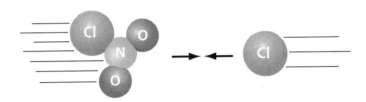

8. Use collision theory to explain each of the following.
    (a) Food found in camps half way up Mount Everest is still edible once thawed.

    (b) Campers react magnesium shavings with oxygen to start fires.

    (c) A thin layer of platinum in a vehicle's exhaust system converts oxides of nitrogen into non-toxic nitrogen gas.

2.4 Determining Rate Laws from Experimental Data

Warm Up

In section 2.3, we introduced the concept of a *rate law*. Rate laws express rates of reaction in the following form: reaction rate = $k[A]^x[B]^y$, where [A] and [B] represent the concentrations of the reactants, and x and y represent the orders with respect to reactants A and B.

The following diagrams represent systems of gaseous reactants A (symbolized by O) and B (symbolized by ■) at a fixed temperature and volume. The equation for the reaction is A(*g*) + B(*g*) → C(*g*).

The rate law equation uses only the reactant concentrations, so we did not depict the presence of the product C in these diagrammatic representations. Below the containers, we have provided the instantaneous rate of reaction for each system in units of mol/L of C produced per second.

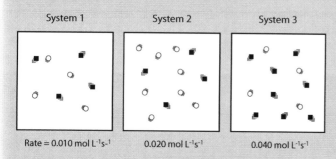

System 1	System 2	System 3
Rate = 0.010 mol L⁻¹s⁻¹	0.020 mol L⁻¹s⁻¹	0.040 mol L⁻¹s⁻¹

1. By what factor did the concentration of A (O) change from System 1 to 2?

   _____

2. How did this affect the reaction rate?

   _____

3. By what factor did the concentration of B (■) change from System 1 to 3?

   _____

4. How did this affect the reaction rate?

   _____

5. Complete the following expression:

   rate = k[A]$^\square$[B]$^\square$

Determining an Initial Reaction Rate

In section 2.1, we discussed methods of determining rates of chemical reactions. In that same section, we determined both the average and instantaneous rates of reaction from a graph of data we collected for the decomposition of thionyl chloride. We call the instantaneous rate determined at the very beginning of a reaction the **initial rate** (Figure 2.4.1).

© Edvantage Interactive 2016

Concentration of Product vs. Time

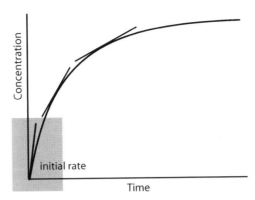

Figure 2.4.1 *The slope of a tangent line drawn to the curve at the beginning of a reaction is greater than that of any other tangent. This slope gives the initial rate of a reaction.*

As predicted by collision theory, the initial rate of a reaction depends on the concentration of the reactants present. Increasing the number of reactant particles in a particular volume leads to more frequent collisions between particles, which usually increases the reaction rate. Performing multiple trials with different concentrations of reactants shows how varying the reactant concentration affects the rate of a reaction (Figure 2.4.2).

Concentration of Reactants vs. Time

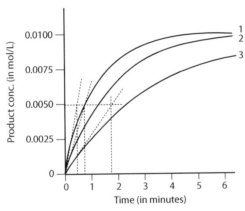

Figure 2.4.2 *The graph shows the relationship between concentration and time for three different initial reactant concentrations. Trial 1 has the greatest initial reactant concentration. The reaction rate increases from Trial 3 to 2 to 1. We determine the initial rate of each reaction from the slope of the tangent at the beginning of the reaction.*

Determining Reaction Orders

We can summarize data from a series of trials such as those shown in the Warm Up in a tabular form. If we assume that each O represents 1.00 mmol of A, and each ■ represents 1.00 mmol of B, all of which are contained in a 1.00 L container, the table would look like Table 2.4.1.

Table 2.4.1 *Data Table for Three Trials*

Trial Number	Initial Rate (mol L⁻¹s⁻¹)	Initial [A] (mol/L)	Initial [B] (mol/L)
1	0.010	0.00400	0.00400
2	0.020	0.00800	0.00400
3	0.040	0.00400	0.00800

From Trial 1 to 2, we double [A] and hold [B] constant. The result is a doubling of the reaction rate. This implies that the rate is directly proportional to the [A], and the process is first order with respect to A. We can demonstrate the relationship mathematically by setting up a ratio of the rate laws for the two trials:

$$\frac{\text{rate 2}}{\text{rate 1}} = \frac{k[A]^x[B]^y}{k[A]^x[B]^y} \quad \text{thus} \quad \frac{0.020 \text{ mol/L/s}}{0.010 \text{ mol/L/s}} = \frac{\cancel{k}(0.00800 \text{ mol/L})^x \cancel{(0.00400 \text{ mol/L})^y}}{\cancel{k}(0.00400 \text{ mol/L})^x \cancel{(0.00400 \text{ mol/L})^y}}$$

or $2 = 2^x$ so $x = 1$ (first order with respect to A)

From Trial 1 to 3, [A] is constant, while [B] doubles. The result is a quadrupling of the reaction rate. This implies an exponential relationship between the reaction rate and [B] in which the rate is proportional to the [B] squared, and the process is second order with respect to B. Setting up a ratio of the rate laws for these two trials gives:

$$\frac{\text{rate 3}}{\text{rate 1}} = \frac{k[A]^x[B]^y}{k[A]^x[B]^y} \quad \text{thus} \quad \frac{0.040 \text{ mol/L/s}}{0.010 \text{ mol/L/s}} = \frac{\cancel{k}\cancel{(0.00400 \text{ mol/L})^x}(0.00800 \text{ mol/L})^y}{\cancel{k}\cancel{(0.00400 \text{ mol/L})^x}(0.00400 \text{ mol/L})^y}$$

or $4 = 2^y$ so $y = 2$ (second order with respect to B)

The data indicates the following rate law:

reaction rate = $k[A][B]^2$

The **overall order** for a reaction is the sum of the orders with respect to each reactant; hence, in this case, the overall reaction order is $1 + 2 = 3$ or third order.

Determining the Rate Constant

Once we have determined the orders with respect to each of the individual reactants, we can determine the numerical rate constant by substituting the rate and concentration values from any of the trials. In the example from the Warm Up, the rate law is: reaction rate = $k[A][B]^2$.

Therefore, the rate constant, $k = \dfrac{\text{reaction rate}}{[A][B]^2}$

Substitution of the values from Trial 1 in the table gives

$$k = \frac{0.010 \text{ mol/L/s}}{(0.00400 \text{ mol/L})(0.00400 \text{ mol/L})^2} = 1.6 \times 10^5 \text{ L}^2\text{mol}^{-2}\text{s}^{-1}$$

We determine the units for the rate constant by canceling the units in the substituted equation. As the overall orders for reactions become larger, the units for rate constants become more complex. We observe a general pattern for the rate constant units as shown in Table 4.4.2.

Table 2.4.2 *Pattern of Rate Constants from Zero to nth Order*

Zero Order	First Order	Second Order	*n*th Order (n >1)
$M \text{ L}^{-1}\text{s}^{-1}$	s^{-1}	$M^{-1} \text{ L s}^{-1}$	$\text{mol}^{(1-n)} \text{ L}^{(n-1)}\text{s}^{-1}$

The magnitude of rate constants varies from one reaction to another. However, for a particular reaction, the value of the rate constant changes only if the temperature changes. In an actual experiment, the process of substitution to determine the numerical value of the rate would be repeated for each trial and all values would be averaged.

© Edvantage Interactive 2016

Sample Problem — Determining a Rate Law from Experimental Data

Bromate and bromide ions react in acidic solution to form bromine:

$$BrO_3^-(aq) + 5\ Br^-(aq) + 6\ H^+(aq) \rightarrow 3\ Br_2(l) + 3\ H_2O(l)$$

Use the data from this table to determine the rate law expression and the rate constant for the reaction.

Run	$[BrO_3^-]_{initial}$ (mol/L)	$[Br^-]_{initial}$ (mol/L)	$[H^+]_{initial}$ (mol/L)	Initial Rate (mol/L^{-1}s^{-1})
1	0.10	0.10	0.10	0.00080
2	0.20	0.10	0.10	0.00160
3	0.20	0.20	0.10	0.00320
4	0.10	0.10	0.20	0.00320

What to Think About

1. Identify two trials for which the concentration of only one reactant changes.

2. Set up a ratio to compare these two trials to one another. The value of the exponent that makes the ratio of the concentration change equal the ratio of the rates is the order with respect to the reactant for which the concentration changes between the two trials.

3. Repeat, comparing trials for which the concentration of a different reactant changes while the concentration of all other reactants remains constant.

4. Repeat this process for all reactants.
   Note that once the order of a particular species is known, we can calculate the order with respect to another reactant even if the concentration of the reactant with the known order changes. We substitute the value of the known order into the equation and attribute the changes in reaction rate to two different concentration changes.

5. Substitute the values for Trial 1 into the rate law and solve for the rate constant, k.

How to Do It

$$\frac{\text{rate } 2}{\text{rate } 1} = \frac{k(0.20)^x(0.10)^y(0.10)^z}{k(0.10)^x(0.10)^y(0.10)^z} = \frac{0.00160 \ M/s}{0.00080 \ M/s}$$

hence $2^x = 2$; therefore $x = 1$

$$\frac{\text{rate } 3}{\text{rate } 2} = \frac{k(0.20)^x(0.20)^y(0.10)^z}{k(0.20)^x(0.10)^y(0.10)^z} = \frac{0.00320 \ M/s}{0.00160 \ M/s}$$

hence $2^y = 2$; therefore $y = 1$

$$\frac{\text{rate } 4}{\text{rate } 1} = \frac{k(0.10)^x(0.10)^y(0.20)^z}{k(0.10)^x(0.10)^y(0.10)^z} = \frac{0.00320 \ M/s}{0.00080 \ M/s}$$

hence $2^z = 4$; therefore $z = 2$

$$\text{rate} = k[BrO_3^-][Br^-][H^+]^2$$

$$k = \frac{\text{rate}}{[BrO_3^-][Br^-][H^+]^2}$$

$$k = \frac{0.00080 \ mol/L \cdot s}{(0.10 \ mol/L)(0.10 \ mol/L)(0.10 \ mol/L)^2}$$

$$k = 8.0 \ L^3 mol^{-3} s^{-1}$$

Practice Problems — Determining Rate Laws from Experimental Data

1. Use the information in the table below to write the rate-law expression for the reaction, and explain how you obtained your answer. Determine the rate constant with units.

    $2\,NO(g) + O_2(g) \rightarrow 2\,NO_2(g)$

Experiment Number	Initial $[O_2]$ (mol·L^{-1})	Initial $[NO]$ (mol·L^{-1})	Initial Rate of Formation of NO_2 (mol·L^{-1}·s^{-1})
1	0.0010	0.0010	x
2	0.0010	0.0020	$2x$
3	0.0020	0.0010	$2x$
4	0.0020	0.0020	$4x$

2. Consider an imaginary reaction: $2\,X + Y \rightarrow Z$. Determine the rate law and the rate constant, with units, from the experimental data in the table below.

Initial Rate of Formation of Z (mol·L^{-1}·s^{-1})	Initial $[X]_o$ (mol·L^{-1})	Initial $[Y]_o$ (mol·L^{-1})
7.0×10^{-4}	0.20	0.10
1.4×10^{-3}	0.40	0.20
2.8×10^{-3}	0.40	0.40
4.2×10^{-3}	0.60	0.60

3. The following systems represent gaseous reactants A (symbolized by $\mathbf{O}$) and B (symbolized by ■) at a fixed temperature and volume. The equation for the reaction is $A(g) + B(g) \rightarrow C(g)$.

    Assume the rate law for the reaction is: rate $= k[A][B]^3$

    System 1 represents a reaction with a rate of 0.010 molL^{-1}s^{-1}. Complete the diagrams for the other systems as follows:

    (a) Adding enough particles of A $\mathbf{O}$) to System 2 to represent a system that would react with an initial rate of 0.020 molL^{-1}s^{-1}.

    (b) Adding enough particles of B (■) to System 3 to represent a system that would react with an initial rate of 0.080 molL^{-1}s^{-1}.

    System 1   System 2   System 3

    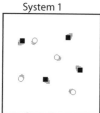   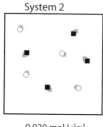   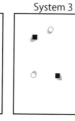

    Rate = 0.010 mol L^{-1}s^{-1} 0.020 mol L^{-1}s^{-1} 0.080 mol L^{-1}s^{-1}

© Edvantage Interactive 2016

In summary, to determine a rate law for a reaction, we start by measuring the initial rate of reaction for at least two trials while varying the concentration of one of the reacting species and keeping the concentrations of the other reactants constant. We continue the experimental analysis by continuing to perform comparison trials varying the concentration of each reacting species while keeping the concentrations of the other reactants constant until we collect enough data to determine the rate law (Figure 2.4.3). Once we have determined the general rate law expression, we can calculate the rate constant by algebraic substitution.

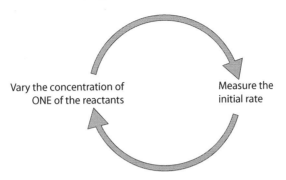

Vary the concentration of
ONE of the reactants

Measure the
initial rate

Figure 2.4.3 *A cycle to determine rate laws from experimental data. Continue this cycle until the orders with respect to all reactants have been determined.*

2.4 Review Questions

1. Consider the hypothetical reaction: $X + Y \rightarrow Z$ and the following data:

Initial Rate of Appearance of Z (mol L^{-1}s^{-1})	[X]$_0$ (mol/L)	[Y]$_0$ (mol/L)
0.053	0.05	0.25
0.127	0.10	0.15
1.02	0.20	0.30
0.254	0.10	0.30
0.509	0.20	0.15

(a) Use the data in the table to determine the rate law for the reaction.

(b) Determine the value of the rate constant with units.

(c) Determine the initial rate of appearance of Z when the concentration of X is 0.15 mol/L and that of Y is 0.20 mol/L.

2. Nitrosyl fluoride, NO_2F, can be made by reacting NO_2 and F_2 gases as follows:

$$2\,NO_2(g) + F_2(g) \rightarrow 2\,NO_2F(g)$$

The following table represents data collected for the rate of formation of nitrosyl fluoride at room temperature. Recall that mol L^{-1} is equivalent to mol/L.

[NO$_2$]$_0$ (mol·L^{-1})	[F$_2$]$_0$ (mol·L^{-1})	Rate (mol·L^{-1}·s^{-1})
0.00100	0.00100	4.00×10^{-5}
0.00100	0.00300	1.20×10^{-4}
0.00500	0.00300	6.00×10^{-4}
0.00500	0.00500	1.00×10^{-3}

(a) Use the data in the table to determine the rate law for the reaction.

(b) Calculate the rate constant at room temperature. Include appropriate units.

© Edvantage Interactive 2016

3. The following trials were performed during the kinetic study of an oxidation-reduction reaction:

$$2 MnO_4^-(aq) + 5 H_2C_2O_4(aq) + 6 H^+(aq) \rightarrow 2 Mn^{2+}(aq) + 10 CO_2(g) + 8 H_2O(l)$$

$[MnO_4^-]_{initial}$ (mol/L)	$[H_2C_2O_4]_{initial}$ (mol/L)	$[H^+]_{initial}$ (mol/L)	Initial Rate of Formation of Mn^{2+} (mol $L^{-1}s^{-1}$)
1.0×10^{-3}	1.0×10^{-3}	1.0	2.0×10^{-4}
2.0×10^{-3}	1.0×10^{-3}	1.0	8.0×10^{-4}
2.0×10^{-3}	2.0×10^{-3}	1.0	1.6×10^{-3}
2.0×10^{-3}	2.0×10^{-3}	2.0	1.6×10^{-3}

(a) Use the data in the table for the initial rates of formation of the manganese(II) ion to determine the rate law and the rate constant for the redox reaction.

(b) By what factor would the initial reaction rate change if the concentrations of all three reactants doubled?

(c) By what factor would the initial reaction rate change if the volume of the reaction system doubled due to the addition of distilled water?

4. The equation for a general reaction is: $2 A(g) + 2 B(g) \rightarrow C(g) + 2 D(g)$. The initial rate of formation of C is determined in four trials with various initial concentrations of reactants as shown in the table.

Trial Number	Initial [A] (mol·L^{-1})	Initial [B] (mol·L^{-1})	Initial Reaction Rate (mol·L^{-1}·s^{-1})
1	0.100	0.100	4.00×10^{-5}
2	0.200	0.100	1.60×10^{-4}
3	0.100	0.200	4.00×10^{-5}
4	0.300	0.200	?

(a) Determine the rate law for the reaction.

(b) Determine the rate constant with units.

(c) Calculate the initial reaction rate for Trial 4.

5. The table below provides data obtained under lab conditions for the reaction:

$$2\,MnO_4^{2-} + H_3IO_6^{2-} \rightarrow 2\,MnO_4^{-} + IO_3^{-} + 3\,OH^{-}$$

The experimental trials involved measuring the initial rate of formation of the iodate (IO_3^{-}) ion with varying initial concentrations of reactants.

Experimental Trial	$[MnO_4^{2-}]_0$ (mol·L^{-1})	$[H_3IO_6^{2-}]_0$ (mol·L^{-1})	Initial Rate (M L^{-1}min^{-1})
1	1.6×10^{-4}	3.1×10^{-4}	2.6×10^{-6}
2	6.4×10^{-4}	3.1×10^{-4}	4.2×10^{-5}
3	1.6×10^{-4}	6.2×10^{-4}	2.6×10^{-6}
4	3.2×10^{-4}	3.1×10^{-4}	?
5	?	6.2×10^{-4}	2.3×10^{-5}

(a) Determine the rate law for the reaction.

(b) Calculate the rate constant with units.

(c) What is the initial rate of formation of IO_3^{-} ion for Trial 4?

(d) What is the required initial concentration of MnO_4^{2-} ion for Trial 5?

(e) What is the initial rate of formation of MnO_4^{-} ion for Trial 1?

6. The equation for the bromination of acetone in acidic solution is:

$$CH_3COCH_3(aq) + Br_2(aq) \rightarrow CH_3COCH_2Br(aq) + H^+(aq) + Br^-(aq)$$

The following data were collected in four trials by varying the concentration of reactants and measuring the initial rate of disappearance of aqueous bromine ($Br_2(aq)$).

Trial Number	$[CH_3COCH_3]_0$ (mol/L)	$[Br_2]_0$ (mol/L)	$[H^+]_0$ (mol/L)	Initial Rate (mol L^{-1}s^{-1})
1	0.30	0.050	0.050	5.7×10^{-5}
2	0.30	0.100	0.050	5.7×10^{-5}
3	0.30	0.100	0.100	1.4×10^{-4}
4	0.40	0.050	0.200	3.2×10^{-4}

Determine the rate law and the rate constant (with appropriate units) for the acidic bromination of acetone.

© Edvantage Interactive 2016

2.5 Reaction Mechanisms, Catalysis, and Rate Laws

Warm Up

Study the following series of molecular collisions representing the catalyzed decomposition of formic acid.

$$H^+ \quad HCOOH \quad HCOOH_2^+ \quad H_2O \quad HCO^+ \quad H_2O \quad CO \quad H^+$$

1. How many reactions are shown in the series above? _____

2. In the format provided below question 3, write the balanced chemical equation for each reaction in the series. As it is a product of the overall series of collisions, the H_2O produced in the second step should *not* be shown as a reactant *or* product in the *third* step.

3. Algebraically sum the three equations to give the overall reaction. (Species that appear as reactants in one step and products in another should be cancelled.) What is the overall reaction once the three steps have been added together?

Step 1: $\rightarrow$

Step 2: $\rightarrow$

Step 3: _____ $\rightarrow$ _____

Overall Reaction: $\rightarrow$

Reaction Mechanisms

A balanced equation for a chemical reaction shows us what substances are present before and after the reaction. Unfortunately, it tells us nothing about the detailed steps occurring at the molecular level in between. Studies have shown that most reactions occur by a series of steps called the reaction mechanism. The individual steps in such a series are called **elementary processes.** These steps are themselves individual *balanced* chemical reactions that may be added together algebraically to give the overall balanced chemical equation.

> A **reaction mechanism** is a series of steps that may be added together to give an overall chemical reaction.

In section 2.3 we learned that successful collisions require sufficient energy and appropriate orientation. As a consequence, the simultaneous collision of more than two reactant molecules with good geometry and E_a is highly unlikely. It's not surprising then that reactions having more than two reactant particles almost always involve more than one step in their reaction mechanism.

As mentioned above, each step in a reaction mechanism is called an elementary process. The **molecularity** of each elementary process is defined as the number of reactant species that must collide to produce the reaction indicated by that step. A reaction involving one molecule only is called a **unimolecular** step. A reaction involving the collision of two species is called a **bimolecular** step, and a reaction involving three species is called a **termolecular** step. Termolecular steps are extremely rare.

Quick Check

1. Why are termolecular steps extremely rare?

   _____

2. Indicate the molecularity of each of the following reactions.

   (a) $NO(g) + Br_2(g) \rightarrow NOBr_2(g)$ _____

   (b) $HCOOH(aq) \rightarrow H_2O(l) + CO(g)$ _____

   (c) $2 NO(g) + Cl_2(g) \rightarrow 2 NOCl(g)$ _____

3. An overall reaction is the sum of two or more elementary processes. Is each reaction above likely to be an elementary process or an overall reaction?

   _____

Species Identification: Intermediates and Catalysts

Since we can't actually *see* reacting particles colliding, flying apart, and reassembling, the mechanisms we use to describe chemical reactions are really just theoretical models. Chemists determine these models by altering the concentration of species involved in the mechanism and examining the effects these alterations produce. Computer models are also very useful in understanding mechanisms.

In any multi-step reaction mechanism the first collision, or decomposition of an energized reactant, always produces some product that is consumed in a later step of the mechanism. Such a species is called a reaction intermediate.

An **intermediate** is a species that is formed in one step and consumed in a subsequent step and so does not appear in the overall reaction.

As was described briefly in earlier sections, a catalyst functions by "providing an alternate, lower-energy pathway" for a reaction to follow. We now know this "alternate pathway" is actually a different reaction mechanism. In essence, most catalysts function by allowing the assembly of a different, lower-energy activated complex than would have formed if the catalyst was not present. Since catalysts are present before and after a reaction is complete, they must be used to facilitate the formation of the lower-energy activated complex in one step and then be reformed in some later step.

Catalysts in biological systems are referred to as **enzymes**. Enzymes are proteins that have an *active site*. This active site is exposed to assist a biological reaction in one step of a mechanism so an *enzyme-substrate* complex can form. Once the substrate reacts, the complex comes apart and the enzyme is regenerated for use again (Figure 2.5.1).

A *catalyst* is consumed in one step and regenerated in a subsequent or later step.

© Edvantage Interactive 2016

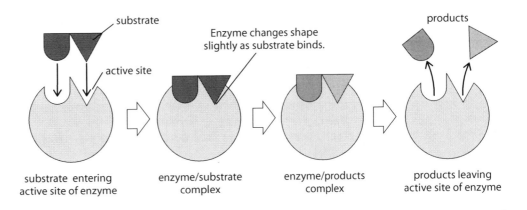

substrate

Enzyme changes shape slightly as substrate binds.

products

active site

substrate entering active site of enzyme

enzyme/substrate complex

enzyme/products complex

products leaving active site of enzyme

Figure 2.5.1 *Notice that the catalyst (in this case the enzyme) is consumed and then regenerated in its original form.*

Reaction Mechanisms and Potential Energy Diagrams

Despite the fact that many reactions involve only two reactant particles, studies show that the majority of chemical changes occur by mechanisms that involve at least two steps. Often one step is much slower than the other(s). The overall reaction rate cannot exceed the rate of the slowest elementary process. Because this slow step limits the overall reaction rate it is called the **rate-determining step**. A variety of conditions may cause a particular step to limit the overall reaction rate. These include the step having:

- complex collision geometry
- a high activation energy
- low concentrations of reactants
- a termolecular collision

A good analogy for this concept occurred back in the days before collating copy machines were available. In those days, teachers had to assemble pages of students' notes by hand and staple them together individually.

If several teachers were teaching the same course, they might get together with each taking on a portion of the job. One teacher would pull the pages off the copier and pass them to another who would assemble the pages in the correct order. Another would tap each pile on the table to make sure the edges were all aligned. Finally, a fourth teacher would staple the pile together. Which of these jobs would be the rate-determining step? Would it increase the rate of the job if a math teacher were asked to assist with passing the papers from the copier or tapping or stapling them? Clearly the assembler is the rate-determining step in such a job. Calling in a math teacher to assist with passing papers would have no effect on the overall rate at all. In fact, it might only serve to annoy the assembler.

As the analogy implies, adding reactants that appear in the non-rate-determining steps of a mechanism will have no effect on the reaction rate. To increase the rate of a reaction, it is necessary to increase the concentration of the reactants that appear in the rate-determining step.

The slowest elementary process in a reaction mechanism determines the overall reaction rate and is called the *rate-determining step*.

Each step in a reaction mechanism involves different chemical species with different bonding arrangements and hence different potential energies or enthalpies. Each step also has its own *rate constant* and its own *activation energy*, depending on the activated complex formed for that step. As a consequence, the potential energy diagram for a particular reaction will have the same number of *peaks,* as there are *steps* in the reaction mechanism.

Calculation of the activation energy for a multi-step reaction mechanism can be confusing. The activation energy for any particular step is simply the potential energy change from the reactants for an elementary process to the activated complex for that process. Consequently, the rate-determining step is the step with the highest activation energy. This value, however, is *not necessarily* the overall activation energy for the reaction. Rather, the overall activation energy is the difference between the potential energy of the activated complex with the highest energy and the potential energy of the reactants for the reaction as a whole.

E_a for a reaction with a multi-step mechanism is equal to

$$PE_{\text{highest energy activated complex}} - PE_{\text{reactants}}$$

As an example, consider the potential energy profile for the reaction in the Warm Up. Figures 2.5.2 and 2.5.3 are for the uncatalyzed reaction followed by the catalyzed reaction. In Figure 2.5.2, a methanoic acid molecule (HCOOH) is energized and forms an activated complex by shifting a hydrogen ion. The energized molecule then decomposes into water and carbon monoxide. This occurs in a single step.

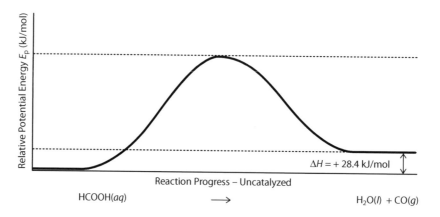

Figure 2.5.2 *A methanoic acid molecule (HCOOH) forms water and carbon monoxide in a single step.*

Notice that Figure 2.5.3 has three "peaks" corresponding to the three steps in the catalyzed reaction mechanism. The rate-determining step is the second one. This step would also determine E_a for the overall reaction. The enthalpy change or ΔH value is unaffected by catalysis as the reactants and products remain the same.

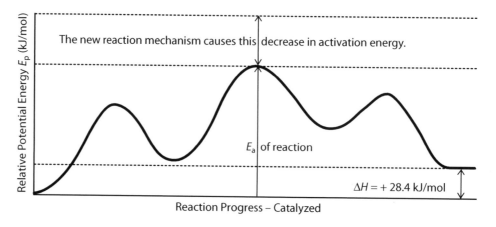

Figure 2.5.3 *This diagram shows the three peaks representing the three steps in a catalyzed reaction.*

© Edvantage Interactive 2016

Sample Problem — Identifying Intermediates and Catalysts in a Mechanism

Use the reaction mechanism produced in the Warm Up for this section to identify reaction intermediates and catalysts.

What to Think About

1. To describe the reaction mechanism, write three reactions for the reactants listed on the left side of each arrow to form the products on the right. As water was an overall product, do not include it as a reactant or product in step 3.

2. Sum the three steps algebraically to give the overall reaction. Cancel species appearing on both sides of the arrows. Identify species based on the definitions in the grey boxes above.

3. Intermediates appear as *products* first *(on the right side)* and as *reactants* later *(on the left side)*. Identify them by drawing a slash from the upper right to the lower left through intermediates.

4. Catalysts are consumed, so they appear as *reactants* first *(left)* and *products* later *(right)*, as they are regenerated. Identify catalysts by drawing a slash from the upper left to the lower right through them.

How to Do It

$$H^+ + HCOOH \rightarrow HCOOH_2^+$$
$$HCOOH_2^+ \rightarrow H_2O + HCO^+$$
$$\frac{HCO^+}{HCOOH} \rightarrow \frac{CO + H^+}{H_2O + CO}$$

Intermediates include: $HCOOH_2^+$ and HCO^+ ions.

There is only one catalyst (as is typically the case). It is homogeneous and is in solution in this case. Specifically the catalyst is the H^+ ion.

Practice Problems — Identifying Intermediates and Catalysts in a Mechanism

For each of the following reaction mechanisms, determine the overall reaction and identify all catalysts and intermediates (some may not have catalysts). Then sketch a potential energy diagram for the reaction. Indicate E_a for the overall reaction. A numerical value is *not* expected.

1. $O_3(g) \rightarrow O_2(g) + O(g)$ (slow)

   $O(g) + O_3(g) \rightarrow 2\,O_2(g)$ (ΔH value for entire reaction = –284.6 kJ/mol)

2. Palladium catalyzes the hydrogenation of ethene (commonly called ethylene) in a reaction having a ΔH value of –136.9 kJ/mol. The mechanism is as follows.

   $$H_2(g) + 2\,Pd(s) \rightleftharpoons 2\,Pd\text{-}H(s)$$
   $$C_2H_4(g) + Pd\text{-}H(s) \rightarrow C_2H_5\text{-}Pd(s) \quad \text{(slowest step)}$$
   $$C_2H_5\text{-}Pd(s) + Pd\text{-}H(s) \rightarrow C_2H_6(g) + 2\,Pd(s)$$

Continued

Practice Problems (Continued)

3. A "chain reaction" often involves *free radical* halogen or hydrogen atoms. These are atoms with an unpaired electron. Free radicals are high energy, unstable, and therefore very reactive. The formation of two free radical atoms in the first step of this mechanism makes the first step the rate-determining one. The first step in a chain mechanism is called the *initiation step*. The second step, however, has the highest energy activated complex. The overall reaction is slightly exothermic.

$$Cl_2(g) \rightarrow Cl(g) + Cl(g) \qquad \text{initiation step}$$
$$(CH_4(g) + Cl(g) \rightarrow CH_3Cl(g) + H(g) \times 2 \qquad \text{propagation steps}$$
$$H(g) + H(g) \rightarrow H_2(g) \qquad \text{termination step}$$

Heterogeneous Catalysts

Catalysts may be classified as one of two types, heterogeneous or homogeneous. **Heterogeneous catalysts** are those in which reactions are limited to their surface area only. Most heterogeneous catalysts are solids. The most common are transition metals such as platinum or nickel. Catalysts of this type undergo *adsorption* of reactants onto their surface. The catalyst energizes the reactants and holds them in a position that allows easy interaction between them and other reacting species. Figure 2.5.4 describes the function of a typical heterogeneous metal catalyst in an addition reaction involving ethene (ethylene), a component of natural gas and hydrogen.

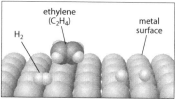

1. H_2 and C_2H_4 approach and adsorb to metal surface.

2. Rate-limiting step is H—H bond breakage.

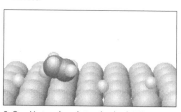

3. One H atom bonds to adsorbed C_2H_4.

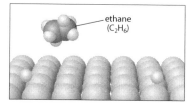

4. Another C—H bond forms and C_2H_6 is released.

Figure 2.5.4 *This process reduces the double bond in $CH_2CH_2(g)$ to a single bond in $CH_3CH_3(g$ by addition of $H_2(g$*

© Edvantage Interactive 2016

Heterogeneous catalysis also occurs inside the exhaust system of our automobiles. A device called a **catalytic converter** activates several oxidation and/or reduction reactions. These transform harmful pollutants such as carbon monoxide, a variety of hydrocarbons, and nitrogen oxides into harmless carbon dioxide, water, and nitrogen gas. The converter contains a series of honeycomb-patterned channels lined with the catalyst, platinum (Figure 2.5.5). A number of other transition metals may function as catalysts in a catalytic converter.

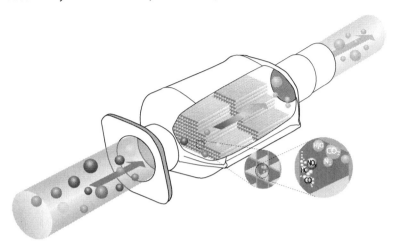

Figure 2.5.5 *Vehicles with properly functioning catalytic converters nearly always pass emissions tests.*

Homogeneous Catalysts

Many reactions are catalyzed by the presence of an acid. In such a case, the hydrogen ions from the acid react with and somehow modify the structure of a reactant to make it more susceptible to reaction with another reagent. The decomposition of methanoic acid using an acid catalyst is shown in the Warm Up and the Sample Problem 4.6.1 in this section. Catalysts such as this, which exist in the same phase as the rest of the reaction system, are sometimes called **homogeneous catalysts**.

One of the most important catalysts in the world is the enzyme, *nitrogenase*. Nitrogenase catalyzes the life-sustaining process of nitrogen fixation. Microorganisms convert the nitrogen in animal waste and dead plants and animals into $N_2(g)$, which is returned to the atmosphere. For the food chain to be sustained, however, there must be a means of converting atmospheric nitrogen back into a form plants can use. This process is called *nitrogenfixation*. The fixing of nitrogen involves the high activation energy reduction of elemental nitrogen into ammonia. Sometimes atmospheric lightning can provide the energy. Bacteria that live in the root nodules of certain plants carry out most of the nitrogen fixation. These bacteria contain **metalloenzymes** that are particularly useful for catalyzing oxidation and in this case, reduction, reactions. Nitrogenase contains an iron-molybedenum-sulfur cofactor in its structure. A cofactor, sometimes called a coenzyme, is a secondary substance that is required for an enzyme to function properly.

Reaction Mechanisms and Rate Laws

A valid reaction mechanism for a particular chemical reaction must fit these criteria:
1. The elementary steps must algebraically sum to the overall balanced equation.
2. Each elementary step is most commonly unimolecular or bimolecular. The chances of more than two particles colliding at once with sufficient energy and proper geometry are infinitesimally small.
3. The reaction mechanism must correlate with the rate law. The steps involved in correlating a mechanism with a rate law are outlined below.

There are four steps involved in the deduction of a rate law from a reaction mechanism:

1. Locate the *rate-determining step*.

As indicated earlier in this section, the *rate-determining step* is the slowest elementary process in the reaction mechanism and determines the overall reaction rate. This step is labeled "slow" or "rate determining."

2. Write a temporary *rate law expression*.

The temporary rate law expression uses the reactants in the rate-determining step and their molecularity. The coefficients for each reactant (the reactant *molecularity*) become the exponents of that reactant's concentration in the temporary rate law (the *order* with respect to that reactant).

3. Write an *equilibrium expression* or a *"fast-forward reversible"* expression.

We will delve into the rate law expression for a fast-forward reversible equilibrium elementary step in more detail in section 2.5. The *double arrow* in the equation indicates that an elementary step is in equilibrium.

4. Use the expression to *substitute for appropriate species* in the temporary rate law.

As the final rate law is determined experimentally, it must ONLY contain reactant species (or in rare cases, a catalyst) that a chemist can manipulate directly. This means we must substitute actual reactants for intermediates or products that appear in the temporary rate law. We can algebraically manipulate the equilibrium expression to allow substitutions to occur.

Sample Problem — Deducing a Rate Law from a Mechanism

The reaction of nitrogen monoxide and chlorine gas occurs via the following two step mechanism:

fast-forward reversible: $NO(g) + Cl_2(g) \rightleftharpoons NOCl_2(g)$ (step 1)

slow: $\underline{NOCl_2(g) + NO(g) \rightarrow 2\,NOCl(g)}$ (step 2)

overall reaction: $2\,NO(g) + Cl_2(g) \rightarrow 2\,NOCl(g)$

Determine the rate law for the overall reaction.

What to Think About	**How to Do It**
1. Step 2 in the given mechanism is rate determining and the coefficients of both species in this step are 1's. Consequently both of these species are first order in the *temporary rate law*.	The temporary rate law based on the slow step in the given mechanism is $$\text{rate} = k'[NOCl_2][NO]$$ Note: The rate constant is also temporary and so is shown as k' ("*k* prime").
2. Write an expression for the *equilibrium* or *fast-forward reversible* step. The first elementary step is an equilibrium, as indicated by the presence of the double arrow.	The equilibrium expression for the reaction in the first elementary step is: $$K_{eq} = \frac{[NOCl_2]}{[NO][Cl_2]}$$ According to the K_{eq} expression above, $$[NOCl_2] = K_{eq}[NO][Cl_2]$$

Continued

© Edvantage Interactive 2016

Sample Problem (Continued)

3. Substitute the $[NOCl_2]$ in the temporary rate law since it is an intermediate and does not appear in the overall reaction. The product of two constants such as $k' \times K_{eq}$ is equal to a new constant, in this case, the overall rate constant, k.

Substitute this expression into the temporary rate law to give:

$rate = k'K_{eq}[NO][Cl_2][NO]$

This rate law simplifies to:

$rate = k[NO]^2[Cl_2]$

Practice Problems — Deducing a Rate Law from a Mechanism

1. The reaction of the iodide ion and the hypochlorite ion is an oxidation-reduction reaction occurring in basic solution:

$$I^-(aq) + OCl^-(aq) \rightarrow IO^-(aq) + Cl^-(aq) \quad (basic)$$

The three-step mechanism is represented as follows:

fast-forward reversible: $OCl^-(aq) + H_2O(l) \rightleftharpoons HOCl(aq) + OH^-(aq)$

rate-determining step: $I^-(aq) + HOCl(aq) \rightarrow HIO(aq) + Cl^-(aq)$

                               $\underline{HIO(aq) + OH^-(aq) \rightarrow H_2O(l) + IO^-(aq)}$

(a) Show how the above steps combine mathematically to give the overall reaction. Identify all *intermediates* and *catalysts*. (Show work directly on the mechanism provided.)

(b) Show that the mechanism provided gives the rate law: $rate = k[I^-][OCl^-][OH^-]^{-1}$
(Note: Because this *redox* reaction is occurring in a basic solution, $[OH^-]$ can appear in the rate law expression.)

Continued

Practice Problems (*Continued*)

2. Although fractional orders are rare, they can occur. Consider the following overall equation for a substitution reaction to form carbon tetrachloride from chloroform:

$$Cl_2(g) + CHCl_3(g) \rightarrow CCl_4(g) + HCl(g)$$

Here are the three elementary steps in the mechanism:

fast-forward reversible reaction: $\qquad Cl_2(g) \rightleftharpoons 2\,Cl(g)$

$\qquad\qquad$ *slow reaction:* $\quad Cl(g) + CHCl_3(g) \rightarrow HCl(g) + CCl_3(g)$

$\qquad\qquad$ *fast reaction:* $\quad \underline{Cl(g) + CCl_3(g) \rightarrow CCl_4(g)}$

(a) Show how the reactants and products of the elementary steps cancel to produce the overall reaction.

(b) Identify any *intermediates or catalysts*. (Show work for parts (a) and (b) on the steps provided above.)

(c) Determine the overall rate law for the reaction.

Equation Coefficients and Rate Law Exponents

It is impossible to deduce a reaction mechanism from an equation alone. The rate law provides guidance as to what occurs on the pathway between the reactants and products. It helps us determine what is formed and consumed during the mechanism for a reaction. Rate laws are determined experimentally. They relate the rate of a reaction to the concentration of the reactants. Rate laws help us determine whether the equation for an overall reaction represents an elementary process, and if it is not, rate laws help us deduce a reaction mechanism.

If the coefficients in an equation match the exponents in a rate law, the reaction *may* consist of *one step*. However, if they do *not*, there is no doubt that the reaction *must* consist of more than one step. Information such as this can be helpful in determining the relationship between a rate law and a reaction mechanism.

© Edvantage Interactive 2016

2.5 Activity: A Molecular View Of a Reaction Mechanism

Question

How can you determine the mechanism for a reaction given a "molecular view"?

Background

Two series of "snapshots" of a reacting system taken several microseconds apart are available for viewing. The first set is of an uncatalyzed reaction. The second set is of the same reaction, but it is catalyzed.

Uncatalyzed reaction: Reactants are B + G; Product is BG.

Snapshot 1

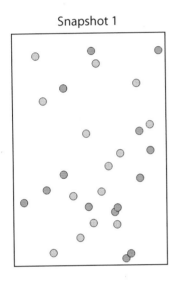

Snapshot 2

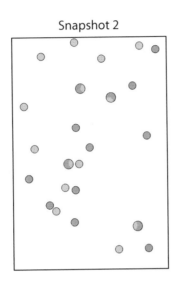

Snapshot 3

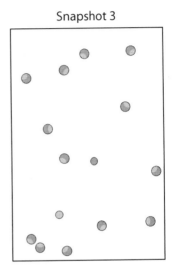

Catalyzed reaction: Reactants are the same as above. Catalyst R added.

Snapshot 1

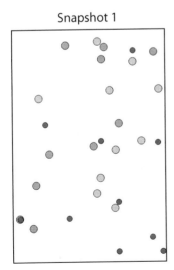

Snapshot 2

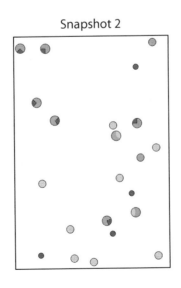

Snapshot 3

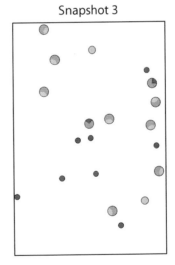

Procedure

1. Determine an equation that represents the uncatalyzed reaction.

2. Determine the reactions that represent the two-step mechanism for the catalyzed reaction.

   Step 1:

   Step 2:

   _____

   Overall Reaction:

Results and Discussion

1. Show how steps 1 and 2 sum to give the overall catalyzed reaction.

2. How does the overall reaction compare with the uncatalyzed reaction?

3. Identify the catalyst in the mechanism.

4. Identify any and all intermediates in the mechanism.

5. How would the time passed from snapshots 1 through 3 in the catalyzed series compare with the time for the uncatalyzed series?

6. Assume the second step in the catalyzed series is rate-determining. How would the time passed between snapshots 1 and 2 compare to the time passed between snapshots 2 and 3?

7. For the catalyzed reaction, how would the addition of more B affect the overall reaction rate? More G? Explain your answers.

© Edvantage Interactive 2016

2.5 Review Questions

1. What is a reaction mechanism?

2. What is a rate-determining step?

3. How do chemists determine reaction mechanisms?

4. Indicate whether each of the following reactions involves heterogeneous or homogeneous catalysis:

   (a) $H_2(g) + CH_2CH_2(g) \xrightarrow{Pt(s)} CH_3CH_3(g)$ hydrogenation of ethylene

   (b) Chlorofluorocarbons (CFCs) catalyze the conversion of ozone ($O_3(g)$) to oxygen gas (O_2).

   $2 O_3(g) \xrightarrow{CFC(g)} 3 O_2(g)$

   (c) Manganese(IV) oxide catalyzes the decomposition of hydrogen peroxide.

   $2 H_2O_2(aq) \xrightarrow{MnO_2(s)} 2 H_2O(l) + O_2(g)$

5. The oxygen produced by the decomposition of hydrogen peroxide may be used to clean a variety of items from contact lenses to dentures. The decomposition may be initiated by the addition of small disks. Study the following mechanism:

   1st: $H_2O_2(aq) + I^-(aq) \rightarrow H_2O(l) + IO^-(aq)$ slow

   2nd: $H_2O_2(aq) + IO^-(aq) \rightarrow H_2O(l) + O_2(g) + I^-(aq)$ fast

   Overall reaction:

   (a) Determine the overall reaction.

   (b) Identify any intermediate(s) present.

   (c) What is the material contained on the disks?

---

6. Examine the following potential energy diagram and use it to construct a reaction mechanism. Show each step and the overall reaction. Label the rate-determining step.

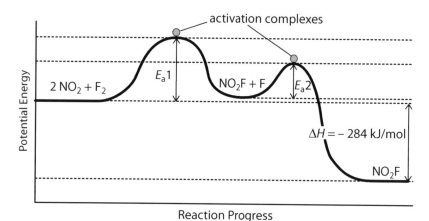

7. Look at the PE diagram shown here and answers the questions below. Write your answers at the end of each question.

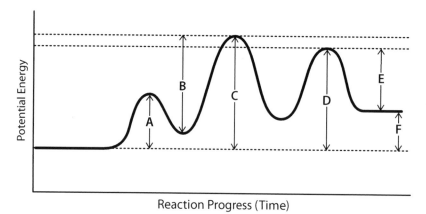

(a) How many steps are in the reaction represented by this potential energy profile?

(b) Which step is rate determining?

(c) What arrow represents E_a for the forward reaction?

(d) What arrow represents E_a for the rate-determining step?

(e) What arrow represents ΔH for the reaction?

(f) Is this an endo- or exothermic reaction?

© Edvantage Interactive 2016

8. The reaction, $CO(g) + NO_2(g) \rightarrow CO_2(g) + NO(g)$ may occur by either of the following two mechanisms:

Mechanism 1: Step 1: $2\,NO_2(g) \rightarrow NO_3(g) + NO(g)$ slow

          Step 2: _____   fast

          Reaction:

Mechanism 2: Step 1: $2\,NO_2(g) \rightarrow N_2O_4(g)$ fast

          Step 2: _____   slow

          Reaction:

(a) Fill the reaction in and use it to discern the missing step 2 for each mechanism.

(b) Experimental data shows that increasing the [CO] has *no effect* on the overall reaction rate. Based on this data, which mechanism must be correct?

9. Consider the reaction: $4\,HBr(g) + O_2(g) \rightarrow 2\,H_2O(g) + 2\,Br_2(g) + \text{heat}$
   (a) Does this reaction represent an elementary process? Explain

   (b) Propose a reaction mechanism for the overall reaction, given the following clues: There are two intermediates in the reaction. The first to form is $HOOBr(g)$ and the second is $HOBr(g)$.

   (c) Experimental data shows that a change in [HBr] has the same effect on the rate of the reaction as an identical change in [O_2]. What is the rate-determining step?

(d) Sketch a potential energy profile for the reaction. Recall that two identical steps involving the same potential bond energies will be shown as the *same step* in a potential energy diagram.

10. Sketch a potential energy diagram for the following reversible reaction:

$$\text{heat} + 2\,A + 2\,B \rightleftharpoons 3\,C$$

Be sure to label the axes. Indicate the following features on the diagram:
(a) reverse activation energy
(b) ΔH
(c) potential energy of activated complex
(d) use a dotted line to represent the pathway for a catalyzed reaction

11. Consider the following mechanism for a chemical reaction.
    Step 1: $2\,NO(g) \rightleftharpoons N_2O_2(g)$ *fast-forward reversible*
    Step 2: $N_2O_2(g) + O_2(g) \rightarrow 2\,NO_2(g)$ *slow*

    (a) Determine the overall reaction. Indicate any catalysts or intermediates.

    (b) Determine the rate law for the overall reaction.

© Edvantage Interactive 2016

12. A hypothetical reaction, 2 A + B→ C + D, has the rate law, rate = k [A][B].
Your teacher proposes the following three reaction mechanisms for the reaction. Which of these mechanisms is consistent with the rate law ? Consider and address each mechanism in turn and justify your choice.

Mechanism 1: A + B ⇌ C + M   *fast-forward reversible*
          M + A → D   *slow*

Mechanism 2: B ⇌ M   *fast-forward reversible*
       M + A → C + X   *slow*
       A + X → D   *fast*

Mechanism 3: A + B ⇌ M   *fast-forward reversible*
       M + A → C + X   *slow*
          X → D   *fast*

13. The reaction of NO and O_2 gases likely occurs according to the following mechanism.
Step 1: $NO(g) + O_2(g) ⇌ NO_3(g)$ *fast-forward reversible*
Step 2: $NO_3(g) + NO(g) → 2 NO_2(g)$ *slow*

(a) Show how the two steps combine to give the overall reaction.

(b) Determine the rate law for the overall reaction.

14. You propose the following three-step mechanism for a reaction. The second step is rate determining.

$NH_3(aq) + OBr^-(aq) \rightleftharpoons NH_2Br(aq) + OH^-(aq)$

$NH_2Br(aq) + NH_3(aq) \rightarrow N_2H_5^+(aq) + Br^-(aq)$

$N_2H_5^+(aq) + OH^-(aq) \rightarrow N_2H_4(aq) + H_2O(l)$

(a) Show how the three steps combine to give the overall reaction.

(b) Identify any catalysts and/or intermediates.

(c) Determine the rate law predicted by this mechanism.

3 Chemical Equilibrium

By the end of this chapter, you should be able to do the following:

- Explain the concept of chemical equilibrium with reference to reacting systems
- Predict, with reference to entropy and enthalpy, whether reacting systems will reach equilibrium
- Apply Le Châtelier's principle to the shifting of equilibrium
- Apply the concept of equilibrium to a commercial or industrial process
- Draw conclusions from the equilibrium constant expression
- Perform calculations to evaluate the changes in the value of K_{eq} and in concentrations of substances within an equilibrium system

By the end of this chapter, you should know the meaning of these **key terms**:

- chemical equilibrium
- closed system
- dynamic equilibrium
- enthalpy
- entropy
- equilibrium concentration
- equilibrium constant expression
- equilibrium shift
- Haber process

- heterogeneous reaction
- homogeneous reaction
- ICE table
- K_{eq}
- Le Châtelier's principle
- macroscopic properties
- open system
- PE diagram

When the number of shoppers travelling between the two floors on the escalators is equal, the crowd has reached equilibrium.

3.1 Introduction to Dynamic Equilibrium

Warm Up

Every weekday from 7 a.m. to 9 a.m. a large volume of traffic flows into Toronto as people who live in the surrounding communities drive to work.

1. Are there any cars leaving Toronto between 7 a.m. and 9 a.m.?

_____

2. Explain how the number of cars in Toronto remains relatively constant between 10 a.m. to 2 p.m. when cars are still entering the city.

_____

3. The number of cars in Toronto decreases between 3 p.m. and 7 p.m. Describe the traffic flow during this period.

_____

Defining Chemical Equilibrium

Many chemical reactions are reversible. For example a decomposition reaction is the reverse of a synthesis reaction. This reversibility of chemical reactions facilitates an important phenomenon known as chemical equilibrium.

> **Chemical equilibrium** exists when the forward rate of a chemical reaction equals its reverse rate.

Chemical equilibria are said to be *dynamic*, which means they are active. In chemical equilibria, the forward and reverse reactions continue to occur. This contrasts with a *static* equilibrium of forces, such as the equal and opposite forces acting on a weight hanging motionless on the end of a string. In a chemical equilibrium, each reactant is being "put back" by the reverse reaction at the same rate that it is being "used up" by the forward reaction and vice versa for each product. Note that the rate at which one chemical is being consumed and produced is not necessarily the same as the rate at which another chemical is being consumed and produced. The consumption and production ratios are provided by the coefficients in the balanced chemical equation. The example below describes the synthesis and decomposition of water. The equation shows that hydrogen is consumed and produced at twice the rate in moles per second that oxygen is.

$$2\,H_2(g) + O_2(g) \rightleftharpoons 2\,H_2O(g)$$

Sample Problem — Determining Equivalent Reaction Rates at Equilibrium

NO_2 is being consumed at a rate of 0.031 mol/s in the equilibrium below. How many moles of N_2O_4 are being consumed each second?

$$2\,NO_2(g) \rightleftharpoons N_2O_4(g)$$

What to Think About	How to Do It
1. Recall that, at equilibrium, the rate of any chemical's consumption equals the rate of its production. Therefore, NO_2 is also being produced at 0.031 mol/s.	$0.031\,\dfrac{mol\ NO_2}{s} \times \dfrac{1\ mol\ N_2O_4}{2\ mol\ NO_2} = \dfrac{0.016\ mol\ N_2O_4}{s}$
2. Look at the coefficients.	The coefficients in the balanced equation indicate that 1 mol of N_2O_4 is consumed for each 2 mol of NO_2 produced.

Practice Problems — Determining Equivalent Reaction Rates at Equilibrium

SO_2 and O_2 are placed in a sealed flask where they react to produce SO_3. When equilibrium is achieved, SO_3 is being produced at a rate of 0.0082 mol/s.

$$2\,SO_2(g) + O_2(g) \rightleftharpoons 2\,SO_3(g)$$

1. How many moles of SO_3 are being consumed each second?

2. How many moles of O_2 are being produced each second?

3. How many grams of O_2 are being consumed each second?

Recognizing Chemical Equilibrium

How do chemists recognize a chemical equilibrium? There are three criteria for a system to be at chemical equilibrium. It must:
1. have constant **macroscopic** properties. Macroscopic properties are those that are large enough to be measured or observed with the unaided eye.
2. be closed.
3. shift when conditions change.

1. Constancy of Macroscopic Properties

A system at equilibrium has constant macroscopic properties such as color, pH, temperature, and pressure because the amount of each reactant and product remains constant. Each chemical is being produced (put back) at the same rate that it is being consumed (removed). There is no macroscopic activity in a system at equilibrium because the continuing forward and reverse reactions are not observable because we cannot see atoms or molecules. Minor unobservable fluctuations in rates and concentrations are presumed to occur in equilibria since reaction rates are dependent on random collisions between reactant species. Another notable characteristic of equilibria is that they are self-perpetuating because the forward and the reverse reactions continuously supply each other with reactants.

2. Closed System

A system is **closed** if no chemicals are entering or leaving the defined system. If a system's properties are constant but the system is open then it is a **steady state** rather than an equilibrium (Figure 3.1.1). In a steady state, components enter and leave the system at the same rate rather than going back and forth within an equilibrium system. A steady state exists when the water level behind Cleveland dam stays constant because water is flowing into Capilano Lake, the lake behind the dam, at the same rate that it is flowing through the dam.

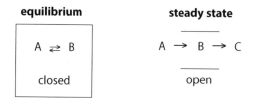

Figure 3.1.1 *Equilibrium occurs only in a closed system. In an open system, steady state can be reached, but not equilibrium.*

A reaction occurring in aqueous solution may only achieve equilibrium if all the reactant particles, product particles, and solvent water molecules remain in the solution. If an equilibrium system is temporarily disrupted by opening it and removing chemicals, the remaining chemicals will re-establish equilibrium if the system is closed again. Chemicals could be removed in a disruption, for example, if a chemical in the aqueous equilibrium is precipitated out or evaporates.

For a system to be at equilibrium, it must be closed and at a constant temperature (constancy of macroscopic properties). The intent of these conditions is to hold the amount of matter and energy constant within the system. For a system to be at a constant temperature it must be at thermal equilibrium with its surroundings, meaning that kinetic energy must be entering and leaving the system at the same rate.

3. A Shift due to Changed Conditions

The world is full of closed systems at constant temperatures in which nothing appears to be happening. In the vast majority of these, there really is nothing happening. They are just chemical mixtures. Equilibrium exists in only a small percentage of those systems that meet the first two criteria. Just as a child might poke a snake to see if it's alive, chemists "poke" chemical systems by changing their conditions. A change in temperature usually forces an equilibrium to reveal itself by causing a change or a *shift* in the amounts of reactants and products. When the solution's original temperature is restored, so are the original amounts. The equilibrium shifts back. Various shifts in response to changes of conditions will be discussed in sections 3.2 and 3.3. If the reaction is photoactivated, it will respond to a change in lighting conditions rather than a change in temperature.

Quick Check

1. Why are chemical equilibria referred to as dynamic? _____

2. List three criteria that must be satisfied for chemical equilibrium to exist.

   _____   _____

   _____

3. What is a closed chemical system? _____

4. What is a macroscopic property? _____

© Edvantage Interactive 2016

Recall that, as a reaction proceeds, reactant concentrations fall. Hence, the forward rate of the reaction (r_f) decreases. In a closed system, the product concentrations rise at the same time as the reactant concentrations are falling. Hence, the reverse rate of the reaction (r_r) increases. This continues until $r_r = r_f$ and equilibrium is established (Figure 3.1.2).

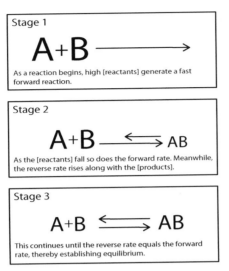

Stage 1

$$A+B \longrightarrow$$

As a reaction begins, high [reactants] generate a fast forward reaction.

Stage 2

$$A+B \underset{\longrightarrow}{\overset{\longleftarrow}{}} AB$$

As the [reactants] fall so does the forward rate. Meanwhile, the reverse rate rises along with the [products].

Stage 3

$$A+B \underset{\longrightarrow}{\overset{\longleftarrow}{}} AB$$

This continues until the reverse rate equals the forward rate, thereby establishing equilibrium.

Figure 3.1.2 *Diagrammatic representation of chemical equilibrium being established*

Figure 3.1.3 shows equilibrium being achieved at about $t = 7$ s when the reactant and product concentrations become constant. It is important to note that the concentrations of reactants are not equal to the concentration of products at equilibrium. Only the forward and reverse reaction *rates* are equal.

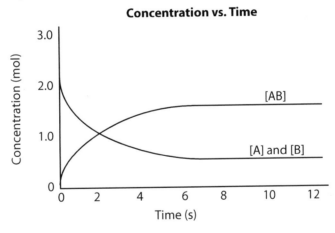

Concentration vs. Time

Figure 3.1.3 *This graph shows what happens with reactant and product concentrations as a function of time as equilibrium is established.*

Quick Check

Is each question below true or false? Place T or F in the places provided.

1. The reactant concentrations always equal the product concentrations at equilibrium. _____

2. When approaching equilibrium, [reactants] decreases while the [products] increases. _____

3. The [reactants] hold steady at equilibrium. _____

4. Before achieving equilibrium, the forward rate (r_f) is less than the reverse rate (r_r). _____

3.1 Review Questions

1. Identify each of the following as being either an *equilibrium* or a *steady state*:

   (a) As bees go back and forth from their hive to a flowerbed, the number of bees inside the hive and at the flowerbed remains constant.

   (b) Despite people checking in and out of a motel each day, the number of guests registered at the motel each night remains constant.

   (c) During a basketball game, team members are frequently being substituted in and out of the game. There are always five players on the floor and seven players on the bench.

   (d) Two new students enrol in your chemistry class each day because they hear from their friends how interesting the class is. Unfortunately two students also withdraw each day.

   (e) Shoppers at the Hotel California Mall can never leave (but it's a lovely place). Shoppers travel back and forth on escalators between the mall's two levels though the number of shoppers on each level never changes.

2. An equilibrium exists when a reaction's forward rate equals its reverse rate. Answer the questions below for the following equilibrium:

$$2\,NO(g) + Cl_2(g) \rightleftharpoons 2\,NOCl(g)$$

   (a) Do the moles of NO consumed per second equal the moles of NO produced per second?

   (b) Do the moles of NO consumed per second equal the moles of NOCl consumed per second?

   (c) Do the moles of NOCl produced per second equal the moles of Cl_2 consumed per second?

   (d) Do the grams of NO consumed per second equal the grams of NO produced per second?

   (e) Do the grams of NO consumed per second equal the grams of NOCl consumed per second?

© Edvantage Interactive 2016

3. $H_2(g)$ is being consumed at a rate of 0.012 mol/s in the following equilibrium:

$$N_2(g) + 3\,H_2(g) \rightleftharpoons 2\,NH_3(g)$$

(a) How many moles of N_2 are being produced and consumed each second?

(b) How many grams of NH_3 are being produced and consumed each second?

4. Melting and evaporating are physical changes, not chemical changes, but changes of physical state can also form dynamic equilibria.
   (a) An ice cube floats in a water bath held at 0°C. The size of the ice cube remains constant because the ice is melting at the same rate as the water is freezing. Describe and explain what you would observe if the temperature of the water bath was increased slightly.

   (b) The water level in a flask drops as water evaporates from it. The flask is then closed using a rubber stopper. The water level continues to drop for a while but eventually holds steady. Explain why the water level is no longer falling. (Has the evaporation stopped?)

5. A chemist observes a closed system at a constant temperature in which no macroscopic changes are occurring. To determine whether or not the system is at equilibrium, the chemist increases its temperature and notes a change in the properties of the system. Can you be sure that this system is at equilibrium? Explain your answer.

6. Nobel laureate (prize winner) Ilya Prigogine coined the term *dissipative structures* for systems such as candle flames that are in steady state. The chemical reaction for burning one type of wax is:

$$C_{25}H_{52}(g) + 38\,O_2(g) \;\rightarrow\; 25\,CO_2(g) + 26\,H_2O(g)$$

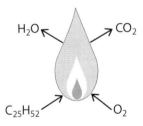

A continuous reaction occurs in a flame. The amount of each reactant and product in the flame remains relatively constant as reactants are continuously drawn in to replace those consumed and the products continuously dissipate into the surrounding air.
(a) How is this situation like an equilibrium?

(b) How is this situation different from an equilibrium?

Fascinate your friends by blowing out a candle flame and then re-igniting the evaporating paraffin gas by placing a lit match a couple centimeters above the wick. Try it!

7. Clock reactions are often used to demonstrate the effect of concentration and temperature on reaction rates. The distinctive aspect of clock reactions is a long delay followed by a sudden appearance of product. This peculiar behavior frequently results from a cyclic mechanism. Consider the mechanism of the iodine clock reaction below:

Step 1 $3\,HSO_3^- + IO_3^- \rightarrow I^- + 3\,H^+ + 3\,SO_4^{2-}$
Step 2 $10\,I^- + 12\,H^+ + 2\,IO_3^- \rightarrow 6\,I_2 + 6\,H_2O$
Step 3 $I_2 + H_2O + HSO_3^- \rightarrow 2\,I^- + 3\,H^+ + SO_4^{2-}$

Why is the two-step iodine cycle at the end of this mechanism not an equilibrium even when the two steps are proceeding at the same rate?

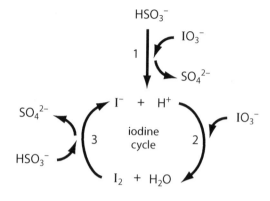

8. When considering equilibria, chemists sometimes forget that the forward and reverse reactions may occur through a series of steps. Consider the following reaction mechanism approaching equilibrium:

Step 1: $2\,NO + H_2 \rightarrow N_2 + H_2O_2$
Step 2: $H_2O_2 + H_2 \rightarrow 2\,H_2O$
Overall: $2\,NO + 2\,H_2 \rightarrow N_2 + 2\,H_2O$

If a reaction is at equilibrium, every step in its mechanism must be at equilibrium. When the above reaction establishes equilibrium, how do you know that:
(a) step 1 must be at equilibrium?

(b) step 2 must be at equilibrium?

© Edvantage Interactive 2016

9. A chemical reaction achieves equilibrium 20 s after it is initiated. Plot and label the forward reaction rate and the reverse reaction rate as a function of time from $t = 0$ s (initiation) until $t = 30$ s. (Caution: This is **not** the same kind of plot as in Figure 5.1.3. Here you are plotting the rate as a function of time whereas in Figure 5.1.3, we plotted the concentration of reactants and products as a function of time.)

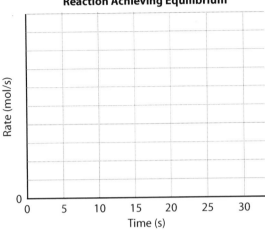

10. Nitrogen dioxide gas is placed in a sealed flask.

$$2\,NO_2(g) \;\rightarrow\; N_2O_4(g)$$

    orange   colorless

    (a) What would you see as the reaction approaches equilibrium?

    (b) Describe the change in the concentrations of reactants and products as the reaction approaches equilibrium.

    (c) Describe the change in the forward and reverse rates as the reaction approaches equilibrium.

11. A system at equilibrium has all of its reactants suddenly removed. Describe how the system would restore equilibrium in terms of its forward and reverse reaction rates and its reactant and product concentrations.

3.2 The Equilibrium Constant

Warm Up

A **constant** is a specific piece of information that does not change value, possibly within a set of described parameters. You have already used many constants in your science and mathematics classes. Some constants simply relate one system of measurement to another. For example, there are 2.54 cm in an inch.

1. Pi (π) is a mathematical constant that relates the circumference of a circle to its radius. What is the approximate value of pi?

   _____

2. The speed of light (c) in a vacuum is a physical constant with a value of 3.00×10^8 m/s. What famous formula of Albert Einstein's uses the speed of light to relate energy to mass?

   _____

3. State the name, symbol, and value of a chemical constant that provides the number of items in a mole of anything.

   _____

4. Why is it important to scientists to have accurate constants?

   _____

Deriving the Equilibrium Expression

Figure 3.2.1 provides the forward and reverse rate equations for the following reaction at equilibrium:

$$H_2(g) + I_2(g) \rightleftharpoons 2\,HI(g)$$

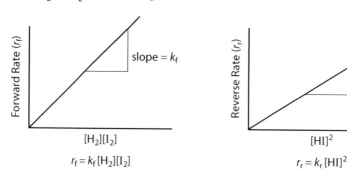

$$r_f = k_f\,[H_2][I_2] \qquad\qquad r_r = k_r\,[HI]^2$$

Figure 3.2.1 *Forward and reverse reaction rates for the equation above*

At equilibrium: $r_f = r_r$

Therefore: $k_f\,[H_2][I_2] = k_r\,[HI]^2$

Rearranging to isolate the constants we get:

$$\frac{k_f}{k_r} = \frac{[HI]^2}{[H_2][I_2]}$$

A constant divided by another constant equals a third constant. In this case $k_f \div k_r$ provides a constant that chemists call the equilibrium constant, K_{eq}.

Therefore: $K_{eq} = \dfrac{[HI]^2}{[H_2][I_2]}$

Regardless of the initial concentrations of reactants and possibly products, when equilibrium is achieved and the equilibrium concentrations are substituted into this expression, the calculated value

© Edvantage Interactive 2016

will always be the same at any given temperature. Since the rate constants k_f and k_r are temperature dependent, so too is the equilibrium constant, K_{eq}, that can be derived from them. This relationship is the mathematical "hook" we needed to quantify our understanding and descriptions of equilibrium. It provides chemists and chemical engineers with the ability to predict the concentrations that will be present when equilibrium is achieved.

The **equilibrium expression** refers to *the formula* for the equilibrium constant in terms of the equilibrium concentrations of reactants and products. The **equilibrium constant** refers to *the numerical value* provided by the equilibrium expression. The units of equilibrium constants vary too much from equation to equation to be useful and are therefore not required for this course.

The *equilibrium law* states that for the general equation:

$$pA + qB \rightleftharpoons rC + sD$$

$$K_{eq} = \frac{[C]^r[D]^s}{[A]^p[B]^q}$$

where p, q, r, and s are the coefficients in the balanced chemical equation.

The equilibrium law is valid for both single-step equilibria and multiple-step equilibria. In other words, the equilibrium expression and constant are independent of the reaction mechanism. Consider the following reaction mechanism:

Step 1	$NO_2 + F_2 \rightleftharpoons NO_2F + \cancel{F}$
Step 2	$\cancel{F} + NO_2 \rightleftharpoons NO_2F$
Net reaction	$2 NO_2 + F_2 \rightleftharpoons 2 NO_2F$

If the reaction is at equilibrium, then step 1 must be at equilibrium to maintain the reactants at a constant concentration. Step 2 must be at equilibrium to maintain the products at a constant concentration. The equilibrium expression for the overall reaction can be derived from the equilibrium expressions for each individual step:

$$K_{eq1} = \frac{[NO_2F][F]}{[NO_2][F_2]} \qquad K_{eq2} = \frac{[NO_2F]}{[F][NO_2]}$$

$$K_{eq1} \times K_{eq2} = \frac{[NO_2F][\cancel{F}]}{[NO_2][F_2]} \times \frac{[NO_2F]}{[\cancel{F}][NO_2]} = \frac{[NO_2F]^2}{[NO_2]^2[F_2]} = K_{eq}$$

The most common and reliable means of determining a reaction's equilibrium constant is to simply substitute equilibrium concentrations into the equilibrium expression.

Sample Problem — Determining K_{eq} from the Equilibrium Concentrations

For the following equation, 0.19 mol NO_2 and 0.64 mol N_2O_4 are found at equilibrium in a 250 mL flask at 92°C.

$$2 NO_2(g) \rightleftharpoons N_2O_4(g)$$

What is the equilibrium constant for this reaction at 92°C?

What to Think About	**How to Do It**
1. Write the equilibrium expression for the reaction. As indicated by the notation [ ], K_{eq} values are determined using molar concentrations so it is important to consider the units provided for the reacting species (moles or M) and the container size if the concentrations need to be calculated.	$K_{eq} = \dfrac{[N_2O_4]}{[NO_2]^2}$
2. Substitute the equilibrium concentrations into the expression.	$K_{eq} = \dfrac{(0.64 \text{ mol}/0.25 \text{ L})}{(0.19 \text{ mol}/0.25 \text{ L})^2} = 4.4$

Practice Problems — Determining K_{eq} from the Equilibrium Concentrations

1. The following gases are at equilibrium in a flask at 423°C: 4.56×10^{-3} M H_2, 7.4×10^{-4} M I_2, and 1.35×10^{-2} M HI. What is the equilibrium constant for the reaction at this temperature?

$$2\,HI(g) \rightleftharpoons H_2(g) + I_2(g)$$

2. A quantity of 3.88×10^{-3} M NO_2 is at equilibrium with 1.73×10^{-4} M N_2O_4 at 60°C.

$$2\,NO_2(g) \rightleftharpoons N_2O_4(g)$$

    (a) What is the equilibrium constant for the reaction at 60°C?

    (b) State whether this reaction is endothermic or exothermic by comparing the equilibrium constant for this reaction at 60°C to the constant at 92°C provided in the preceding sample problem. Explain your reasoning.

3. As a slight variation on this type of problem, you could be asked to determine an equilibrium concentration from the K_{eq} and the other equilibrium concentrations. For example, 0.14 M NH_3 is at equilibrium with 0.020 M N_2 at 225°C. What is the equilibrium concentration of H_2 in the reacting mixture?

$$N_2(g) + 3\,H_2(g) \rightleftharpoons 2\,NH_3(g) \qquad K_{eq} = 1.7 \times 10^2 \text{ at } 225°C$$

What Does a Bigger Equilibrium Constant Mean?

Recall our derivation of K_{eq}. For the equilibrium system, $H_2(g) + I_2(g) \rightleftharpoons 2\,HI(g)$:

$$\frac{k_f}{k_r} = \frac{[HI]^2}{[H_2][I_2]} = K_{eq} \qquad \text{but } \frac{k_r}{k_f}, \text{ which equals } \frac{[H_2][I_2]}{[HI]^2}, \text{ is also a constant.}$$

Presumably, chemists chose the numerical value provided by the first expression, $[HI]^2/[H_2][I_2]$ to be K_{eq} because the product concentration is in its numerator and the reactant concentrations are in its denominator. This means that the size of the equilibrium constant indicates the extent of the reaction's progress towards products.

> The further a given reaction progresses to the right to achieve equilibrium, the greater its equilibrium constant will be.

This appeals to us because it is consistent with the number line, which also has numbers increasing from left to right. Here we are combining the chemical equation metaphor that changing from reactants to products is proceeding to the right with the number line metaphor that proceeding to the right is increasing in numerical value.

Knowing what a bigger equilibrium constant *does not mean* is perhaps just as important as knowing what it *does mean*. Chemists must be careful not to attempt to infer too much from equilibrium constants. The following two points outline important information about interpreting equilibrium constants:

© Edvantage Interactive 2016

1. It is impossible to infer anything about an equilibrium's position solely from its equilibrium constant. An equilibrium's position depends on the initial reactant concentrations as well as the equilibrium constant. A given reaction therefore has a wide range of equilibrium positions that result from the same equilibrium constant. Consider the following equilibrium:

$$CH_3COOH(aq) \rightleftharpoons H^+(aq) + CH_3COO^-(aq) \qquad K_{eq} = 1.8 \times 10^{-5}$$

   If the initial concentration of CH_3COOH is 1.0 M then there will be a 0.42% yield at equilibrium, but if its initial concentration is 1.0×10^{-6} M then there will be a 95% yield at equilibrium. From Le Châtelier's perspective, diluting the system causes a shift to the right to partially restore the osmotic pressure.

2. Even with the same initial reactant concentrations, it is difficult to make meaningful comparisons between the equilibrium constants of different equilibria unless their expressions have identical forms. The following two equilibria have radically different percent yields even when they have the same equilibrium constant (at different temperatures) and the same initial reactant concentrations. The first equilibrium can have a greater K_{eq} than the second one and still have a lower percent yield.

$$Ni(CO)_4(g) \rightleftharpoons Ni(s) + 4\,CO(g) \qquad K_{eq} = 1$$

   When the initial $[Ni(CO)_4] = 1.0$ M there is a 23% yield at equilibrium.

$$2\,NO(g) \rightleftharpoons N_2(g) + O_2(g) \qquad K_{eq} = 1$$

   When the initial $[NO] = 1.0$ M there is an 83% yield at equilibrium.

Does an Equilibrium Constant Change When the Equilibrium System Shifts?

When an equilibrium is stressed by changing concentration(s), the new concentrations will not provide the equilibrium constant when plugged into the equilibrium expression. The equilibrium will shift to restore a set of concentrations that once again provide the equilibrium constant. It is after all, a constant.

On the other hand, the shift caused by a temperature change makes all the product concentrations increase and all the reactant concentrations decrease or vice versa so it must change the equilibrium constant. Equilibrium constants are temperature dependent. A shift to the right in response to a temperature change causes the equilibrium constant to increase. A shift to the left in response to a temperature change causes the equilibrium constant to decrease.

> Changing the temperature is the only way to change a chemical equation's equilibrium constant.

When a temperature change causes an equilibrium system to shift to the right, its [products] increase and its [reactants] decrease; therefore its equilibrium position also shifts to the right. Conversely, when a temperature change causes an equilibrium system to shift to the left, its [reactants] increase and its [products] decrease; therefore its equilibrium position also shifts to the left.

Table 3.2.1 *The Effect of Stresses on the Equilibrium System, Position, and Constant*

$2\,SO_2(g) + O_2(g) \rightleftharpoons 2\,SO_3(g)$		$\Delta H = -198$ kJ/mol	
Stress	**Equilibrium System**	**Equilibrium Position**	**Equilibrium Constant**
Add reactant	shifts right	may shift left or right	no change
Decrease volume	shifts right	shifts right	no change
Decrease temperature	shifts right	shifts right	increases

Quick Check

1. Consider the following equilibrium: $Ag^+(aq) + 2\,NH_3(aq) \rightleftharpoons Ag(NH_3)_2^+(aq)$

   (a) In what direction will the system shift if some ammonia (NH_3) is added to it? _____

   (b) How will this affect the equilibrium constant? _____

2. Consider the following equilibrium: $PCl_5(g) + 92.5\,kJ \rightleftharpoons PCl_3(g) + Cl_2(g)$

   A decrease in temperature will cause the equilibrium system to shift _____

   causing its percent yield to _____ and its equilibrium constant to

   _____.

3. Consider the following equilibrium: $C_2H_2(g) + 3\,H_2(g) \rightleftharpoons 2\,CH_4(g)$ $K_{eq} = 0.36$

   True or False? We know that reactants are favored in this reaction because $K_{eq} < 1$. _____

No Liquids or Solids in Equilibrium Expressions

Chemicals in liquid or solid states are not included in equilibrium expressions.

For example, the equilibrium formed when common salt dissolves in water is:

$$NaCl(s) \rightleftharpoons Na^+(aq) + Cl^-(aq)$$

Its equilibrium expression is simply: $K_{eq} = [Na^+][Cl^-]$

While the term *concentration* normally refers the amount of one chemical per unit volume of a mixture, it is sometimes used to describe how concentrated particles of pure matter are. For example, [pure $H_2O(l)$] = 55.6 M. However, the *concentration* of a pure solid or liquid is fixed by its density while the concentration of a solute is not. Regardless, this is a heterogeneous reaction, and it is the surface area of the NaCl that affects the reaction rate, not its concentration. So why is the surface area of the salt not part of the equilibrium expression? Increasing the surface area by grinding the salt or by adding more salt increases the rate of dissolving but does not affect the equilibrium concentrations because the rate of recrystallizing increases equally.

Although our example was a physical equilibrium, this principle holds true for heterogeneous chemical equilibria as well. A solid's surface area, although affecting the rate at which equilibrium is achieved, does not affect the equilibrium position. Solids therefore do not appear in equilibrium expressions. Likewise, adding or removing solids from an equilibrium affects the forward and reverse rates equally and therefore does not cause a shift.

The same logic applies to pure liquids involved in heterogeneous reactions but liquids involved as solvents are not included for a different reason. For example:

$$Cr_2O_7^{2-}(aq) + H_2O(l) \rightleftharpoons 2\,H^+(aq) + 2\,CrO_4^{2-}(aq)$$

$$K_{eq} = \frac{[H^+]^2[CrO_4^{2-}]^2}{[Cr_2O_7^{2-}]}$$

The [$H_2O(l)$] is not included in any equilibrium expression. In the above chemical equation, water is a reactant and a solvent for the reactant and product ions. Since water's concentration is nearly constant, we omit it from equilibrium expressions.

There is one situation where liquids appear in equilibrium expressions. When there is more than one liquid in the chemical equation, the liquids dilute each other so these chemicals are included in the equilibrium expression.

© Edvantage Interactive 2016

Quick Check

Write the equilibrium expression for the following reactions:

1. $B_2H_6(g) + 3\,O_2(g) \rightleftharpoons B_2O_3(s) + 3\,H_2O(g)$ _____

2. $4\,HCl(g) + O_2(g) \rightleftharpoons 2\,Cl_2(g) + 2\,H_2O(g)$ _____

3. $H_2(g) + Br_2(l) \rightleftharpoons 2\,HBr(g)$ _____

4. $CaCO_3(s) \rightleftharpoons Ca^{2+}(aq) + CO_3^{2-}(aq)$ _____

The Equilibrium Constant and the Form of the Chemical Equation

The form in which a chemical equation is written affects its K_{eq} expression and constant. To avoid possible ambiguity, chemists should provide the chemical equation with the K_{eq} value.

$$H_2(g) + \tfrac{1}{2}\,O_2(g) \rightleftharpoons H_2O(g)$$

At a particular temperature, 2.0 mol H_2, 4.0 mol O_2, and 12.0 mol H_2O are discovered at equilibrium in a 1.0 L flask.

$$K_{eq} = \frac{[H_2O]}{[H_2][O_2]^{\frac{1}{2}}} = \frac{12.0}{(2.0)(4.0)^{\frac{1}{2}}} = 3.0$$

The same reaction has a different equilibrium expression and a different constant when the coefficients in its equation are doubled:

$$2\,H_2(g) + O_2(g) \rightleftharpoons 2\,H_2O(g)$$

$$K_{eq} = \frac{[H_2O]^2}{[H_2]^2[O_2]} = \frac{(12.0)^2}{(2.0)^2(4.0)} = 9.0$$

The exact same equilibrium concentrations, when substituted into the new expression, provide a value that is the square of the original chemical equation's constant. Doubling a chemical equation's coefficients has the effect of squaring its K_{eq}. This is reasonable since the coefficients in the chemical equation appear as powers in the equilibrium expression.

Reversing a chemical equation has the effect of inverting its equilibrium expression and constant. The K_{eq} for any reaction is the reciprocal of the K_{eq} for its reverse reaction. Reversing the original equation we get:

$$H_2O(g) \rightleftharpoons H_2(g) + \tfrac{1}{2}\,O_2(g)$$

$$K_{eq} = \frac{[H_2][O_2]^{\frac{1}{2}}}{[H_2O]} = \frac{(2.0)(4.0)^{\frac{1}{2}}}{12.0} = 0.33$$

Quick Check

$$2\,HI(g) \rightleftharpoons H_2(g) + I_2(g) \qquad K_{eq} = 0.018 \text{ at } 423°C$$

1. What is the K_{eq} at 423°C of $H_2(g) + I_2(g) \rightleftharpoons 2\,HI(g)$? _____

2. What is the K_{eq} at 423°C of $HI(g) \rightleftharpoons \tfrac{1}{2}\,H_2(g) + \tfrac{1}{2}\,I_2(g)$? _____

3. What is the K_{eq} at 423°C of $\tfrac{1}{2}\,H_2(g) + \tfrac{1}{2}\,I_2(g) \rightleftharpoons HI(g)$? _____

The Reaction Quotient

The numerical value derived when *any* set of reactant and product concentrations is plugged into an equilibrium expression is called the **trial K_{eq}** or the **reaction quotient, Q**. This value tells chemists whether a reaction is at equilibrium and, if not, the direction that the reaction will proceed or shift to achieve equilibrium. If the trial K_{eq} is less than the actual K_{eq} then the reaction must proceed to the right to achieve equilibrium. The reaction quotient's numerator must increase and its denominator decrease until the quotient itself has risen to equal the equilibrium constant. If the trial K_{eq} is greater than the actual K_{eq} then the reaction must proceed to the left to achieve equilibrium. The reaction quotient's numerator must decrease and its denominator increase until the quotient itself has dropped to equal the equilibrium constant.

Sample Problem — Determining the Direction a System Will Proceed to Achieve Equilibrium, Given its Reactant and Product Concentrations

The following gases are introduced into a closed flask: 0.057 M SO_2, 0.057 M O_2, and 0.12 M SO_3. In which direction will the reaction proceed to establish equilibrium?

$$2 SO_2(g) + O_2(g) \rightleftharpoons 2 SO_3(g) \qquad K_{eq} = 85$$

What to Think About	How to Do It
1. Write the equilibrium expression for the reaction provided.	$\text{Trial } K_{eq} = \dfrac{[SO_3]^2}{[SO_2]^2[O_2]}$
2. Substitute the concentrations into the equilibrium expression and solve for the trial K_{eq}. Compare the trial K_{eq} to the actual K_{eq}.	$= \dfrac{(0.12)^2}{(0.057)^2\, 0.057} = 78 < 85$
3. Note that, by shifting to the right, the $[SO_3]$ will rise while the $[SO_2]$ and $[O_2]$ fall, causing the trial K_{eq} to increase toward 85 and the establishment or restoration of equilibrium.	Therefore this reaction must proceed or shift to the right to achieve equilibrium.

© Edvantage Interactive 2016

Practice Problems — Determining the Direction a System Will Proceed to Achieve Equilibrium, Given its Reactant and Product Concentrations

1. The industrial synthesis of hydrogen involves the reaction of steam and methane to produce *synthesis gas*, a mixture of hydrogen and carbon monoxide.

   $$CH_4(g) + H_2O(g) \rightleftharpoons CO(g) + 3\,H_2(g) \qquad K_{eq} = 4.7 \text{ at } 1127°C$$

   A mixture at 1127°C contains 0.045 M H_2O, 0.025 M CH_4, 0.10 M CO, and 0.30 M H_2. In which direction will the reaction proceed to establish equilibrium?

2. The following gases are introduced into a closed 0.50 L flask: 1.5 mol NO_2 and 4.0 mol N_2O_4. In which direction will the reaction proceed to achieve equilibrium?

   $$2\,NO_2(g) \rightleftharpoons N_2O_4(g) \quad K_{eq} = 0.940.$$

3. In a container, 0.10 M H^+ and 0.10 M SO_4^{2-} exist in equilibrium with 0.83 M HSO_4^-. A buffer is added that increases the concentration of both the bisulphate and sulfate ions by 0.10 M. What happens to the $[HSO_4^-]$ as equilibrium is restored?

   $$HSO_4^-(aq) \rightleftharpoons H^+(aq) + SO_4^{2-}(aq)$$

Reactants or Products?

It is awkward to call some chemicals "reactants" and others "products" if they are all present when the reaction starts. It is nevertheless convenient to use these terms so chemists write the chemical equation with the chemicals on the left side of the arrow being called the reactants and those on the right side of the arrow being called the products. Which direction the equation is written and therefore which chemicals are called reactants and which chemicals are called products is arbitrary. Of course, once decided, reversing the equation would invert the equilibrium expression and provide a K_{eq} that is the reciprocal of the original one.

An Addendum to Le Châtelier's Principle

Le Châtelier's principle of *partially* alleviating a stress is based on more than one chemical concentration being involved in the equilibrium process. When an equilibrium removes some of an added chemical, other chemicals' concentrations also change along with it. The changing concentrations of these others essentially prevent the stressed chemical from reaching its original equilibrium concentration before equilibrium is re-established. Consider the following hypothetical equilibrium's response to the stress of adding some A.

$$A + B \rightleftharpoons AB$$

If all the added A were removed (by reacting it with B to form AB) then the forward rate would be less than it was at the original equilibrium (due to the decreased [B]) but the reverse rate would be greater than at the original equilibrium (due to the increased [AB]). To re-establish equilibrium the forward rate must be greater than it was at the original equilibrium and therefore all the added A cannot be removed.

Some heterogeneous chemical reactions and physical processes involve only one chemical concentration. When such a system is stressed by changing that concentration, equilibrium is not re-established until the entire stress is removed and the original concentration restored.

Chapter 3 Chemical Equilibrium

Equilibria that have only one chemical concentration in their equilibrium expression *completely* alleviate any stress that changes that concentration.

For example, any stress that changes the concentration of the lone gaseous product in the following equilibria will be completely, rather than partially, alleviated.

- Water evaporating and condensing in a closed vessel
  $$H_2O(l) \rightleftharpoons H_2O(g) \qquad K_{eq} = [H_2O(g)]$$

- Calcium carbonate decomposing and synthesizing within a closed vessel
  $$CaCO_3(s) \rightleftharpoons CaO(s) + CO_2(g) \qquad K_{eq} = [CO_2]$$

These equilibrium expressions have only one chemical concentration in them. As this implies, this value is constant at a given temperature. When these systems are stressed by removing some of this chemical, the entire loss must be replaced to restore the reaction quotient back to that of the equilibrium constant.

Quick Check

State whether each of the following equilibria would partially or completely alleviate a stress that changes a reactant's or product's concentration.

1. $CoCl_2(s) + 6\,H_2O(g) \rightleftharpoons CoCl_2 \cdot 6\,H_2O(s)$ _____

2. $NH_4Cl(s) \rightleftharpoons NH_3(g) + HCl(g)$ _____

3. $CO_2(g) + NaOH(s) \rightleftharpoons NaHCO_3(s)$ _____

3.2 Activity: What's My Constant?

Question
How can you determine the mathematical relationship that is common to three sets of numbers? Of course, it's a lot easier to discover the relationship when you know that one actually exists!

Background
Do you think that you could have reasoned or recognized that different sets of equilibrium concentrations have a common mathematical relationship? The Norwegian chemists Cato Maximilian Guldberg and Peter Waage proposed the equilibrium law in 1864 after observing many different sets of equilibrium concentrations.

Procedure
Each set of numbers in the table below satisfies the formula $A - B + C = 5$.

Set	A	B	C
1	10	6	1
2	3	1	3
3	− 4	2	11

$$\frac{A - B + C = 5}{}$$

Continued on next page

© Edvantage Interactive 2016

3.2 Activity: *Continued*

1. Each set of numbers in the table below can also be substituted into a common formula yielding a constant. Determine that formula.

Set	A	B	C
1	18	3	9
2	6	22	2
3	5	10	15

Easy

_____

2. Repeat procedure step 1 for each table below.

Set	A	B	C
1	3	4	20
2	5	37	3
3	14	24	88

Challenging

_____

Set	A	B	C
1	7	13	20
2	0	5	9
3	3	10	33

Really Hard

_____

Results and Discussion

1. Briefly describe the method(s) you used to determine the expression for each collection of data.

2. How successful were you and your colleagues at this task?

3. Why do you not need anyone to mark this activity to know whether or not you were successful?

3.2 Review Questions

1. At a given temperature the forward and reverse rate equations for the following reaction are as shown (the units for the rate constants are left out for simplicity):

   $2 N_2O_5(g) \rightleftharpoons 2 N_2O_4(g) + O_2(g)$

   $r_f = 2.7 \times 10^{-3} [N_2O_5]^2$ $\qquad$ $r_r = 4.3 \times 10^{-2} [N_2O_4]^2[O_2]$

   Derive the equilibrium constant, K_{eq}, for this reaction at this temperature.

2. A student claims that the coefficients in balanced chemical equations provide the ratio of the chemicals present at equilibrium? For example, consider the following equation.

   $2 NO(g) + Cl_2(g) \rightleftharpoons 2 NOCl(g)$

   The student asserts that the equation tells us that the ratio of the equilibrium concentrations will be 2 NO: 1 Cl_2: 2 NOCl. Is the student correct? If not, what do the coefficients represent?

3. Write the equilibrium expression for each of the following:

   (a) $HNO_2(aq) \rightleftharpoons H^+(aq) + NO_2^-(aq)$

   (b) $2 SO_3(g) \rightleftharpoons 2 SO_2(g) + O_2(g)$

   (c) $4 NH_3(g) + 5 O_2(g) \rightleftharpoons 4 NO(g) + 6 H_2O(g)$

4. A 2.0 L flask contains 0.38 mol $CH_4(g)$, 0.59 mol $C_2H_2(g)$, and 1.4 mol $H_2(g)$ at equilibrium. Calculate the equilibrium constant, K_{eq}, for the reaction:

   $2 CH_4(g) \rightleftharpoons C_2H_2(g) + 3 H_2(g)$

© Edvantage Interactive 2015

5. A cylinder contains 0.12 M $COBr_2$, 0.060 M CO, and 0.080 M Br_2 at equilibrium. The volume of the cylinder is suddenly doubled.

$COBr_2(g) \rightleftharpoons CO(g) + Br_2(g)$

(a) What is the molar concentration of each gas immediately after the volume of the cylinder is doubled?

(b) Explain, in terms of Le Châtelier's principle, why the system shifts right to restore equilibrium.

(c) The system re-equilibrates by converting 0.010 M $COBr_2$ into CO and Br_2. Verify that the original equilibrium concentrations and the re-established equilibrium concentrations provide the same value when substituted into the reaction's equilibrium expression.

6. A closed flask contains 0.65 mol/L N_2 and 0.85 mol/L H_2 at equilibrium. What is the $[NH_3]$?

$N_2(g) + 3 H_2(g) \rightleftharpoons 2 NH_3(g) \qquad K_{eq} = 0.017$

7. A 1.0 L flask is injected simultaneously with 4.0 mol N_2, 3.0 mol H_2, and 8.0 mol NH_3. In what direction will the reaction proceed to achieve equilibrium? Show your mathematical reasoning.

$N_2(g) + 3 H_2(g) \rightleftharpoons 2 NH_3(g) \qquad K_{eq} = 1.0$

8. Write the equilibrium expression for each of the following:

(a) $Fe(s) + 2 H^+(aq) \rightleftharpoons H_2(g) + Fe^{2+}(aq)$

(b) $2 I^-(aq) + Cl_2(aq) \rightleftharpoons I_2(s) + 2 Cl^-(aq)$

(c) $CaO(s) + CO_2(g) \rightleftharpoons CaCO_3(s)$

(d) $CO_2(g) \rightleftharpoons CO_2(aq)$ (Include each chemical's phase in the equilibrium expression.)

(e) $2 Na_2O(s) \rightleftharpoons 4 Na(l) + O_2(g)$

9. Write the chemical equation and the equilibrium expression for the equilibrium that develops when:
   (a) Gaseous chlorine dissolves in water.

   (b) Gaseous carbon tetrachloride decomposes into solid carbon and chlorine gas.

   (c) Solid magnesium oxide reacts with sulfur dioxide gas and oxygen gas to produce solid magnesium sulfate.

10. $2 NOCl(g) \rightleftharpoons 2 NO(g) + Cl_2(g)$ $K_{eq} = 8.0 \times 10^{-2}$ at 462°C
    For each of the following, what is the K_{eq} at 462°C?
    (a) $NOCl(g) \rightleftharpoons NO(g) + \frac{1}{2} Cl_2(g)$

    (b) $2 NO(g) + Cl_2(g) \rightleftharpoons 2 NOCl(g)$

    (c) $NO(g) + \frac{1}{2} Cl_2(g) \rightleftharpoons NOCl(g)$

© Edvantage Interactive 2016

11. How would each of the following stresses affect the equilibrium constant, K_{eq}, for:

$2 CO(g) + O_2(g) \rightleftharpoons 2 CO_2(g)$ $\Delta H = -31$ kJ/mol

(a) Add some $CO_2(g)$?

(b) Decrease the volume of the reaction vessel (at a constant temperature)?

(c) Increase the temperature?

(d) Add a catalyst?

12. Can you infer that reactants are favored in the reaction below because $K_{eq} < 1$? Explain.

$C(s) + H_2O(g) \rightleftharpoons CO(g) + H_2(g)$ $K_{eq} = 0.16$

13. Consider the following two equilibria:

(a) $2 SO_3(g) \rightleftharpoons 2 SO_2(g) + O_2(g)$ $K_{eq} = 0.25$

(b) $PCl_5(g) \rightleftharpoons PCl_3(g) + Cl_2(g)$ $K_{eq} = 0.50$

Given that their initial reactant concentrations are equal, can you infer from their equilibrium constants that the first equilibrium has a lower percent yield than the second equilibrium? Explain.

14. Consider the following equilibrium:

$2 KClO_3(s) \rightleftharpoons 2 KCl(s) + 3 O_2(g)$ $\Delta H = 56$ kJ/mol

Compare the $[O_2]$ when equilibrium is re-established to its concentration before:

(a) some $KClO_3(s)$ is added.

(b) some $O_2(g)$ is removed.

(c) the temperature is decreased.

3.3 Equilibrium Problems

Warm Up

Chemists use a simple table called an **ICE table** to help solve equilibrium problems. ICE is an acronym for **I**nitial concentration, **C**hange in concentration, and **E**quilibrium concentration. All the units are molarity (M). ICE tables are like Sudoku for chemists and are fun to solve!

The following ICE table shows a system that initially had 3.0 M N_2 and an unknown concentration of Cl_2. In the system, 2.0 M of the N_2 was consumed before achieving equilibrium. Complete the ICE table to determine the initial concentration of Cl_2. The steps following the table will assist you if you need help.

$K_{eq} = 0.128$	$N_2(g)$	$+$	$3 Cl_2(g)$	$\rightleftharpoons$	$2 NCl_3(g)$
I	3.0		?		0
C	-2.0				
E					

1. Solve for the equilibrium concentration (E) of N_2. 3.0 − 2.0 = ?
2. Solve for the change of concentration (C) of Cl_2 and NCl_3 using the coefficients in the balanced chemical equation.
3. Solve for the equilibrium concentration (E) of NCl_3.
4. Solve for the equilibrium concentration (E) of Cl_2 using K_{eq}.
5. Solve for the initial concentration (I) of Cl_2.

Solving Equilibrium Problems

There are three related values in any chemical system that develops an equilibrium:
- the equilibrium constant
- the initial concentrations
- the equilibrium concentrations

In equilibrium problems, you will be given two of these values and asked to determine the third. The only two chemical concepts used to solve equilibrium problems are:
- reaction stoichiometry — the mole ratio in which the reactants are consumed and the products are formed
- the equilibrium law — the relationship between the equilibrium constant and any set of equilibrium concentrations

Determining K_{eq} from Initial Concentrations and One Equilibrium Concentration

The coefficients in a balanced chemical equation provide the mole ratios in which the reactants are consumed and the products are formed. Thus, if you know how much the concentration of one chemical changed in reaching equilibrium, you can easily determine how much the others have changed. The C in the ICE table stands for *change* but it can also remind you to pay attention to the *coefficients*.

It's important as well to pay attention to the units provided and requested in equilibrium problems. In this type of problem, you may be given the number of moles and liters, thus requiring you to calculate the molar concentrations, or you may have the molarity provided directly.

Sample Problem — Determining K_{eq} from Initial Concentrations and One Equilibrium Concentration

A student placed 7.00 mol NH_3 in a 0.500 L flask. At equilibrium, 6.2 M N_2 was found in the flask. What is the equilibrium constant, K_{eq}, for this reaction?

$$2 NH_3(g) \rightleftharpoons N_2(g) + 3 H_2(g)$$

What to Think About

1. Draw an ICE table and fill in the information provided in the question.

$$\frac{7.00 \text{ mol}}{0.500 \text{ L}} = 14.0 \text{ M}$$

2. Use the coefficients in the balanced chemical equation to relate (in the C row) the moles of reactant consumed to the moles of each product formed.
   For every 2 mol of NH_3 that are consumed, 1 mol of N_2 and 3 mol of H_2 are produced.

3. Do the math.

4. Calculate K_{eq} using the equilibrium expression and concentrations.
   Exercise caution indicating your final answer to the appropriate degree of certainty. ICE tables involve subtraction and addition. In subtraction and addition, the answer must be rounded to the number of decimal places that the least precise piece of data is rounded to.

How to Do It

	$2 NH_3(g) \rightleftharpoons$	$N_2(g) +$	$3 H_2(g)$
I	14.0	0	0
C			
E		6.2	

	$2 NH_3(g) \rightleftharpoons$	$N_2(g) +$	$3 H_2(g)$
I	14.0	0	0
C	−12.4	+ 6.2	+ 18.6
E		6.2	

	$2 NH_3(g) \rightleftharpoons$	$N_2(g) +$	$3 H_2(g)$
I	14.0	0	0
C	−12.4	+ 6.2	+ 18.6
E	1.6	6.2	18.6

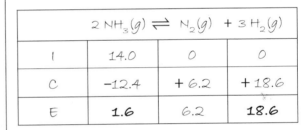

$$K_{eq} = \frac{[N_2][H_2]^3}{[NH_3]^2} = \frac{(6.2)(18.6)^3}{(1.6)^2} = 1.6 \times 10^4$$

Practice Problems — Determining K_{eq} from Initial Concentrations and One Equilibrium Concentration

1. The following gases were placed in a 4.00 L flask: 8.00 mol N_2 and 10.00 mol H_2. After equilibrium was achieved, 1.20 M NH_3 was found in the flask. Complete the ICE table below and determine the equilibrium constant, K_{eq}.

	$N_2(g) +$	$3 H_2(g) \rightleftharpoons$	$2 NH_3(g)$
I			
C			
E			

Continued opposite

Chapter 3 Chemical Equilibrium

Practice Problems — *Continued*

2. Equal volumes of 1.60 M Ag^+ and 2.60 M $S_2O_3^{2-}$ were mixed. The $[Ag(S_2O_3)_2^{3-}]$ at equilibrium was 0.35 M. Complete the ICE table below and determine K_{eq}. (Reminder: Whenever you mix aqueous solutions, there is a dilution effect. Mixing equal volumes doubles the solution's volume and halves the concentration of both solutes.)

	$Ag^+(aq)$	+ $2\,S_2O_3^{2-}(aq)$ $\rightleftharpoons$	$Ag(S_2O_3)_2^{3-}(aq)$
I			
C			
E			

3. A sample of 6.0 g of carbon was placed in a 1.0 L flask containing 1.4 mol O_2. When equilibrium is established, 1.2 g of carbon remains. Determine K_{eq}. (Note: Because carbon is a solid it is crossed out in the ICE table but the moles of carbon consumed must be calculated — outside the ICE table — to determine the equilibrium concentrations of O_2 and CO.)

	$2\,C(s)$ +	$O_2(g)$ $\rightleftharpoons$	$2\,CO(g)$
I			
C			
E			

Determining Equilibrium Concentrations from K_{eq} and the Initial Concentrations

The equilibrium law provides chemists with the ability to predict the concentrations that will be present when equilibrium is achieved from any initial set of concentrations. This includes determining the concentrations that will be reached when a stressed system restores equilibrium. In re-equilibration problems, the initial concentrations are created by stressing a previous equilibrium. Such calculations will allow you to verify Le Châtelier's principle.

Chemists solve this type of problem algebraically. There are questions in this course that require the quadratic equation or synthetic division to obtain the answer.

Sample Problem — Determining Equilibrium Concentrations from K_{eq} and the Initial Concentrations

The following gases are injected into a 1.00 L flask: 1.20 mol of $H_2(g)$ and 1.20 mol of $F_2(g)$. What will the concentration of HF be when equilibrium is achieved? (Note: There is no dilution effect when gases are mixed because the mixture's volume isn't increased. Injecting another gas into the same flask is possible because there is so much space between gas particles.)

$$H_2(g) + F_2(g) \rightleftharpoons 2\,HF(g) \qquad K_{eq} = 2.50$$

What to Think About	**How to Do It**

What to Think About

1. Draw an ICE table and fill in the information provided in the question.

2. Set up an algebraic solution using the coefficients in the balanced chemical equation to relate the moles of reactants consumed to each other and to the moles of the product formed.
   For every x moles of H_2 and F_2 that are consumed, $2x$ moles of HF are produced.

3. Complete the ICE table.

4. Solve for x using the equilibrium expression and constant:

   (i) Find the square root of each side.

   (ii) Multiply each side by $1.20 - x$.
   (iii) Expand.
   (iv) Add $1.58x$ to both sides.
   (v) Divide each side by 3.58.

5. Don't forget to answer the question!
   How could you check your answer?

How to Do It

$H_2(g) + F_2(g) \rightleftharpoons 2\,HF(g)$

I	1.20	1.20	0
C			
E			

$H_2(g) + F_2(g) \rightleftharpoons 2\,HF(g)$

I	1.20	1.20	0
C	$-x$	$-x$	$+2x$
E			

$H_2(g) + F_2(g) \rightleftharpoons 2\,HF(g)$

I	1.20	1.20	0
C	$-x$	$-x$	$+2x$
E	$1.20 - x$	$1.20 - x$	$2x$

$$K_{eq} = \frac{[HF]^2}{[H_2][F_2]} = \frac{(2x)^2}{(1.20 - x)^2} = 2.50$$

$$\frac{2x}{1.20 - x} = (2.50)^{1/2} = 1.58$$

$$2x = 1.58\,(1.20 - x)$$
$$2x = 1.896 - 1.58x$$
$$3.58x = 1.896$$
$$x = 0.530\ M$$

$$[HF]_{eq} = 2x = 2(0.530\ M) = 1.06\ M$$

Sample Problem — Determining Equilibrium Concentrations from K_{eq} and the Initial Concentrations

A 3.00 L flask contains 6.00 M H_2, 6.00 M Cl_2, and 3.00 M HCl at equilibrium. An additional 15 mol of HCl is injected into the flask. What is [Cl_2] when equilibrium is re-established?

$$H_2(g) + Cl_2(g) \rightleftharpoons 2\,HCl(g)$$

What to Think About	How to Do It
1. Draw an ICE table and fill in the information provided in the question. E_f = final (re-established) equilibrium. Adding $\dfrac{15.0\ mol}{3.00\ L}$ increases the [HCl] by 5.00 M.	$H_2(g) + Cl_2(g) \rightleftharpoons 2\,HCl(g)$ 		$H_2(g)$	$Cl_2(g)$	$2\,HCl(g)$	 |---|---|---|---| | I	6.00	6.00	8.00	 | C				 | E_f				
2. Le Châtelier predicts that the system will shift to the left to remove some of the added HCl. For every x moles of H_2 and Cl_2 that are produced in the shift, $2x$ moles of HCl are consumed.	
3. Complete the ICE table.	$H_2(g) + Cl_2(g) \rightleftharpoons 2\,HCl(g)$ 		$H_2(g)$	$Cl_2(g)$	$2\,HCl(g)$	 |---|---|---|---| | I	6.00	6.00	8.00	 | C	$+x$	$+x$	$-2x$	 | E_f	$6.00 + x$	$6.00 + x$	$8.00 - 2x$	
4. Calculate K_{eq} by substituting the original equilibrium concentrations into the equilibrium expression.	$K_{eq} = \dfrac{[HCl]^2}{[H_2][Cl_2]} = \dfrac{(3.00)^2}{(6.00)^2} = 0.250$
5. Solve for x using the equilibrium expression and constant and by taking the square root of each side. Note that this value corroborates our qualitative prediction based on Le Châtelier's principle. The system re-establishes equilibrium by removing only 4 M of the added 5 M HCl.	$K_{eq} = \dfrac{[HCl]^2}{[H_2][Cl_2]} = \dfrac{(8.00 - 2x)^2}{(6.00 + x)^2} = 0.250$ $\dfrac{8.00 - 2x}{6.00 + x} = (0.250)^{\frac{1}{2}} = 0.500$ $x = 2.00\ M$
6. Don't forget to answer the question!	
7. Check your answer by substituting your value for x back into the equilibrium expression.	[Cl_2] when equilibrium is restored is: $6.00\ M + x = 6.00\ M + 2.00\ M = 8.00\ M$ $\dfrac{(8.00 - 4.00)^2}{(6.00 + 2.00)^2}$ does indeed equal 0.250.

Practice Problems — Determining the Equilibrium Concentrations from K_{eq} and the Initial Concentrations

1. In the lab, 4.5 mol of HCl(g) are pumped into a 3.00 L flask and heated to 80°C. How many moles of Cl_2 will be found in the flask after equilibrium is established? K_{eq} at 80°C = 0.36

	2 HCl(g) $\rightleftharpoons$	$H_2(g)$ +	$Cl_2(g)$
I			
C			
E			

2. As part of an experiment, 4.00 mol H_2, 4.00 mol C_2N_2, and 8.00 mol HCN are injected into a 2.00 L flask where they establish equilibrium. What is the $[C_2N_2]$ when equilibrium is achieved? K_{eq} = 5.00

	$H_2(g)$ +	$C_2N_2(g)$ $\rightleftharpoons$	2 HCN(g)
I			
C			
E			

3. The table below shows the molarity of three gases at equilibrium. The concentration of HCl is then decreased as shown. What is the [HCl] when equilibrium is re-established?

	$H_2(g)$ +	$Cl_2(g)$ $\rightleftharpoons$	2 HCl(g)
E_o	6.00	6.00	12.0
I	6.00	6.00	5.00
C			
E_f			

Determining Initial Concentrations from K_{eq} and the Equilibrium Concentrations

Determining past conditions from present ones is perhaps even more remarkable than predicting future conditions. In solving the previous type of problem, we predicted a future event by determining the concentrations that will be reached at equilibrium from the system's initial concentration. In solving the type of problem covered in this section, we will do exactly the opposite as we travel back into the past to determine what initial concentrations would have resulted in the current equilibrium concentrations. We've outlined one method of solving this type of problem below but many variations exist.

Sample Problem — Determining Initial Concentrations from K_{eq} and the Equilibrium Concentrations

Some CH_3OH was injected into a flask where it established equilibrium with a [CO] = 0.15 M. What was the initial concentration of CH_3OH?

$$CH_3OH(g) \rightleftharpoons 2 H_2(g) + CO(g) \qquad K_{eq} = 0.040$$

What to Think About	**How to Do It**
1. Draw an ICE table and fill in the information provided in the question.	<table><tr><td></td><td>$CH_3OH(g) \rightleftharpoons$</td><td>$2 H_2(g) +$</td><td>$CO(g)$</td></tr><tr><td>I</td><td>x</td><td>0</td><td>0</td></tr><tr><td>C</td><td></td><td></td><td></td></tr><tr><td>E</td><td></td><td></td><td>0.15</td></tr></table>
2. Use the coefficients in the balanced chemical equation to relate the moles of reactant consumed to the moles of each product formed. For each mole of CH_3OH that is consumed, 2 mol of H_2 and 1 mol of CO are produced.	<table><tr><td></td><td>$CH_3OH(g) \rightleftharpoons$</td><td>$2 H_2(g) +$</td><td>$CO(g)$</td></tr><tr><td>I</td><td>x</td><td>0</td><td>0</td></tr><tr><td>C</td><td>−0.15</td><td>+0.30</td><td>+0.15</td></tr><tr><td>E</td><td></td><td></td><td></td></tr></table>
3. Complete the ICE table.	<table><tr><td></td><td>$CH_3OH(g) \rightleftharpoons$</td><td>$2 H_2(g) +$</td><td>$CO(g)$</td></tr><tr><td>I</td><td>x</td><td>0</td><td>0</td></tr><tr><td>C</td><td>−0.15</td><td>+0.30</td><td>+0.15</td></tr><tr><td>E</td><td>$x - 0.15$</td><td>0.30</td><td>0.15</td></tr></table>
4. Solve for x using the equilibrium expression and constant.	$$K_{eq} = \frac{[H_2]^2[CO]}{[CH_3OH]} = \frac{(0.30)^2(0.15)}{x - 0.15} = 0.040$$ $$\frac{(0.30)^2(0.15)}{0.040} = x - 0.15$$ $$x = 0.49 \text{ M}$$

© Edvantage Interactive 2016

Practice Problems — Determining Initial Concentrations from K_{eq} and the Equilibrium Concentrations

1. NiS reacted with O_2 in a 2.0 L flask. When equilibrium was achieved 0.36 mol of SO_2 were found in the flask. What was the original $[O_2]$ in the flask? $K_{eq} = 0.30$

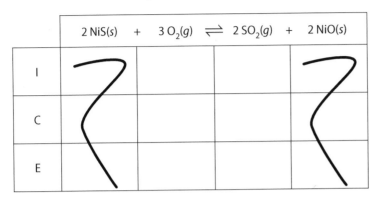

	2 NiS(s) +	3 O_2(g) ⇌	2 SO_2(g) +	2 NiO(s)
I				
C				
E				

2. Some HI is pumped into a flask. At equilibrium, the [HI] = 0.60 mol/L. What was the initial [HI]? $K_{eq} = 0.25$

	2 HI(g) ⇌	H_2(g) +	I_2(g)
I			
C			
E			

3. Some SO_2 and O_2 are injected into a flask. At equilibrium, the $[SO_2] = 0.050$ M and the $[O_2] = 0.040$ M. What was the initial $[O_2]$? $K_{eq} = 100$

	2 SO_2(g) +	O_2(g) ⇌	2 SO_3(g)
I			
C			
E			

                              © Edvantage Interactive 2016

The equilibrium position of a reaction is characterized by a mathematical value often referred to as the **mass action expression**. For the reaction:

$$dD + eE \rightleftharpoons fF + gG$$

where D, E, F, and G represent chemical formulas, and d, e, f, and g are coefficients, the mass action expression is:

$$\frac{(aF)^f (aG)^g}{(aD)^d (aE)^e}$$

where a stands for the *activity* of each of the species in the equation.

The activity of a chemical species may be represented by its concentration (e.g., [F]) in the case of species present in solution or as gases, or by its partial pressure (e.g., P_F) in the case of a reaction where all species are present as gases. If the activities are represented by concentrations and the system is at equilibrium, the mass action expression is called an equilibrium constant K_c (as described in section 5.2). If, however, the activities are represented by partial pressures and the system is at equilibrium, the expression is still called an equilibrium constant, but it is represented by K_p. To summarize:

$$K_c = \frac{[F]^f [G]^g}{[D]^d [E]^e} \qquad K_p = \frac{[P_F]^f [P_G]^g}{[P_D]^d [P_E]^e}$$

Note: K_p should always be *calculated* using partial pressures in *atmospheres*.

The numerical values of K_c and K_p are usually different. Their relationship becomes clear if you remember the ideal gas law, which states that $PV = nRT$. Rearrangement of the ideal gas law shows:

Concentration, $C = n/V$ and $n/V = P/RT$, hence $C = P/RT$, thus $P = CRT$

Substitution of CRT for P into the K_p expression above allows you to derive the relationship between K_p and K_c as follows:

$$K_p = K_c(RT)^{\Delta n}$$

Because K_p is determined using partial pressures in atmospheres, it follows that the ideal gas constant value, $R = 0.08206$ L·atm/mol·K. Additionally,

T = temperature in K, and
$\Delta n = (f + g) - (d + e)$ (the difference in the sums of the coefficients
for the *gaseous* reactants and products)

Sample Problem — Conversion Between K_c and K_p

The Haber process for the formation of ammonia establishes equilibrium at 498 K. Under these circumstances, $[N_2] = 0.020$ mol/L, $[H_2] = 0.18$ mol/L, and $[NH_3] = 0.14$ mol/L. Determine the numerical value of K_c and K_p.

What to Think About	How to Do It
1. Determine the balanced chemical equation that describes the equilibrium.	$N_2(g) + 3H_2(g) \rightleftharpoons 2NH_3(g)$
2. Write an appropriate K_c expression for the equation.	$K_c = \dfrac{[NH_3]^2}{[N_2][H_2]^3} = \dfrac{(0.14)^2}{(0.020)(0.18)^3} = 170$
3. Substitute concentrations and solve for K_c.	
4. Determine Δn and substitute into the appropriate equation to determine K_p. (Be sure to apply the exponent Δn to the *entire product* of R x T. Also take care with the *sign* of Δn and substitution of the correct R value.)	$\Delta n = 2 - (1 + 3) = -2 \quad K_p = K_c(RT)^{\Delta n}$ $\quad = 170(0.08206\ L\ atm/mol\ K \times 498\ K)^{-2}$ $\quad = 170 \times 0.000599 = 0.10$ Notice that NO units are included in a K_c or K_p value.

Practice Problems — Conversion Between K_c and K_p

1. Given the equilibrium quantities stated below each species, determine K_p for the following reactions at a fixed temperature:

   (a) $N_2O_4(g) \rightleftharpoons 2NO_2(g)$
   2.71 atm   0.600 atm

   (b) $CaCO_3(s) \rightleftharpoons CaO(s) + CO_2(g)$
   15.6 g/L   0.02 g/L   1.04 atm

2. Given the equilibrium partial pressures stated below each species, and the K_p value at a fixed temperature, determine the missing partial pressure.

   (a) $2NO(g) \quad + \quad O_2(g) \quad \rightleftharpoons \quad 2NO_2(g) \quad K_p = 1.6 \times 10^{12}$
   6.5×10^{-5} atm 4.5×10^{-5} atm   ?

   (b) $N_2O_4(g) \rightleftharpoons 2NO_2(g) \qquad K_p = 0.715$
   ?   15.8 atm

3. At 500.°C, the reaction between N_2 and H_2 to form ammonia has a $K_p = 1.5 \times 10^{-5}$. What is the numerical value of K_c for this reaction?

4. For which of the following reactions would $K_p = K_c$? Explain your choice.

   (a) $N_2(g) + O_2(g) \rightleftharpoons 2NO(g)$

   (b) $2NO(g) + O_2(g) \rightleftharpoons 2NO_2(g)$

3.3 Activity: Visualizing Equilibria

Question

How could you determine an equilibrium system's constant if you were able to count the number of molecules present at equilibrium?

Background

The amount of each reactant and product remains constant at equilibrium because each chemical is being produced at the same rate that it is being consumed. The diagrams below represent the interconversion of A (dark) molecules and B (light) molecules:

$$A \text{ (dark)} \rightleftharpoons B \text{ (light)}$$

Procedure

1. Each row of drawings represents a separate trial that results in equilibrium. Answer the questions below about the trials.

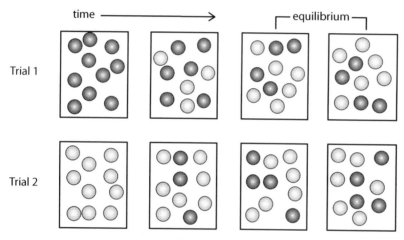

Results and Discussion

1. State a property of chemical equilibrium that is evident by observing trials 1 and 2.

2. What is the equilibrium constant for A $\rightleftharpoons$ B? The container could be any volume because the volumes cancel in this particular equilibrium expression.

3. In another trial, 20 A molecules and 50 B molecules were counted in a reaction vessel. How many A molecules will there be in the vessel when equilibrium is established?

4. After equilibrium was established in trial 2, the temperature was decreased. When equilibrium was restored, there were 7 A molecules and 3 B molecules in the container. State whether A $\rightleftharpoons$ B is exothermic or endothermic.

© Edvantage Interactive 2016

3.3 Review Questions

1. Complete the following ICE tables.

(a)

	$2\,CH_4(g) \rightleftharpoons$	$C_2H_2(g)$ +	$3\,H_2(g)$
I	6.0	0	0
C			
E		1.5	

(b)

	$N_2(g)$ +	$3\,H_2(g) \rightleftharpoons$	$2\,NH_3(g)$
I		5.0	0
C			
E	2.0		1.0

2. During an experiment, 3.0 mol of NO_2 are injected into a 1.0 L flask at 55°C. At equilibrium, the flask contains 1.2 mol of N_2O_4.

$$2\,NO_2(g) \rightleftharpoons N_2O_4(g)$$

(a) What is the $[NO_2]$ at equilibrium?

(b) What is K_{eq} for this reaction at 55°C?

3. Equal volumes of 3.60 M A^{2+} and 6.80 M B^- are mixed. After the reaction, equilibrium is established with $[B^-] = 0.40$ M.

$$A^{2+}(aq) + 3B^-(aq) \rightleftharpoons AB_3^-(aq)$$

(a) What is the $[A^{2+}]$ at equilibrium?

(b) Determine K_{eq}.

4. Complete the following ICE tables:

(a)

K_{eq} = 1.20	$H_2(g)$	+ $C_2N_2(g)$ ⇌	2 HCN(g)
I			0
C			
E	5.0	1.5	

(b)

K_{eq} = 1.20	$H_2(g)$	+ $C_2N_2(g)$ ⇌	2 HCN(g)
I	5.4		0
C			
E			3.6

5. The interconversion of the structural isomers glyceraldehyde-3-phospate (G3P) and dihydroxyacetone phosphate (DHAP) is a biochemical equilibrium that occurs during the breakdown of glucose in our cells. What will their concentrations be at equilibrium if the initial concentration of each isomer is 0.020 M?

   G3P(aq) ⇌ DHAP(aq) K_{eq} = 19

6. A 1.00 L flask is injected with 0.600 mol of each of the following four gases: H_2, CO_2, H_2O, and CO.

   $H_2(g) + CO_2(g)$ ⇌ $H_2O(g) + CO(g)$ K_{eq} = 1.69

   (a) What is the $[H_2]$ at equilibrium?

   (b) What is the [CO] at equilibrium?

7. A 500 mL flask is injected with 0.72 mol of C_2N_2 and 0.72 mol of H_2. What will the [HCN] be when the system reaches equilibrium?

   $H_2(g) + C_2N_2(g)$ ⇌ 2 HCN(g) K_{eq} = 1.20

© Edvantage Interactive 2016

8. A 1.0 L flask containing 4.0 mol of H_2 and a 1.0 L flask containing 4.0 mol of F_2 are connected by a valve. The valve is opened to allow the gases to mix in the 2.0 L combined volume.

$$H_2(g) + F_2(g) \rightleftharpoons 2\,HF(g) \qquad\qquad K_{eq} = 121$$

How many moles of H_2 will be present in the system when it equilibrates?

9. A 250 mL flask containing 1.0 g of excess BN(s) is injected with 0.21 mol of $Cl_2(g)$.

$$2\,BN(s) + 3\,Cl_2(g) \rightleftharpoons 2\,BCl_3(g) + N_2(g) \qquad\qquad K_{eq} = 0.045$$

(a) What will the $[BCl_3]$ equal when the system attains equilibrium? (Hint: The math is a bit trickier on this one; you need to take the cube root of each side.)

(b) Would the reaction achieve equilibrium if the flask initially contained 1.0 g of BN(s)? Support your answer with calculations.

10. A flask is injected with 0.60 M C_2H_2 and 0.60 M H_2. Determine the $[H_2]$ at equilibrium by trial and error. Lower the $[C_2H_2]$ and the $[H_2]$ and raise the $[CH_4]$ in appropriate increments until you find a set of concentrations that provides the K_{eq} value when substituted into the equilibrium expression.

$$2\,CH_4(g) \rightleftharpoons C_2H_2(g) + 3\,H_2(g) \qquad K_{eq} = 2.8$$

11. In a 2.00 L flask, 3.00 M H_2, 3.00 M Cl_2, and 7.50 M HCl coexist at equilibrium. A student removes 7.00 mol of HCl from the flask.

(a) What would the concentration of each gas be when equilibrium re-establishes?

	$H_2(g)$	+	$Cl_2(g)$	$\rightleftharpoons$	$2\,HCl(g)$
E_o					
I					
C					
E_f					

(b) Describe how the system's response is consistent with Le Châtelier's principle.

12. A 200.0 mL solution of 0.10 M Fe^{3+}, 0.10 M SCN^-, and 1.8 M $FeSCN^{2+}$ is at equilibrium. The solution is diluted by adding water up to 500.0 mL. Complete the ICE table below and show the algebraic equation that would allow you to solve for the ion concentrations when equilibrium is restored. Do **NOT** solve for x.

	$Fe^{3+}(aq)$	+	$SCN^-(aq)$	$\rightleftharpoons$	$FeSCN^{2+}(aq)$
E_o	0.10		0.10		1.8
I					
C					
E_f					

13. In a 500.0 mL flask, 2.5 mol of H_2, 2.5 mol of Br_2, and 5.0 mol of HBr coexist at equilibrium. At 35 s, 2.5 mol of Br_2 is injected into the flask, and the system re-establishes equilibrium at 55 s. Use three different-colored plots on the graph below to show how the concentration of each chemical changes during this period. (This question can be solved algebraically without using the quadratic formula despite not providing a perfect square.)

$$H_2(g) + Br_2(g) \rightleftharpoons 2\,HBr(g)$$

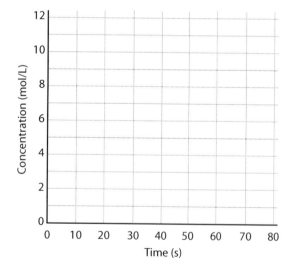

© Edvantage Interactive 2016

14. Some SO_3 is injected into a 500 mL flask. At equilibrium the $[O_2] = 1.80$ M.

$$2\,SO_3(g) \rightleftharpoons 2\,SO_2(g) + O_2(g) \qquad K_{eq} = 3.83 \times 10^{-2}$$

   (a) What is the $[SO_3]$ at equilibrium?

   (b) How many moles of SO_3 were originally injected into the flask?

15. Equal quantities of $H_2(g)$ and $I_2(g)$ are pumped into a flask. At equilibrium the $[HI] = 1.0$ M. What was the initial $[H_2]$?

$$H_2(g) + I_2(g) \rightleftharpoons 2\,HI(g) \qquad K_{eq} = 4.0$$

16. Some PCl_5 is pumped into a 500 mL flask. The $[PCl_3] = 1.50$ M at equilibrium. What was the initial $[PCl_5]$?

$$PCl_5(g) \rightleftharpoons PCl_3(g) + Cl_2(g) \qquad K_{eq} = 2.14$$

17. A reaction mixture contains 0.24 mol of NO, 0.10 mol of O_2, and 1.20 mol of NO_2 at equilibrium in a 1.0 L container. How many moles of O_2 would need to be added to the mixture to increase the amount of NO_2 to 1.30 mol when equilibrium is re-established?

$$2\,NO(g) + O_2(g) \rightleftharpoons 2\,NO_2(g)$$

18. Write the K_p expression for each of the following equations:

   (a) $PCl_5(g) \rightleftharpoons PCl_3(g) + Cl_2(g)$

   (b) $P_4(s) + 5\,O_2(g) \rightleftharpoons 2\,P_2O_5(g)$

   (c) $CO_2(g) + CaO(s) \rightleftharpoons CaCO_3(s)$

19. Calculate K_p for the equilibria in Review Questions 4, 6, and 7 in section 5.2.
    Review Question 4:

    Review Question 6:

    Review Question 7:

20. Consider the following reaction:
    $$2\,SO_2(g) + O_2(g) \rightleftharpoons 2\,SO_3(g) \qquad K_p = 0.14 \text{ at } 625°C$$

    If a reaction vessel is filled with SO_3 at a partial pressure of 0.10 atm and 0.20 atm each of SO_2 and O_2 gas, is the reaction at equilibrium? If not, in which direction does it proceed to reach equilibrium?

21. The following graph represents partial pressure vs. time for the reaction between A and B gas to form C gas. Gas A is present in excess.

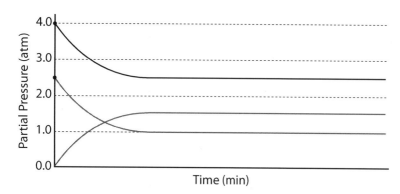

    (a) Write a balanced chemical equation for the equilibrium in the question.

    (b) Write the equilibrium expression K_p for the reaction.

    (c) Calculate the numerical value for K_p for this reaction.

    (d) Calculate the numerical value for K_c for this reaction.

22. In a container, 1.00 mol of N_2 and 3.00 mol of H_2 are mixed together to produce ammonia. At equilibrium, the total pressure of the system is 1.8×10^6 Pa and the mixture contains only 50% of the N_2 that was present originally. Calculate K_p for this reaction at this temperature.

23. A lab technician places 0.300 atm of SO_2, 0.400 atm O_2, and 0.020 atm of SO_3 into a 10.0 L bulb. Once equilibrium is established, the partial pressure of SO_3 is found to be 0.140 atm. What is the value of K_p for the reaction under these conditions?

24. $PCl_5(g)$ decomposes into $PCl_3(g)$ and $Cl_2(g)$. A pure sample of phosphorus pentachloride is placed into an evacuated 1.00 L glass bulb. The temperature remains constant while the pure sample decomposes as shown below:

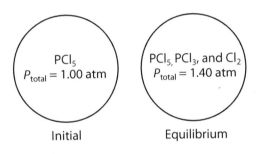

Initial   Equilibrium

(a) Explain why the pressure increases in the container as the reaction reaches equilibrium.

(b) Determine the partial pressure of each gas when the system reaches equilibrium.

(c) Calculate K_p for the equilibrium system.

(d) If the decomposition were to go to completion, what would the total pressure be in the system?

3.4 Le Châtelier's Principle

Warm Up

Consider the following equilibrium: $2 SO_2(g) + O_2(g) \rightleftharpoons 2 SO_3(g)$

1. What is equal at equilibrium?

   _____

2. What would happen to the forward rate if some O_2 were removed from this equilibrium?

   _____

3. Explain why, in terms of collision theory.

   _____

4. Would the reaction still be at equilibrium at this point?

   _____

Equilibria Response to Reactant or Product Removal

In 1888, the French chemist Henry Le Châtelier wrote, "Every change of one of the factors of an equilibrium occasions a rearrangement of the system in such a direction that the factor in question experiences a change in a sense opposite to the original change." Le Châtelier's principle has since been expressed in many different ways that are fortunately easier to understand than Le Châtelier's own wording.

> **Le Châtelier's principle**: An equilibrium system subjected to a stress will shift to partially alleviate the stress and restore equilibrium.

In other words, when an equilibrium system is disrupted, it will shift its reactant and product concentrations, changing one into the other, to reduce the disruption and re-establish equilibrium. Le Châtelier's principle allows chemists to predict what will happen to an equilibrium's reactant and product concentrations when its conditions change.

> When a quantity of reactant or product is added to an equilibrium system, the system will shift to remove *some* of the added chemical.

> When a quantity of reactant or product is removed from an equilibrium system, the system will shift to replace *some* of the removed chemical.

An **equilibrium system** is a reacting system that is at or approaching equilibrium. When we change the concentration of a reactant or a product, we "stress" the equilibrium system by temporarily destroying the equilibrium condition. When a system responds by changing some reactants into products, the response is referred to as a "**shift right**" because the products are on the right side of a chemical equation. When a system responds by changing some products into reactants, the response is called a "**shift left**."

© Edvantage Interactive 2016

Sample Problem — Predicting How an Equilibrium System Will Respond to the Addition of Reactant or Product

Some HI is added to the system below. In what direction will the system shift to restore equilibrium? When equilibrium is restored, how will the concentration of each substance compare to its concentration before the HI was added?

$$H_2(g) + I_2(g) \rightleftharpoons 2\,HI(g)$$

What to Think About	How to Do It
1. Using Le Châtelier's principle, determine that the system will shift to remove some of the added HI.	The system must *shift left* (toward reactants) to consume some of the added HI.
2. Infer from Le Châtelier's principle that the shift left produces H_2 and I_2. Note that Le Châtelier's principle doesn't explicitly state what happens to the concentrations of H_2 and I_2, but you can infer what happens from your understanding of the principle	Since not all of the added HI will be removed, the [HI] will increase. The [H_2] and [I_2] will also increase

How does a chemist remove chemicals from an equilibrium system? Obviously you can't simply reach in and pick some ions or molecules out. Chemists usually remove one chemical by reacting it with another. The reaction that removes the chemical might also arrive at equilibrium. We'll discuss this situation in later chapters.

Students often state that a stressed equilibrium system "*tries to* restore equilibrium" or "*tries to* remove some of the added chemical." As Yoda of *Star Wars* says, "Do or do not. There is no try." A stressed system doesn't *try to* restore equilibrium; it *does* restore equilibrium. When a reactant or product is added to an equilibrium system, it doesn't *try to* remove some of the added chemical; it *does* remove some of the added chemical.

Sample Problem — Predicting How an Equilibrium System Will Respond to the Removal of Reactant or Product

Some solid calcium hydroxide is in equilibrium with a saturated solution of its ions.

$$Ca(OH)_2(s) \rightleftharpoons Ca^{2+}(aq) + 2\,OH^-(aq)$$

This is a solubility equilibrium. The rate of dissolving equals the rate of recrystallizing. Some OH^- is removed by adding some hydrochloric acid to the solution. (The H^+ in the acid neutralizes some OH^- to produce H_2O.) In what direction will the equilibrium shift? When equilibrium is restored, how will the calcium ion and the hydroxide ion concentrations compare to their concentrations before the acid was added?

What to Think About	How to Do It
1. Using Le Châtelier's principle, determine that the system will shift to replace some of the removed OH^-.	The system must <u>shift right</u> (towards products) to replace some of the removed OH^-.
2. Determine the effect of the shift right. The shift right also produces some Ca^{2+} and causes more of the $Ca(OH)_2(s)$ to dissolve.	Since not all of the removed OH^- is replaced, the [OH^-] will decrease. The [Ca^{2+}] will increase.

Practice Problems — Predicting How an Equilibrium System Will Respond to the Addition or Removal of Reactant or Product

Use the following system for questions 1 and 2:

$$Fe^{3+}(aq) + SCN^-(aq) \rightleftharpoons FeSCN^{2+}(aq)$$

1. (a) What does Le Châtelier's principle say will occur if some $Fe(NO_3)_3$ is added to the system? ($Fe(NO_3)_3$ dissociates into independent Fe^{3+} and NO_3^- ions in solution.)

    (b) In what direction will the system shift?

    (c) When equilibrium is restored, how will the concentration of each substance compare to its concentration before the $Fe(NO_3)_3$ was added?

2. (a) What does Le Châtelier's principle say will occur if some sodium biphosphate is added to the system? (The HPO_4^{2-} ion reacts with the Fe^{3+} ion to produce $FeHPO_4^+$.)

    (b) In what direction will the system shift?

    (c) When equilibrium is restored, how will the concentration of each substance compare to its concentration before the sodium biphosphate was added?

3. Look at the graph below. At t_1 more H_2 was suddenly added to the closed system as shown. Equilibrium was re-established at t_2. Complete the plots to show how the system would respond.

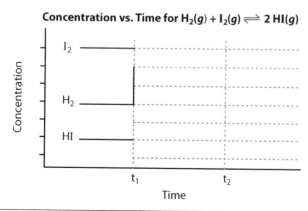

Concentration vs. Time for $H_2(g) + I_2(g) \rightleftharpoons 2\,HI(g)$

The Shift Mechanism: Effects of Stress on Forward and Reverse Reaction Rates

Le Châtelier's principle describes how an equilibrium system responds to a stress without offering any explanation of the response. The explanation is related to the effect of the stress on the equilibrium's forward and reverse reaction rates. To an equilibrium system, a **stress** is any action that has a different effect on the forward reaction rate than it does on the reverse reaction rate, thus disrupting the equilibrium. In other words, a disrupted or stressed equilibrium system is no longer at equilibrium because its forward and reverse reaction rates are not equal.

Sample Problem — Describing the Shift Mechanism

Explain in terms of forward and reverse reaction rates how the following equilibrium system would respond to adding some iron(III) chloride. ($FeCl_3$ dissociates into independent Fe^{3+} and Cl^- ions in solution.)

$$Fe^{3+}(aq) + SCN^-(aq) \rightleftharpoons FeSCN^{2+}(aq)$$

What to Think About	How to Do It
1. Determine the immediate effect of the stress on the forward and/or reverse reaction rates	Adding some Fe^{3+} increases the forward reaction rate (r_f).
2. Decide if this results in a net forward or net reverse reaction.	This results in a net forward reaction, also known as a shift right.

The system in Sample Problem above would re-equilibrate in the same manner that it established equilibrium in the first place. Figure 3.4.1(a) shows the rates when the system is initially at equilibrium (E_i), when the system is stressed (S), and when the system restores equilibrium (E_f). The net forward reaction would cause the reactant concentrations and the forward rate (r_f) to decrease, while the product concentrations and the reverse rate (r_r) increase, until r_f once again equals r_r.

The graph in Figure 3.4.1(b) is the more traditional way of depicting the same information shown in the arrow diagram in (a). In (b), the solid line represents the forward rate and the dotted line represents the reverse rate.

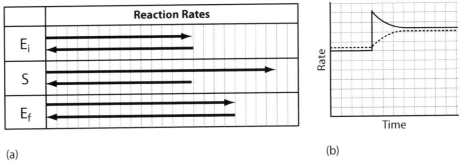

(a)

(b)

Figure 3.4.1 *Two different ways of representing a reaction in a diagram*

Sample Problem — Describing the Shift Mechanism

Explain in terms of forward and reverse reaction rates how the following reaction would respond to removing some SO_2.

$$2\,SO_2(g) + O_2(g) \rightleftharpoons 2\,SO_3(g)$$

What to Think About	How to Do It
1. Determine the immediate effect of the stress on the forward and/or reverse reaction rates.	Removing some SO_2 decreases the forward reaction rate (r_f).
2. Decide if this results in a net forward or net reverse reaction.	This results in a net reverse reaction, also known as a shift left.

The kinetics diagram on the right illustrates the rates at the initial equilibrium, at the time of the stress, and when equilibrium is restored. Note that the rates are lower when equilibrium is restored than they were at the initial equilibrium. This is logical since some chemical was removed from the system.

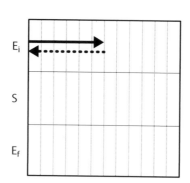

Practice Problems — Describing the Shift Mechanism

Consider the following equilibrium system:

$$2\,NOCl(g) \rightleftharpoons 2\,NO(g) + Cl_2(g)$$

1. Explain in terms of forward and reverse reaction rates how the equilibrium would respond to each of the following changes.
   (a) adding some NO
   (b) removing some Cl_2
   (c) removing some NOCl

2. Show how the forward and the reverse reaction rates respond to a sudden addition of NO to the system at t_1. Use a solid line for the forward rate and a dotted line for the reverse rate. The system re-equilibrates at t_2. The arrow diagram on the right of the graph is another way of depicting the same information. You may use it to do your rough work.

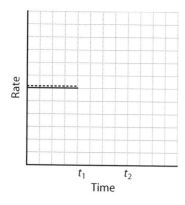

© Edvantage Interactive 2016

Changing Surface Area and Adding Catalysts

In heterogeneous reactions, an increase in surface area increases the forward and reverse rates equally since both forward and reverse reactions occur at the same surface. Adding more solid or crushing the solid present at equilibrium therefore has no effect on the equilibrium concentrations of the reactants and products in solution. When the initial reactants have a greater surface area, the system reaches equilibrium sooner. Likewise, adding a catalyst increases the forward and reverse rates equally and therefore has no effect on the position of the equilibrium. When a catalyst is added to the initial reactants, the system reaches equilibrium sooner.

The Equilibrium Position

The phrase **equilibrium position** refers to the relative concentrations of reactants and products at equilibrium and is usually expressed as percent yield. In Grade 11, you learned that percent yield is the amount of a product formed or recovered as a percentage of what the complete reaction will theoretically produce.

$$\text{percent yield} = \frac{\text{actual yield}}{\text{theoretical yield}} \times 100$$

An equilibrium system with an increased percent yield is said to have an equilibrium position farther to the right. "The equilibrium *position* shifted right" translates to: "the system has a greater percent yield than it had at the previous equilibrium." It is important to make a distinction between the equilibrium system shifting in response to a stress (as described by Le Châtelier's principle) and the equilibrium position shifting as a possible result. When you lose your balance snowboarding, you shift your weight to regain your balance. Sometimes you also shift your balance farther forward or backward on your board. Likewise, when an equilibrium system shifts to remove some of an added chemical or to replace some of a removed chemical, the system may "overshoot" or "undershoot" the original equilibrium position, depending on the circumstance. Consider the following equilibrium:

$$\text{HP}(aq) \rightleftharpoons \text{H}^+(aq) + \text{P}^-(aq)$$
yellow   blue

A green solution indicates equal concentrations of HP and P^- and therefore a 50% yield. If some yellow HP is added to a green equilibrium mixture, the *system will shift right* to remove some of the added HP. However, when equilibrium is restored, the solution is still yellow so we know that *the equilibrium position has shifted left*.

The expression "products are favored" is sometimes used to describe an equilibrium system. Be careful making inferences from this expression. Let's examine what the phrase does and, perhaps more importantly, does not mean. Products are *favored* when the equilibrium has a greater than 50 percent yield. This means that more than half of the limiting reactant has been converted into product.

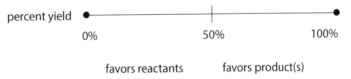

If a reaction has a limiting reactant, you cannot infer that any one reactant or product has a higher or lower concentration than any other reactant or product solely from the products being favored. For example:

$$\text{H}_3\text{BO}_3(aq) + \text{CN}^-(aq) \rightleftharpoons \text{H}_2\text{BO}_3^-(aq) + \text{HCN}(aq)$$

Even though products are favored in the above equilibrium, the [HCN] may be less than the [CN^-] if the CN^- is in excess. Likewise, the [HCN] may be less than the [H_3BO_3] if the H_3BO_3 is in excess. Furthermore, a reasonable excess of either reactant ensures that the total [reactants] will be greater than the total [products] even though the products are favored.

3.4 Review Questions

1. Consider the following equilibrium system: $2\,NO(g) + Cl_2(g) \rightleftharpoons 2\,NOCl(g)$

   (a) What does Le Châtelier's principle say will occur if some NO is added to the system?

   (b) In which direction will this system shift in response to the stress?

   (c) Compare the $[Cl_2]$ when equilibrium is reestablished to its concentration before the NO was added.

2. Consider the following equilibrium system: $2\,NO(g) + O_2(g) \rightleftharpoons 2\,NO_2(g)$
   (a) Explain in terms of forward and reverse reaction rates how the system responds to removing some O_2.

   (b) Compare the rates of the forward and reverse reactions when equilibrium is reestablished with the rates before some O_2 was removed.

3. Silver nitrate is added to the equilibrium system:
   $$Ag(S_2O_3)_2{}^{3-}(aq) \rightleftharpoons Ag^+(aq) + 2\,S_2O_3{}^{2-}(aq)$$

   When equilibrium is restored, how will each ion's concentration compare with its concentration before the silver nitrate was added? Explain how you arrived at your answer.

4. Cholesterol is a component of cell membranes and a building block for hormones such as estrogen and testosterone. About 80% of the body's cholesterol is produced by the liver, while the rest comes directly from our diet. There are two forms of cholesterol: a "good" form (HDL) that helps lubricate blood vessels and a "bad" form (LDL) that deposits on the inside of artery walls where it can restrict blood flow. Suppose these two forms could be converted from one to the other via the following "equilibrium" reaction:
   $$LDL + X \rightleftharpoons HDL + Y$$

   (a) Briefly explain why a drug that removes the bad cholesterol (LDL) would not be completely effective (i.e., it would have a bad side-effect).

   (b) Referring to the above equilibrium, how could a drug company effectively treat people with too high an LDL:HDL ratio?

© Edvantage Interactive 2016

5. Sulfur dioxide is an important compound in wines, where it acts as an antimicrobial and antioxidant to protect the wine from spoiling. The following equilibrium exists in wines:

    $SO_2(aq) + H_2O(l) \rightleftharpoons H^+(aq) + HSO_3^-(aq)$

    State whether a winemaker should increase the wine's pH (by removing H^+) or decrease the wine's pH (by adding H^+) to shift the equilibrium toward the active SO_2?

6. Complete the following table using the words "decrease," "same," or "increase" to indicate how the equilibrium concentrations are affected by the stated stress. "Increase" means that when equilibrium is restored, the chemical's concentration is greater than it was before the stress.

    $$2\,NH_3(g) \rightleftharpoons N_2(g) + 3\,H_2(g)$$

		Add NH$_3$	Remove some H$_2$	Add N$_2$
Equilibrium Concentration	N$_2$			
	H$_2$			
	NH$_3$			

7. $HP \rightleftharpoons H^+ + P^-$

    red   yellow

    The above equilibrium system appears orange due to equal concentrations of HP and P^-.
    (a) What action will shift the equilibrium so the solution turns red?

    (b) What could be done to shift the equilibrium so the solution turns yellow?

8. Hemoglobin is the protein in red blood cells that transports oxygen to cells throughout your body. Each hemoglobin (Hb) molecule attaches to four oxygen molecules:

    $Hb(aq) + 4\,O_2(aq) \rightleftharpoons Hb(O_2)_4(aq)$

    In which direction does the above equilibrium shift in each of the following situations:
    (a) At high elevations the air pressure is lowered reducing the $[O_2]$ in the blood.

    (b) At high altitude, climbers sometimes breathe pressurized oxygen from a tank to increase the $[O_2]$ in the blood.

    (c) People who live at higher altitudes produce more hemoglobin.

    (d) Carbon monoxide poisoning occurs when carbon monoxide molecules bind to hemoglobin instead of oxygen molecules. Carboxyhemoglobin is even redder than oxyhemoglobin; therefore, one symptom of carbon monoxide poisoning is a flushed face.

9. Explain why neither adding a catalyst nor increasing the surface area of S(s) stresses the following equilibrium, even though each of these actions increases the forward reaction rate.

$$2\,S(s) + 3\,O_2(g) \rightleftharpoons 2\,SO_3(g)$$

10. The following equilibrium exists in an aqueous solution of copper(II) chloride:

$$CuCl_4{}^{2-}(aq) + 4\,H_2O(l) \rightleftharpoons Cu(H_2O)_4{}^{2+}(aq) + 4\,Cl^-(aq)$$
green   blue

(a) Some Cl⁻ is removed by adding some silver nitrate to the solution. The Ag⁺ in the silver nitrate precipitates with the Cl⁻ to produce AgCl(s). In what direction will the equilibrium shift?

(b) If the initial equilibrium mixture was blue, what would you observe as a sodium chloride solution was added dropwise to the equilibrium mixture?

11. At t_1 some CO was suddenly removed from the closed system shown below. Equilibrium was reestablished at t_2. Complete the plots to show how the system would respond.

$$Ni(s) + 4\,CO(g) \rightleftharpoons Ni(CO)_4(g)$$

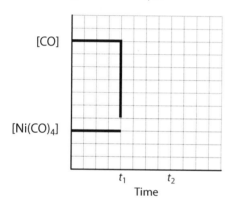

12. Show how the forward and reverse reaction rates respond to having some HOCl suddenly removed from the following system at t_1.

$$H_2O(g) + Cl_2O(g) \rightleftharpoons 2\,HOCl(g)$$

Use a solid line for the forward rate and a dotted line for the reverse rate. The system re-equilibrates at t_2. The arrow diagram on the right is another way of displaying the same information. You may use it to do your rough work.

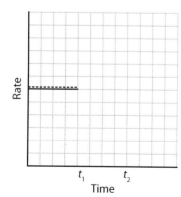

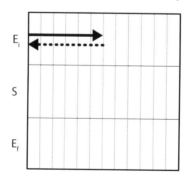

13. Equilibria are often linked through one chemical common to both. Even two equilibria coupled together present an interesting dynamic.

Equilibrium 1
$$Cu^{2+} + 4\,NH_3 \rightleftharpoons Cu(NH_3)_4^{2+}$$
$$+$$
$$4\,H^+$$

Equilibrium 2 $\upharpoonleft\downharpoonright$

$$4\,NH_4^+$$

How would the $[Cu^{2+}]$ be affected by adding some H^+ to this coupled system? Briefly explain using Le Châtelier's principle.

14. Silver acetate has a low solubility in water. A small amount of solid silver acetate is in equilibrium with a saturated solution of its ions.

Equilibrium 1
$$AgCH_3COO(s) \rightleftharpoons Ag^+(aq) + CH_3COO^-(aq)$$
$$+$$
$$H^+(aq)$$

Equilibrium 2 $\upharpoonleft\downharpoonright$

$$CH_3COOH(aq)$$

What would you observe occurring in the beaker as $H^+(aq)$ is added dropwise to the solution? Briefly explain using Le Châtelier's principle.

15. Consider the following equilibrium:

$$2\,NO(g) + O_2(g) \rightleftharpoons 2\,NO_2(g)$$

Describe how [NO] could be greater than the $[NO_2]$ despite the products being favored at equilibrium.

16. Because few natural systems are closed, many of nature's reversible reactions are perpetually "chasing after" equilibrium. In *At Home in the Universe*, the author, Stuart Kauffman, describes living systems as "persistently displaced from chemical equilibrium." Describe one way to ensure that a reversible reaction never achieves equilibrium.

3.5 Le Châtelier's Principle and Volume and Temperature Changes

Warm Up

1. What is the scientific meaning of *pressure*?

   _____

2. To increase gas pressure, we _____ the gas into less space.

3. What is temperature a measure of?

   _____

4. An increase in temperature increases the rate of reactions because the molecules collide more
   _____ and _____.

How Equilibria Respond to Volume Changes

We've described and explained how equilibria respond to changing the concentration of a single reactant or product. The concentrations of all the reactants and products can be changed simultaneously by changing the volume of the reacting system. The volume of a gaseous system can be changed by compressing or decompressing it. The volume of an aqueous system can be changed by evaporating water from it or by diluting it. A change in volume changes all the reactants' and products' concentrations.

It isn't possible for a shift to partially restore all the chemicals' concentrations but some equilibria can shift to partially restore the total or combined concentration of the chemicals. For example, if an aqueous equilibrium is diluted then all the chemical concentrations are decreased. A shift can't increase the concentrations of chemicals on both sides of the equation but some equilibria can increase the total chemical concentration by shifting to the side of the equation with the greater number of particles. Le Châtelier views this situation from the perspective of pressure.

> Equilibria respond to volume changes by shifting to relieve some of the added pressure or to replace some of the lost pressure.

You are probably familiar with the concept of gas pressure, but you may not be familiar with the concept of solute (osmotic) pressure. A detailed discussion of osmosis and osmotic pressure is not required here. You need only know that osmotic pressure is to dissolved particles what gas pressure is to gas particles. In 1901, the Dutch chemist Jacobus van't Hoff discovered that dissolved particles in an aqueous solution behave just like gas particles in a container. The relationship between the concentration, temperature, and pressure is the same for gas particles and dissolved particles. Van't Hoff won the first Nobel Prize in chemistry for his work on osmotic pressure and chemical equilibrium. Just as a gas's pressure is proportional to its concentration of gas particles, an aqueous solution's osmotic pressure is proportional to its concentration of solute particles. Decompressing a gas lowers its gas pressure. Diluting a solute lowers its osmotic pressure.

Chemists sometimes refer to the partial pressure of a gas. **Partial pressure** is the gas's part of the total gas pressure or the pressure exerted by this gas alone in a mixture of gases. The sum of the partial pressures equals the total pressure of the gas mixture. A gas's partial pressure is proportional to its concentration. The same concepts and principles apply to solutes and their partial osmotic pressures.

© Edvantage Interactive 2016

Consider the following equilibrium:

$$H_2(g) + F_2(g) \rightleftharpoons 2\,HF(g)$$

This equilibrium doesn't respond to a volume change. It cannot partially restore the pressure by shifting in either direction since there are the same number of gas particles on each side of the equation.

Quick Check

1. According to Le Châtelier's principle, how will an equilibrium respond to being compressed?

   _____

2. What is *partial pressure*?

   _____

3. According to Le Châtelier's principle, how will an aqueous equilibrium respond to being diluted?

   _____

Sample Problem — Predicting How an Equilibrium Will Respond to a Decrease in Volume

The system described by the equation below is compressed. In what direction will the system shift to restore equilibrium? When equilibrium is restored, how will the number of each type of molecule and the concentration of each substance compare to those before the system was compressed?

$$PCl_3(g) + Cl_2(g) \rightleftharpoons PCl_5(g)$$

What to Think About	How to Do It
1. Recall that Le Châtelier's principle says the system will shift to relieve *some* of the added pressure.	The system must <u>shift right</u> to reduce the pressure.
2. Consider the effect the stress has on the system to determine the number of each type of molecule. The stress changed the amount of space that the particles move around in, not the number of particles. Only the system's response to the stress changes the number of particles. The forward reaction converts two molecules into one molecule. Thus a shift right reduces the total number of particles and the pressure of the system.	The number of PCl_5 molecules will increase, while the number of PCl_3 and Cl_2 molecules will decrease.
3. Determine the effect of compression on the concentrations of the substances in the system. The situation regarding concentration is illustrated below: 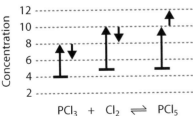 In this diagram, all the original concentrations are doubled by the compression so the volume must have been halved.	Because the system was compressed, every substance has a higher concentration or partial pressure at the new equilibrium than it did at the initial equilibrium. (Although the shift can't reduce all the chemicals' concentrations or partial pressures, it is reducing most of them (2/3) by shifting to the right. The result is that some of the added pressure is relieved.)

© Edvantage Interactive 2016

Sample Problem — Predicting How an Equilibrium Will Respond to an Increase in Volume

The system below is diluted. In what direction will the system shift to restore equilibrium? When equilibrium is restored, how will the number of each type of particle and the concentration of each species compare to those before the system was diluted?

$$H^+(aq) + NO_2^-(aq) \rightleftharpoons HNO_2(aq)$$

What to Think About

1. Recall that Le Châtelier's principle says that equilibrium will be restored by replacing *some* of the lost osmotic pressure.

2. Consider the effect the stress has on the system to determine the number of each type of molecule. Only the system's response to the stress, not the stress itself, changes the number of particles. The reverse reaction converts one particle into two particles thus a shift left increases the total number of particles and the osmotic pressure of the system.

3. Determine the effect of dilution on the concentrations of the substances in the system. The situation regarding concentration is illustrated below:

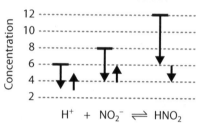

$$H^+ + NO_2^- \rightleftharpoons HNO_2$$

In this diagram, all the original concentrations are halved by the dilution so the volume must have been doubled.

How to Do It

The system must <u>shift left</u> to increase the pressure.

The number of HNO_2 molecules will decrease while the number of H^+ and NO_2^- ions will increase.

Because the system was diluted, every substance has a lower concentration at the new equilibrium than it did at the initial equilibrium.

Practice Problems — Predicting How an Equilibrium Will Respond to a Volume Change

1. The system below is compressed:

   $$2\,NOCl(g) \rightleftharpoons 2\,NO(g) + Cl_2(g)$$

   In what direction will the system shift to restore equilibrium? When equilibrium is restored, how will the number of each type of molecule and the concentration of each substance compare to those before the system was compressed?

2. The system below is diluted:

   $$Ag(S_2O_3)_2^{3-}(aq) \rightleftharpoons Ag^+(aq) + 2\,S_2O_3^{2-}(aq)$$

   In what direction will the system shift to restore equilibrium? When equilibrium is restored, how will the number of each type of particle and the concentration of each species compare to those before the system was diluted?

Continued opposite

© Edvantage Interactive 2016

Practice Problems — *Continued*

3. The volume of the system below is decreased:

$$CO_2(g) + H_2(g) \rightleftharpoons CO(g) + H_2O(g)$$

Will the equilibrium system respond? Explain.

The Shift Mechanism: The Effect of Volume Change on Forward and/or Reverse Reaction Rates

For an explanation of what causes this shift, we must once again turn to chemical kinetics. When the volume of an equilibrium system changes, all the reactant and product concentrations change proportionately. Nevertheless, the forward and reverse reaction rates may change by different amounts. In doing so, they become unequal. From Le Châtelier's predictions, we can infer the following:

> The direction (forward or reverse) that has the greater sum of gaseous or aqueous reactant coefficients is the more sensitive of the two directions to volume changes.

By "more sensitive," we mean that a volume change will decrease or increase the rate of that direction more than that of the opposite direction. At equilibrium, the relationship between concentration and the reaction rate depends only on the coefficients in the balanced equation. For example, consider the following system:

$$Fe^{3+}(aq) + SCN^-(aq) \rightleftharpoons FeSCN^{2+}(aq)$$

Diluting this aqueous system decreases its forward rate more than its reverse rate because the sum of the reactant coefficients for the forward reaction is 2 whereas the lone reactant coefficient for the reverse reaction is only 1. If the sum of gaseous or aqueous reactant coefficients equals the sum of the gaseous or aqueous product coefficients then the equilibrium is not stressed by volume changes. This is because any volume change will have the same effect on the forward and reverse rates. For example, consider the following system:

$$H_2(g) + F_2(g) \rightleftharpoons 2\,HF(g)$$

Compressing this gaseous system increases its forward and reverse rates equally and therefore does not disrupt the equilibrium.

The only external factors that affect reaction rates are the reactant concentrations and temperature. A pressure change only stresses an equilibrium if the pressure change reflects a change in the reactant and product concentrations. The pressure of an equilibrium system can be changed without changing its concentrations by, for example, adding an inert gas to the system. Since this pressure change does not reflect any change of reactant or product concentrations, it does not affect the equilibrium.

Sample Problem — Describing the Shift Mechanism for a Decrease in Volume

Explain in terms of forward and reverse reaction rates how the equilibrium system below would respond to a decrease in volume.

$$2\,SO_2(g) + O_2(g) \rightleftharpoons 2\,SO_3(g)$$

What to Think About	How to Do It
1. Determine the immediate effect of the stress on the forward and/or reverse reaction rates.	Compressing the system increases the forward rate (r_f) more than the reverse rate (r_r).
2. Decide if this would result in a net forward or net reverse reaction.	This results in a net forward reaction, also known as a shift right.

The arrow diagram on the right illustrates the rates at the initial equilibrium, at the time of the stress, and when equilibrium is restored.

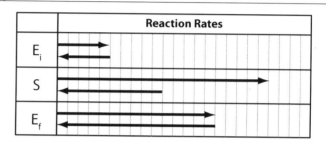

Sample Problem — Describing the Shift Mechanism for a Volume Change

Explain in terms of forward and reverse reaction rates how the equilibrium system below would respond to being diluted.

$$H^+(aq) + SO_4^{2-}(aq) \rightleftharpoons HSO_4^-(aq)$$

What to Think About	How to Do It
1. Determine the immediate effect of the stress on the forward and/or reverse reaction rates.	Diluting the system decreases the forward rate (r_f) more than the reverse rate (r_r).
2. Decide if this would result in a net forward or net reverse reaction.	This results in a net reverse reaction, also known as a shift left.

The arrow diagram on the right illustrates the rates at the initial equilibrium, at the time of the stress, and when equilibrium is restored.

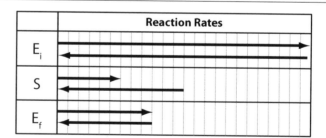

© Edvantage Interactive 2016

Practice Problems — Describing the Shift Mechanism for Changes in Volume

1. Explain in terms of forward and reverse reaction rates how the equilibrium system below would respond to a decrease in volume.
$$2\,NOCl(g) \rightleftharpoons 2\,NO(g) + Cl_2(g)$$

2. Explain in terms of forward and reverse reaction rates how the equilibrium system below would respond to being diluted.
$$Ag(S_2O_3)_2{}^{3-}(aq) \rightleftharpoons Ag^+(aq) + 2\,S_2O_3{}^{2-}(aq)$$

3. Show how the forward and reverse reaction rates respond to a sudden compression of the system at t_1. Use a solid line for the forward rate and a dotted line for the reverse rate. The system restores equilibrium at t_2. The arrow diagram on the right is another way of depicting the same information. You may use it to do your rough work.
$$2\,SO_2(g) + O_2(g) \rightleftharpoons 2\,SO_3(g)$$

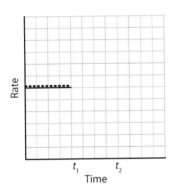
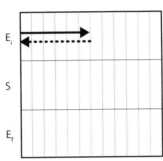

How Equilibria Respond to Temperature Changes

Le Châtelier's principle states the following:

> Equilibria respond to changing temperatures by shifting to remove some of the added kinetic energy or to replace some of the removed kinetic energy.

Sample Problem — Predicting How an Equilibrium Will Respond to an Increase in Temperature

The system below is heated. In what direction will the system shift to restore equilibrium? When equilibrium is restored, how will the concentration of each species compare to its concentration before the system was heated?

$$N_2(g) + O_2(g) \rightleftharpoons 2\,NO(g) \qquad \Delta H = 181\ kJ/mol$$

What to Think About	How to Do It
1. Recall that Le Châtelier's principle says the system will shift to remove *some* of the added kinetic energy and cool itself.	The system must <u>shift right</u> (in the endothermic direction) to convert some of the added KE into PE.
2. Determine the effect of heating on the concentrations of the substances in the system. Note that 2 NO molecules are formed for each N₂ and O₂ molecule that react.	The $[N_2]$ and $[O_2]$ will decrease and the $[NO]$ will increase.

Note that ΔH can be included as part of a thermochemical equation:

$$N_2(g) + O_2(g) + 181\,\text{kJ} \rightleftharpoons 2\,NO(g)$$

In that case, the kinetic energy can be treated just as though it were a chemical. Adding O_2 would cause a shift to the right to remove some of the added O_2. Likewise, adding kinetic energy causes a shift to the right to remove some of the added kinetic energy.

Sample Problem — Predicting How an Equilibrium Will Respond to a Decrease in Temperature

The system below is cooled. In what direction will the system shift to restore equilibrium? When equilibrium is restored, how will the concentration of each species compare to its concentration before the system was cooled?

$$N_2(g) + O_2(g) \rightleftharpoons 2\,NO(g) \qquad \Delta H = 181\,\text{kJ/mol}$$

What to Think About	How to Do It
1. Recall that Le Châtelier's principle says the system will shift to replace *some* of the lost kinetic energy and warm itself.	The system must shift left (in the exothermic direction) to convert some PE into KE.
2. Determine the effect of cooling on the concentrations of the substances in the system. Note that 2 NO molecules are consumed for each N_2 and O_2 molecule formed.	The [NO] will decrease. The [N_2] and [O_2] will increase.

Practice Problems — Predicting How an Equilibrium Will Respond to a Temperature Change

1. The system below is heated. In what direction will the system shift to restore equilibrium? When equilibrium is restored, how will the concentration of each species compare to its concentration before the system was heated?

$$2\,SO_2(g) + O_2(g) \rightleftharpoons 2\,SO_3(g) \qquad \Delta H = -198\,\text{kJ/mol}$$

2. The system below is cooled. In what direction will the system shift to restore equilibrium? When equilibrium is restored, how will the concentration of each species compare to its concentration before the system was cooled?

$$H_2(g) + I_2(g) \rightleftharpoons 2\,HI(g) + 17\,\text{kJ/mol}$$

Effects of Volume and Temperature Changes

Figure 3.5.1 depicts the situation described in Sample Problem above. When the stress is a sudden concentration or volume change it appears as a spike(s) on plots of concentrations versus time. Temperature changes do not appear on these plots so the system responds to an invisible stress. Another difference is that concentration changes, both individual and those resulting from volume changes, can be very sudden. However, the temperature of a system, particularly an aqueous system, cannot change rapidly. This means that chemical systems begin responding while the temperature is still changing. In other words, the response begins before the stress is complete.

© Edvantage Interactive 2016

Neither volume nor temperature change itself changes the percent yield so a system's response to these stresses shifts its equilibrium position in the same direction that the system shifted in response to the stress.

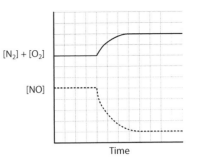

Figure 3.5.1 *Changes in concentration show up in the graph but the temperature change doesn't.*

Pressure-Temperature Relationships

Increasing the temperature of gases in a closed container increases their pressure. The temperature change itself affects the equilibrium. However, the resulting pressure change is irrelevant to the equilibrium because it does not reflect a change of concentrations. The same cannot be said for the reverse. Some of the kinetic energy of gas particles transforms into potential energy as the particles speed up, escaping their mutual attractions and spreading apart.

When a gas is compressed, its temperature rises because some of the particles' potential energy converts to kinetic energy as the particles are forced closer together. The temperature change resulting from compressing or decompressing a gas mixture does affect its equilibrium. In questions where a gaseous equilibrium is compressed or decompressed, assume that its temperature was held constant unless otherwise stated. Such a stipulation allows you to deal with only one variable at a time.

The Shift Mechanism: The Effect of Temperature Change on Forward and Reverse Reaction Rates

If the collision geometry requirements are the same for the forward and reverse reactions, then their rates depend solely on the frequency of collisions possessing the activation energy. The forward and reverse reaction rates are equal at equilibrium. Therefore the frequency of collisions possessing the activation energy must be the same for the forward and reverse reactions. The percentage of the area under a collision energy distribution curve that is at or beyond the activation energy (E_a) represents the percentage of collisions having enough energy to react.

For an endothermic reaction, like that represented in Figures 3.5.2 and 3.5.3, the forward reaction has a lower percentage of collisions with the activation energy needed than the reverse reaction does. The forward reaction must therefore have a greater frequency of collisions to achieve the same frequency of successful collisions as the reverse reaction. For example, 4% of the forward reaction's 800 collisions per second and 20% of the reverse reaction's 160 collisions per second would both equal 32 successful collisions per second. For an endothermic reaction, a higher concentration of reactants is therefore required to generate the same rate as a lower concentration of products because a lower percentage of the reactant collisions are successful.

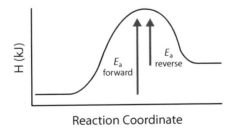

Figure 3.5.2 *Potential energy diagram.*

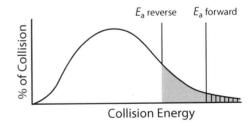

Figure 3.5.3 *Collision energy diagram*

Increases in temperature cause a shift in the endothermic direction because they increase the rate of the endothermic direction more than they increase the rate of the exothermic direction. The endothermic direction has the harder task due to its higher activation energy so it benefits more from the assistance provided by the increased temperature. Likewise, decreases in temperature cause a shift in the exothermic direction because they decrease the rate of the endothermic direction more than they decrease the rate of the exothermic direction. The endothermic direction is hindered more than the exothermic direction by the decreased temperature.

An equilibrium's endothermic direction is more sensitive to temperature changes than its exothermic direction due to the endothermic direction's greater activation energy.

Sample Problem — Describing the Shift Mechanism for an Increase in Temperature

Explain in terms of forward and reverse reaction rates how the system below would respond to being heated.

$$N_2(g) + O_2(g) \rightleftharpoons 2 NO(g) \qquad \Delta H = 181 \text{ kJ/mol}$$

What to Think About	How to Do It
1. Determine the immediate effect of the stress on the forward and/or reverse reaction rates.	Heating the system increases the forward rate (r_f) more than the reverse rate (r_r).
2. Decide if this would result in a net forward or net reverse reaction.	This results in a net forward reaction, also known as a shift right.

The arrow diagram on the right illustrates the rates at the initial equilibrium, at the time of the stress, and when equilibrium is restored.

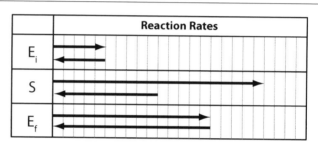

Sample Problem — Describing the Shift Mechanism for a Decrease in Temperature

Explain in terms of forward and reverse reaction rates how the system below would respond to being cooled.

$$N_2(g) + O_2(g) \rightleftharpoons 2 NO(g) \qquad \Delta H = 181 \text{ kJ/mol}$$

What to Think About	How to Do It
1. Determine the immediate effect of the stress on the forward and/or reverse reaction rates?	Cooling the system decreases the forward rate (r_f) more than the reverse rate (r_r).
2. Decide if this would result in a net forward or net reverse reaction.	This results in a net reverse reaction, also known as a shift left.

The arrow diagram on the right illustrates the rates at the initial equilibrium, at the time of the stress, and when equilibrium is restored.

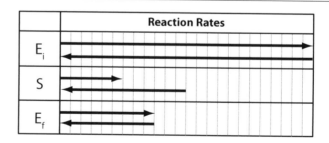

© Edvantage Interactive 2016

Practice Problems — Describing the Shift Mechanism for Changes in Temperature

1. Explain in terms of forward and reverse reaction rates how the system below would respond to being heated.

$$2 SO_2(g) + O_2(g) \rightleftharpoons 2 SO_3(g) \qquad \Delta H = -198 \text{ kJ/mol}$$

2. Explain in terms of forward and reverse reaction rates how the system below would respond to being cooled.

$$2 Cl_2(g) + 2 H_2O(g) + 113 \text{ kJ/mol} \rightleftharpoons 4 HCl(g) + O_2(g)$$

3. Show how the forward and reverse reaction rates in the system below would respond to a temperature increase at t_1. Use a solid line for the forward rate and a dotted line for the reverse rate. The system restores equilibrium at t_2. The arrow diagram on the right is another way of depicting the same information. You may use it to do your rough work.

$$2 NCl_3(g) \rightleftharpoons N_2(g) + 3 Cl_2(g) \qquad \Delta H = -460 \text{ kJ/mol}$$

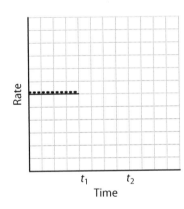
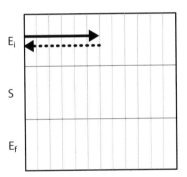

The Haber-Bosch Process

Almost all of the world's ammonia is produced via the Haber-Bosch process and almost all of our inorganic nitrogen compounds are produced from this ammonia. More than 100 million tonnes of ammonia with a value in excess of $600 million are produced annually. About 80% of the world's ammonia is used to produce fertilizers. Other products include explosives, plastics, fibres, and dyes.

German chemist Fritz Haber developed the equipment and procedures for producing ammonia (NH_3) from its constituent elements (N_2 and H_2) in 1910. In 1918, he received the Nobel Prize in chemistry for this accomplishment. In 1931, another German chemist, Carl Bosch, won the Nobel Prize in chemistry, in part for transforming the process to an industrial scale. The balanced equation and enthalpy for the reaction are:

$$N_2(g) + 3 H_2(g) \rightleftharpoons 2 NH_3(g) \qquad \Delta H = -92.4 \text{ kJ/mol}$$

Process Production Rate and Temperature Considerations

Consider the plight of a chemist who wants to produce NH_3 in his or her laboratory by allowing a single set of reactants to achieve equilibrium within a closed container. The percent yield and the reaction rate both need to be considered in choosing the optimal temperature. Lower temperatures produce higher percent yields of NH_3 at equilibrium since lower temperatures shift this equilibrium toward products. However, at lower temperatures the reaction proceeds at slower rates in both

© Edvantage Interactive 2016

forward and reverse directions. Therefore it takes longer to produce any given amount of product. In other words, a higher temperature generates a faster forward rate but sustains it for a much shorter time period, both because the reaction rate is faster and the percent yield is less. To use a racing analogy, at higher temperatures the reaction runs faster toward a closer finish line (lower % yield).

Reactions proceeding at lower temperatures will eventually produce the amount produced at higher temperatures and then just keep rumbling along. This is the chemical version of the familiar tale of the tortoise versus the hare. Maximum productivity might be achieved by initially establishing equilibrium at a high temperature and then shifting the equilibrium toward products by lowering the temperature. Using a catalyst allows chemists to increase the reaction rate at a lower temperature that produces a higher percent yield.

> For the Haber-Bosch process, lower temperatures produce a higher percent yield but at a lower rate.

The chemical industry does not produce ammonia by allowing single sets of reactants to establish equilibria within closed containers. As the reacting mixture is cycled and recycled through a Haber reactor, N_2 and H_2 are continuously fed in at one location while NH_3 is continuously liquefied and removed at another. The ammonia can be selectively removed because hydrogen bonding between NH_3 molecules causes them to condense at a higher temperature than hydrogen and nitrogen. The temperatures in the reactor are adjusted to maximize the concentration of NH_3, when and where it is extracted. The forward rate is kept high by replacing the consumed reactants while the reverse rate is kept low by removing product. Percent yield ceases to be a consideration if the system doesn't achieve equilibrium.

An industrial chemist must strike a compromise between the increased rate provided by a greater temperature and the increased cost to produce it. The reaction rate is also increased by using a catalyst. The "bottom line" for industry is its annual profit, not its annual production of ammonia. A plant strives to generate the greatest possible amount of ammonia for the lowest possible cost. The industry is obviously influenced by a tremendous number of commercial and economic factors as well as chemical factors.

Process Production Rate and Pressure Considerations

Higher pressures generate faster rates and push the reaction toward a higher percent yield.

According to Le Châtelier's principle, the system partially relieves the increased pressure by shifting right as the forward reaction converts four molecules into two. Compressing the gases also raises their temperature. High compression systems are expensive to build and to operate. Most Haber reactors operate at about 3.5×10^4 kPa. The increased yield at this pressure more than compensates for the higher construction and operation costs.

Quick Check

1. Name the chemical produced by the Haber-Bosch process.

   _____

2. What increases the rate of the Haber-Bosch process without decreasing its percent yield?

   _____

© Edvantage Interactive 2016

3.5 Activity: Dealing With Pressure

Question

What will a gaseous equilibrium mixture look like at the molecular level as it responds to being compressed?

Background

An equilibrium mixture of colorless dinitrogen tetroxide, $N_2O_4(g)$, and orange nitrogen dioxide, $NO_2(g)$, forms when nitric acid is poured over copper. When this equilibrium mixture is compressed in a plugged syringe, the mixture becomes darker orange as a result of concentrating the NO_2 molecules. Within seconds the mixture's color changes slightly, yet unmistakeably, as the equilibrium shifts in response to the stress.

$$N_2O_4(g) + energy \rightleftharpoons 2 NO_2(g)$$
$$\text{colorless} \qquad\qquad \text{orange}$$

Procedure

1. The three diagrams below represent the tube in a syringe. Complete the third diagram by drawing in a possible number of NO_2 and N_2O_4 molecules after the system has responded to the stress and restored equilibrium.
2. Color in the circle underneath each syringe to indicate how pale or dark orange the gas would appear.

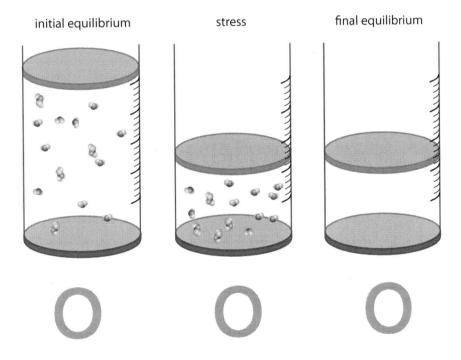

initial equilibrium   stress   final equilibrium

Results and Discussion

1. In response to the compression, the number of NO_2 molecules _____ and the number of N_2O_4 molecules _____.

2. Describe the molecules' behavior when the reaction in the syringe is at equilibrium.

3. How would the color of the equilibrium mixture change when the syringe is plunged into an ice bath? Explain.

3.5 Review Questions

1. Consider the following equilibrium: $Fe^{3+}(aq) + SCN^-(aq) \rightleftharpoons FeSCN^{2+}(aq)$
   (a) In which direction will the system shift if it is diluted? Explain your answer in terms of Le Châtelier's principle.

   (b) Compare the number and the concentration of SCN^- ions when equilibrium is restored to their number and concentration before the system was diluted.

2. Explain *in terms of forward and reverse reaction rates* how this system responds to an increase in volume.
$$PCl_5(g) \rightleftharpoons PCl_3(g) + Cl_2(g)$$

3. In which direction does the following equilibrium shift when the gas mixture is compressed? Explain using Le Châtelier's principle *and* in terms of forward and reverse reaction rates.
$$2\,C(s) + O_2(g) \rightleftharpoons 2\,CO(g)$$

4. Describe a situation when equilibrium concentrations change but no stress occurs.

5. Complete the following plots. The system is at equilibrium prior to t_1. At t_1 the volume of the system is suddenly doubled. The system responds to this stress between t_1 and t_2 until it re-equilibrates at t_2.
$$N_2O_4(g) \rightleftharpoons 2\,NO_2(g)$$

6. Show how the forward and reverse reaction rates respond to a sudden increase in the volume of the system at t_1. Use a solid line for the forward rate and a dotted line for the reverse rate. The system restores equilibrium at t_2. The arrow diagram on the right is another way of depicting the same information. You may use it to do your rough work.

$$N_2O_4(g) \rightleftharpoons 2\,NO_2(g)$$

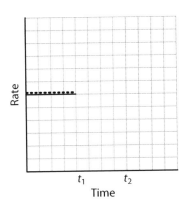
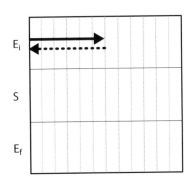

7. The solubility of a substance is its highest possible concentration at a given temperature. Any further solid added to the solution will remain undissolved in equilibrium with the dissolved state. Dissolving sodium sulfate in water is exothermic.

$$Na_2SO_4(s) \rightleftharpoons 2\,Na^+(aq) + SO_4^{2-}(aq) + heat$$

State whether sodium sulfate will be less soluble or more soluble when the temperature of the solution is increased. Explain.

8. In which direction will the following equilibrium system shift when it is heated?

$$2\,SO_3(g) + 192\ kJ/mol \rightleftharpoons 2\,SO_2(g) + O_2(g)$$

Provide two ways to arrive at this answer.

9. Complete the following plots. The system below is at equilibrium prior to t_1. The system is suddenly cooled at t_1. The system responds to this stress between t_1 and t_2 until it re-equilibrates at t_2.

$$N_2O_4(g) + 57\ kJ \rightleftharpoons 2\,NO_2(g)$$

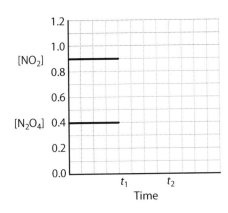

10. Show how the forward and reverse reaction rates respond to a sudden increase in the temperature of the system below at t_1. Use a solid line for the forward rate and a dotted line for the reverse rate. The system restores equilibrium at t_2. The arrow diagram on the right is another way of depicting the same information. You may use it to do your rough work.

$$Ni(s) + 4\,CO(g) \rightleftharpoons Ni(CO)_4(g) \qquad \Delta H = -603 \text{ kJ/mol}$$

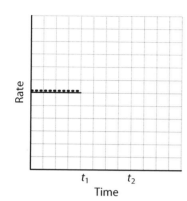 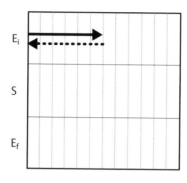

11. $Co(H_2O)_6^{2+}(aq) + 2\,Cl^-(aq) \rightleftharpoons Co(H_2O)_4Cl_2(aq) + 2\,H_2O(l)$
    pink   purple

A flask containing the above equilibrium turns from purple to pink when cooled. State whether the forward reaction is endothermic or exothermic. Explain how you arrived at your answer.

12. $A + B \rightleftharpoons AB + 16.8 \text{ kJ/mol}$

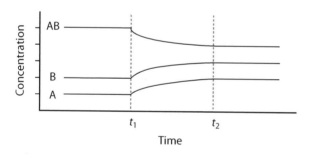

(a) In which direction is the equilibrium system shifting?

(b) What specifically was done to this system at t_1?

13. Explain *in terms of forward and reverse reaction rates* how the equilibrium below responds to a decrease in temperature:

$$N_2(g) + 3 H_2(g) \rightleftharpoons 2 NH_3(g) \qquad \Delta H = -92.4 \text{ kJ/mol}$$

14. Why is an equilibrium's endothermic direction more sensitive to temperature changes than its exothermic direction?

15. What conditions of temperature and pressure favor products in the following reaction:

$$PCl_5(g) \rightleftharpoons PCl_3(g) + Cl_2(g) \qquad \Delta H = 238 \text{ kJ/mol}$$

16. Briefly describe the conflicting factors that chemists face when choosing a temperature to perform the Haber-Bosch process.

17. Consider the system below. When equilibrium is restored, how will the number of each type of molecule and the concentration of each substance compare to those before the stress was introduced? Complete the following table using the words "decrease," "same," or "increase."

$$2 NH_3(g) \rightleftharpoons N_2(g) + 3 H_2(g) \qquad \Delta H = 92.4 \text{ kJ/mol}$$

		Decrease Volume	Decrease Temperature
Equilibrium concentration	N_2		
	H_2		
	NH_3		
Equilibrium number	N_2		
	H_2		
	NH_3		

18. The graph below shows how forward and reverse reaction rates change as an exothermic reaction goes from initiation to equilibrium. Plot the forward and reverse reaction rates for the same reaction at a higher temperature.

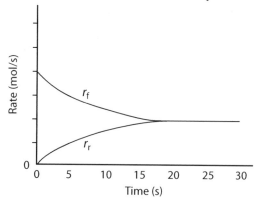

Rate (forward and reverse) vs. Time for a Reaction as It Approaches and Achieves Equilibrium

19. Nitric acid is produced commercially by the Ostwald process. The first step of the Ostwald process is:

$$4 \, NH_3(g) + 5 \, O_2(g) \rightleftharpoons 4 \, NO(g) + 6 \, H_2O(g) + energy$$

In which direction will the above system shift in the following situations:

(a) Some NO is added.

(b) Some NH_3 is removed.

(c) The pressure of the system is decreased by increasing the volume.

(d) The temperature of the system is decreased.

20. A piston supported by gas trapped in a cylinder is a fixed pressure apparatus. As long as the gas in the cylinder is supporting the same piston then its pressure must be constant because it is exerting the same force over the same bottom surface of the piston. If the piston weighs more, then the fixed pressure is greater. Consider the following equilibrium system trapped in a cylinder:

$$PCl_5(g) \rightleftharpoons PCl_3(g) + Cl_2(g)$$

(a) In which direction will the system shift when some weight is added to the piston?

(b) How would this shift affect the apparatus?

21. Complete the following review table.

$$N_2(g) + 3 H_2(g) \rightleftharpoons 2 NH_3(g) \qquad \Delta H = -92.4 \text{ kJ/mol}$$

Stress	Le Châtelier Predicts		Chemical Kinetics Explains	
	Response	Shift	Effect	Net Rx
Add H_2	some of the added H_2 removed			
Add NH_3		left		
Remove N_2			r_f decreases	
Decrease volume (compress)				net forward rx
Decrease temperature			r_r decreases more than r_f	

Extension

22. Holding the temperature and pressure constant when a reactant or product is added to an equilibrium system is easier said than done. Some SO_3 is added to the following system. Its temperature and pressure are *not* fixed.

$$2 SO_2(g) + O_2(g) \rightleftharpoons 2 SO_3(g) + 198 \text{ kJ/mol}$$

(a) In which direction will the system shift in response to the added SO_3?

(b) In which direction will the system shift in response to the small change in pressure resulting from the added SO_3?

(c) In which direction will the system shift in response to the small change in temperature resulting from the increased pressure?

(d) In which direction will the system shift in response to the change in temperature resulting from the system's shift to the added SO_3?

4 Acid-Base Equilibrium

By the end of this chapter, you should be able to do the following:

- Identify acids and bases through experimentation
- Identify various models for representing acids and bases
- Analyze balanced equations representing the reaction of acids or bases with water
- Classify an acid or base in solution as either weak or strong, with reference to its electrical conductivity
- Analyze the equilibria that exist in weak acid or weak base systems
- Identify chemical species that are amphiprotic
- Analyze the equilibrium that exists in water
- Perform calculations relating pH, pOH, [H_3O^+], and [OH^-]
- Explain the significance of the K_a and K_b equilibrium expressions
- Perform calculations involving K_a and K_b

By the end of this chapter, you should know the meaning of these **key terms**:

- acid
- acid ionization constant (K_a)
- amphiprotic
- Arrhenius
- base
- base ionization constant (K_b)
- Brønsted-Lowry
- conjugate acid-base pair
- electrical conductivity
- ion product constant
- mass action expression
- pH
- pK_w
- pOH
- polarized
- strong acid
- strong base
- water ionization constant (K_w)
- weak acid
- weak base

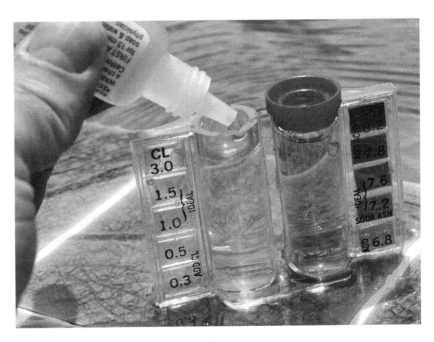

Testing swimming pool water involves acid-base interactions.

4.1 pH and pOH Review Questions

(Assume all solutions are at 25°C unless otherwise indicated.)

1. Define pH and pOH using a statement and an equation for each.

2. Why do we use Sorensen's pH and pOH scales to express hydronium and hydroxide concentrations in aqueous solutions?

3. Complete the following table, expressing each value to the proper number of significant figures.

$[H_3O^+]$	pH	Acidic/Basic/Neutral
3.50×10^{-6} M		
	11.51	
0.00550 M		
	0.00	
6.8×10^{-9} M		

4. Complete the following table, expressing each value to the proper number of significant figures.

$[OH^-]$	pOH	Acidic/Basic/Neutral
7.2×10^{-9} M		
	9.55	
4.88×10^{-4} M		
	14.00	
0.000625 M		

5. Complete the following statements:
   (a) As a solution's pOH value and $[H_3O^+]$ both decrease, the solution becomes more _____ (acidic or basic).

   (b) As a solution's pH value and $[OH^-]$ both decrease, the solution becomes more _____ (acidic or basic)

   (c) The _____ (sum or product) of the $[H_3O^+]$ and $[OH^-]$ equals K_w.

   (d) The _____ (sum or product) of pH and pOH equals pK_w.

© Edvantage Interactive 2016

6. Complete the following table, expressing each value to the proper number of significant figures.

[H$_3$O$^+$]	pOH	Acidic/Basic/Neutral
0.0342 M		
	8.400	
7.2 × 10^{-12} M		
	3.215	

7. For pure water at 60.0°C, the value of pK_w = 13.02. Calculate the pH at this temperature and decide if the water is acidic, basic, or neutral.

8. Calculate the pH of a 0.30 M solution of Sr(OH)$_2$.

9. A 2.00 g sample of pure NaOH is dissolved in water to produce 500.0 mL of solution. Calculate the pH of this solution.

10. A sample of HI is dissolved in water to make 2.0 L of solution. The pH of this solution is found to be 2.50. Calculate the mass of HI dissolved in this solution.

11. Complete the following table, expressing each value to the proper number of significant figures.

[H$_3$O$^+$]	[OH$^-$]	pOH	pH	Acidic/Basic/Neutral
5.620 × 10^{-5} M				
	0.000450 M			
		12.50		
			10.5	

12. Calculate the pH resulting from mixing 75.0 mL of 0.50 M HNO_3 with 125.0 mL of a solution containing 0.20 g NaOH.

13. Calculate the pH of the solution that results from mixing 200.0 mL of a solution with a pH of 1.50 with 300.0 mL of a solution having a pOH of 1.50.

14. Calculate the pH of a solution that is produced when 3.2 g of HI is added to 500.0 mL of a solution having a pH of 13.00. Assume no volume change.

15. The following three solutions are mixed together:
    25.0 mL of 0.20 M HCl + 35.0 mL of 0.15 M HNO_3 + 40.0 mL of 0.30 M NaOH
    Calculate the pH of the final solution.

16. What mass of HCl should be added to 450.0 mL of 0.0350 M KOH to produce a solution with a pH of 11.750? (Assume no volume change.)

17. What mass of LiOH must be added to 500.0 mL of 0.0125 M HCl to produce a solution with a pH of 2.75? (Assume no volume change.)

© Edvantage Interactive 2016

4.2 The Ionization of Water

Warm Up

1. Describe the difference between a weak acid and a strong acid.

   _____

   _____

2. Compare the relative electrical conductivities of 1.0 M HCl, 1.0 M CH_3COOH, and distilled water. Explain your reasoning.

   _____

   _____

3. On your K_a table, find the equation for water acting as an acid and reproduce it here. Write the K_a expression for water.

The Ion-Product Constant of Water

Earlier in this course, you saw that water can act as either a Brønsted-Lowry weak acid or weak base. Water is amphiprotic and so can form both hydronium and hydroxide ions. In a Brønsted-Lowry equilibrium, we can see how one water molecule donates a proton to another water molecule (Figure 4.2.1). This is called **autoionization**.

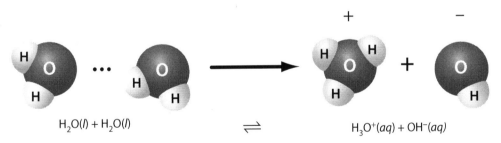

$$H_2O(l) + H_2O(l) \rightleftharpoons H_3O^+(aq) + OH^-(aq)$$

Figure 4.2.1 *Autoionization of water*

As with any equilibrium equation, we can write a corresponding equilibrium constant expression:

$$K_w = [H_3O^+][OH^-]$$

where K_w is the **water ionization constant** or **ion product constant**.

Remember that the value of an equilibrium constant depends on the temperature.

At 25°C, $K_w = 1.00 \times 10^{-14} = [H_3O^+][OH^-]$

From this information, we can calculate the $[H_3O^+]$ and $[OH^-]$ in water at 25°C. It is obvious from the equilibrium that the $[H_3O^+] = [OH^-]$ at any temperature. Because of this, water is neutral.

$$H_2O(l) + H_2O(l) \rightleftharpoons H_3O^+(aq) + OH^-(aq)$$
$$\qquad\qquad x \qquad\quad x$$

$$K_w = 1.00 \times 10^{-14} = [H_3O^+][OH^-]$$
$$= (x)(x) = x^2$$
$$x = 1.00 \times 10^{-7} \text{ M}$$
$$[H_3O^+] = [OH^-] = 1.0 \times 10^{-7} \text{ M}$$

Quick Check

1. The autoionization of water is endothermic. If the temperature of water is increased, what happens to the concentration of hydronium ion, hydroxide ion, and K_w?

    _____

    _____

2. At higher temperatures, how will the concentration of hydronium ion and hydroxide ion compare to each other?

    _____

    _____

3. At 10°C, $K_w = 2.9 \times 10^{-15}$. Calculate $[H_3O^+]$ and $[OH^-]$ in water at this temperature.

Adding Acid or Base to Water

When we add an acid or base to water, we cause the equilibrium present in water to shift in response. In 1.0 M HCl, HCl, which is a strong acid, thus ionizes 100% to produce 1.0 M H_3O^+ and 1.0 M Cl^- ions:

$$HCl(aq) + H_2O(l) \rightarrow H_3O^+(aq) + Cl^-(aq)$$
$$\qquad\qquad\qquad\quad 1.0 \text{ M} \qquad 1.0 \text{ M}$$

The added hydronium ions cause the water equilibrium to shift left and the concentration of hydroxide to decrease.

Likewise, when a strong base dissolves in water, the added hydroxide ions cause a shift left, and a corresponding hydronium ion concentration to decrease.

An increase in $[H_3O^+]$ causes a decrease in $[OH^-]$, and vise versa. The $[H_3O^+]$ is inversely proportional to $[OH^-]$.

Both H_3O^+ and OH^- ions exist in all aqueous solutions:
*   If $[H_3O^+] > [OH^-]$, the solution is acidic.
*   If $[H_3O^+] = [OH^-]$, the solution is neutral.
*   If $[H_3O^+] < [OH^-]$, the solution is basic.

© Edvantage Interactive 2016

Sample Problem — Calculating [H₃O⁺] and [OH⁻] in Solutions of a Strong Acid or Strong Base

What is the $[H_3O^+]$ and $[OH^-]$ in 0.50 M HCl? Justify that the solution is acidic.

What to Think About	How to Do It
1. HCl is a strong acid and so will ionize 100%. Thus $[HCl] = [H_3O^+]$.	$[H_3O^+] = 0.50\ M$
2. The temperature is not specified. Assume 25°C.	$K_w = 1.00 \times 10^{-14} = [H_3O^+][OH^-]$
3. Substitute into K_w and solve for $[OH^-]$.	$1.00 \times 10^{-14} = (0.50\ M)[OH^-]$ $[OH^-] = 2.0 \times 10^{-14}\ M$ Because the $[H_3O^+] > [OH^-]$, the solution is acidic.

Practice Problems — Calculating [H₃O⁺] and [OH⁻] in Solutions of a Strong Acid or Strong Base (Assume the temperature in each case is 25°C.)

1. Calculate the $[H_3O^+]$ and $[OH^-]$ in 0.15 M $HClO_4$. Justify that this solution is acidic.

2. Calculate the $[H_3O^+]$ and $[OH^-]$ in a saturated solution of magnesium hydroxide. (Hint: this salt has low solubility, but is a strong base.)

3. A student dissolved 1.42 g of NaOH in 250. mL of solution. Calculate the resulting $[H_3O^+]$ and $[OH^-]$. Justify that this solution is basic.

Mixing Solutions of Strong Acids and Bases

When we react strong acids with strong bases, we need to consider two factors: solutions will dilute each other when mixed, and then acids will neutralize bases. The resulting solution will be acidic, basic, or neutral depending on whether more acid or base is present after neutralization.

Sample Problem — What Happens When a Strong Acid Is Added to a Strong Base?

What is the final $[H_3O^+]$ in a solution formed when 25 mL of 0.30 M HCl is added to 35 mL of 0.50 M NaOH?

What to Think About	How to Do It
1. When two solutions are combined, both are diluted. Calculate the new concentrations of HCl and NaOH in the mixed solution.	HCl is a strong acid, so $[HCl] = [H_3O^+]$ NaOH is a strong base, so $[NaOH] = [OH^-]$ $[HCl] = \dfrac{0.30 \text{ mol}}{\cancel{L}} \times \dfrac{0.025 \cancel{L}}{0.060 \text{ L}} = 0.125 \text{ M}$ $[NaOH] = \dfrac{0.50 \text{ mol}}{\cancel{L}} \times \dfrac{0.035 \cancel{L}}{0.060 \text{ L}} = 0.292 \text{ M}$
2. The hydronium ions and hydroxide ions will neutralize each other. Since there is more hydroxide, there will be hydroxide left over. Calculate how much will be left over.	$[H_3O^+]_{initial} = 0.125 \text{ M}$ $[OH^-]_{initial} = 0.292 \text{ M}$ $[OH^-]_{excess} = [OH^-]_{initial} - [H_3O^+]_{initial}$ $= 0.292 \text{ M} - 0.125 \text{ M}$ $= 0.167 \text{ M} = 0.17 \text{ M}$
3. Use K_w to calculate the hydronium ion concentration from the hydroxide ion concentration.	$K_w = [H_3O^+][OH^-]$ $1.00 \times 10^{-14} = [H_3O^+](0.17 \text{ M})$ $[H_3O^+] = 6.0 \times 10^{-14} \text{ M}$

Practice Problems — What Happens When a Strong Acid Is Added to a Strong Base?

1. Calculate the final $[H_3O^+]$ and $[OH^-]$ in a solution formed when 150. mL of 1.5 M HNO_3 is added to 250. mL of 0.80 M KOH.

2. Calculate the mass of solid NaOH that must be added to 500. mL of 0.20 M HI to result in a solution with $[H_3O^+] = 0.12$ M. Assume no volume change on the addition of solid NaOH.

3. Calculate the resulting $[H_3O^+]$ and $[OH^-]$ when 18.4 mL of 0.105 M HBr is added to 22.3 mL of 0.256 M HCl.

© Edvantage Interactive 2016

4.2 Activity: Counting Water Molecules and Hydronium Ions

Question
How many water molecules does it take to produce one hydronium ion?

Procedure
1. Calculate the number of water molecules present in 1.0 L of water using the density of water (1.00 g/mL) and its molar mass.
2. Calculate the number of hydronium ions in 1.0 L of water. (Hint: You need the $[H_3O^+]$ in pure water from step 1.)
3. Using the above answers, calculate the ratio of ions/molecules. This is the percentage ionization of water.
4. Using the ratio above, calculate the number of water molecules required to produce one hydronium ion.

Results and Discussion
1. From the ratio of ions to molecules, it is evident that an extremely small percentage of water molecules actually ionize. Because there are an enormously large number of molecules present in the solutions we use, a reasonable number of hydronium and hydroxide ions are present. What volume of water contains only one hydronium ion?

4.2 Review Questions

1. In its pure liquid form, ammonia (NH_3) undergoes autoionization. Write an equation to show how ammonia autoionizes.

2. Complete the following table:

[H₃O⁺]	[OH⁻]	Acidic, Basic, or Neutral?
	6.0 M	
3.2×10^{-4} M		
	9.2×10^{-12} M	
2.5 M		
	4.7×10^{-5} M	

3. The autoionization of water has $\Delta H = 57.1$ kJ/mol. Write the equation for the autoionization of water including the energy term. Explain how the value of K_w changes with temperature.

4. The K_w for water at 1°C is 1.0×10^{-15}. Calculate the [H₃O⁺] and [OH⁻] in 0.20 M HI at this temperature.

5. Human urine has a [H₃O⁺] = 6.3×10^{-7} M. What is the [OH⁻], and is urine acidic, basic, or neutral?

6. Complete the table:

Temperature	K_w	[H₃O⁺]	[OH⁻]	Acidic, Basic, or Neutral?
50° C	5.5×10^{-14}			
100° C	5.1×10^{-13}			

© Edvantage Interactive 2016

7. Heavy water (D_2O) is used in CANDU reactors as a moderator. In heavy water, the hydrogen atoms are H-2 called *deuterium* and symbolized as D. In a sample of heavy water at 50°C, $[OD^-] = 8.9 \times 10^{-8}$ M. Calculate K_w for heavy water.

8. Calculate the $[H_3O^+]$ and $[OH^-]$ in a saturated solution of calcium hydroxide. ($K_{sp} = 4.7 \times 10^{-6}$)

9. A student combines the following solutions:
    Calculate the $[H_3O^+]$ and $[OH^-]$ in the resulting solution.

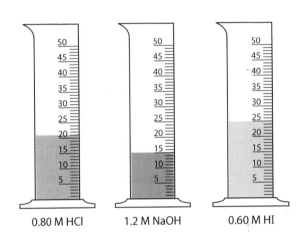

0.80 M HCl   1.2 M NaOH   0.60 M HI

10. What mass of strontium hydroxide must be added to 150. mL of 0.250 M nitric acid to produce a solution with $[OH^-] = 0.010$ M?

4.3 Identifying Acids and Bases

Warm Up

A student tested a number of unknown solutions and recorded the following observations. Based on each observation, place a check mark in the corresponding column that identifies the unknown solution as containing an acid, a base, or either one.

Observation	Acid	Base
Turns phenolphthalein pink		
Feels slippery		
Has pH = 5.0		
Tastes sour		
Conducts electricity		
Reacts with metal to produce a gas		

The Arrhenius Theory of Acids and Bases

In previous courses, you learned how to identify an acid or base using a concept developed by a chemist named Svante Arrhenius. According to the Arrhenius theory, acids release H^+ ions in solution, and bases release OH^- ions.

Typically, when an Arrhenius acid and base react together, a salt and water form. A salt is an ionic compound that does not contain H^+ or OH^- ions. The cation from the base and the anion from the acid make up the salt.

$$\text{Example: } HCl(aq) + NaOH(aq) \rightarrow NaCl(aq) + H_2O(l)$$
$$\text{acid} \qquad \text{base} \qquad \text{salt} \qquad \text{water}$$

Sample Problem — Identifying Arrhenius Acids and Bases

Classify each of the following substances as an Arrhenius acid, an Arrhenius base, a salt or a molecular compound.
(a) HNO_3
(b) $Al(OH)_3$
(c) $Al(NO_3)_3$
(d) NO_2

What to Think About	How to Do It
(a) An acid releases H^+ ions.	HNO_3 is an acid.
(b) A base releases OH^- ions.	$Al(OH)_3$ is a base.
(c) A salt is an ionic compound not containing H^+ or OH^- ions.	$Al(NO_3)_3$ is a salt.
(d) A molecule is not made up of ions.	NO_2 is a molecular compound.

© Edvantage Interactive 2016

Practice Problems — Identifying Arrhenius Acids and Bases

1. Classify each of the following as an Arrhenius acid, an Arrhenius base, a salt, or a molecular compound.

   (a) H_2SO_4 _____

   (b) XeF_6 _____

   (c) CH_3COOH _____

   (d) $NaCH_3COO$ _____

   (e) KOH _____

   (f) NH_3 _____

2. Complete the following neutralization equations. Make sure each equation is balanced, and circle the salt produced.

   (a) $CH_3COOH + LiOH \rightarrow$

   (b) $HI + Ca(OH)_2 \rightarrow$

   (c) $Mg(OH)_2 + H_3PO_4 \rightarrow$

3. Write the formula of the parent acid and the parent base that react to form each salt listed.

   Parent Acid   **Parent Base**

   (a) KNO_2

   (b) NH_4Cl

   (c) CuC_2O_4

   (d) $NaCH_3COO$

Brønsted-Lowry Acids and Bases

Arrhenius' definition worked well to classify a number of substances that displayed acidic or basic characteristics. However, some substances that acted like acids or bases could not be classified using this definition. A broader definition of acids and bases was required.

In the practice problem above, you may have classified NH_3 as molecular. While it is molecular, a solution of NH_3 also feels slippery, has a pH greater than 7, and turns phenolphthalein pink. It clearly has basic characteristics, but it is not an Arrhenius base.

Chemists Johannes Brønsted and Thomas Lowry suggested a broader definition of acids and bases:

> **Brønsted-Lowry acid** — a substance or species that donates a hydrogen ion, H^+ (a proton)
> **Brønsted-Lowry base** — a substance or species that accepts a hydrogen ion, H^+

Consider the reaction that occurs in aqueous HCl:

$$HCl(aq) + H_2O(l) \rightarrow H_3O^+(aq) + Cl^-(aq)$$
acid   base   hydronium

In this example, the HCl donates a hydrogen ion (H^+) to the water molecule. The HCl is therefore acting as a Brønsted-Lowry acid. The water accepts the H^+ ion so it is acting as a Brønsted-Lowry base.

The H_3O^+ ion is called a **hydronium ion**. It is simply a water molecule with an extra H^+ ion (Figure 4.3.1). It is also called a protonated water molecule.

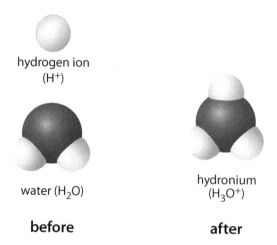

hydrogen ion
(H^+)

water (H_2O)

hydronium
(H_3O^+)

before

after

Figure 4.3.1 *A hydronium ion is a water molecule with an extra H+ ion.*

Let's look at NH_3 now. In a solution of ammonia (NH_3) the following reaction occurs:

$$NH_3(aq) + H_2O(l) \rightleftharpoons NH_4^+(aq) + OH^-(aq)$$
$\quad$ base $\qquad$ acid

The ammonia molecule accepted a H^+ ion from the water, so NH_3 is acting as a Brønsted-Lowry base, and water is acting as a Brønsted-Lowry acid.

You may notice that in the equation for HCl, a one-way arrow was used, but in the equation for NH_3, an equilibrium arrow was used. The reasons for this will be explained in the next section. Just remember that if you see an equilibrium arrow, then equilibrium is established. More importantly, in an equilibrium, you have both reactants and products present in the system. Both forward and reverse reactions occur. If we look at the reverse reaction for the ammonia system, we can identify Brønsted-Lowry acids and bases:

$$NH_3(aq) + H_2O(l) \rightleftharpoons NH_4^+(aq) + OH^-(aq)$$
$\quad$ base $\qquad$ acid $\qquad\quad$ acid $\qquad$ base

In the reverse reaction, the NH_4^+ ion donates a proton to the OH^- ion. According to Brønsted-Lowry definitions, the NH_4^+ ion is acting as an acid, and the OH^- ion is acting as a base.

In a Brønsted-Lowry equilibrium, there are two acids and two bases: one for the forward reaction, and one for the reverse reaction. An acid and a base react to form a different acid and base.

Two substances that differ by one H^+ ion are called a **conjugate acid-base pair.**

In the example above, the NH_3 and NH_4^+ together form one conjugate acid-base pair, and the H_2O and OH^- form the other conjugate acid-base pair.

© Edvantage Interactive 2016

Sample Problems — Identifying Conjugate Acid-Base Pairs

1. In the following equilibrium, identify the acids and bases, and the two conjugate acid-base pairs:

$$HF(aq) + CN^-(aq) \rightleftharpoons HCN(aq) + F^-(aq)$$

2. Complete the following table:

Conjugate Acid	Conjugate Base
$H_2C_2O_4$	
	SO_3^{2-}
HCO_3^-	
	H_2O

3. Complete the following equilibrium, which represents the reaction of a Brønsted-Lowry acid and base. Circle the substances that make up one of the conjugate acid-base pairs.

$$NO_2^-(aq) + H_2CO_3(aq) \rightleftharpoons$$

What to Think About

1. An acid donates a proton and a base accepts a proton.

   In the forward reaction, the HF is the acid and the CN– is the base. In the reverse reaction, the HCN is the acid and the F– is the base.

   The substances in a conjugate acid-base pair differ by one H^+ ion.

2. An acid donates a proton. Find the conjugate base of an acid by removing one H^+. Be careful of your charges on the ions! A base accepts a proton. Find the conjugate acid of a given base by adding one H^+.

3. An acid must be able to donate a H^+ ion. Only the H_2CO_3 has a H^+ to donate. When it donates a H^+ ion, HCO_3^- forms. The NO_2^- ion is forced to accept the H^+, making the NO_2^- a base. When the NO_2^- accepts a proton, it forms HNO_2. The total charge on the reactant side should equal the total charge on the product side. Balance reactions for both.

Note: H_2CO_3 only donates ONE H^+ ion. Substances in a conjugate acid-base pair differ by only ONE H^+ ion. Balance both sides of the equation for number of atoms and charge.

How to Do It

The two conjugate acid-base pairs are: HF/F^- and CN^-/HCN.

$$HF(aq) + CN^-(aq) \rightleftharpoons HCN(aq) + F^-(aq)$$
$$\text{acid} \qquad \text{base} \qquad \text{acid} \qquad \text{base}$$

Conjugate acid   Conjugate base

$H_2C_2O_4$	→ remove H^+	$HC_2O_4^-$
HSO_3^-	← add H^+	SO_3^{2-}
HCO_3^-	→ remove H^+	CO_3^{2-}
H_3O^+	← add H^+	H_2O

$$NO_2^-(aq) + H_2CO_3(aq) \rightleftharpoons$$
$$HNO_2(aq) + HCO_3^-(aq)$$

Circle around either of the following:
NO_2^-/HNO_2 or H_2CO_3/HCO_3^-

Practice Problems — Identifying Conjugate Acid-Base Pairs

1. For the following equilibria, label the acids and bases for the forward and reverse reactions.

   (a) $HIO_3 + NO_2^- \rightleftharpoons HNO_2 + IO_3^-$

   (b) $HF + HC_2O_4^- \rightleftharpoons H_2C_2O_4 + F^-$

   (c) $Al(H_2O)_6^{3+} + SO_3^{2-} \rightleftharpoons HSO_3^- + Al(H_2O)_5OH^{2+}$

2. Complete the following table:

Conjugate Acid	Conjugate Base
H_2O_2	
	$H_2BO_3^-$
HCOOH	
	$C_6H_5O_7^{3-}$

3. Complete the following equilibria. Label the acids and bases for the forward and reverse reactions. Circle one conjugate acid-base pair in each equilibria.

   (a) $HNO_2 + NH_3 \rightleftharpoons$

   (b) $H_3C_6H_5O_7 + CN^- \rightleftharpoons$

   (c) $PO_4^{3-} + H_2S \rightleftharpoons$

Amphiprotic Species

Consider the two equilibria below:

$$NH_3(aq) + H_2O(l) \rightleftharpoons NH_4^+(aq) + OH^-(aq) \qquad HF(aq) + H_2O(l) \rightleftharpoons H_3O^+(aq) + F^-(aq)$$
$$\text{acid} \qquad\qquad\qquad\qquad\qquad\qquad\qquad \text{base}$$

In the first reaction, water acts as a Brønsted-Lowry acid. In the second reaction, water acts as a Brønsted-Lowry base. An **amphiprotic** species has the ability to act as an acid or a base, depending on what it is reacting with. Water is a common amphiprotic substance. Many anions also display amphiprotic tendencies. For a species to be amphiprotic, it must have a proton to donate and be able to accept a proton. Examples of amphiprotic anions include HCO_3^-, $HC_2O_4^-$, and $H_2PO_4^-$. Uncharged species, with the exception of water, are generally not amphiprotic. For example, HCl will donate one H^+ ion (proton) to form Cl^-, but will not accept a proton to form H_2Cl^+. You should recognize many of the species that form.

Quick Check

1. Write an equation for a reaction between HCO_3^- and CN^- where HCO_3^- acts as an acid.

2. Write an equation for a reaction between HCO_3^- and H_2O where HCO_3^- acts as a base.

3. Circle amphiprotic species in the following list:

   (a) CH_3COOH (b) $H_2PO_4^-$ (c) PO_4^{3-} (d) $H_2C_2O_4$ (e) $HC_2O_4^-$

© Edvantage Interactive 2016

4.3 Activity: Conjugate Pairs Memory Game

Question
How many conjugate acid-base pairs can you identify?

Materials
- grid of conjugate pairs, cut into cards
- scissors

Procedure
1. Go to edvantagescience.com for a page of symbols and formulae.
2. Cut along the grid lines to make a set of cards. Each card will have one symbol or formula on it.
3. Place the cards face down on the table in a 6×6 grid.
4. Play in groups of two or three. The first player turns over two cards. If the two substances are a conjugate acid-base pair, the player keeps the two cards and gets one more turn. If they are not a conjugate acid-base pair, the player turns the cards face down again after everyone has seen them.
5. The next player turns over two cards, again looking for a conjugate pair.
6. The play continues until all conjugate acid-base pair cards are collected. The winner is the player with the most cards.

Results and Discussion
1. Define an acid-base conjugate pair.

2. Explain why H_2SO_3 and SO_3^{2-} are not a conjugate pair.

4.3 Review Questions

1. How are the Arrhenius and Brønsted-Lowry definitions of an acid and base similar? How are they different? Use examples.

2. Explain why the H^+ ion is the same as a proton.

3. A hydronium ion is formed when water accepts a proton. Draw a Lewis structure for water, and explain why water will accept a proton. Draw the Lewis structure for a hydronium ion.

4. In the following equations, identify the acids and bases in the forward and reverse reactions. Identify the conjugate acid-base pairs.

   (a) $NH_3 + H_3PO_4 \rightleftharpoons NH_4^+ + H_2PO_4^-$

   (b) $H_2PO_4^- + SO_3^{2-} \rightleftharpoons HSO_3^- + HPO_4^{2-}$

   (c) $CH_3NH_2 + CH_3COOH \rightleftharpoons CH_3COO^- + CH_3NH_3^+$

5. Formic acid, HCOOH, is the substance responsible for the sting in ant bites. Write an equation showing it acting as an acid when reacted with water. Label the acids and bases in the forward and reverse reactions. Identify the two conjugate acid-base pairs.

6. Pyridine, C_5H_5N, is a Brønsted-Lowry base. It is used in the production of many pharmaceuticals. Write an equation showing it acting as a base when reacted with water. Label the acids and bases in the forward and reverse reactions. Identify the two conjugate acid-base pairs.

© Edvantage Interactive 2016

7. Sodium hypochlorite solution is also known as bleach. It contains the hypochlorite ion ClO^-.
   (a) Write an equation for the reaction between hypochlorite ion and ammonium ion. Label the acids and bases in the forward and reverse reactions. Identify the two conjugate acid-base pairs.

   (b) This equilibrium favors the reactants. Which of the acids is stronger and donates protons more readily?

8. (a) Explain how to write the formula for the conjugate acid of a given base. Use an example.

   (b) Explain how to write the formula for the conjugate base of a given acid. Use an example.

9. (a) Hydrogen peroxide, H_2O_2, is a Brønsted Lowry acid. It is used as an antiseptic and bleaching agent. Write the formula for the conjugate base of hydrogen peroxide.

   (b) Hydrazine, N_2H_4, is a Brønsted-Lowry base used as a rocket fuel. Write the formula for the conjugate acid of hydrazine.

   (c) Phenol, HOC_6H_5, is a Brønsted-Lowry acid used to make plastics, nylon, and slimicides. Write the formula for its conjugate base.

   (d) Aniline, $C_6H_5NH_2$, is a Brønsted-Lowry base used to make polyurethane. Write the formula for its conjugate acid.

10. Define the term *amphiprotic*. List four amphiprotic species.

11. Baking soda contains sodium bicarbonate.
    (a) Write two equations demonstrating the amphiprotic nature of the bicarbonate ion with water. Describe a test you could perform to identify which equilibrium is more likely to occur.

    (b) Bicarbonate produces CO_2 gas in the batter of cookies or cakes, which makes the batter rise as it bakes. Which of the two equations in (a) represents the action of bicarbonate ion in baking?

12. Water is amphiprotic. Write a reaction showing a water molecule acting as an acid reacting with a water molecule acting as a base. Label the acids and bases for the forward and reverse reactions. Identify the conjugate acid-base pairs.

© Edvantage Interactive 2016

4.4 The Strengths of Acids and Bases

Warm Up

Consider Figure 4.4.1, which shows electricity being conducted through two solutions of different acids.

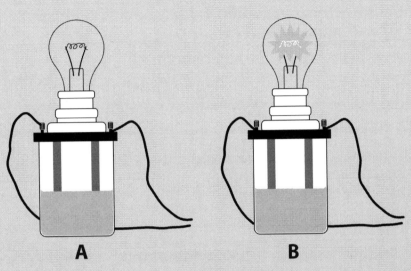

Figure 4.4.1 *Although these acids are the same concentration, they don't both conduct electricity.*

One of the solutions is 1.0 M hydrochloric acid and one is 1.0 M acetic acid. Hypothesize which beaker contains which acid, and write a paragraph that explains your reasoning.

_____

_____

_____

The Acid and Base Ionization Constant

Let's go back to our discussion of CH_3COOH. The equilibrium present is:

$$CH_3COOH(aq) + H_2O(l) \rightleftharpoons H_3O^+(aq) + CH_3COO^-(aq)$$

As with all equilibria, we can write a K_{eq} expression for acetic acid, which is customized for acids by calling it a K_a expression. The K_a is called the **acid ionization constant**.

$$K_a = \frac{[H_3O^+][CH_3COO^-]}{[CH_3COOH]}$$

Notice that we do not include the $[H_2O]$ in the K_a expression. As you learned earlier, the concentration of water does not change appreciably, so it is treated as part of the constant. For any weak acid in solution, we can write a general equation and K_a expression:

$$HA(aq) + H_2O(l) \rightleftharpoons H_3O^+(aq) + A^-(aq) \qquad K_a = \frac{[H_3O^+][A^-]}{[HA]}$$

In a weak acid solution of appreciable concentration, most of the acid molecules remain intact or un-ionized. Only a few ions are formed. Equal concentrations of different acids produce different H_3O^+ concentrations. The K_a values for weak acids are less than 1.0. The K_a corresponds to the percentage ionization. A greater K_a signifies a greater $[H_3O^+]$ in solution.

Likewise, a weak Brønsted-Lowry base such as ammonia establishes an equilibrium in solution:

$$NH_3(aq) + H_2O(l) \rightleftharpoons NH_4^+(aq) + OH^-(aq)$$

$$K_b = \frac{[NH_4^+][OH^-]}{[NH_3]}$$

where K_b is called the **base ionization constant**. Generally, for a molecule acting as a weak Brønsted-Lowry base in aqueous solution:

$$B(aq) + H_2O(l) \rightleftharpoons HB^+(aq) + OH^-(aq) \qquad K_b = \frac{[HB^+][OH^-]}{[B]}$$

Quick Check

1. HF is a weak acid. Write an equation showing how HF acts in solution; then write the K_a expression for HF.

2. Explain why we would not typically write a K_b expression for NaOH.

    _____

    _____

3. Ethylamine is a weak base with the formula $CH_3CH_2NH_2$. Write an equation showing how ethylamine acts in water, then write the K_b expression.

4. The hydrogen oxalate ion is amphiprotic. Write two equations, one showing how this ion acts as an acid and the other showing this ion acting as a base. Beside each equation, write its corresponding K_a or K_b expression.

Comparing Acid and Base Strengths

Recall that the larger the K_a or K_b, the greater the $[H_3O^+]$ or $[OH^-]$ respectively. To compare the relative strengths of weak acids and bases, we can use a Table of relative strengths of acids and bases.

As you look at the table, note the following points:

*   Acids are listed on the left of the table, and their conjugate bases are listed on the right.
*   The strong acids are the top six acids on the table. Their ionization equations include a one-way arrow signifying that they ionize 100%. Their K_a values are too large to be useful.

© Edvantage Interactive 2016

- The other acids between, and including, hydronium and water are weak. Their ionization equations include an equilibrium arrow and an associated K_a value.
- Even though OH$^-$ and NH$_3$ are listed on the left of the table, they do NOT act as acids in water. The reaction arrow does not go in the forward direction. They do NOT give up H$^+$ ions in water.
- There are two bold arrows along the sides of the table. On the left, acid strength increases going up the table. Notice that this arrow stops for OH$^-$ and NH$_3$ because they are not weak acids; they will not donate a hydrogen ion in water. On the right, base strength increases going down the table. This arrow stops for the conjugate bases of the strong monoprotic acids because these ions (Cl$^-$, Br$^-$, and so on) do not act as weak bases. They will not accept a hydrogen ion from water.
- The K_a values listed are for aqueous solutions at room temperature. Like any equilibrium constant, K_a and K_b values are temperature dependent.
- The table lists the K_a values for weak acids. You will learn how to calculate the K_b of a weak base in section 5.5. For now, you can rank the relative strength of a base from its position on this table. The lower a base is on the right side, the stronger it is. This means that the stronger an acid is, the weaker its conjugate base will be and vice versa. The more willing an acid is to donate a hydrogen ion, the more reluctant its conjugate base will be to take it back.
- Some ions appear on both sides of the table. They are amphiprotic and able to act as an acid or a base. One example of this is the bicarbonate ion, HCO$_3^-$.

Quick Check

1. Classify the following as a strong acid, strong base, weak acid, or weak base.

   (a) sulfuric acid   _____

   (b) calcium hydroxide   _____

   (c) ammonia   _____

   (d) benzoic acid   _____

   (e) cyanide ion   _____

   (f) nitrous acid   _____

2. For the weak acids or bases above, write an equation demonstrating their behavior in water and their corresponding K_a or K_b expression.

3. A student tests the electrical conductivity of 0.5 M solutions of the following: carbonic acid, methanoic acid, phenol, and boric acid. Rank these solutions in order from most conductive to least conductive.

   _____

   _____

Chapter 4 Acid-Base Equilibrium

Effects of Structure on Acid Strength

Strong acids ionize to produce more hydronium ions than weak acids when placed in water. That is, strong acids donate their hydrogen ions more readily. Why do some acids ionize more than others? To answer this question, we must examine an acid's structure. The structure of an acid influences how readily a hydrogen ion may leave the molecule (Figure 4.4.2).

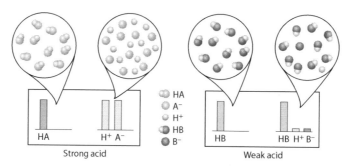

Figure 4.4.2 *Strong acids ionize completely in water. Weak acids ionize only partially. The weaker the acid, the lower the degree of ionization. In this representation, hydronium ion, H_3O^+ is simplified to H^+.*

Binary Acid Strength

The strength of a binary acid, HX depends primarily on the attraction between the nucleus of the hydrogen atom and the electrons that surround the atom X. There is also an attractive force between the electron of the hydrogen atom and the nucleus of X. As the size of X increases, the distance between the nucleus of one atom and the electrons of its neighbor increases. An increased distance results in a longer bond length, less bond strength, and a stronger acid. Binary acids of the halogen family provide a good illustration (Figure 4.4.3).

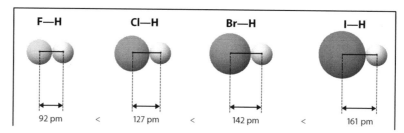

Figure 4.4.3 *Hydrofluoric acid is the weakest member of the hydrohalic acids due to the strong bond between hydrogen and fluorine. Binary acids of the halogen family increase in strength as the bond length increases—the longer the bond length, the more easily they can ionize.*

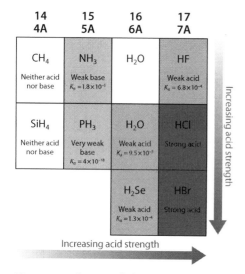

Figure 4.4.4 *In general, the acidity of binary acids increases as the non-metal attached to the hydrogen is further to the right in a period or closer to the bottom in a family of the periodic table.*

Binary acids containing more than one hydrogen atom are weaker than the hydrohalic acid in the same period (Figure 4.4.4). The presence of more hydrogen atoms bound to the central non-metal strengthens the H–X bonds in an H_nX molecule.

Acids weaker than water do not behave as acids in aqueous solution. Thus ammonia and methane are not commonly considered to be acids. Water is only treated as an acid in the context of aqueous solution chemistry.

© Edvantage Interactive 2016

Ternary Acid Strength

The strength of ternary or oxo-acids depends on two things:
1. the number of oxygen atoms, and
2. the electronegativity of the central non-metal atom

Ternary acids ionize more easily when the O–H bond is readily **polarized** (Figure 4.4.5). The bond is polarized when the pair of electrons shared between the oxygen and hydrogen atoms is drawn away from the hydrogen toward the center of the molecule. This occurs most readily when there are more oxygen atoms and the central non-metal atom is highly electronegative.

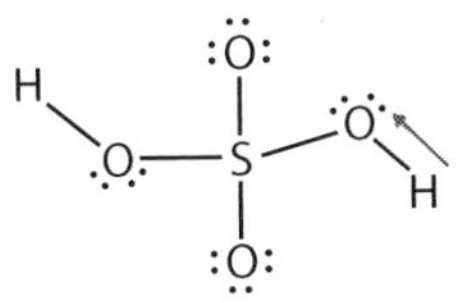

Figure 4.4.5 *Polarization of the O–H bond in an oxo-acid such as sulfuric acid (H_2SO_4) leads to increased strength*

Carboxylic Acids

The strength of carboxylic acids also depends on polarization of the O–H bond. The bond is more easily polarized if the carbon skeleton is shorter and if there are electronegative atoms attached to the carbon skeleton of the molecule (Figure 4.4.6).

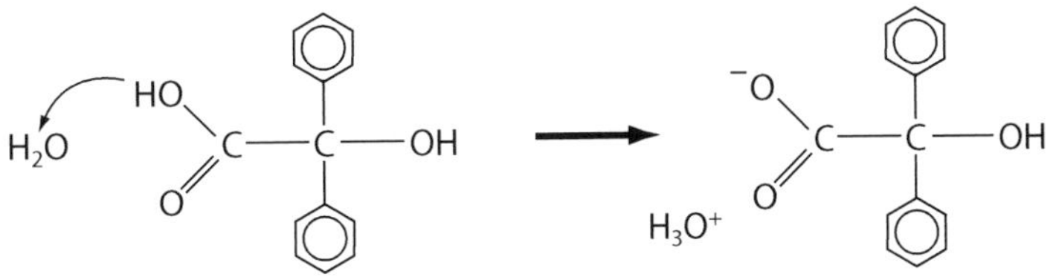

Figure 4.4.6 *The H atom from the carboxylic acid group (–COOH) on the left side of benzillic acid is the most ionizable H atom due to electron withdrawal by the extra oxygen double bonded to the carbon in the group. The electron withdrawal polarizes the H–O bond, causing the acid to ionize.*

Quick Check

1. Study the acids shown here. Which acid is stronger? Clearly explain your answer.

Acid 1

Acid 1

_____

_____

_____

_____

2. Study this table of binary acids. Rank the compounds below from strongest to weakest in terms of acid strength. Give a complete explanation of your reasoning.

Binary compound	Hydro-bromic acid (HBr)	Hydro-chloric acid (HCl)	Hydro-iodic acid (HI)	Hydro-selenic acid(H_2Se)	Hydro-sulfuric acid (H_2S)	Methane (CH_4)	Water (H_2O)
Lewis structure	H—Br:	H—Cl:	H—I:	Se (H, H)	S (H, H)	C (H, H, H, H)	O (H, H)

_____

_____

3. Study the ternary acids shown here. Rank the compounds below from weakest to strongest in terms of acid strength. Give a complete explanation of your reasoning.

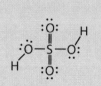

(H₂SO₄)   (HClO₃)   (HBrO₃)   (HClO₄)   (H₂SO₃)

_____

_____

_____

_____

4. Rank benzoic, ethanoic, and methanoic acids in terms of strength. Arrange the acids from greatest to least polarizable O–H bond.

The Position of Equilibrium and Relative Strengths

When a Brønsted-Lowry acid and base react, the position of the equilibrium results from the relative strengths of the acids and bases involved. If K_{eq} is greater than 1, products are favored. If K_{eq} is less than 1, reactants are favored. Acids that are stronger are more able to donate H^+ ions, so the position of the equilibrium is determined by the stronger acid and base reacting. Consider the reaction between ammonia and methanoic acid:

$$NH_3(aq) + HCOOH(aq) \rightleftharpoons NH_4^+(aq) + HCOO^-(aq)$$
$$\text{base} \qquad \text{acid} \qquad\qquad \text{acid} \qquad \text{base}$$

We can label the acids and bases for the forward and reverse reactions as above. The two acids are methanoic acid and the ammonium ion. According to the K_a table, methanoic acid is a stronger acid than the ammonium ion, so it donates H^+ ions more readily. Therefore, the forward reaction happens to a greater extent than the reverse reaction. Additionally, NH_3 is a stronger base than $HCOO^-$, so it accepts H^+ ions more readily. Therefore, the forward reaction proceeds to a greater extent than the reverse reaction, and products are favored at equilibrium.

Equilibrium favors the reaction in the direction of the stronger acid and base forming the weaker acid and base.

Sample Problem — Predicting Whether Reactants or Products Will Be Favored in a Brønsted-Lowry Acid-Base Equilibrium

Predict whether reactants or products will be favored when HCN reacts with HCO_3^-.

What to Think About	How to Do It
1. Recognize that both HCN and HCO_3^- can act as weak acids, but only HCO_3^- can act as a weak base. This means that HCN will be the acid, and HCO_3^- will be the base. The acid donates a H^+ ion and the base accepts the H^+ ion. We can complete the equilibrium.	$HCN + HCO_3^- \rightleftharpoons CN^- + H_2CO_3$
2. The acid in the forward reaction is HCN, and the acid in the reverse reaction is H_2CO_3.	$acid + base \rightleftharpoons base + acid$
3. According to the K_a table, H_2CO_3 is a stronger acid than HCN. H_2CO_3 will donate H^+ ions more readily than HCN. It is evident from the table that CN^- is a stronger base than HCO_3^-. The stronger acid and base will always appear on the same side of an equilibrium.	$weaker\ acid + weaker\ base \rightleftharpoons$ $stronger\ acid + stronger\ base$
4. The equilibrium favors the direction in which the stronger acid and base react to form the weaker conjugate acid and base.	The reverse reaction is favored, so reactants are favored at equilibrium.

Consider the reaction between HSO_4^- and $HC_2O_4^-$. Both of these species are amphiprotic. If two amphiprotic species react, then the stronger acid of the two will donate the H^+ ion, unless one of the species is water. When an amphiprotic species reacts with water, the reaction that occurs to a greater extent is determined by comparing the K_a to the K_b of the amphiprotic species.

Sample Problem — Predicting Whether Reactants or Products Will Be Favored in a Brønsted-Lowry Acid-Base Equilibrium

Predict whether reactants or products will be favored when HSO_4^- reacts with $HC_2O_4^-$.

What to Think About	How to Do It
1. Both substances are amphiprotic. Since HSO_4^- is a stronger acid than $HC_2O_4^-$, the HSO_4^- acts as the acid and donates a H^+ ion to $HC_2O_4^-$.	$HSO_4^- + HC_2O_4^- \rightleftharpoons SO_4^{2-} + H_2C_2O_4$
2. The acid in the forward reaction is HSO_4^-, and the acid in the reverse reaction is $H_2C_2O_4$.	$acid + base \rightleftharpoons base + acid$
3. According to the K_a table, $H_2C_2O_4$ is a stronger acid than HSO_4^-. $H_2C_2O_4$ will donate H^+ ions more readily than HSO_4^-. It is evident from the table that SO_4^{2-} is a stronger base than $HC_2O_4^-$. The stronger acid and base will always appear on the same side of an equilibrium.	$weaker\ acid + weaker\ base \rightleftharpoons$ $stronger\ acid + stonger\ base$
4. The equilibrium favors the direction in which the stronger acid and base react to form the weaker conjugate acid and base.	Reverse reaction favored, so reactants are favored at equilibrium.

Practice Problems — Predicting Whether Reactants or Products Will Be Favored in a Brønsted-Lowry Acid-Base Equilibrium

1. For the following, complete the equilibrium and predict whether reactants or products are favored at equilibrium.

    (a) hydrogen peroxide + hydrogen sulfite ion $\rightleftharpoons$

    (b) citric acid + ammonia $\rightleftharpoons$

    (c) hydrogen carbonate ion + dihydrogen phosphate ion $\rightleftharpoons$

2. Arsenic acid (H_3AsO_4) reacts with an equal concentration of sulfate ion. At equilibrium, $[H_3AsO_4] > [HSO_4^-]$. Write the equation for this reaction and state which acid is the stronger one.

3. Consider the reaction between the sulfite ion and the hexaaquochromium ion. Write the equation for this reaction, and predict whether K_{eq} is greater or less than 1.

The Levelling Effect

According to the K_a table, all strong acids in water are equally strong. Remember that "strong" means that it ionizes 100%. When each of the strong acids ionizes in water, hydronium ions form:

$$HCl(aq) + H_2O(l) \rightarrow H_3O^+(aq) + Cl^-(aq)$$

$$HBr(aq) + H_2O(l) \rightarrow H_3O^+(aq) + Br^-(aq)$$

Therefore, in a solution of a strong acid, no molecules of the strong acid remain — only the anion and hydronium ion are left. In the same manner, all strong bases dissociate completely to form OH^- ions.

In aqueous solution, the strongest acid actually present is H_3O^+ and the strongest base actually present is OH^-. Water levels the strength of strong acids and bases.

All strong acids in aqueous solution have equal ability to donate a H^+ ion to form H_3O^+. This is analogous to your chemistry teacher and a football player being able to lift a 5 kg weight. Both are able to lift the weight easily, so there is no observed difference in their strengths. Increasing the difficulty of the task (by increasing the amount of weight) would allow us to observe a difference in strength. Likewise, HCl and HI have no observable difference in strength when reacting with water, but when reacting with pure CH_3COOH, their different strengths become apparent.

4.4 Activity: Determining the Relative Strengths of Six Acids

Question

You are given six unknown weak acid solutions of the same concentration. The three weak acid indicators (HIn) are first mixed with HCl and NaOH. Can you build a table of relative acid strengths for six unknown solutions?

Procedure

1. Consider the following data collected when the indicated solutions are mixed:

	HIn_1/In_1^-	HIn_2/In_2^-	HIn_3/In_3^-
HCl	red	yellow	colorless
NaOH	yellow	red	purple
HA_1/A_1^-	red	yellow	purple
HA_2/A_2^-	red	yellow	colorless
HA_3/A_3^-	yellow	yellow	purple

2. There are six unknown weak acid solutions containing a conjugate acid-base pair. Three of the acids are HA_1, HA_2, and HA_3. The other three acids are chemical indicators HIn_1, HIn_2, and HIn_3. A chemical indicator is a weak acid in which its conjugate acid has a different color than its conjugate base. In the indicator solution, both the acid form (HIn) and the base form (In^-) exist in equilibrium.

3. When indicator 1 (HIn_1) is mixed with HCl, the HCl will donate a H^+ ion because it is a strong acid. If HCl acts as an acid, then it will donate a H^+ ion to the base form of the indicator:

   $$HCl + In_1^- \rightarrow HIn_1 + Cl^-$$

   According to the data in step 1, indicator 1 turns red in HCl. Therefore, HIn must be red. Likewise, In^- must be yellow because the OH^- in NaOH accepts a H^+ ion from HIn to form In^-. We know then that HIn = red and In^- = yellow.

4. When we mix unknown acid 1 (HA_1) with indicator 1 (HIn_1) we see red. The equilibrium established may be written as:

   $$HA_1 + In_1^- \rightleftharpoons HIn_1 + A_1^-$$

   $\quad\quad$ yellow $\quad\quad$ red

   Knowing that HIn_1 is red, we conclude that products are favored in this equilibrium. Therefore, HA_1 is a stronger acid than HIn_1.

5. Fill in the table below by comparing the strength of each pair of acids HA to HIn. The first one has been filled in for you from the discussion above.

	HIn_1/In_1^-	HIn_2/In_2^-	HIn_3/In_3^-
HA_1/A_1^-	$HA_1 > HIn_1$		
HA_2/A_2^-			
HA_3/A_3^-			

Results and Discussion

1. Rank the six unknown acids in order from strongest to weakest:

   _____ > _____ > _____ > _____ > _____ > _____

2. Construct a table similar to a table of Relative Strengths of Brønsted-Lowry Acids and Bases using the six unknown acids. Be sure to include ionization equations and arrows on each side of the table labelled: "Increasing strength of acid" and "Increasing strength of base."

4.4 Review Questions

1. Classify the following as strong or weak acids or bases.
   (a) sodium oxide — used in glass making

   (b) boric acid — used to manufacture fiberglass, antiseptics, and insecticides

   (c) perchloric acid — used to make ammonium perchlorate for rocket fuel

   (d) phosphate ion — present in the cleaner TSP (trisodium phosphate)

2. For any of the substances above that are weak, write an equation showing how they react in water, then write its corresponding K_a or K_b expression.

3. A student tests the electrical conductivity of a 2.0 M oxalic acid solution and compares it to the conductivity of 2.0 M hydroiodic acid. Explain how the hydroiodic acid could have a greater conductivity than the oxalic acid.

4. Calculate the total ion concentration in a solution of 2.0 M nitric acid. Explain why you cannot use this method to calculate the concentration of ions in 2.0 M nitrous acid.

5. Give an example of a
   (a) concentrated weak base

   (b) dilute strong acid

6. (a) Rank the following 0.1 M solutions in order from least electrical conductivity to greatest electrical conductivity: carbonic acid, citric acid, sulfuric acid, sulfurous acid, and water.

    (b) Rank the following bases in order from strongest to weakest: monohydrogen phosphate ion, carbonate ion, fluoride ion, ammonia, nitrite ion, and water.

7. Write the equation for the reaction of each of the following acids in water and its corresponding K_a expression:
    (a) monohydrogen citrate ion

    (b) dihydrogen citrate ion

    (c) aluminum ion

    (d) hydrogen peroxide

8. Write the equation for the reaction of each of the following bases in water and its corresponding K_b expression:
    (a) ammonia

    (b) benzoate ion

    (c) acetate ion

    (d) monohydrogen citrate ion

    (e) pyradine (C_5H_5N).

© Edvantage Interactive 2016

9. For the following, complete the equilibria, then state whether reactants or products are favored.

(a)

$$Fe(H_2O)_6^{3+}(aq) + HO_2^-(aq) \rightleftharpoons$$

(b)

$$H_2SO_3(aq) + IO_3^-(aq) \rightleftharpoons$$

(c)

$$CN^-(aq) + H_2PO_4^-(aq) \rightleftharpoons$$

10. Using the substances H_2CO_3, HCO_3^-, $H_2C_2O_4$ and $HC_2O_4^-$, write an equilibrium equation with a $K_{eq} > 1$.

11. Consider the following equilibria:

$$H_2SiO_3 + BrO^- \rightleftharpoons HBrO + HSiO_3^- \quad K_{eq} = 0.095$$

$$HClO + BrO^- \rightleftharpoons HBrO + ClO^- \quad K_{eq} = 14$$

Rank the acids H_2SiO_3, $HClO$, and $HBrO$ from strongest to weakest.

12. Explain why HCl, HBr, and HI are equally strong in water. Use balanced chemical equations in your answer.

4.5 Calculations Involving K_a and K_b

Warm Up

Three of the binary acids containing halogens (hydrohalic acids) are strong acids, while one of them is a weak acid.

1. (a) Write a chemical equation representing the reaction of hydrochloric acid with water and identify the two conjugate acid-base pairs.

   (b) If the concentration of this *strong* acid solution is 0.50 M, what would you expect the $[H_3O^+]$ and the pH of the solution to be?

2. (a) Write a chemical equation representing the reaction of hydrofluoric acid with water and identify the two conjugate acid-base pairs. Which side of this equilibrium is favored?

   (b) If the concentration of this *weak* acid solution is also 0.50 M, would you expect the pH of this solution to be the same as for 0.50 M HCl? Why or why not?

3. Write K_a or K_b expressions for the following species in aqueous solutions:

   (a)

   K_a for $HNO_2 =$

   (b)

   K_b for $C_2O_4^{2-} =$

   (c)

   K_a for $HC_2O_4^- =$

   (d)

   K_b for $NH_3 =$

Part A: Calculations for Weak Acids

Most of the substances that we identify as acids ionize only to a slight extent in water and are therefore considered to be weak acids. As you learned earlier, the following equilibrium exists in an aqueous solution of a weak acid HA:

$$HA(aq) + H_2O(l) \rightleftharpoons A^-(aq) + H_3O^+(aq)$$

In this chemical equilibrium system, the weaker an acid HA is, the less ionization occurs, the more the reactants are favored, and the smaller the value of the acid ionization constant K_a. In strong acids, the ionization is effectively 100%. In weak acids, because most of the original HA remains intact, the concentration of hydronium ions at equilibrium is *much less* than the original concentration of the acid.

Consider the data presented in one of the sample questions in the previous section:

"A 0.10M solution of Aspirin (acetylsalicylic acid) at 25°C is found to have a pH of 2.27."

This pH corresponds to a hydronium ion concentration of only 5.4×10^{-3} M. It tells us that acetylsalicylic acid must be a weak acid because only a small percentage of the original 0.10 mol/L of the acid has ionized. If the ionization were complete, we would expect the hydronium ion concentration to also be 0.10M, corresponding to a pH of 1.00.

For a strong acid, because almost all of the original acid has been converted to hydronium ions, the $[H_3O^+]$ in the solution is the same as the original acid concentration.

Is there also a way that we could calculate the equilibrium concentration of hydronium ions (and therefore the pH) of a *weak acid* solution if we knew the initial acid concentration? The answer is yes because using an ICE table, you learned how to calculate equilibrium concentrations of chemical species given initial concentrations and a value for the equilibrium constant K_{eq}. Let's begin the discussion of calculating this value and others for weak acid equilibria.

In section 6.4, you were introduced to the acid ionization constant K_a which is given by:

$$K_a = \frac{[A^-][H_3O^+]}{[HA]}$$

This equation will be used to solve the majority of calculations that you will perform, and the three values that we normally care most about are K_a, [HA], and $[H_3O^+]$. Because we are concerned with three variables, there are really three types of problems that you will be expected to solve for weak acids. Let's consider examples of each.

Problem Type 1: Calculating $[H_3O^+]$ (and so usually pH) given K_a and $[HA]_{initial}$

Let's return to our Warm Up example:
Calculate the pH of 0.50 M solution of hydrofluoric acid (HF). K_a for HF = 3.5×10^{-4}

Note the following:
1. The concentration given refers to how the solution *was prepared* — namely, $[HA]_{initial}$.
2. The question is asking us to determine the *equilibrium* concentration of hydronium ions (from which we calculate pH), given the *initial* concentration of the acid and the value of K_a. This suggests the use of an ICE table.
3. We are given the value for K_a. If the value is not given, you will be expected to find that value by referring to a Table of Relative Strengths of Brønsted-Lowry Acids and Bases.
4. For most weak acid problems, it will be necessary to construct an ICE table underneath the balanced equation for the equilibrium existing in the aqueous solution.
5. Any problem that requires us to calculate a value *on the ICE table itself* will also require us to define a value for that unknown (as *x*, for example). These problems usually involve $[H_3O^+]$ or the $[HA]_{initial}$
6. HF is a monoprotic acid, but even if we are given a polyprotic weak acid, *the first ionization* (donation of the first proton) is *the predominant reaction determining pH*. Subsequent ionizations with much smaller K_a values are of no relative consequence in determining pH and can therefore be considered insignificant.
7. As only the first proton is donated, there is always a 1:1:1 mole ratio in the change line of such problems.
8. You should always read the question carefully — more than once if necessary — so that you are certain of the type of problem you are given, and what you are being asked to calculate.

Let's begin solving this problem: Let *x* equal the equilibrium concentration of hydronium ions: $[H_3O^+]_{eq}$
Now let's construct the ICE table, fill it in, and discuss the entries in Table 4.5.1.

Table 4.5.1 *ICE Table for Example Problem*

		HF +	H₂O ⇌	F⁻ +	H₃O⁺
Initial Concentration	(I)	0.50		0	0
Change in Concentration	(C)	−x		+x	+x
Equilibrium Concentration	(E)	0.50 − x		x	x

When filling in the table, we start by making two assumptions:

1. We don't include the concentration of water for the same reason we don't include it in a K_a expression. We can assume the $[H_2O]$ remains constant because the extent to which the large concentration of water (55.6 M) actually *changes* is insignificant, given the relatively tiny amount of ionization that actually occurs.

2. We know that the initial $[H_3O^+]$ in pure water (prior to the ionization of the weak acid) is really 10^{-7} M. However, the fact that the K_a of this acid is so much greater than K_w means that we can assume that this initial $[H_3O^+]$ (resulting from the autoionization of water) is insignificant compared to the equilibrium $[H_3O^+]$ resulting from the ionization of this weak acid. Consequently, the initial $[H_3O^+]$ is given as zero.

At this point we could attempt to solve for x:

$$K_a = \frac{[F^-][H_3O^+]}{HF} = \frac{x^2}{0.50 - x} = 3.5 \times 10^{-4}$$

However, that process would require the use of the quadratic formula. We can avoid this if we make another simplifying assumption based on the relative magnitudes of $[HF]_{initial}$ and K_a. The value of K_a is so small compared to the initial concentration of the acid that the percent of the acid that actually ionizes will not significantly change the original concentration. As a result, we can make the following assumption:

$[HF]_{eq} = 0.50 - x \approx 0.50$

It is important to note that the assumption *is not always* justified. This assumption is valid if the percent ionization of the weak acid is $\leq 5\%$. The percent ionization is given by the following equation:

$$\% \text{ ionization} = \frac{[H_3O^+]_{eq}}{[HA]_{initial}} \times 100\%$$

A good rule-of-thumb is:

If the $[HA]_{initial}$ is at least 10^3 times larger than the K_a value, the assumption is valid.

It may surprise you to know that, as the initial concentration of the acid decreases, the percent ionization *increases*. This means that the assumption is normally only valid for relatively high weak-acid concentrations. Table 4.5.2 demonstrates this, using data for three different concentrations of acetic acid.

Table 4.5.2 *Data for Three Concentrations of Acetic Acid*

[CH$_3$COOH]	Percent Ionization	Assumption
0.15 M	1.1%	valid
0.015 M	3.5%	valid
0.0015 M	11%	invalid

In most, if not all of the problems you will encounter in this course, the assumption will be justified and the use of the quadratic formula can therefore be avoided. However, it is still necessary to *explicitly state the assumption each time you solve such a problem*. If you simply ignore x, it constitutes a chemical error. Having made the assumption, let's return to our example. We now have:

$$\frac{x^2}{0.50} = 3.5 \times 10^{-4} \qquad x = \sqrt{(3.5 \times 10^{-4})(0.50)} = 0.0132 \ M\ H_3O^+$$

$$pH = -\log(0.0132) = 1.88 \text{ (two significant figures)}$$

Let's calculate the % ionization as a check to see if our most recent assumption was valid:

$$\% \text{ ionization} = \frac{[H_3O^+]_{eq}}{[HF]_{initial}} \times 100\% = \frac{0.0132\ M}{0.50\ M} \times 100\% = 2.6\% \text{ (the assumption was valid)}$$

Quick Check

1. Why don't we include water's concentration when we complete an ICE table?

   _____

   _____

2. Why are we justified in assuming that the initial concentration of hydronium ions prior to the ionization of a weak acid is effectively zero?

   _____

   _____

3. What allows us to assume that $[HA]_{eq} \approx [HA]_{initial}$ in weak acid equilibria?

   _____

   _____

Sample Problem — Calculating pH given K_a and $[HA]_{initial}$

Hydrogen sulfide is a poisonous flammable gas whose "rotten egg" smell is perceptible at concentrations as low as 0.00047 ppm. It is also a weak acid when dissolved in water. Calculate the pH of 0.0500M H_2S.

What to Think About

1. The K_a value isn't given. Refer to the table.:
   $K_a = 9.1 \times 10^{-8}$
   This value has two significant figures so our final pH should reflect that.

2. H_2S is a diprotic acid, but the first ionization is all that significantly determines pH.

3. Define x and solve for it using an ICE table.

4. Remember to state the assumption mentioned above.

How to Do It

Let $x = [H_3O^+]_{eq}$

$$H_2S + H_2O \rightleftharpoons HS^- + H_3O^+$$

	H_2S		HS^-	H_3O^+
I	0.0500		0	0
C	$-x$		$+x$	$+x$
E	$0.0500 - x$		x	x

Assume $0.0500 - x \approx 0.0500$

$$K_a = \frac{[HS^-][H_3O^+]}{[H_2S]} = \frac{x^2}{0.0500} = 9.1 \times 10^{-8}$$

$$x = \sqrt{(9.1 \times 10^{-8})(0.0500)} = \underline{6.7}4 \times 10^{-5}\ M$$

$$pH = -\log(\underline{6.7}4 \times 10^{-5}) = 4.\underline{17} \text{ (two sig figs)}$$

Practice Problems — Calculating pH given K_a and $[HA]_{initial}$

1. Methanoic acid is the simplest carboxylic acid and is found naturally in the venom of bee and ant stings. (It is also called formic acid, from the Latin word for ant, *formica*). Calculate the pH of a 0.50 M solution of methanoic acid.

2. Household vinegar is an aqueous solution of acetic acid. A sample of vinegar is analyzed by titration and found to be 0.850 M CH_3COOH. Calculate the pH of this solution.

3. Calculate the percent ionization in a 0.10 M solution of aspirin with a pH of 2.27. Would our simplifying assumption stated above be valid in this case?

Problem Type 2: Calculating $[HA]_{initial}$ given K_a and pH

In this type of problem, we are given the pH of the solution from which we calculate the equilibrium concentration of hydronium ions. We then use that value and the K_a to calculate the initial concentration of the weak acid.

As we are once again solving for an unknown on the ICE table, we still must define x as that unknown. However, there are a couple of differences between this unknown and the one in the previous problem type:

1. We place this "x" in the "**I**nitial" row, rather than the "**E**quilibrium" row of the table.
2. This unknown will be the largest of any quantity appearing in the ICE table because it's the initial concentration of the acid. Therefore, no assumption regarding its insignificance applies.

Consider the sample problem below. Note that the use of the quadratic isn't necessary to solve this problem. Therefore, there is no need to assume that the amount of ionization of the benzoic acid that occurs relative to the initial concentration is insignificant. However, if the $[H_3O^+]_{eq}$ is sufficiently large relative to the K_a value, the assumption may be valid. Even so, until you have acquired ample experience solving these types of problems, if you don't *have to* make such an assumption to solve the problem, then don't. (Calculate the percentage ionization in the sample problem to see if such an assumption would have been valid in this case.)

© Edvantage Interactive 2016

Sample Problem — Calculating $[HA]_{initial}$, given K_a and pH

Benzoic acid is used as a food preservative and a precursor in many organic synthesis reactions. It is the most commonly used chemical standard in calorimetry. What concentration of benzoic acid is required to produce a solution with a pH of 3.30?

What to Think About

1. Once again an ICE table and a "Let $x = $" statement are required.

2. The unknown now represents the initial acid concentration.

3. Use the given pH to calculate the $[H_3O^+]_{eq}$.

4. Look up the value of K_a for benzoic acid: $K_a = 6.5 \times 10^{-5}$

How to Do It

Let $x = [C_6H_5COOH]_{initial}$

$$[H_3O^+]_{eq} = 10^{-3.30} = 0.000501 \text{ M}$$

$$C_6H_5COOH + H_2O \rightleftharpoons C_6H_5COO^- + H_3O^+$$

	x		0	0
I	x		0	0
C	-0.000501		$+0.000501$	$+0.000501$
E	$x - 0.000501$		0.000501	0.000501

$$K_a = \frac{[C_6H_5COO^-][H_3O^+]}{[C_6H_5COOH]} = \frac{(0.000501)^2}{(x - 0.000501)}$$

$$= 6.5 \times 10^{-5}$$

$$x - 0.000\underline{501} = \frac{(0.000\underline{501})^2}{6.5 \times 10^5}$$

$$x = 0.00\underline{44} \text{ M (2 significant figures)}$$

Practice Problems — Calculating $[HA]_{initial}$, given K_a and pH

1. Citric acid is one of the acids responsible for the sour taste of lemons. What concentration of citric acid would be required to produce a solution with a pH of 2.50?

2. Rhubarb's sour taste is due in part to the presence of oxalic acid. A solution of oxalic acid has had the label removed. What concentration should appear on the label if the pH of the solution is found to be 0.55?

3. Nitrous acid is one of the components of acid rain. An aqueous solution of nitrous acid is found to have a pH of 1.85. Calculate the concentration of the acid.

This type of problem does not require us to solve for an unknown x on the ICE table because all of the entries in the table are available directly or indirectly from the information provided in the question. The pH allows us to determine $[H_3O^+]_{eq}$. Although there is *no need* for a simplifying assumption, we are given enough information to calculate percentage ionization to determine if the assumption is justified.

Let's return to acetylsalicylic acid in the following sample problem.

Sample Problem — Calculating K_a, given $[HA]_{initial}$ and pH

A 0.100 M solution of acetylsalicylic acid (Aspirin) is found to have a pH of 2.27. Calculate the K_a for this acid. The formula for acetylsalicylic acid is $C_8H_7O_2COOH$.

What to Think About	**How to Do It**
1. Use pH to calculate $[H_3O^+]_{eq}$ and then use that value to complete the entries in the ICE table. Note that we cannot ignore 0.00537 M compared to 0.10 M.	$[H_3O^+]_{eq} = 10^{-2.27} = 0.00537\ M$ $C_8H_7O_2COOH + H_2O \rightleftharpoons C_8H_7O_2COO^- + H_3O^+$ <table><tr><td>I</td><td>0.100</td><td></td><td>0</td><td>0</td></tr><tr><td>C</td><td>−0.00537</td><td></td><td>+0.00537</td><td>+0.00537</td></tr><tr><td>E</td><td>0.0946</td><td></td><td>0.00537</td><td>0.00537</td></tr></table>
2. Record the K_a value to two significant figures.	$K_a = \dfrac{[C_8H_7O_2COOH^-][H_3O^+]}{[C_8H_7O_2COOH]} = \dfrac{(0.00537)^2}{0.0946}$ $= \underline{3.0} \times 10^{-4}$ (2 significant figures)

Practice Problems — Calculating K_a, given $[HA]_{initial}$ and pH

1. One form of vitamin C is ascorbic acid, $H_2C_6H_6O_6$. The name originates from the fact that ascorbic acid prevents scurvy — a fact first discovered in 1747 by British surgeon John Lind. This subsequently resulted in citrus juice (from limes and lemons) being supplied to sailors in the Royal Navy. A 0.100 M solution of ascorbic acid is found to have a pH of 3.00. Calculate the K_a for ascorbic acid.

2. Lactic acid ($C_3H_6O_3$) is a weak acid produced in muscle tissue during anaerobic respiration and is the acid present in sour milk. It's also responsible for the sour taste of sauerkraut. A 0.025 M solution of lactic acid is found to have a pH of 2.75. Calculate the K_a for lactic acid.

Part B: Calculations for Weak Bases

As with acids, most bases are weak. As you learned earlier, water can both accept and donate a proton (hydrogen ion), so weak bases also participate in equilibria with water. Using the symbol "B" for a weak base, we can represent this as:

$$B(aq) + H_2O(l) \rightleftharpoons HB^+(aq) + OH^-(aq)$$

We can therefore write the following expression for the base ionization constant. K_b:

$$K_b = \frac{[HB^+][OH^-]}{[B]}$$

Although the three main types of problems associated with weak bases that you will be expected to solve are similar to those identified above for weak acids, additional calculations are often required.

For example, if you are given a problem that includes a weak base from a Table of Relative Strengths of Brønsted-Lowry Acids and Bases, you cannot simply look up the K_b value as you are able to with K_a values. Rather, you must *calculate the K_b for that base by using the K_a value of its conjugate acid*. Let's derive the equation that you will need to perform that calculation below.

Consider the conjugate acid/base pair of NH_4^+ and NH_3 and their respective K_a and K_b expressions:

$$K_a \text{ for } NH_4^+ = \frac{[NH_3][H_3O^+]}{[NH_4^+]} \quad \text{and} \quad K_b \text{ for } NH_3 = \frac{[NH_4^+][OH^-]}{[NH_3]}$$

Note that two common terms appear in each equation. Let's take advantage of that by multiplying the two expressions together and cancelling those common terms:

$$K_a \times K_b = \frac{[NH_3][H_3O^+]}{[NH_4^+]} \times \frac{[NH_4^+][OH^-]}{[NH_3]} = [H_3O^+][OH^-] = K_w$$

This allows us to formulate the following relationship for *conjugate acid-base pairs*:

$$K_a \text{ (conjugate acid)} \times K_b \text{ (conjugate base)} = K_w = 1.00 \times 10^{-14} \text{ (at 25°C)}$$

Taking the negative logarithm of both sides of the above equation, we obtain:

$$pK_a \text{ (conjugate acid)} + pK_b \text{ (conjugate base)} = pK_w = 14.00 \text{ (at 25°C)}$$

This allows us to calculate the K_b value for any weak base in the table. For example:

$$K_b \text{ for } NH_3 = \frac{K_w}{K_a \text{ for } NH_4^+} = \frac{1.00 \times 10^{-14}}{5.6 \times 10^{-10}} = 1.8 \times 10^{-5}$$

You must be careful to use the *correct K_a* value when performing this calculation, especially when dealing with amphiprotic ions. Before you begin the calculation, first locate the weak base on the *right side* of the table. Then look over to the left side of that equation to find the appropriate conjugate acid. The K_a value for *that acid* is the correct value to use in the calculation.

Quick Check

1. Complete the following table by choosing the correct conjugate acid and corresponding K_a value and then calculating the K_b value for each weak base. Consider carefully the first three that are done for you.

	Weak Base	Conjugate Acid	Appropriate K_a Value	Calculated K_b
(a)	$HC_2O_4^-$	$H_2C_2O_4$	5.9×10^{-2}	1.7×10^{-13}
(b)	$H_2PO_4^-$	H_3PO_4	7.5×10^{-3}	1.3×10^{-12}
(c)	HPO_4^{2-}	$H_2PO_4^-$	6.2×10^{-8}	1.6×10^{-7}
(d)	NO_2^-			
(e)	$HC_6H_5O_7^{2-}$			
(f)	HCO_3^-			
(g)	CN^-			

2. Calculate the pK_a and pK_b values for all of the chemical species above. How do the sizes of pK_a values for acids and pK_b values for bases relate to their strength?

Problem Type 1: Calculating [OH⁻] (and usually pH) given K_b and $[B]_{initial}$

In the same way we discussed each of the three main problem types associated with weak acids, let's now begin that discussion for solutions of weak bases.

Remember that if the question involves a weak base from the table, we have to calculate the K_b rather than simply looking it up and also that solving for "x" gives us [OH⁻] rather than [H_3O^+]. This means that an extra calculation will be necessary if we are asked to determine pH. Remember this point. Consider the sample problems below.

Notice that, in the second sample problem, the cyanide *ion* is reacting with water and functioning as a weak base. Such an event is known as **hydrolysis**. A detailed treatment of hydrolysis will appear in Chapter 5. For now, simply treat ions as you would any other weak base in water.

Note that the only *uncharged* weak base (except for water) in the table of acids and bases is NH_3. Most of the remaining weak bases on the table are anions. Many neutral weak bases are organic compounds called amines containing nitrogen whose lone electron pair is available to accept a proton from water.

Sample Problem — Calculating [OH$^-$] and pH using K_b and [B]$_{initial}$

One of the compounds responsible for the odor of herring brine is methylamine, CH_3NH_2. ($K_b = 4.4 \times 10^{-4}$) Calculate the pH of a 0.50 M solution of methylamine.

What to Think About	**How to Do It**
1. Once again, construct an ICE table. Add the proton from water to the nitrogen in methylamine. Be careful with charges.	Let $x = [OH^-]_{eq}$
	$$CH_3NH_2 + H_2O \rightleftharpoons CH_3NH_3^+ + OH^-$$
2. A value on the ICE table is being solved so, once again, define x.	
3. The K_b value is provided so you don't have to calculate it.	
4. The relative magnitudes of K_b and [OH$^-$]$_{initial}$ allow the assumption to be valid.	

ICE table:

	CH_3NH_2	H_2O	$CH_3NH_3^+$	OH^-
I	0.50		0	0
C	$-x$		$+x$	$+x$
E	$0.50 - x$		x	x

Assume $0.50 - x \approx 0.50$

$$K_b = \frac{[CH_3NH_3^+][OH^-]}{[CH_3NH_2]} = \frac{x^2}{0.50} = 4.4 \times 10^{-4}$$

$x = 0.0148\ M\ OH^-$ so $pOH = -\log 0.0148 = 1.829$

$pH = 14.00 - 1.829 = 12.17$

Sample Problem — Calculating [OH$^-$] and pH using K_b and [B]$_{initial}$

Calculate the pH of a solution containing 0.20 M CN$^-$.

What to Think About	**How to Do It**
1. Calculate the K_b value using the K_a for HCN.	K_b for $CN^- = \dfrac{K_w}{K_a\ \text{for HCN}} = \dfrac{1.00 \times 10^{-14}}{4.9 \times 10^{-10}}$
2. As CN$^-$ is a relatively strong weak base, expect this solution to have a relatively high pH.	$= 2.04 \times 10^{-5}$
	Let $x = [OH^-]_{eq}$
3. Remember to convert the [OH$^-$] to pH.	$$CN^- + H_2O \rightleftharpoons HCN + OH^-$$

ICE table:

	CN^-	H_2O	HCN	OH^-
I	0.20		0	0
C	$-x$		$+x$	$+x$
E	$0.20 - x$		x	x

Assume $0.20 - x \approx 0.20$

$$K_b = \frac{[HCN][OH^-]}{[CN^-]} = \frac{x^2}{0.20} = 2.04 \times 10^{-5}$$

$x = 0.00202\ M\ OH^-$ so $pOH = -\log (0.00202)$

$= 2.695$

$pH = 14.00 - 2.695 = 11.31$

Practice Problems — Calculating [OH⁻] and pH using K_b and $[B]_{initial}$

1. Hydrazine, N_2H_4 is used in rocket fuel, in producing polymer foams, and in the production of air bags. The K_b for hydrazine is 1.7×10^{-6}. Calculate the pH of the solution prepared by dissolving 12.0 g of hydrazine in 500.0 mL of solution.

2. Calculate the $[OH^-]$, $[H^+]$, pOH, and pH of a 0.60 M solution of $HCOO^-$.

3. Calculate the K_a and pK_a values for the following:
   (a) methylammonium, $CH_3NH_3^+$

   (b) hydrazinium, $N_2H_5^+$

Problem Type 2: Calculating $[B]_{initial}$, given K_b and pH (or pOH)

This type of problem may require us to calculate both $[OH^-]_{eq}$ (from pH) and K_b (from a K_a) at the beginning of the solution process. We then continue in much the same way as we would for this type of problem when dealing with weak acids. Consider the sample problem below.

Sample Problem — Calculating $[B]_{initial}$, given K_b and pH (or pOH)

What concentration of NH_3 would be required to produce a solution with a pH = 10.50?

What to Think About

1. Calculate both the K_b for NH_3 (using the K_a for NH_4^+) and the $[OH^-]_{eq}$ (from the given pH).

2. The unknown x will represent the $[NH_3]_{initial}$.

3. No assumption regarding x is part of solving this problem.

How to Do It

$$K_b \text{ for } NH_3 = \frac{K_w}{K_a \text{ for } NH_4} = \frac{1.00 \times 10^{-14}}{5.6 \times 10^{-10}} = 1.78 \times 10^{-5}$$

$$pOH = 14.00 - 10.50 = 3.50$$

$$[OH^-]_{eq} = 10^{-3.50} = 3.16 \times 10^{-4} \text{ M}$$

Let $x = [NH_3]_{initial}$

	NH_3	$+ H_2O \rightleftharpoons$	NH_4^+	$+$	OH^-
I	x		0		0
C	-3.16×10^{-4}		$+3.16 \times 10^{-4}$		$+3.16 \times 10^{-4}$
E	$x - 3.16 \times 10^{-4}$		3.16×10^{-4}		3.16×10^{-4}

$$K_b = \frac{[NH_4^+][OH^-]}{[NH_3]} = \frac{(3.16 \times 10^{-4})^2}{x - 3.16 \times 10^{-4}}$$

$$= 1.78 \times 10^{-5}$$

$$x - 3.16 \times 10^{-4} = \frac{(3.16 \times 10^{-4})^2}{1.78 \times 10^{-5}}$$

$$x = 0.0059 \text{ M}$$

Practice Problems — Calculating $[B]_{initial}$ given K_b and pH (or pOH)

1. Ethylamine ($C_2H_5NH_2$) is a pungent colorless gas used extensively in organic synthesis reactions. It is also a weak base with $K_b = 5.6 \times 10^{-4}$. What mass of ethylamine is dissolved in 250.0 mL of a solution having a pH of 11.80?

Continued on the next page

Practice Problems (Continued)

2. What concentration of CN^- would produce a solution with a pH of 11.50?

3. Using the K_b provided above for hydrazine, calculate the $[N_2H_4]$ required to produce a solution with a $[H_3O^+] = 1.0 \times 10^{-10}$ M.

Problem Type 3: Calculating K_b given $[B]_{initial}$ and pH (or pOH)

As was the case with an acidic system, this final type of problem requires no simplifying assumption (although it may prove to be justified), and no unknown to be solved in the ICE table. All of the entries in the table are available, either directly or indirectly, from the information provided in the question. Consider the sample problem below.

Sample Problem — Calculating K_b, given $[B]_{initial}$ and pH (or pOH)

A solution is prepared by dissolving 9.90 g of the weak base hydroxylamine, NH_2OH, in enough water to produce 500.0 mL of solution. The pH of the solution is found to be 9.904. Calculate the K_b for hydroxylamine.

What to Think About	**How to Do It**
1. Convert grams of the compound dissolved in 500.0 mL to moles per liter to determine $[NH_2OH]_{initial}$.	$[NH_2OH]_{initial} = 9.90 \text{ g} \dfrac{NH_2OH}{0.5000 \text{ L}} \times \dfrac{1 \text{ mol}}{33.0 \text{ g}} = 0.600 \text{ M}$
2. Use the pH to determine $[OH^-]_{eq}$. That value shows that the % ionization is small enough to assume $0.600 - x \approx 0.600$.	$pOH = 14.000 - 9.904 = 4.096$ $[OH^-]_{eq} = 10^{-4.096} = 8.0168 \times 10^{-5}$ M

$$NH_2OH + H_2O \rightleftharpoons NH_2OH_2^+ + OH^-$$

I	0.600		0	0
C	-8.0168×10^{-5}		$+8.0168 \times 10^{-5}$	$+8.0168 \times 10^{-5}$
E	≈ 0.600		8.0168×10^{-5}	8.0168×10^{-5}

3. Record the final answer to three significant figures.

$$K_b = \frac{[NH_2][OH_2^-]}{[NH_2OH]} = \frac{(8.0168 \ 10^{-5})^2}{0.600} = 1.07 \times 10^{-8}$$

Practice Problems — Calculating K_b, given $[B]_{initial}$ and pH (or pOH)

1. A 0.400 M solution of the weak base methylamine, CH_3NH_2, is found to have a pH of 12.90. Calculate the K_b of methylamine and the percentage ionization. Compare your calculation of this K_b value with the sample problem above involving methylamine. What might this indicate about the temperature of this solution?

2. One of the most effective substances at relieving intense pain is morphine. First developed in about 1810, the compound is also a weak base. In a 0.010 M solution of morphine, the pOH is determined to be 3.90. Calculate the K_b and pK_b for morphine. (Let "Mor" and "HMor$^+$" represent the conjugate pair in your equilibrium reaction.)

3. Quinine, $C_{20}H_{24}N_2O_2$, is a naturally occurring white crystalline base used in the treatment of malaria. It is also present in tonic water. Calculate the K_b for this weak base if a 0.0015 M solution has a pH of 9.84. (Let "Qui" and "HQui$^+$" represent the conjugate pair in your equilibrium reaction.)

4.5 Activity: An Organically Grown Table of Relative Acid Strengths

Question

Can you construct your own table of relative acid strengths using the relationships you have learned in this section to calculate the K_a values for a series of organic compounds?

Background

The vast majority of chemical compounds are organic (carbon-based) compounds and some of those are weak acids and bases. Given sufficient data, you can use various calculations to organize a collection of these compounds into a table from strongest to weakest acids similar to a Table of Relative Strengths of Brønsted-Lowry Acids and Bases, which you have already seen.

Procedure

1. You will be given data relating to 15 organic compounds, 9 of which are weak acids, and 6 of which are weak bases. The data could include K_b, pK_b, pK_a, pH, and pOH information. None of the compounds appear on a Table of Relative Strengths of Brønsted-Lowry Acids and Bases. The data will not be presented in any particular order.
2. If given the acid, write the formula for the conjugate base and vice versa.
3. Use the data given to calculate the K_a value for each weak acid or for the conjugate acid of each weak base using any of the relationships discussed in this section. Before beginning, you may want to review the relationships below.
4. Place the equilibrium equation for each weak acid (or conjugate acid) reacting with water in order from strongest down to weakest acid as in an example provided.
5. Include in the right-hand section of the table you construct the K_a value you have calculated.
6. All of the acids are monoprotic carboxylic acids (containing –COOH) and so all of their conjugate bases will appear as $-COO^-$ following donation of the proton to water.
7. All of the weak bases are neutral amines containing nitrogen and so all of their conjugate acids will have an extra "H" on the nitrogen and a "+" charge following acceptance of a proton from the hydronium ion.
8. Consider the following when calculating the K_a values (Assume 25°C):

    - For conjugate acid-base pairs: $K_a \times K_b = K_w = 1.00 \times 10^{-14}$

    - For conjugate acid-base pairs: $pK_a + pK_b = pK_w = 14.00$

    - Review how to calculate K_a and K_b, given pH (or pOH) and $[HA]_{initial}$ (or $[B]_{initial}$).

9. Fill in the missing items in the table below and use the data provided to calculate the K_a values for all the acids and conjugate acids of the bases given in the table.
10. Then arrange all of the acids and conjugate acids in the correct order in the table, including the appropriate equilibrium equation for the examples given. Note that "soln" stands for "solution."

Compound Name	Formula for Conjugate Acid	Formula for Conjugate Base	Calculate K_a for Acid or Conjugate Acid Given
Acids			
chloroacetic acid	$ClCH_2COOH$		$pK_a = 2.85$
phenylacetic acid	C_7H_7COOH		pH of 1.0 M soln = 2.155
propanoic acid	C_2H_5COOH		K_b for conjugate base = 7.7×10^{-10}
pyruvic acid	C_2H_3OCOOH		pK_b for conjugate base = 11.45
lactic acid	C_2H_5OCOOH		pOH of 0.10 M soln = 11.57
acetylsalicylic acid	$C_8H_7O_2COOH$		K_b for conjugate base = 2.8×10^{-11}
glycolic acid	CH_3OCOOH		$pK_a = 3.82$
glyoxylic acid	$CHOCOOH$		pK_b for conjugate base = 10.54
glyceric acid	$C_2H_5O_2COOH$		pH of 1.0 M soln = 1.77
Bases			
pyridine		C_5H_5N	$K_b = 1.7 \times 10^{-9}$
trimethylamine		$(CH_3)_3N$	pOH of 0.10 M soln = 2.60
piperidine		$C_5H_{10}NH$	$pK_b = 2.89$
tert-butylamine		$(CH_3)_3CNH_2$	pH of a 1.0 M soln = 12.34
ethanolamine		$C_2H_5ONH_2$	pK_a of conjugate acid = 9.50
n-propylamine		$C_3H_7NH_2$	$pK_b = 3.46$

Relative Strengths of Some Organic Acids and Bases

Strength of Acid	Equilibrium Reaction With Water					K_a Value	Strength of Base
	Acid + H_2O	$\rightleftharpoons$	H_3O^+ +	Base			
Stronger ↑		$\rightleftharpoons$					**Weaker** ↓
		$\rightleftharpoons$					
		$\rightleftharpoons$					
		$\rightleftharpoons$					
		$\rightleftharpoons$					
		$\rightleftharpoons$					
		$\rightleftharpoons$					
		$\rightleftharpoons$					
		$\rightleftharpoons$					
		$\rightleftharpoons$					
		$\rightleftharpoons$					
		$\rightleftharpoons$					
		$\rightleftharpoons$					
		$\rightleftharpoons$					
Weaker		$\rightleftharpoons$					**Stronger**

Sample:

HCOOH (given an acid)	+ H_2O	$\rightleftharpoons$	H_3O^+	+ $HCOO^-$		1.8×10^{-4}	
NH_4^+	+ H_2O	$\rightleftharpoons$	H_3O^+	+ **NH_3** (given a base)		5.6×10^{-10}	

Results and Discussion

1. Are the K_a values for these monoprotic carboxylic acids significantly different from each other in their orders of magnitude? _____

2. Which acid is the strongest and which base is the strongest? _____

3. Use the K_a vlaues you have calculated to expand the Table of Relative Strengths of Acids and Bases, if you want to include these organic compounds.

4.5 Review Questions

1. Calculate the $[H_3O^+]$, $[OH^-]$, pH, and pOH that results when 23.0 g of HCOOH is dissolved in enough water to produce 500.0 mL of solution.

2. At standard temperature and pressure, 5.6 L of H_2S is dissolved in enough water to produce 2.50 L of solution. Calculate the pH of this solution and percent ionization of H_2S.

3. The percent ionization of 0.100 M solution of an unknown acid is 1.34%. Calculate the pH of this solution and identify the acid.

4. Because of its high reactivity with glass, hydrofluoric acid is used to etch glass. What mass of HF would be required be required to produce 1.5 L of an aqueous solution with a pH of 2.00?

5. Phosphoric acid is used in rust removal and also to add a tangy sour taste to cola soft drinks. A solution of phosphoric acid is found to have a pOH of 12.50. Calculate the concentration of this acid.

6. Oxalic acid is a white crystalline solid. Some of its uses include rust removal, bleaching pulpwood, and even as an ingredient in baking powder. A 250.0 mL sample of an oxalic solution is found to have a pH of 2.35. What mass of oxalic acid would remain if this aqueous solution were evaporated to dryness?

7. Hypochlorous acid (HClO) is used mainly as an active sanitizer in water treatment. A 0.020 M solution of hypochlorous acid is found to have a pH of 4.62. Calculate the K_a for hypochlorous acid.

8. Phenylacetic acid ($C_6H_5CH_2COOH$) is used in some perfumes and in the production of some forms of penicillin. A 0.100 M solution of phenylacetic acid has a pOH of 11.34. Calculate the K_a of phenylacetic acid.

9. Complete the following table:

Conjugate Acid	Conjugate Base	K_a for Acid	pK_a	K_b for Base	pK_b
	NO_2^-				
H_2O_2					
	$C_6H_5O^-$				
HSO_4^-					

10. Complete the following table of amphiprotic ions:

Conjugate Acid	Conjugate Base	K_a for Acid	pK_a	K_b for Base	pK_b
	HPO_4^-				
$H_2C_6H_5O_7^-$					
	$H_2BO_3^-$				
HCO_3^-					

© Edvantage Interactive 2016

11. An aqueous solution is prepared by dissolving 5.6 L of NH_3 gas, measured at STP, in enough water to produce 750.0 mL of solution. Calculate the pH of this solution.

12. Isopropylamine, $(CH_3)_2CHNH_2$, is a weak base ($K_b = 4.7 \times 10^{-4}$) used in herbicides such as Roundup and some chemical weapons. Calculate the pOH and pH of a 0.60 M solution of isopropylamine.

13. What concentration of sulfite ions will produce a solution with a pH of 10.00?

14. Trimethylamine, $(CH_3)_3N$ is a weak base ($K_b = 6.3 \times 10^{-5}$). It is one of the compounds responsible for the smell of rotting fish and is used in a number of dyes. What volume of this gas, measured at STP, must be dissolved in 2.5 L of solution to give that solution a pOH of 2.50?

15. A 0.10 M solution of ethylamine, $C_2H_5NH_2$, is found to have a pOH of 2.14. Calculate the K_b for ethylamine.

5 Applications of Acid-Base Reactions

By the end of this chapter, you should be able to do the following:

- Demonstrate an ability to design, perform, and analyze a titration experiment involving the following:
  - primary standards
  - standardized solutions
  - titration curves
  - appropriate indicators
- Describe an indicator as an equilibrium system
- Perform and interpret calculations involving the pH in a solution and K_a for an indicator
- Describe the hydrolysis of ions in salt solutions
- Analyse the extent of hydrolysis in salt solutions
- Describe buffers as equilibrium systems
- Describe the preparation of buffer systems
- Predict what will happen when oxides dissolve in rain water

By the end of this chapter, you should know the meaning of these **key terms**:

- acid rain
- buffers
- dissociation
- equation
- equivalence point (stoichiometric point)
- hydrolysis
- hydrolysis reaction
- indicator
- primary standards
- salt
- titration
- titration curve
- transition point

The freshwater African chichlid requires water having a pH between 8.0 and 9.2 to survive. The South American chichlid requires water with a pH between 6.4 and 7.0.

5.1 Hydrolysis of Salts — The Reactions of Ions with Water

Warm Up

Consider the neutralization reactions described below.

1. (a) When equal volumes of 0.10 M HNO_3 and 0.10 M KOH solutions react together, what salt solution exists in the reaction vessel following the reaction?

   _____

   (b) Consider the dissociated ions of this salt. Is either of the ions located on a table of relative strengths of Brønsted-Lowry acids and bases ? If so, where? Does this help you predict if the pH of this solution will be equal to, above, or below 7?

   _____

   _____

2. (a) When equal volumes of 0.10 M CH_3COOH and 0.10 M NaOH solutions react together, what salt solution exists in the reaction vessel following the reaction?

   _____

   (b) Consider the dissociated ions of the salt. Is either of the ions located on a table of relative strengths of acids and bases? If so, where? Does this help you predict if the pH of this solution will be equal to, above, or below 7?

   _____

   _____

Neutralization Reactions

In previous years you were introduced to several reaction types, which were then discussed in more detail in Grade 11. One of those reaction types is *neutralization* in which an acid and a base react to produce a salt and water. The name suggests that when an equal number of moles of hydronium ions from an acid and hydroxide ions from a base react together, the resulting solution will be neutral and thus have a pH of 7.

It might surprise you to know that many such neutralizations produce salt solutions that are actually acidic or basic. This phenomenon occurs because one or both of the dissociated *ions of the product salt* behave as weak acids or bases and thus react with water to generate hydronium or hydroxide ions. This is known as hydrolysis.

> **Hydrolysis** is the reaction of an ion with water to produce either the conjugate base of the ion and *hydronium ions* or the conjugate acid of the ion and *hydroxide ions*.

Whether or not the ions of a salt will hydrolyze can often be determined by considering the acids and bases from which the salt was produced. In each case, we look at the dissociated ions of each type of salt individually and assess their ability to either donate protons to or accept protons from water. This allows us to predict if aqueous solutions of those salts will be acidic, basic, or neutral. Let's begin that discussion below.

© Edvantage Interactive 2016

A. Neutral Salts: Salts Containing the Anion of a Strong Acid and the Cation of a Strong Base

Consider the first Warm Up question above. When equal amounts of nitric acid and potassium hydroxide solutions are combined, an aqueous solution of potassium nitrate is produced. The dissociated ions present in this solution are the K^+ cations from the strong base and the NO_3^- anions from the strong acid.

Like all aqueous ions, the alkali ions in the solution become surrounded by water molecules in the hydration process, but no reaction between those ions and water occurs. The same is true for all alkali (Group 1) ions and most alkaline earth (Group 2) ions (except beryllium). *These are the cations of strong bases and they do not hydrolyze.* We therefore consider them *spectator ions.*

Like all ions that are the conjugate bases of strong acids, NO_3^- ions have no measurable ability to accept protons from water. Notice on a table of relative strengths of Brønsted-Lowry acids and bases that all such anions of strong acids are located at the top right corner of the table and on the receiving end of a *one-way arrow* — they are thus incapable of accepting protons and so cannot function as bases. Like the cations mentioned above, all anions of strong monoprotic acids are hydrated in water, but no further reaction occurs. *The anions of strong monoprotic acids do not hydrolyze.* They are considered *spectator ions in water.* (Note that the bisulphate anion, HSO_4^-, although unable to *accept* protons from water, is a relatively strong weak acid and therefore *donates* protons to water.) We can generalize these results into the conclusion stated below.

A salt containing the anion of a strong monoprotic acid and the cation of a strong base will produce a neutral solution in water because neither of the ions undergoes hydrolysis.

Quick Check

1. Circle the ions in the following list that represent cations of strong bases.

    Al^{3+} Rb^+ Fe^{3+} Cr^{3+} Ca^{2+} Sn^{4+} Cs^+ Ba^{2+}

2. Circle the ions in the following list that represent the conjugate bases of strong acids.

    F^- ClO_2^- ClO_4^- SO_4^{2-} Cl^- NO_2^- CH_3COO^- CN^- NO_3^-

3. Circle the following salts whose ions will not hydrolyze when dissociated in water.

    NH_4Cl Na_2CO_3 $RbClO_4$ Li_2SO_3 BaI_2 NH_4HCOO KIO_3 CsF $CaBr_2$

B. Basic Salts: Salts Containing the Anion of a Weak Acid and the Cation of a Strong Base

Look at the second Warm Up question at the beginning of this section. When equal amounts of acetic acid and sodium hydroxide solutions are combined, an aqueous solution of sodium acetate is produced. The dissociated ions present in this solution are the Na^+ ions from the strong base and the CH_3COO^- ions from the weak acid. We have already stated that alkali ions are incapable of undergoing hydrolysis and thus cannot affect the solution's pH.

However, the acetate anion is the conjugate base of a weak acid and therefore has a measurable ability to accept protons from water. Being a weak base, the acetate anion will react with water by accepting protons in the following hydrolysis reaction:

$$CH_3COO^-(aq) + H_2O(l) \rightleftharpoons CH_3COOH(aq) + OH^-(aq)$$

As a result of the hydrolysis, this solution will be basic with a pH above 7.

A salt containing the anion of a weak monoprotic acid and the cation of a strong base will produce a basic solution in water because the anion acts as a weak base, producing hydroxide ions, and the cation does not react.

Quick Check

1. Which of the following salts contain the anion of a weak acid?

   NH_4Cl $NaClO_4$ $Fe(CH_3COO)_3$ KF $LiCl$

   $Al(NO_3)_3$ NH_4HSO_4 $Pb(NO_2)_2$ NH_4I $Ba(CN)_2$

2. Which of the following salts will produce a basic aqueous solution due to anionic hydrolysis?

   $AlBr_3$ $Ca(HCOO)_2$ $RbClO_4$ $SrCO_3$ $Mg(CN)_2$

   $NaCH_3COO$ $Cr(NO_3)_3$ LiC_6H_5COO FeI_3 K_3PO_4

Qualitatively, we can predict that such solutions will be basic due to anionic hydrolysis, but we can also perform all of the same types of calculations for these dissolved anions that we introduced in the previous section for any weak base in water. Consider Sample Problem below.

Sample Problem — Calculating the pH of a Basic Salt Solution

A 9.54 g sample of $Mg(CN)_2$ is dissolved in enough water to make 500.0 mL of solution. Calculate the pH of this solution.

What to Think About

1. First calculate the concentration of the compound and then write the dissociation equation to determine the initial concentration of each ion.

2. Then consider each of the dissociated ions separately and decide if either is capable of hydrolyzing.

3. Mg^{2+} will not hydrolyze, but CN^- is the conjugate base of a very weak acid and is therefore a relatively strong weak base. Consequently, expect the pH of this solution to be well above 7.

4. Write an equilibrium equation under which you can construct an ICE table.

5. To calculate the $[OH^-]_{eq}$, first calculate the K_b of the cyanide anion.

6. Remember that you are solving for $[OH^-]_{eq}$ on the ICE table and so an extra step is required to determine pH.

How to Do It

$$\frac{9.54 \cancel{g}}{0.5000\ L} \times \frac{1\ mol\ Mg(CN)_2}{76.3 \cancel{g}} = 0.250\ M$$

$$Mg(CN)_2(s) \rightarrow Mg^{2+}(aq) + 2\ CN^-(aq)$$
$$0.250\ M \qquad\qquad 0.250\ M \qquad\quad 0.500\ M$$

$$K_b\ for\ CN^- = \frac{K_w}{K_a\ for\ HCN} = \frac{1.00 \times 10^{-14}}{4.9 \times 10^{-10}}$$
$$= 2.04 \times 10^{-5}$$

Let $x = [OH^-]_{eq}$

$$CN^- + H_2O \rightleftharpoons HCN + OH^-$$

I	0.500		0	0
C	$-x$		$+x$	$+x$
E	$0.500 - x$		x	x

Assume $0.500 - x \approx 0.500$

$$K_b = \frac{[HCN][OH^-]}{[CN^-]} = \frac{x^2}{0.500} = 2.04 \times 10^{-5}$$

$$x = 3.19 \times 10^{-3}\ M = [OH^-]_{eq}$$

$$pOH = -log\ (0.00319) = 2.496$$

$$pH = 14.00 - 2.496 = 11.50\ (2\ sig.\ figures)$$

© Edvantage Interactive 2016

Practice Problems — Basic Salt Solutions

1. Without performing any calculations, rank the following salts in order of decreasing pH of their 0.10 M aqueous solutions:

   Na_2SO_3 LiF KNO_2 RbCN $Na_2C_2O_4$ K_2CO_3

   _____ > _____ > _____ > _____ > _____ > _____

2. Sodium carbonate is used in the manufacture of glass and also as a laundry additive to soften water. A 200.0 mL aqueous solution of 0.50 M Na_2CO_3 is diluted to 500.0 mL. Calculate the pH of the resulting solution.

3. What concentration of NaHCOO would be required to produce an aqueous solution with a pH of 9.20? Begin by writing the equation for the predominant equilibrium present in the solution.

C. Acidic Salts I: Salts Containing the Conjugate Base of a Strong Acid and the Conjugate Acid of a Weak Base

When equal amounts of NH_3 (a weak base) and HCl (a strong acid) are combined, the neutralization reaction that occurs is:

$$NH_3(aq) + HCl(aq) \rightarrow NH_4Cl(aq)$$

Following the reaction, the two ions present in the solution are NH_4^+ and Cl^-. We have already noted that chloride ions, like all conjugate bases of the strong acids, are incapable of accepting protons by reacting with water. However, the ammonium cation is the conjugate acid of a weak base and is therefore a weak acid capable of donating protons to water in the cationic hydrolysis reaction shown below:

$$NH_4^+(aq) + H_2O(l) \rightleftharpoons NH_3(aq) + H_3O^+(aq)$$

As a result of the hydrolysis, this solution will be acidic with a pH below 7.

> A salt containing the cation of a weak base and the anion of a strong monoprotic acid will produce an acidic solution in water because the cation acts as a weak acid producing hydronium ions and the anion does not react.

Quick Check

1. Write the hydrolysis equation for the conjugate acids of the following weak bases reacting with water and the appropriate K_a expressions:

   (a) methylamine, CH_3NH_2

   (b) n-propylamine, $C_3H_7NH_2$

   (c) trimethylamine $(CH_3)_3N$

2. Calculate the K_a for the conjugate acids of the above weak bases given the following data:

   (a) K_b for methylamine $= 4.4 \times 10^{-4}$

   (b) K_b for n–propylamine $= 3.5 \times 10^{-4}$

   (c) K_b for trimethylamine $= 6.3 \times 10^{-5}$

Sample Problem — Calculating the pH of an Acidic Salt

The K_b for pyridine, C_5H_5N, is 4.7×10^{-9}. Calculate the pH of a 0.10 M solution of $C_5H_5NHNO_3$.

What to Think About	How to Do It
1. The dissociation equation yields $C_5H_5NH^+$ and NO_3^- ions, each at 0.10 M concentrations. The NO_3^- ion will not hydrolyze as it is the conjugate base of a strong acid. The $C_5H_5NH^+$ cation, however will donate protons to water as it is the conjugate acid of a weak base. That hydrolysis will make the solution acidic.	$C_5H_5NHNO_3\,(s) \rightarrow \underset{0.10\text{ M}}{C_5H_5NH^+\,(aq)} + \underset{0.10\text{ M}}{NO_3^-\,(aq)}$
2. Calculate the K_a for the cation using K_w and the given K_b for pyridine.	$K_a \text{ for } C_5H_5NH^+ = \dfrac{K_w}{K_b \text{ for } C_5H_5N} = \dfrac{1.00 \times 10^{-14}}{4.7 \times 10^{-9}}$ $= 2.13 \times 10^{-6}$ Let $x = [H_3O^+]_{eq}$
5. Construct an ICE table under the equilibrium equation for hydrolysis of the cation.	$C_5H_5NH^+ + H_2O \rightleftharpoons C_5H_5N + H_3O^+$

$$C_5H_5NH^+ + H_2O \rightleftharpoons C_5H_5N + H_3O^+$$

I	0.10		0	0
C	$-x$		$+x$	$+x$
E	$0.10 - x$		x	x

Assume $0.10 - x \approx 0.10$

$$K_a \text{ for } C_5H_5NH^+ = \frac{[C_5H_5N]\,[H_3O^+]}{[C_5H_5NH^+]} = \frac{x^2}{0.10}$$

$$= 2.13 \times 10^{-6}$$

$$x = \sqrt{2.13 \times 10^{-7}} = 4.61 \times 10^{-4}$$

6. Calculate the pH.

$$pH = -\log(4.61 \times 10^{-4}) = 3.34 \text{ (2 sig. figures)}$$

© Edvantage Interactive 2016

Practice Problems — Acidic Salt Solutions

1. Ammonium nitrate is used in fertilizers, the production of explosives, and instant cold packs. Calculate the pH of the solution produced when 16.0 g of NH_4NO_3 is dissolved in enough water to produce 500.0 mL of solution.

2. The pH of a 0.50 M solution of N_2H_5Cl is found to be 4.266. Calculate the K_a for $N_2H_5^+$. Check your answer, given that the K_b for $N_2H_4 = 1.7 \times 10^{-6}$.

3. What mass of C_5H_5NHCl would be required to produce 250.0 mL of an aqueous solution with a pH = 3.00? (See Sample Problem 6.1.2 above for K_a value.)

D. Acidic Salts II: Salts Containing the Anion of a Strong Acid and a Small Highly Charged Metal Cation

Look closely at a table of relative strengths of acids and bases that you were introduced to earlier in this text. Notice that several of the weak acids are actually hydrated metal cations that are capable of donating protons to water. For example, consider the Al^{3+} cation. The ion itself is not a Brønsted-Lowry acid. However, when it is surrounded by six water molecules in its hydrated form, the combination of its small size and relatively high charge (called a high "charge density" by chemists) draws the oxygens of the attached water molecules very close. This further polarizes their O–H bonds. This increases the tendency of those molecules to donate protons, making the hydrated cation complex a weak acid. Consider the diagram of the hydrated cation in Figure 5.1.1.

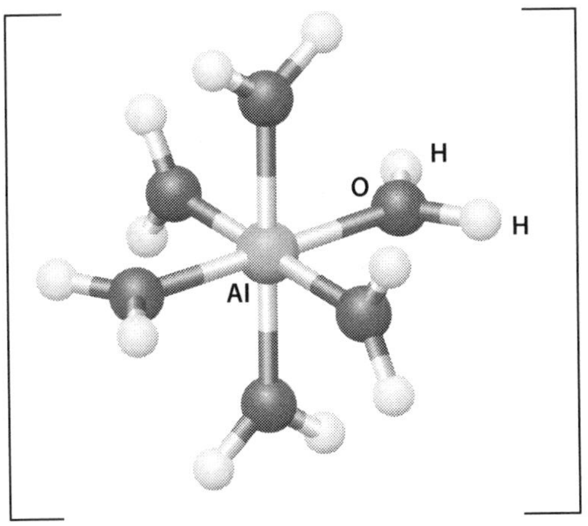

We would not expect this to occur when larger cations with charge are hydrated. This explains why the alkali metals and all but one of the alkaline earth cations do not hydrolyze. Can you suggest a reason why Be^{2+} *does* react with water to some extent?

The hydrolysis reaction for the hexaaquoaluminum cation is shown below:

$$Al(H_2O)_6^{3+}(aq) + H_2O(l) \rightleftharpoons Al(H_2O)_5OH^{2+}(aq) + H_3O^+(aq)$$

Figure 5.1.1 *The hydrated cation formed from the Al^{3+} cation surrounded by six water molecules*

Note that in the hydrolysis reaction, the number of bound water molecules decreases by one (from six to five) when the proton is donated to water and generates an OH⁻. This reduces the overall charge of the cation from 3+ to 2+.

Other hydrated cations such as Fe^{3+}, Cr^{3+}, Sn^{2+}, and Cu^{2+} show similar behavior. Generally, each ion will form an acidic hydrate with the number of water molecules equal to twice the magnitude of the charge on the cation. As a result, a salt containing one of these cations and an anion from a strong monoprotic acid would produce an acidic aqueous solution.

> A salt containing the anion of a strong monoprotic acid and a small highly charged metal cation will produce an acidic solution in water because the hydrated cation acts as a weak acid producing hydronium ions and the anion does not react.

Quick Check

1. Circle the salts below that will produce acidic aqueous solutions.

   $NaNO_2$ NH_4I $CaBr_2$ $CrCl_3$ $Sr(CN)_2$ $RbCH_3COO$ $Fe(NO_3)_3$ Li_2SO_3

2. Write the hydrolysis reactions for the following hydrated cations:

   (a) $Sn(H_2O)_4^{2+}$

   (b) $Cu(H_2O)_4^{2+}$

   (c) $Fe(H_2O)_6^{3+}$

Sample Problem — Acidic Salts II

What mass of $CrCl_3$ would be required to produce 250.0 mL of an aqueous solution with a pH of 2.75?

What to Think About

1. The aqueous solution contains Cl⁻ ions which will not hydrolyze and hydrated Cr^{3+} ions which will react with water to produce H_3O^+ ions.

2. Use the pH to determine the $[H_3O^+]_{eq}$. Use the $[H_3O^+]_{eq}$, together with the K_a value for $Cr(H_2O)_6^{3+}$ from the table, to calculate the $[Cr^{3+}]_{initial}$.

How to Do It

$$[H_3O^+]_{eq} = 10^{-pH} = 10^{-2.75} = 0.00178 \text{ M}$$

$$\text{Let } x = [Cr^{3+}]_{initial} = [Cr(H_2O)_6^{3+}]_{initial}$$

$$Cr(H_2O)_6^{3+} + H_2O \rightleftharpoons Cr(H_2O)_5OH^{2+} + H_3O^+$$

I	x		0	0
C	-0.00178		$+0.00178$	$+0.00178$
E	$x - 0.00178$		0.00178	0.00178

Continued opposite

© Edvantage Interactive 2016

What to Think About	**How to Do It**
3. $[CrCl_3]_{initial} = [Cr^{3+}]_{initial} = [Cr(H_2O)_6{}^{3+}]_{initial}$	$K_a = \dfrac{[Cr(H_2O)_5OH^{2+}]\,[H_3O^+]}{[Cr(H_2O)_6{}^{3+}]} = \dfrac{(0.00178)^2}{x - 0.00178}$ $= 1.5 \times 10^{-4}$ $1.5 \times 10^{-4}x - 2.67 \times 10^{-7} = 3.17 \times 10^{-6}$ $x = 2.29 \times 10^{-2}$ mol/L $2.29 \times 10^{-2}\, \dfrac{\text{mol CrCl}_3}{\cancel{L}} \times \dfrac{158.5\ g}{\cancel{mol}} \times 0.2500\ \cancel{L}$ $= 0.91\ g\ (2\ \text{sig. figures})$

Practice Problems — Acidic Salts II

1. Iron(III) nitrate solutions are used by jewellers to etch silver and silver alloys. Calculate the pH of a 6.0 M $Fe(NO_3)_3$ solution.

2. What concentration of $AlBr_3$ would be required to produce an aqueous solution with a pH of 3.25?

3. Unlike the other alkaline earth cations, the hydrated beryllium ion will hydrolyze by donating protons to water. The K_a for $Be(H_2O)_4{}^{2+}$ is 3.2×10^{-7}. Calculate the pH of a 0.400 M aqueous solution of BeI_2.

Magnitudes of K_a and K_b Values

Whether the two remaining classes of salts produce acidic, basic, or neutral solutions depends on the relative magnitudes of the K_a and K_b values for their ions. For the most part, you will not be expected to calculate the pH of such solutions, but calculations will be necessary to determine if those pH values will be above, below, or equal to 7.

E. Salts Containing Weakly Acidic Cations and Weakly Basic Anions

Consider the ions present in a 0.10 M solution of NH_4CN. The ammonium ion is the conjugate acid of a weak base (NH_3), and the cyanide ion is the conjugate base of a weak acid (HCN). As a result, both dissociated ions will react with water and influence the pH of the salt solution. Those two hydrolysis reactions and the corresponding equilibrium constant values are shown below:

$$NH_4^+(aq) + H_2O(l) \rightleftharpoons NH_3(aq) + H_3O^+(aq) \qquad K_a = 5.6 \times 10^{-10}$$

$$CN^-(aq) + H_2O(l) \rightleftharpoons HCN(aq) + OH^-(aq) \qquad K_b = 2.0 \times 10^{-5}$$

Note that the K_b of the cyanide ion is greater than the K_a of the ammonium ion. This tells us that the anionic hydrolysis reaction that generates hydroxide ions occurs to a much greater extent than the cationic hydrolysis reaction that produces hydronium ions. Consequently the [OH⁻] will exceed the [H₃O⁺] and the solution will be basic with a pH greater than 7.

Thus by comparing the K_a and the K_b values of the ions which hydrolyze, we can determine if the solution will be acidic, basic, or neutral. Below are guides for using this comparison to determine the acidity of a solution.

> A salt containing a weakly acidic cation and a weakly basic anion will produce a solution that is:
> acidic if K_a for the cation > K_b for the anion
> basic if K_a for the cation < K_b for the anion
> neutral if K_a for the cation = K_b for the anion

Quick Check

1. Which of the following salts will dissociate into ions that will *both* react with water?

   KI NH_4NO_2 $Fe(CN)_3$ $Sn(NO_3)_2$ $Rb_2C_2O_4$ $CrBr_3$ $NaCH_3COO$ AlF_3

2. Write out the two hydrolysis reactions that occur when a sample of NH_4F dissolves in water.

3. Which of the two hydrolysis reactions in question 2 above will occur to a greater extent? How do you know?

   _____

   _____

Sample Problem — Determining if a Salt Solution is Acidic, Basic, or Neutral Determine if an aqueous solution of $Cr(CH_3COO)_3$ will be acidic, basic, or neutral and include the hydrolysis reactions that occur.

What to Think About	How to Do It
1. Both of the dissociated ions will hydrolyze.	$Cr(H_2O)_6^{3+}(aq) + H_2O(l) \rightleftharpoons Cr(H_2O)_5OH^{2+}(aq) + H_3O^+(aq)$ $K_a = 1.5 \times 10^{-4}$
2. Use the K_a for the hydrated Cr^{3+} ion.	$CH_3COO^-(aq) + H_2O(l) \rightleftharpoons CH_3COOH(aq) + OH^-(aq)$ $K_b = \dfrac{K_w}{K_a \text{ for } CH_3COOH} = \dfrac{1.00 \times 10^{-14}}{1.8 \times 10^{-5}} = 5.6 \times 10^{-10}$
3. Calculate the K_b for the acetate ion using K_w and the K_a for acetic acid.	As the value of K_a for $Cr(H_2O)_6^{3+}$ is greater than the value of K_b for CH_3COO^-, the hydrolysis of the cation-producing hydronium ions predominates. We would expect this solution to be acidic.

© Edvantage Interactive 2016

Practice Problems — Determining if a Salt Solution is Acidic, Basic, or Neutral

1. Determine if a solution of NH_4CH_3COO will be acidic, basic, or neutral, and include the hydrolysis reactions that occur. Can you predict the approximate pH of this solution?

2. Ammonium phosphate is used in fire extinguishers and also in bread making to promote the growth of the yeast. Determine if an aqueous solution of $(NH_4)_3PO_4$ will be acidic, basic, or neutral and include the hydrolysis reactions that occur.

3. Arrange the following 0.10 M salt solutions in order of decreasing pH:

   $FeCl_3$ $(NH_4)_2CO_3$ $Al(CH_3COO)_3$ $NaNO_3$

   _____ > _____ > _____ > _____

F. Salts Containing the Cation of a Strong Base and an Amphiprotic Anion

When aqueous solutions containing an equal number of moles of NaOH and H_3PO_4 are combined, only a *partial neutralization* of the triprotic acid occurs, producing an aqueous solution of NaH_2PO_4. This solution contains sodium ions, which we know will not hydrolyze, and the amphiprotic dihydrogen phosphate ion, which is capable of both donating protons to and accepting protons from water. To determine which hydrolysis reaction predominates, we must once again compare a K_a to a K_b value, except in this case those values are for the *same ion*.

A salt containing a cation of a strong base and an amphiprotic anion will produce a solution that is: acidic if K_a for the anion > K_b for the anion
basic if K_a for the anion < K_b for the anion

Table 5.1.1 *Summary Table of Hydrolysis*

Type of Salt		Examples	Ion That Hydrolyzes	Result for Solution
Cation	**Anion**			
A. Of a strong base	Of a strong acid	KNO_3, NaCl	neither	neutral
B. Of a strong base	Of a weak acid	KCN, $NaCH_3COO$	anion	basic
C. Of a weak base[†]	Of a strong acid	NH_4I, NH_4Br	cation	acidic
D. Small highly charged	Of a strong acid	$FeCl_3$, $Al(NO_3)_3$	cation	acidic
E. Weakly acidic	Weakly basic	NH_4CN, $Fe(NO_2)_2$	both	acidic or basic*
F. Of a strong base	Amphiprotic	$NaHCO_3$, $KHSO_3$	anion	acidic or basic*

[†] *Conjugate acid of* weak base
*Acidic if $K_a > K_b$, basic if $K_a < K_b$

Sample Problem — Determining if a Salt Solution Containing the Cation of a Strong Base and an Amphiprotic Anion Will be Acidic or Basic

Determine if a 0.10 M solution of NaH_2PO_4 will be acidic or basic and include the hydrolysis reactions that occur.

What to Think About	How to Do It
1. The sodium ions will not hydrolyze, but the dihydrogen phosphate anion can. It is amphiprotic.	$H_2PO_4^-(aq) + H_2O(l) \rightleftharpoons HPO_4^{2-}(aq) + H_3O^+(aq)$ $K_a = 6.2 \times 10^{-8}$
2. Use the K_a for the anion. Calculate the K_b using K_w and the K_a for phosphoric acid.	$H_2PO_4^-(aq) + H_2O(l) \rightleftharpoons H_3PO_4(aq) + OH^-(aq)$ $K_b = \dfrac{K_w}{K_a \text{ for } H_3PO_4} = \dfrac{1.00 \times 10^{-14}}{7.5 \times 10^{-3}} = 1.3 \times 10^{-12}$ As the value of K_a is greater than the value of K_b for the anion, the hydrolysis reaction producing hydronium ions is the predominant one and the solution will therefore be slightly acidic.

Practice Problems — Determining if a Salt Solution Containing the Cation of a Strong Base and an Amphiprotic Anion Will be Acidic or Basic

1. Determine if a 0.10 M solution of K_2HPO_4 will be acidic or basic and include the hydrolysis reactions that occur.

2. Arrange the following 0.10 M aqueous solutions in order of increasing pH:

   $NaHSO_3$ $LiHCO_3$ $KHSO_4$

   _____ < _____ < _____

3. Are any calculations required to determine if an aqueous solution of $KHSO_4$ will be acidic or basic? Why or why not?

© Edvantage Interactive 2016

5.1 Activity: Hydrolysis — A Rainbow of Possibilities

Question

Can you predict the color that a universal indicator solution will display when added to a series of 10 different 0.1 M aqueous salt solutions?

Background

A universal indicator solution is a mixture of several chemical indicators, each of which undergoes a different color change over a different pH range. When the indicators are mixed, their colors and color changes combine over the entire range of the pH scale to display a series of rainbow-like hues depending on the hydronium concentration of the particular solution as shown in the table below.

pH	1	2	3	4	5	6	7	8	9	10	11	12	13	14
Colour	RED		ORANGE		YELLOW		GREEN			BLUE		PURPLE-VIOLET		

Procedure

1. Calculate the pH of the following 0.1 M aqueous solutions to determine the color displayed by the universal indicator when added to that solution. (The pH values for the first two salts are provided for you.)

   (a) $NaHSO_4$ (pH ≤ 3)

   (b) K_3PO_4 (pH ≥ 11)

   (c) NH_4NO_3

   (d) $Na_2C_2O_4$

2. Write the formula for each salt underneath the appropriate pH value and color in the diagram below.

3. Determine if the following 0.1 M aqueous solutions are acidic, basic, or neutral by comparing the K_a value for the cation to the K_b value for the anion in each salt.

   (a) $(NH_4)_2CO_3$

(b) $Fe_2(SO_4)_3$

(c) $(NH_4)_2C_2O_4$

4. The three solutions above have the following three pH values: 3.8, 6.5, and 8.5. Match each solution above to one of the pH values and write the formula for that salt underneath the appropriate pH value and color in the diagram below.

5. Determine if the following 0.1 M aqueous solutions should be acidic, basic, or neutral by comparing the K_a value to the K_b value for the anion in each salt.
   (a) KH_2PO_4

   (b) $NaHSO_3$

   (c) $KHCO_3$

6. The three solutions above have the following three pH values: 5.5, 4.0, and 9.0. Match each solution above to one of the pH values and write the formula for that salt underneath the appropriate pH value and color in the diagram below.

pH	1	2	3	4	5	6	7	8	9	10	11	12	13	14
Colour	RED		ORANGE		YELLOW		GREEN			BLUE		PURPLE-VIOLET		

_____

_____

_____

Formulas

Results and Discussion

1. If possible, ask your teacher if you can test the results of your calculations by preparing as many of the above solutions as possible. Add a few drops of universal indicator to each and/or measure the pH values with a pH meter.

© Edvantage Interactive 2016

5.1 Review Questions

1. Three separate unmarked beakers on a lab bench each contain 200 mL samples of 1.0 M clear, colorless aqueous solutions. You are told that one beaker contains $Ca(NO_3)_2$, one beaker contains K_3PO_4, and one beaker contains $Al(NO_3)_3$. Using the principles learned in this section, describe a simple test to identify the solutes in each solution.

2. Complete the following table for the six aqueous solutions by filling in the missing entries.

Salt Formula	Ion(s) that Hydrolyze(s)	Result for Aqueous Solution (Acidic, Basic, or Neutral)	Equation(s) for Hydrolysis Reaction(s) (if any)
$(NH_4)_2SO_3$			
$Al(IO_3)_3$			
RbF			
SrI_2			
KHC_2O_4			
$Fe_2(SO_4)_3$			

3. A 50.0 mL solution of 0.50 M KOH is combined with an equal volume of 0.50 M CH_3COOH.
    (a) Write the chemical equation for this neutralization reaction.

    (b) What salt concentration exists in the reaction vessel following the reaction?

(c) Calculate the pH of this solution. Begin by writing the equation for the predominant equilibrium that exists in the solution.

4. A 25.2 g sample of Na_2SO_3 is dissolved in enough water to make 500.0 mL of solution. Calculate the pH of this solution.

5. Copper(II) chloride dihydrate is a beautiful blue-green crystalline solid. The K_a for the tetraaquocopper(II) ion is 1.0×10^{-8}. What mass of $CuCl_2 \cdot 2\ H_2O$ would be required to produce 250.0 mL of an aqueous solution with a pH of 5.00?

6. Sodium cyanide is mainly used to extract gold and other precious metals in mining. Cyanide salts are also among the most rapidly acting of all poisons. A 300.0 mL aqueous solution of sodium cyanide is found to have a pH of 9.50. What mass of NaCN exists in this solution?

7. One of the main uses for ammonium perchlorate is in the production of solid rocket propellants. Calculate the pH of the solution produced by dissolving 470 g of the salt in enough water to make 5.0 L of solution.

8. Without performing any calculations, arrange the following 0.1 M aqueous solutions in order of increasing pH.

RbI NH_4Br KCN Li_2CO_3 $NaHSO_4$ $Cr(NO_3)_3$ Na_3PO_4 $FeCl_3$

_____ < _____ < _____ < _____ < _____ < _____ < _____ < _____

9. (a) What mass of KNO_2 will remain when 350.0 mL of an aqueous solution with a pH of 8.50 is evaporated to dryness?

(b) How will you observe the pH change as the volume of the solution decreases? Why?

10. Calculate the pH of a 0.500 M aqueous solution of N_2H_5Cl. The K_b for $N_2H_4 = 1.7 \times 10^{-6}$.

5.2 The Chemistry of Buffers

Warm Up

1. Consider a 1.0 L aqueous solution of 0.10 M CH_3COOH. Calculate the pH of this solution and begin by writing the equation for the predominant chemical equilibrium in the solution.

2. From the $[H_3O^+]$ calculated above, determine the percent ionization of the acetic acid.

3. A student adds 0.10 mol of $NaCH_3COO$ to the solution described in question 1.

   (a) In which direction will the equilibrium shift after the addition of the salt?

   _____

   (b) What is the name of this type of effect? (Hint: You learned about this effect in Chapter 4.)

   _____

   (c) How will the percent ionization of the acetic acid and the pH of the solution be affected?

   _____

   (d) What two chemical species participating in the equilibrium will predominate in the solution following the addition of the salt? Can these species react *with each other*?

   _____

Definition of a Buffer

Most biological fluids are solutions whose pH must be maintained within a very narrow range. In your body for example, the ability of your blood to transport oxygen depends on its pH remaining at or very near 7.35. If the pH of your blood were to deviate much more than one-tenth of a unit beyond that, it would lose the capacity to perform its vital function. Yet many products of the multiple metabolic processes occurring right now in your body are acidic compounds, each potentially able to lower your blood pH to fatal levels. In addition, many of the foods you enjoy are full of acidic compounds. If your blood were a solution incapable of effectively and continually resisting changes to its pH level, these foods would kill you. A solution capable of maintaining a relatively constant pH is known as a buffer.

> An acid-base **buffer** is a solution that resists changes in pH following the addition of relatively small amounts of a strong acid or strong base.

To understand how (and how well) a buffer solution resists pH changes, we must first discuss the *components* of a buffer. Let's start with the same 1.0 L solution of 0.10 M CH_3COOH from the Warm Up above. Only a very small percent of the weak acid is ionized, symbolized using enlarged and reduced fonts in the reaction shown below.

$$CH_3COOH(aq) + H_2O(l) \rightleftharpoons CH_3COO^-(aq) + H_3O^+(aq)$$

If a relatively small amount of a strong base such as NaOH is added to this solution, a "reservoir" of *almost all* of the original 0.10 mol of acetic acid is available to neutralize the added hydroxide ions. However, this same minimal ionization means that the solution has *almost no ability* to counter the effects of added hydronium ions from an acid because the concentration of the conjugate base in this solution is so low. This solution therefore cannot be considered to be a buffer.

To give this solution the ability to also absorb *added acid*, we must increase the concentration of the conjugate base. We can do this by adding a soluble salt of that anion in the form of, for example, sodium acetate. The weak base added is normally *the conjugate base of the weak acid already in solution*. This prevents the two species from neutralizing each other.

Let's now add 0.10 mol of $NaCH_3COO$ to this acidic solution with no volume change and consider the effects. The Na^+ is a spectator ion in the solution, but according to Le Châtelier's principle, the added acetate ions will shift the weak acid equilibrium to the left in favor of the molecular acid and further suppress its already minimal ionization. This qualifies as the common ion effect that you learned about earlier. As the shift occurs, the percent ionization of the acetic acid drops from the original 1.3% to only 0.018%. The corresponding decrease in hydronium concentration results in a pH increase in the solution from 2.87 to 4.74.

Recall the pH calculations for weak acids. There, we assumed that the equilibrium concentrations of those acids were effectively equal to the initial concentrations if the percent ionization was less than 5%. In this solution, the assumption is even more justified. Also, the equilibrium concentration of the acetate ion in this solution is slightly more than 0.10 M because of that very small percent ionization. However, because the ionization is so minimal, the equilibrium concentration of the acetate ion is effectively equal to the concentration of that anion resulting from the added salt. Also any hydrolysis of the acetate ion can be ignored because of the presence of the acetic acid.

Our solution is therefore effectively a 0.10 M solution of both acetic acid and its conjugate base, the acetate anion. Appreciable quantities of each component give the solution the capacity to resist large pH changes equally well following the addition of relatively small amounts of either a strong base or a strong acid.

This is because significant (and approximately equal) reservoirs of *both* a weak acid *and* a weak base are available in the solution to neutralize those stresses. Thus, the buffer has the ability to shift to the left or the right in response to either acidic or basic stress.

$$\underset{\approx 0.10 \text{ M}}{CH_3COOH}(aq) + H_2O(l) \rightleftharpoons \underset{\approx 0.10 \text{ M}}{CH_3COO^-}(aq) + H_3O^+(aq)$$

A buffer solution normally consists of a weak acid and its conjugate weak base in appreciable and approximately equal concentrations.

We refer to this solution as an **acidic buffer** because it will buffer a solution in the acidic region of the pH scale. Note that it's not necessary for the concentrations of the weak acid and its conjugate base to be equal — only that they are each relatively large. Normally, however, we attempt to keep those concentrations as close to equal as possible so as to give the buffer the ability to resist both acid and base stresses equally well. We'll discuss this in more detail below.

To understand how these components allow the buffer to resist significant pH changes, we begin by manipulating the K_a expression for this weak acid. Our goal is to derive an equation that tells us what determines the hydronium concentration of this buffer solution.

Because: $K_a = \dfrac{[CH_3COO^-][H_3O^+]}{[CH_3COOH]}$ then: $[H_3O^+] = K_a \dfrac{[CH_3COOH]}{[CH_3COO^-]}$

Or in general: $[H_3O^+] = K_a \dfrac{[HA]}{[A^-]}$

> This simple but important equation means that the hydronium ion concentration (and therefore the pH) of a buffer solution depends on two factors:
> - the K_a value for the weak acid and
> - the *ratio* of the concentration of that weak acid to its conjugate base in the solution

Examining the above equation more closely reveals some additional details:

1. If the concentrations of the acid and its conjugate base are equal, a ratio of 1 means that the hydronium concentration in the buffer solution is simply equal to the K_a value for the weak acid. Thus, in our example, the $[H_3O^+] = K_a$ for acetic acid $= 1.8 \times 10^{-5}$ M.

2. At a constant temperature, only one of the two factors determining $[H_3O^+]$ (and therefore its maintenance) is variable. As the value of K_a is a constant, only the weak acid/conjugate base concentration ratio can be changed. Specifically: if the $[HA]/[A^-]$ ratio *increases*, the $[H_3O^+]$ *increases*, and if the $[HA]/[A^-]$ ratio *decreases*, the $[H_3O^+]$ *decreases*.

3. When we dilute a buffer solution, the concentrations of both the weak acid and its conjugate base are reduced equally. Therefore, their ratio remains constant. This means that the hydronium ion concentration (and so the pH) *does not change* when a buffer solution is diluted.

Quick Check

1. Why do we normally attempt to make the concentrations of the weak acid and its conjugate base in a buffer solution approximately equal?

   _____

2. In a buffer containing HA and A$^-$, the conjugate base A$^-$ will react to neutralize added acid. As a result, following the addition of a small amount of strong acid to a buffer solution, the $[HA]/[A^-]$ ratio will _____ (increase or decrease), the $[H_3O^+]$ will _____ (increase or decrease) slightly, and the pH will _____ (increase or decrease) slightly.

3. Circle the pairs of chemical species below that could be used to prepare a buffer solution.

   HNO_3 and $NaNO_3$ KF and HF HNO_2 and HNO_3 HCOOH and LiHCOO

   $NaHSO_4$ and Na_2SO_4 K_2CO_3 and $K_2C_2O_4$ HCl and NaCl KH_2PO_4 and K_2HPO_4

pH Change Resistance after the Addition of a Strong Acid to an Acidic Buffer

Let's use some of the above points as we discuss the chemistry of buffers in more detail.

We'll begin by using our acetic acid/acetate ion buffer as an example. First, we'll consider how the components of a buffer allow it to resist pH changes after the addition of a relatively small amount of either a strong acid or a strong base.

When a small amount of strong acid is added to a buffer, the reservoir of conjugate base (resulting from the added salt) reacts with the hydronium ions from the acid. In our example, this yields the following net ionic equation:

$$CH_3COO^-(aq) + H_3O^+(aq) \rightarrow CH_3COOH(aq) + H_2O(l)$$

All of the hydronium ions from the strong acid are converted to the weak acid and water in the reaction. This increases the [CH_3COOH] and decreases the [CH_3COO^-] by a stoichiometric amount equal to the number of moles of hydronium ions added from the strong acid. The result is that the buffer component *ratio* increases, which increases the overall [H_3O^+] but *only by a very small amount*.

Although a quantitative treatment of buffer chemistry will likely not be expected in this course, discussing some numbers will demonstrate how effective a buffer is at maintaining a relatively constant pH.

In our original buffer solution, the component ratio was equal to 1. Therefore, the [H_3O^+] was equal to the K_a for acetic acid, namely 1.8×10^{-5} M. We now add 0.010 mol HCl to 1.0 L of our buffer solution containing 0.10 M CH_3COOH and 0.10 M CH_3COO^- with no volume change. The 0.010 mol H_3O^+ will be consumed according to the above reaction and therefore decrease the [CH_3COO^-] by 0.010 mol/L and increase the [CH_3COOH] by 0.010 mol/L. The result for our 1.0 L buffer solution will be as shown in Table 5.2.1.

Table 5.2.1 *Results of Adding 0.010 mol H_3O^+ to the Buffer Solution*

	[CH_3COOH]	[CH_3COO^-]	[CH_3COOH]/[CH_3COO^-] Ratio
Before 0.010 M H_3O^+ added	0.10 M	0.10 M	0.10 M/0.10 M = 1.0
After 0.010 M H_3O^+ added	0.11 M	0.09 M	0.11 M/0.09 M = 1.222

The initial and final [H_3O^+] are calculated below according to the equation:

$$[H_3O^+] = (K_a \text{ for acetic acid}) \times \frac{[CH_3COOH]}{[CH_3COO^-]}$$

Initial [H_3O^+] = $(1.8 \times 10^{-5}$ M$) \times (1.0)$ = **1.8×10^{-5} M** so pH = $-\log (1.8 \times 10^{-5})$ = **4.74**

Final [H_3O^+] = $(1.8 \times 10^{-5}$ M$) \times (1.22)$ = **2.20×10^{-5} M** so pH = $-\log (2.196 \times 10^{-5})$ = **4.66**

The pH has indeed decreased, but *only* by 0.08 units. To appreciate how effective this buffer is at maintaining the pH, consider the result of adding 0.010 mol HCl to 1.0 L of pure water. The [H_3O^+] would increase from 1.0×10^{-7} M to 1.0×10^{-2} M. This represents a *100 000 times increase* in hydronium ion concentration and a *5 unit decrease* in pH from 7.00 to 2.00!

pH Change Resistance after the Addition of a Strong Base to a Buffer Solution

When a small amount of strong base is added to a buffer, the reservoir of weak acid reacts with the hydroxide ions from the base. For our example, this results in the following net ionic equation:

$$CH_3COOH(aq) + OH^-(aq) \rightarrow CH_3COO^-(aq) + H_2O(l)$$

All of the hydroxide ions from the strong base are converted to the conjugate base of the weak acid and water in the reaction. This decreases the [CH_3COOH] and increases the [CH_3COO^-] by a stoichiometric amount equal to the number of moles of hydroxide ions added from the strong base. The result is that the buffer component *ratio* decreases, which decreases the overall [H_3O^+] but once again, *only by a very small amount*.

Using the same 1.0 L buffer solution containing 0.10 M CH_3COOH and 0.10 M CH_3COO^-, we add 0.010 mol NaOH with no volume change. The 0.010 mol OH^- will be consumed according to the above reaction and therefore decrease the [CH_3COOH] by 0.010 mol/L and increase the [CH_3COO^-] by 0.010 mol/L. The result for our 1.0 L buffer solution is shown in Table 5.2.2.

Table 5.2.2 *Results of Adding 0.010 mol OH^- to the Buffer Solution*

	[CH_3COOH]	[CH_3COO^-]	[CH_3COOH]/[CH_3COO^-] Ratio
Before 0.010 M OH^- added	0.10 M	0.10 M	0.10 M/0.10 M = 1.0
After 0.010 M OH^- added	0.09 M	0.11 M	0.09 M/0.11 M = 0.82

We can once again calculate the final $[H_3O^+]$ by multiplying the K_a for acetic acid by the new reduced ratio:

Final $[H_3O^+] = (1.8 \times 10^{-5}$ M$) \times (0.82) = \mathbf{1.48 \times 10^{-5}}$ **M** so final pH $= -\log (1.48 \times 10^{-5}) = \mathbf{4.83}$

The pH value has increased, but once again only slightly — by just 0.09 units. The effectiveness of this buffer at maintaining a relatively constant pH is again evident if we consider that adding 0.010 mol NaOH to 1.0 L of pure water would reduce the $[H_3O^+]$ from 1.0×10^{-7} M to 1.0×10^{-12} M. This represents a *100 000 times decrease* in hydronium ion concentration and a *5 unit increase* in pH from 7.00 to 12.00!

Figure 5.2.1 summarizes our examples above. Note the appropriate net ionic equation below each section of the diagram.

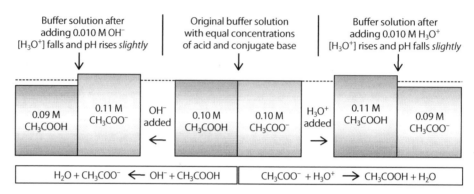

Figure 5.2.1 *The effects on pH of adding a strong base or a strong acid to an acidic buffer*

Sample Problem — Acidic Buffers

Consider a 1.0 L buffer solution composed of 1.0 M HNO_2 and 1.0 M $NaNO_2$.
(a) Write the equation for the weak acid equilibrium in this solution and highlight the predominant species in that equilibrium.
(b) Write the net ionic equation for the reaction that occurs when a small amount of HCl is added to this solution.
(c) How will the $[HNO_2]/[NO_2^-]$ ratio, the $[H_3O^+]$, and the pH change following the addition of this acid? What equation do you use to make these decisions?

What to Think About

1. The concentrations of both HNO_2 and NO_2^- can be safely assumed to be ≈ 1.0 M, making these the major species.

2. The addition of a small amount of the strong acid HCl introduces H_3O^+ ions into the solution, which react with the nitrite anions to form HNO_2 and water.

3. This reduces the $[NO_2^-]$ and increases the $[HNO_2]$ increasing the concentration ratio of weak acid to conjugate base.

   This increases the $[H_3O^+]$ and lowers the pH slightly according to the equation given earlier.

How to Do It

(a) $HNO_2 (aq) + H_2O (l) \rightleftharpoons NO_2^- (aq) + H_3O^+ (aq)$

(b) $NO_2^- (aq) + H_3O^+ (aq) \rightarrow HNO_2 (aq) + H_2O (l)$

(c) The above equation means that the $[HNO_2]/[NO_2^-]$ ratio will increase. This causes the $[H_3O^+]$ to increase slightly and the pH to decrease slightly as per the following equation:

$$[H_3O^+] = (K_a \text{ for } HNO_2) \times \frac{[HNO_2]}{[NO_2^-]}$$

© Edvantage Interactive 2016

Practice Problems — Acidic Buffers

1. (a) Fill in the blanks in the statement below.
   Following the addition of a small amount of strong base to a buffer solution, the [HA]/[A⁻] ratio _____ (increases or decreases), the [H₃O⁺] _____ (increases or decreases) slightly, and the pH _____ (increases or decreases) slightly.

   (b) Write the net ionic equation for the reaction occurring when a small amount of NaOH is added to the buffer solution discussed in Sample Problem 8.2.1 above.

   (c) How will the [HNO₂]/[NO₂⁻] ratio, the [H₃O⁺], and the pH of this solution change following the addition of this strong base?

2. (a) If 100.0 mL of the buffer solution discussed in the sample problem is diluted to 1.0 L, the pH will be the same as the original buffer solution. How many moles of HNO₂ and NO₂⁻ are available to neutralize added H₃O⁺ and OH⁻ ions in 1.0 L of this diluted solution compared with 1.0 L of the undiluted buffer solution?

   (b) If 0.11 mol HCl is now added to each of these 1.0 L buffer solutions, would they be equally able to resist a significant change in their pH levels? Why or why not?

3. Determine if each of the following solutions qualifies as a buffer. Briefly explain your answer in each case.
   (a) 0.10 M HI/0.10 M NaI

   (b) 0.50 M NaF/0.50 M NaCN

   (c) 1.0 M K₂C₂O₄/1.0 M KHC₂O₄

   (d) 0.20 M HF/0.20 M HCN

Buffering a Solution in the Basic pH Region

We can also prepare a solution that buffers in the basic region of the pH scale. This is called a **basic buffer**. Although some minor differences exist, the chemistry associated with the maintenance of solution pH is very similar to the chemistry for an acidic buffer.

Consider 1.0 L of an aqueous solution of 0.10 M $NH_3(aq)$ and 0.10 M NH_4Cl (aq). The equilibrium and predominant participating species can be represented as shown below:

$$\mathbf{NH_3}_{(aq)} + H_2O(l) \rightleftharpoons \mathbf{NH_4}^+_{(aq)} + OH^-(aq)$$
$$\approx 0.10 \text{ M} \qquad\qquad \approx 0.10 \text{ M}$$

This solution has appreciable quantities of both a weak base and its conjugate acid in approximately equal amounts. (Note that the chloride ion from the salt is simply a spectator ion in this aqueous solution.) The buffer solution has the capacity to resist large pH changes equally well following the addition of relatively small amounts of both a strong acid and a strong base because significant (and approximately equal) reservoirs of *both* a weak base and a weak acid are available in the solution to neutralize those stresses.

In terms of the hydroxide concentration in a solution of this basic buffer, we can derive an equation similar to the one when we began with an acid ionization earlier. In our example:

Because: $K_b = \dfrac{[NH_4^+][OH^-]}{[NH_3]}$ then: $[OH^-] = K_b \dfrac{[NH_3]}{[NH_4^+]}$

Or in general for any buffer containing a weak base B: $[OH^-] = K_b \dfrac{[B]}{[HB^+]}$

> The hydroxide ion concentration (and therefore the pH) of this buffer solution depends on two factors:
> - the K_b value for the weak base and
> - the *ratio* of the concentration of that weak base to its conjugate acid in the solution

Similar to an acidic buffer, the equation tells us that the hydroxide ion concentration and ultimately the pH of the solution depend on a constant and the ratio of the concentrations of a conjugate acid-base pair. The equation tells us that *if* the $[B]/[HB^+]$ ratio *increases*, the $[OH^-]$ *increases*, and *if* the $[B]/[HB^+]$ ratio *decreases*, the $[OH^-]$ *decreases*.

As noted earlier, only a qualitative treatment of buffer chemistry will be expected in this course. However, we can appreciate the effectiveness of this basic buffer by quantitatively investigating the results of adding a relatively small amount of both a strong acid and strong base to 1.0 L of the solution. We will add the same amount of each to the basic buffer as we did to the acidic buffer discussed earlier.

pH Change Resistance after the Addition of a Strong Acid

When a small amount of strong acid is added, the reservoir of weak base reacts with the hydronium ions from the acid. In our example, this yields the following net ionic equation:

$$NH_3(aq) + H_3O^+(aq) \rightarrow NH_4^+(aq) + H_2O(l)$$

All of the hydronium ions from the strong acid are converted to the conjugate acid of the weak base and water in the reaction. This increases the $[NH_4^+]$ and decreases the $[NH_3]$ by a stoichiometric amount equal to the number of moles of hydronium ions added from the strong acid. The result is that the buffer component *ratio* decreases, which decreases the overall $[OH^-]$ but *only by a very small amount*.

Assume that we add 0.010 mol HCl to this solution with no volume change. The 0.010 mol H_3O^+ will be consumed according to the above reaction. It will therefore decrease the $[NH_3]$ by 0.010 mol/L and increase the $[NH_4^+]$ by 0.010 mol/L. The result for our 1.0 L buffer solution is shown in Table 5.2.3.

Table 5.2.3 *Results of Adding 0.010 mol H_3O^+ to the Buffer Solution*

	$[NH_3]$	**$[NH_4^+]$**	**$[NH_3]/[NH_4^+]$ Ratio**
Before 0.010 M H_3O^+ added	0.10 M	0.10 M	0.10 M/0.10 M = 1.0
After 0.010 M H_3O^+ added	0.09 M	0.11 M	0.09 M/0.11 M = 0.82

The initial and final $[OH^-]$ along with the initial and final pH values are calculated below:

$[OH^-] = (K_b \text{ for } NH_3) \times \dfrac{[NH_3]}{[NH_4^+]}$ (Remember: K_b for $NH_3 = K_w / K_a$ for NH_4^+)

Initial $[OH^-] = (1.8 \times 10^{-5} \text{ M}) \times (1.0) = \mathbf{1.8 \times 10^{-5}}$ **M**

So initial $[H_3O^+] = \dfrac{1.00 \times 10^{-14}}{1.8 \times 10^{-5}} = \mathbf{5.6 \times 10^{-10}}$ **M** so initial pH = $-\log (5.6 \times 10^{-10}) = \mathbf{9.25}$

Final $[OH^-] = (1.8 \times 10^{-5} \text{ M}) \times (0.82) = \mathbf{1.48 \times 10^{-5}}$ **M**

So final $[H_3O^+] = \dfrac{1.00 \times 10^{-14}}{1.48 \times 10^{-5}} = \mathbf{6.76 \times 10^{-10}}$ **M** so final pH = $-\log (6.76 \times 10^{-10}) = \mathbf{9.17}$

Contrast this minimal increase in hydronium concentration and corresponding minimal decrease in pH with the huge changes to both after the addition of 0.010 mol HCl to 1.0 L of pure water, discussed earlier in the section.

pH Change Resistance after the Addition of a Strong Base

When a small amount of strong base is added, the reservoir of the weak conjugate acid (from the added salt) reacts with the hydroxide ions from the base. For our example, this results in the following net ionic equation:

$NH_4^+ (aq) + OH^-(aq) \longrightarrow NH_3(aq) + H_2O(l)$

All of the hydroxide ions from the strong base are converted to the weak base and water in the reaction. This increases the $[NH_3]$ and decreases the $[NH_4^+]$ by a stoichiometric amount equal to the number of moles of hydroxide ions added from the strong base. The result is that the buffer component *ratio* increases, which increases the overall $[OH^-]$ once again by a very small amount.

Using the same 1.0 L basic buffer solution above, we add 0.010 mol NaOH with no volume change. The 0.010 mol OH^- will be consumed according to the above reaction. It will therefore increase the $[NH_3]$ by 0.010 mol/L7and decrease the $[NH_4^+]$ by 0.010 mol/L. The result for our 1.0 L buffer solution is shown in Table 5.2.4.

Table 5.2.4 *Results of Adding 0.010 mol OH^- to the Buffer Solution*

	$[NH_3]$	**$[NH_4^+]$**	**$[NH_3]/[NH_4^+]$ Ratio**
Before 0.010 M OH^- added	0.10 M	0.10 M	0.10 M/0.10 M = 1.0
After 0.010 M OH^- added	0.11 M	0.09 M	0.11 M/0.09 M = 1.22

We can once again calculate the final $[OH^-]$ according to the following:

Final $[OH^-] = (1.8 \times 10^{-5} \text{ M}) \times (1.222) = \mathbf{2.20 \times 10^{-5}}$ **M**

So final $[H_3O^+] = \dfrac{1.00 \times 10^{-14}}{2.20 \times 10^{-5}} = \mathbf{4.55 \times 10^{-10}}$ **M** and final pH = $-\log (4.55 \times 10^{-10}) = \mathbf{9.34}$

Obviously, if *less* than a 0.10 pH unit change occurs in our basic buffer solution after adding either 0.010 mol of strong acid or 0.010 mol of strong base, the buffer is extremely efficient at maintaining a reasonably constant pH compared to pure water.

Consider once again that the same maintenance of relatively constant pH occurs whether we discuss an acid ionization or a base ionization. Figure 5.2.2 summarizes the changes we have just discussed for this basic buffer. Note again the appropriate net ionic equations beneath each section of the diagram.

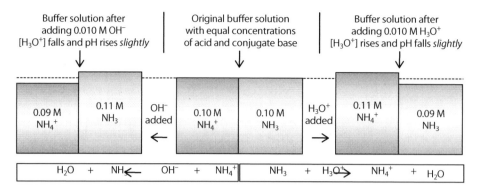

Figure 5.2.2 *The effects on pH of adding a strong base or a strong acid to a basic buffer*

Sample Problem — Basic Buffers

1. Hydrazine, N_2H_4, is a weak base with a $K_b = 1.7 \times 10^{-6}$. What compound could you add to a 0.50 M solution of hydrazine to make a basic buffer solution?

2. Extension: If the concentration of that compound in the final solution were also 0.50 M, what $[H_3O^+]$ would exist in the buffer solution?

What to Think About

1. To make this solution a buffer, add a soluble salt of the conjugate acid of hydrazine.

2. If the concentration of that conjugate acid is also 0.50 M, then according to the equation discussed above, the hydroxide ion concentration in the solution is equal to the K_b for hydrazine. Calculate the hydronium concentration based on that.

How to Do It

The conjugate acid of N_2H_4 is $N_2H_5^+$. Therefore an appropriate compound to add to this solution would be N_2H_5Cl.

If the solution contained 0.50 M N_2H_4 and also 0.50 M N_2H_5Cl, then in the buffer solution:

$$[OH^-] = K_b \text{ for } N_2H_4 = 1.7 \times 10^{-6} \text{ M}$$

Thus: $[H_3O^+] = \dfrac{K_w}{[OH^-]} = \dfrac{100 \times 10^{-14}}{1.7 \times 10^{-6}} = 5.9 \times 10^{-9}$ M

Practice Problems — Basic Buffers

1. Each of the following solutions contains a weak base. What compounds (in what concentrations ideally) would make each a buffer solution?

Weak Base	Added Compound
(a) 1.0 M CH_3NH_2	
(b) 0.80 M N_2H_4	
(c) 0.20 M $(CH_3)_2NH$	

2. Write the six net ionic equations representing the reactions occurring when a small amount of strong acid and also a small amount of strong base are added to each of the above basic buffer solutions.

	Net Ionic Equation When Acid Added	Net Ionic Equation When Base Added
(a)		
(b)		
(c)		

© Edvantage Interactive 2016

The Henderson-Hasselbalch Equation (Extension)

A very useful relationship for buffers can be derived from the equation we have discussed in this section, namely:

$$[H_3O^+] = K_a \times \frac{[HA]}{[A^-]}$$

Taking the negative logarithm of both sides of this equation yields:

$$-\log [H_3O^+] = -\log K_a + -\log \left[\frac{[HA]}{[A^-]} \right]$$

(Note the inversion of the ratio when the sign of the log is changed.)

From which we can obtain: $pH = pK_a + \log \left[\frac{[A^-]}{[HA]} \right]$

If we generalize the ratio for any conjugate acid-base pair, we write what is known as the **Henderson-Hasselbalch equation:**

$$pH = pK_a + \log \left[\frac{[base]}{[acid]} \right]$$

Again, buffer calculations will not likely be required in this course, but any discussion of buffers should include some reference to this equation because, as we will see below, it represents a convenient tool for both analyzing and preparing buffer solutions.

The Capacity of a Buffer

The above equation reinforces that the pH of a given buffer is dependent only on the component ratio in the solution resulting from the relative concentrations of the conjugate base and weak acid. For example, a 0.010 M CH_3COO^-/0.010 M CH_3COOH buffer solution will have the same pH as a buffer solution containing 1.0 M CH_3COO^- and 1.0 M CH_3COOH. However, their ability to *resist changes* to those pH values will be different because that ability depends on the absolute concentrations of their buffer components. The former solution can neutralize only a small amount of acid or base before its pH changes significantly. The latter can withstand the addition of much more acid or base before a significant change in its pH occurs.

> **Buffer capacity** is defined as the amount of acid or base a buffer can neutralize before its pH changes significantly.

A more concentrated or *high-capacity* buffer will experience less of a pH change following the addition of a given amount of strong acid or strong base than a less concentrated or *low-capacity* buffer will. Stated another way, to cause the same pH change, more strong acid or strong base must be added to a high-capacity buffer than to a low-capacity buffer.

> Following the addition of an equal amount of H_3O^+ or OH^- ions, the $[A^-]/[HA]$ ratio (and hence the pH) changes more for a solution of a low-capacity buffer than for a high-capacity buffer.

Preparation of a Buffer

The buffer solutions we have discussed in this section contain equal concentrations of conjugate acid-base pairs. There is a reason for that. The Henderson-Hasselbalch equation clearly shows that the more the component ratio changes, the more the solution pH changes. In addition, simple calculations with the same equation show that the more similar the component concentrations are to each other (the closer the $[A^-]/[HA]$ ratio is to 1) in a buffer solution, the less that ratio changes after the addition of a given amount of strong acid or strong base. Conversely, a buffer solution whose component concentrations are very different will experience a greater change in pH following the addition of the same amount of H_3O^+ or OH^- ions. Practically speaking, if the $[A^-]/[HA]$ ratio is less than 0.1 or greater than 10, the buffer can no longer maintain its pH level when a small amount of strong acid or base is added. This means that a buffer is effective only if the following condition is met:

$$10 \geq \frac{[A^-]}{[HA]} \geq 0.1$$

As a result, when we prepare a buffer, we attempt to find a weak acid whose pK_a is as close as possible to the desired pH so that the component ratio is within the desired range and ideally as close as possible to 1.

More on Buffer Preparation (Extension)

Preparations of buffer solutions for biological and environmental purposes are a common task for researchers and laboratory technicians. The Henderson-Hasselbalch equation and the above rules are routinely employed in the process. The desired pH of the solution usually dictates the choice of the conjugate acid-base pair. Because a buffer is *most effective* when the component concentration ratio is *closest to 1*, the *best weak acid* will be the one whose pK_a is *closest* to that target pH value. Once that acid is chosen, the Henderson-Hasselbalch equation is used to choose the appropriate ratio of $[A^-]/[HA]$ that achieves the desired pH. As mentioned at the beginning of this section, the equilibrium and initial concentrations of the buffer components are almost the same. This allows the equation to yield the following:

$$\text{Desired pH} = pK_a + \log\left[\frac{[A^-]_{initial}}{[HA]_{initial}}\right]$$

When the actual concentrations are chosen, the fact that higher concentrations make better buffers means that low concentrations are normally avoided. For most applications, concentrations between 0.05 M and 0.5 M are sufficient. Sample Problem 8.2.3 is offered for demonstration purposes only.

Sample Problem — Extension: Preparing a Buffer

An environmental chemist requires a solution buffered to pH 5.00 to study the effects of acid rain on aquatic microorganisms. Decide on the most appropriate buffer components and suggest their appropriate relative concentrations.

What to Think About	How to Do It
1. Choose an acid whose pK_a value is close to 5.00. The sodium salt of its conjugate base will then be the second buffer component.	The K_a for acetic acid = 1.8×10^{-5}. This corresponds to a pK_a = 4.74. Therefore this buffer solution can be prepared from acetic acid and sodium acetate. According to the Henderson-Hasselbalch equation, $$pH = 5.00 = 4.74 + \log\left[\frac{[CH_3COO^-]_{initial}}{[CH_3COOH]_{initial}}\right]$$
2. Determine the proper $[A^-]/[HA]$ ratio according to the Henderson-Hasselbalch equation to obtain the desired buffer pH.	so $\log\left[\frac{[CH_3COO^-]_{initial}}{[CH_3COOH]_{initial}}\right] = 0.26$ and thus $\left[\frac{[CH_3COO^-]_{initial}}{[CH_3COOH]_{initial}}\right] = 10^{0.26} = 1.8$ A ratio of 1.8 to 1.0 could be accomplished with many combinations. For example: 1.8 M and 1.0 M, 0.18 M and 0.10 M, and 0.90 M and 0.50 M are all correct concentrations for CH_3COO^- and CH_3COOH respectively in this buffer. The choice depends on the required capacity of the buffer.

© Edvantage Interactive 2016

Practice Problems — Buffer Capacity and Preparation

1. Rank the following four buffer solutions (by letter) in order from lowest to highest capacity.
   - (a) 0.48 M HF and 0.50 M NaF
   - (c) 1.0 M CH_3COOH and 1.0 M $LiCH_3COO$
   - (b) 0.040 M HCOOH and 0.060 M KHCOO
   - (d) 0.10 M H_2S and 0.095 M NaHS

   _____ < _____ < _____ < _____

2. *Buffer range* is the pH range over which a buffer acts effectively. Given that the $[A^-]/[HA]$ ratio should be no less than 0.1 and no more than 10 for a buffer to be effective, use the Henderson-Hasselbalch equation to determine how far away the pH of a buffer solution can be (+ or –) from the pK_a of the weak acid component before that buffer becomes ineffective. Your answer represents the normally accepted range of a buffer.

3. Prior to being used to measure the pH of a solution, pH meters are often calibrated with solutions buffered to pH = 7.00 and also pH = 4.00 or pH = 10.00. Use a table of relative strengths of acids and bases and the Henderson-Hasselbalch equation to select three appropriate conjugate acid-base pairs that could be used to prepare these buffer solutions and complete the table below.

Desired pH	Weak Acid	Weak Acid pK_a	Salt of Conjugate Base
4.00			
7.00			
10.00			

The Maintenance of Blood pH

Two of the most important functions of your blood are to transport oxygen and nutrients to all of the cells in your body and also to remove carbon dioxide and other waste materials from them.

This essential and complex system could not operate without several buffer systems.

The two main components of blood are blood plasma, the straw-colored liquid component of blood, and red blood cells, or *erythrocytes*. Erythrocytes contain a complex protein molecule called hemoglobin, which is the molecule that transports oxygen in your blood. Hemoglobin (which we will represent as HHb) functions effectively as a weak monoprotic acid according to the following equilibrium:

$$HHb(aq) + O_2(aq) + H_2O(l) \rightleftharpoons HbO_2^-(aq) + H_3O^+(aq)$$
hemoglobin   oxyhemoglobin

The system functions properly when oxygen binds to hemoglobin producing oxyhemoglobin. That oxygen is eventually released to diffuse out of the red blood cells to be absorbed by other cells to carry out metabolism. For this to occur properly, several buffer systems maintain the pH of the blood at about 7.35.

If the $[H_3O^+]$ is too low (pH greater than about 7.50), then the equilibrium shown above shifts so far to the right that the $[HbO_2^-]$ is too high to allow for adequate release of O_2. This is called *alkalosis*.

If the $[H_3O^+]$ is too high (pH lower than about 7.20), then the equilibrium shifts far enough to the left that the $[HbO_2^-]$ is too low. The result is that the hemoglobin's affinity for oxygen is so reduced that the molecules won't bind together. This is called *acidosis*.

The most important buffer system managing blood pH involves H_2CO_3 and HCO_3^-. $CO_2(aq)$

produced during metabolic processes such as respiration is converted in the blood to H_2CO_3 by an enzyme called carbonic anhydraze. The carbonic acid then rapidly decomposes to bicarbonate and hydrogen ions. We can represent the process in the equation shown below:

$$CO_2(aq) + H_2O(l) \rightleftharpoons H_2CO_3(aq) \rightleftharpoons HCO_3^-(aq) + H^+(aq)$$

We can clearly see the buffer components in the above equilibrium system. For example, any addition of hydrogen ions will reduce the $[HCO_3^-]/[H_2CO_3]$ ratio and lower the pH only slightly. Coupled with the above system is the body's remarkable ability to alter its breathing to modify the concentration of dissolved CO_2. In the above example, rapid breathing would increase the loss of CO_2 to the atmosphere in the form of gaseous CO_2. This would then lower the concentration of $CO_2(aq)$ and further help to remove any added H^+ by driving the above equilibrium to the left.

Quick Check

1. Another buffer system present in blood and in other cells is the $H_2PO_4^-/HPO_4^{2-}$ buffer system.
    (a) Write the net ionic equation representing the result of adding hydronium ions to a solution containing this buffer system.

    (b) Write the net ionic equation representing the result of adding hydroxide ions to a solution containing this buffer system.

2. People under severe stress will sometimes hyperventilate, which involves rapid inhaling and exhaling. This can lower the $[CO_2]$ in the blood so much that a person may lose consciousness.
    (a) Consider the above equilibrium and suggest the effect of hyperventilating on blood pH if the concentration of carbon dioxide is too low.

    (b) Why might breathing into a paper bag reduce the effects of hyperventilation?

© Edvantage Interactive 2016

5.2 Activity: Over-The-Counter Buffer Chemistry

Question
What kinds of buffers are used in over-the-counter medicines?

Background
Many common over-the-counter medicines employ chemical principles that you are learning about. One of the most common and effective pain relievers or "analgesics" is the weak acid acetylsalicylic acid (ASA), $C_8H_7O_2COOH$. This product is marketed under various brands but the best-known one is Aspirin by the Bayer Corporation. (*Note that anyone under the age of 18 should not use ASA as children may develop Reye's syndrome, a potentially fatal disease that may occur with ASA use in treating flu or chickenpox.*)

One form of the product contains a "buffering agent" because some people are sensitive to the acidity level of this medication. That same "buffering agent" is used in several antacid remedies to neutralize excess stomach acid (HCl).

Procedure
1. Consider the advertisement shown here and answer the questions below.

    (a) Identify the ion in the compound listed on the box that acts as the "acid neutralizer" and buffers the ASA.

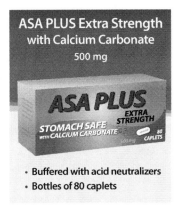

- Buffered with acid neutralizers
- Bottles of 80 caplets

    (b) Write the net ionic equation corresponding to the reaction involving the "acid neutralizer" reacting with a small amount of strong acid.

    (c) Write the net ionic equation corresponding to the reaction occurring when a small amount of strong base is added to a relatively concentrated solution of ASA.

    (d) Consider the above net ionic equations and decide if a solution containing significant quantities of ASA and the ion identified as the acid neutralizer in question 1 would function well as a buffer solution? Why or why not?

2. Consider the antacid label shown here and note that the active ingredient is the same compound used to buffer the ASA above.

(a) Determine the pH of a buffer solution containing a 0.10 M solution of both the anion in the compound listed on the label and its conjugate acid.

(b) Would this solution be considered an acidic or a basic buffer?

3. Next time you're in a pharmacy, locate other antacid or "buffered" products on the shelves. Read the labels to determine if the active ingredient is the same or different than in the products listed here. If different, think about the chemistry associated with that ingredient and try to figure out how it works. (Thinking about the chemistry you encounter every day is *always* a good idea!)

5.2 Review Questions

1. What is the purpose of an acid-base buffer?

2. Why do you think that the components of a buffer solution are normally a conjugate acid-base pair rather than any combination of a weak acid and a weak base?

3. Explain why a solution of 0.10 M HNO_3 and 0.10 M $NaNO_3$ cannot function as a buffer solution.

4. Each of the following compound pairs exists at a concentration 0.50 M in their respective solutions. Circle the solutions that represent buffers:

   Na_2CO_3/KOH   NaCl/HCl C_6H_5COOH/KC_6H_5COO HNO_3/KNO_2

   N_2H_4/NH_3 $CH_3NH_3NO_3$/CH_3NH_2 K_2SO_3/$KHSO_3$ CH_3COOH/HI

   HBr/NaOH KIO_3/HIO_3 $NaHS$/H_2S HF/LiF H_2O_2/$RbHO_2$

5. Consider a buffer solution containing 0.30 M HCN and 0.30 M NaCN.
   (a) Without performing any calculations, state the $[H_3O^+]$ in the solution.

   (b) Is this solution considered to be an acidic or a basic buffer? Why?

   (c) Write the net ionic equation for the reaction occurring when a small amount of HCl is added to the solution. What happens to the pH of the solution after the HCl is added?

   (d) Write the net ionic equation for the reaction occurring when a small amount of NaOH is added to the solution. What happens to the pH of the solution after the NaOH is added?

6. Complete the following table for a buffer solution containing equal concentrations of HA and A⁻ when a small amount of strong acid is added and when a small amount of strong base is added.

Stress Applied	Net Ionic Equation	How [HA]/[A⁻] Changes	How pH Changes
H_3O^+ added			
OH^- added			

7. Without performing any calculations, consult a table of K_a values and arrange the following buffer solutions (by letter) in order from lowest $[H_3O^+]$ to highest $[H_3O^+]$:
    (a) 1.0 M H_2S/1.0 M NaHS   (c) 0.25 M $NaHC_2O_4$/0.25 M $Na_2C_2O_4$
    (b) 0.50 M HCN/0.50 M KCN   (d) 2.0 M HCOOH/2.0 M LiHCOO

    _____ < _____ < _____ < _____

8. What is meant by the term *buffer capacity* and what does it depend upon? Which of the buffer solutions listed in question 7 above would have the highest capacity?

9. List the following four buffer solutions (by letter) in order from highest to lowest capacity.
    (a) 0.010 M KNO_2/0.010 M HNO_2 (c) 0.0010 M NH_3/0.0010 M NH_4Cl
    (b) 0.10 M CH_3COOH/0.10 M $NaCH_3COO$ (d) 1.0 M HF/1.0 M NaF

    _____ > _____ > _____ > _____

10. What is meant by the term *buffer range*? How is it related to the pK_a value for the weak acid component of a buffer solution?

11. Describe the effect of lowering the $[CO_2]$ in blood on the pH of the blood.

12. Describe the effect of *alkalosis* on the ability of hemoglobin to transport oxygen.

13. Describe the effect of *acidosis* on the ability of hemoglobin to transport oxygen.

14. **Challenge:** Consider carefully the components of a buffer solution and decide if a buffer solution could be *prepared* from 1.0 L of 1.0 M HNO_2 and sufficient NaOH? If so, how?

15. Use the Henderson-Hasselbalch equation to calculate the pH of each of the buffers mentioned in question 9 above.

16. Use the Henderson-Hasselbalch equation to answer the following:
    (a) A student requires a solution buffered to pH = 10.00 to study the effects of detergent runoff into aquatic ecosystems. She has just prepared a 1.0 L solution of 0.20 M $NaHCO_3$. What mass of Na_2CO_3 must be added to this solution to complete the buffer preparation? Assume no volume change.

    (b) Calculate the pH of this buffer solution following the addition of 0.0010 mol HCl.

17. Calculate the pH of the following buffer solutions:
    (a) 75.0 mL of 0.200 mol/L CH_3COOH mixed with 75.0 mL of 0.300 mol/L $NaCH_3COO$

    (b) 300. mL of 0.100 mol/L NH_3 combined with 200. mL of 0.200 mol/L NH_4Cl

18. A buffer solution contains 0.400 mol/L of CH_3COOH and 0.400 mol/L of $NaCH_3COO$. What is the pH of the buffer under the following conditions?
    (a) Before any acid or base is added

    (b) After adding 0.050 mol of HCl to 1.00 L of the buffer. Assume the total volume remains constant.

    (c) After adding 0.050 mol of NaOH to 1.00 L of the buffer. Assume the total volume remains constant.

© Edvantage Interactive 2016

19. A solution contains 0.0375 mol of HCOOH and 0.0325 mol of NaHCOO in a total volume of 1.00 L. Determine the pH following the addition of 0.0100 mol of HCl with no significant change in volume.

20. What ratio of [NaF]/[HF] is required to produce a buffer with a pH of 4.25?

21. How many grams of NH_4Br must be added to 0.500 mol of NH_3 to produce 1.00 L of buffer with a pH of 9.05?

22. (a) What is the pH of 1.00 L of buffer containing 0.180 mol of CH_3COOH and 0.200 mol of $NaCH_3C$

   (b) How many moles of HCl must be added to this buffer to change the pH to:
      (i) 4.600

      (ii) 0.900

   (c) The purpose of a buffer is to maintain a relatively constant pH when strong acids or bases are added. What caused the large drop in pH in (b)(ii)?

5.3 Acid-Base Titrations — Analyzing with Volume

Warm Up

1. What is the typical purpose of a titration?

   _____

2. Determine the pH of the following solutions:

0.10 M HCl	0.10 M HCN

3. Assume that 25.0 mL of each of the above solutions is reacted with a 0.10 M NaOH solution. How will the volume of the NaOH solution required to neutralize the HCl compare with that required to neutralize the HCN?

   _____

Criteria for Titration

Titrations are among the most important of all the analytical procedures that chemists use. A titration is a form of volumetric analysis. During a titration, the number of moles of solute in a solution is determined by adding a sufficient volume of another solution of known concentration to *just produce a complete reaction*. Once determined, that number of moles can then be used to calculate other values such as concentration, molar mass, or percent purity.

Any reaction being considered for a titration must satisfy three criteria:
1. Only one reaction can occur between the solutes contained in the two solutions.
2. The reaction between those solutes must go rapidly to completion.
3. There must be a way of signaling the point at which the complete reaction has been achieved in the reaction vessel. This is called the **equivalence point** or **stoichiometric point** of the titration.

> The equivalence point in an acid-base titration occurs in the reaction vessel when the total number of moles of H_3O^+ from the acid equals the total number of moles of OH^- from the base.

To ensure that the reaction between the acid and the base goes to completion, at least one of the two reacting species must be strong. A complete reaction means that *the volume of added solution required to reach the equivalence point depends only on the moles of the acid and base present and the stoichiometry of the reaction*. Prior to the titration, a small amount of an appropriate chemical indicator is added to the reaction vessel containing the solution being analyzed. The correct indicator is one that will undergo a color change *at or very near* the pH associated with the equivalence point. This color change signals when the titration should stop. A pH meter used to monitor the pH of the reaction mixture during the course of a titration will also indicate when the equivalence point has been reached.

Titration Accuracy

Recall from your introduction to titrations in the M4 Chemistry textbook that quantitative analytical procedures such as titrations require precise instruments and careful measurements to ensure the accuracy of the results. Let's review the equipment and procedures associated with a titration. Figure 5.3.1 shows the apparatus used for a typical titration.

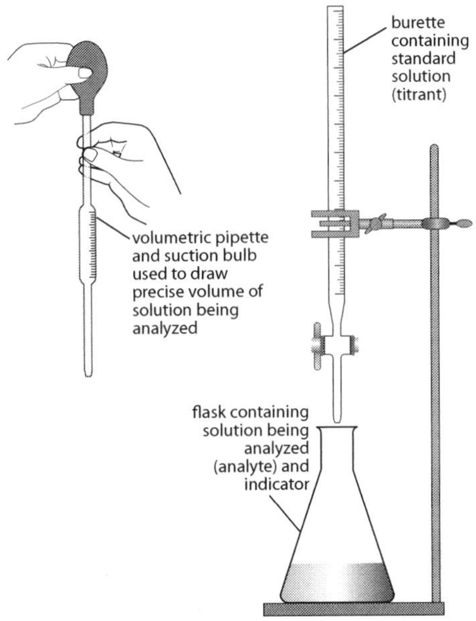

A precise volume of the solution to be analyzed is drawn into a volumetric pipette and transferred into an Erlenmeyer (conical) flask. The shape of the flask allows for swirling of the reaction mixture during the course of the titration without loss of contents. A small amount of an appropriate indicator is then added to this solution. The flask is placed under a burette containing the solution of known concentration called a **standard** or **standardized solution**. The solution in the burette is referred to as the *titrant* and the solution in the flask is called the *analyte*. Normally, the approximate concentration of the analyte is known, which allows a titrant of similar concentration to be prepared. If the titrant is too concentrated, then only a few drops might be required to reach the equivalence point. If the titrant is too dilute, then the volume present in the burette may not be enough to reach the equivalence point.

The standard solution is carefully added to the solution in the flask until the first permanent color change just appears in the indicator. This is called the **transition point** or **endpoint** of the indicator. It should signal when the equivalence point in the titration has been reached.

Figure 5.3.1 *Titration apparatus*

> The transition point is the point in a titration at which the indicator changes color.

At the transition point, the valve on the burette is closed to stop the titration and the volume of standard solution added from the burette is determined.

It is important to remember that *the pH at the transition point is dependent only on the chemical nature of the indicator* and is independent of the equivalence point. The *pH at the equivalence point is dependent only on the chemical nature of the reacting species*. As mentioned above, the pH at which the endpoint occurs should be as close as possible to the pH of the solution at the equivalence point. (Each of these topics will be discussed in greater detail in section 5.4.)

A titration should always be repeated as an accuracy check. Incomplete mixing of solutions, incorrect pipetting techniques, or errors made when reading burettes can contribute to inaccuracies in the data collected, particularly for beginning students.

Those experienced at performing titrations normally expect that the volumes added from the burette in each trial should agree with each other within 0.02 mL (less than a drop). Students performing titrations for the first time should expect agreement within 0.1 mL.

If the volumes delivered from the burette in the first two trials do not agree within the desired uncertainty, then the titration must be repeated until they do. Once agreement between two trials occurs, the volumes added in those trials are averaged, and the other data is discarded. For example, consider Table 5.3.1, which lists the volumes of standard solution required to reach the equivalence point in three separate titration trials.

Table 5.3.1 *Volumes of Standard Solution Required for Equivalence Points*

Titration Trial	Volume of Std. Solution
1	21.36 mL
2	21.19 mL
3	21.21 mL

Note that a third trial was required because the first two volumes differed by 0.17 mL, which is beyond the range of acceptable agreement. The volume recorded for trial 3 agrees well with that of trial 2 and so those two volumes are averaged to obtain the correct volume of standard solution, while the data from trial 1 is discarded. (It is common to overshoot a titration on the first trial.)

$$\text{Average volume of standard solution} = \frac{21.19 \text{ mL} + 21.21 \text{ mL}}{2} = 21.20 \text{ mL}$$

Quick Check

1. What ensures that an acid-base titration goes to completion?

   _____

2. Distinguish between an endpoint and an equivalence point in an acid-base titration.

   _____

   _____

3. A student performing a titration for the first time lists the volumes of standard solution required to reach the equivalence point in three separate titration trials.

Titration Trial	Volume of Std. Solution
1	23.88 mL
2	23.67 mL
3	23.59 mL

   What is the correct volume of standard solution that should be recorded by the student?

   _____

Standard Solutions

A successful titration requires that the concentration of the standard solution be very accurately known. There are two ways to obtain a standard solution.

1. A standard solution can be prepared if the solute is a stable, non-deliquescent, soluble compound available in a highly pure form. Such a compound is known as a **primary standard**.
   - Two examples of **acidic primary standards** are:
   (a) potassium hydrogen phthalate, $KHC_8H_4O_4$, a monoprotic acid often abbreviated as simply KHP.
   (b) oxalic acid dihydrate, $H_2C_2O_4 \cdot 2\ H_2O$, a diprotic acid.
   - A common example of a **basic primary standard** is anhydrous sodium carbonate, Na_2CO_3, which will accept two protons in a reaction with an acid.
   - Each of the above stable, pure compounds can be used to prepare a standard solution whose concentration can be accurately known directly.

2. If the solute is not available in a highly pure form and/or readily undergoes reaction with, for example, atmospheric water vapor or carbon dioxide, then the solution must be *standardized* to accurately determine its concentration before it can be used in a titration. This is accomplished by titrating the solution in question against a primary standard.
   For example, a solution of the strong base sodium hydroxide is often used as a standard solution in a titration. However, solid NaOH rapidly absorbs water vapor from the air. Both solid and

aqueous NaOH readily react with atmospheric CO_2 as shown in the equation below:

$$2\, NaOH + CO_2 \rightarrow Na_2CO_3 + H_2O$$

This means that before a solution of NaOH can be used as a standard solution in a titration, its concentration must first be accurately determined by titrating it against an acidic primary standard such as KHP or $H_2C_2O_4 \cdot 2\, H_2O$. For each titration, phenolphthalein is a suitable indicator. KHP reacts with NaOH as shown in this equation:

$$KHC_8H_4O_4(aq) + NaOH(aq) \rightarrow NaKC_8H_4O_4(aq) + H_2O(l)$$

Oxalic acid dihydrate reacts with NaOH in a 2:1 mole ratio:

$$H_2C_2O_4 \cdot 2\, H_2O(aq) + 2\, NaOH(aq) \rightarrow Na_2C_2O_4(aq) + 4\, H_2O(l)$$

For example, if KHP is used to standardize the NaOH solution, a precise mass of KHP (usually sufficient to prepare a 0.1000 M solution), is dissolved in water, transferred into a volumetric flask, and diluted to the required volume. A volumetric pipette is then used to transfer a precise volume to an Erlenmeyer flask into which a few drops of phenolphthalein indicator are added. The NaOH solution to be standardized is then gradually added from a burette into the acid solution. At the equivalence point, all of the KHP in the flask has been neutralized and so the next drop of NaOH solution added makes the reaction mixture basic enough to cause the indicator to turn pink. The volume of the NaOH solution required in the titration allows for the accurate determination of its concentration. Once that concentration is known, the standardized NaOH solution can then be added to an acid solution in a titration procedure.

To standardize an acidic solution, a titration against a basic primary standard such as Na_2CO_3 is performed. Appropriate indicators for this reaction would be either bromcresol green or methyl red. In a reaction with a monoprotic acid such as HCl, the carbonate anion will react in a 2:1 mole ratio:

$$Na_2CO_3(aq) + 2\, HCl(aq) \rightarrow 2\, NaCl(aq) + CO_2(g) + H_2O(l)$$

When standardizing a solution, its *approximate* concentration is often known. Because the concentration of the other solution is known, the approximate volume required of the solution being standardized in the titration can be estimated before the procedure.

Quick Check

1. Is a 4.00 g sample of NaOH likely to contain 0.100 mol of this compound? Why or why not?

   _____

2. Which piece of equipment and/or procedure employed during a titration ensures the following:
   (a) Accurate and precise measurement of the volume of the solution being analyzed in the reaction flask

   _____

   (b) Accurate and precise determination of the concentration of the titrant

   _____

   (c) Accurate and precise measurement of the volume of titrant required in the titration

   _____

   (d) Correct determination of the equivalence point during the titration

   _____

Sample Problem — Standardizing a Solution

A student standardizing a solution of NaOH finds that 28.15 mL of that solution is required to neutralize 25.00 mL of a 0.1072 M standard solution of KHP. Calculate the [NaOH].

What to Think About	**How to Do It**
1. To solve titration problems, begin with writing the balanced equation for the reaction. The mole ratio in the balanced equation is 1 mol NaOH : 1 mol KHP	$KHC_8H_4O_4 + NaOH \rightarrow NaKC_8H_4O_4 + H_2O$ $$\text{mol KHP} = 0.02500\ \cancel{L} \times 0.1072\ \frac{\text{mol KHP}}{\cancel{L}} = 0.002680\ \text{mol}$$ $$\text{mol NaOH} = \text{mol KHP} = 0.002680\ \text{mol}$$
2. The [NaOH] should be slightly less than 0.107**2** M because the volume of NaOH solution required in the titration is greater than 25.00 mL.	$$[NaOH] = \frac{0.002680\ \text{mol NaOH}}{0.02815\ L} = 0.09520\ M$$ (4 sig. figures) Look at the above solution. Can you identify *three steps* in the solution process?

Practice Problems — Standardizing a Solution

1. If 21.56 mL of a NaOH solution is required to neutralize 25.00 mL of a 0.0521 M standard oxalic acid solution, calculate the [NaOH].

2. A 1.546 g sample of pure anhydrous sodium carbonate is diluted to 250.0 mL in a volumetric flask. A 25.00 mL aliquot of this standard solution required 23.17 mL of a nitric acid solution to be neutralized. Calculate the [HNO$_3$].

Common Titration Calculations

The majority of titration calculations you will be expected to perform in this course involve determining a solution concentration, solution volume, molar mass, or percent purity.

Regardless of which acid or base is involved, *the total number of moles of H$^+$ from the acid equals the total number of moles of OH$^-$ from the base at the equivalence point.* Therefore, for any type of titration problem you are solving, it is *strongly suggested* that you begin by writing the balanced chemical equation for the titration reaction if it isn't provided.

- The first step in the calculation process normally involves using the data provided to determine the number of moles of one of the reactant species used.
- The second step uses the moles determined in the first step and the mole ratio in the balanced equation to determine the moles of the second reactant consumed.
- The third step uses the moles calculated in step 2 to determine a solution concentration, solution volume, molar mass, or percent purity.

Because a titration represents a quantitative analytical procedure, accuracy and precision are paramount. This means that you must pay particular attention to significant figures when performing titration calculations.

Calculating Solution Concentration

This represents the most common type of titration calculation you will encounter in this course. If you look again at Sample Problem above for standardizing a solution, you will recognize this problem type and the application of the above steps to solve it.

Sample Problem — Calculating Solution Concentration

A 25.0 mL sample of H_2SO_4 requires 46.23 mL of a standard 0.203 M NaOH solution to reach the equivalence point. Calculate the $[H_2SO_4]$.

What to Think About	**How to Do It**
1. The balanced equation shows a 2:1 mole ratio between the reacting species.	$2\ NaOH(aq) + H_2SO_4(aq) \rightarrow Na_2SO_4(aq) + 2\ H_2O(l)$ $mol\ NaOH = 0.04623\ L \times \dfrac{0.203\ mol}{L} = 0.009385\ mol$
2. Ensure that your final answer has three significant figures.	$mol\ H_2SO_4 = 0.009385\ \cancel{mol\ NaOH} \times \dfrac{1\ mol\ H_2SO_4}{2\ \cancel{mol\ NaOH}}$ $= 0.004692\ mol\ H_2SO_4$
3. As molarity × mL = millimoles, solve the question using mol and L, *or* mmol and mL.	$[H_2SO_4] = \dfrac{0.004692\ mol\ H_2SO_4}{0.0250\ L} = 0.188\ M$ (3 sig. figures)
4. A solution using each set of units is shown on the right.	*Alternatively:* $mmol\ NaOH = 46.23\ \cancel{mL} \times \dfrac{0.203\ mmol}{\cancel{mL}} = 9.385\ mmol$ $mmol\ H_2SO_4 = 9.385\ \cancel{mmol\ NaOH} \times \dfrac{1\ mmol\ H_2SO_4}{2\ \cancel{mmol\ NaOH}}$ $= 4.692\ mmol\ H_2SO_4$ $[H_2SO_4] = \dfrac{4.692\ mmol\ H_2SO_4}{25.0\ mL} = 0.188\ M$

Practice Problems — Calculating Solution Concentration

1. The equivalence point in a titration is reached when 25.64 mL of a 0.1175 M KOH solution is added to a 50.0 mL solution of acetic acid. Calculate the concentration of the acetic acid.

Continued on next page

Practice Problems (Continued)

2. Lactic acid, C_2H_5OCOOH, is found in sour milk, yogurt, and cottage cheese. It is also responsible for the flavor of sourdough breads. Three separate trials, each using 25.0 mL samples of lactic acid, are performed using a standardized 0.153 M NaOH solution. Consider the following table listing the volume of basic solution required to reach the equivalence point for each trial.

Titration Trial	Volume of NaOH Solution
1	33.42 mL
2	33.61 mL
3	33.59 mL

Calculate the concentration of the lactic acid.

3. Methylamine, CH_3NH_2, is found in herring brine solutions, used in the manufacture of some pesticides, and serves as a solvent for many organic compounds. A titration is performed to determine the concentration of methylamine present in a solution being prepared for a commercial pesticide. A 0.185 M HCl solution is added to 50.0 mL samples of aqueous methylamine in three separate titration trials. The data table below shows the results.

Titration Trial	Burette Readings	
	Initial Volume	Final Volume
1	20.14 mL	47.65 mL
2	9.55 mL	36.88 mL
3	15.84 mL	43.11 mL

Calculate the concentration of the methylamine solution.

Calculating Solution Volume

If you are asked to calculate a solution volume from titration data, you will probably be given the concentrations of both the acid and the base solutions. If you aren't given the concentrations directly, you will be given enough information to calculate them. The final step in the solution process involves converting the moles of reactant determined in the second step into a volume using the appropriate concentration value.

It is important to remember that because *the reaction goes to completion*, the volume of standard solution required in a titration is only dependent on the stoichiometry of the reaction and the moles of the species (acid or base) that it must neutralize. *It does not depend on the strength of those species.*

Review your answer to Warm Up question 3. The volume of standard NaOH solution required to neutralize 25.0 mL of 0.10 M HCl will be *the same* as that required to neutralize 25.0 mL of 0.10 M HCN.

Sample Problem — Calculating Solution Volume

What volume of a standard $Sr(OH)_2$ solution with a pH of 13.500 is needed to neutralize a 25.0 mL solution of 0.423 M HCl?

What to Think About	How to Do It
1. The pH allows the concentration of the basic solution to be calculated.	$2\,HCl(aq) + Sr(OH)_2(aq) \rightarrow SrCl_2(aq) + 2\,H_2O(l)$ $\text{mmol HCl reacting} = 25.0\ \text{mL} \times \dfrac{0.423\ \text{mmol HCl}}{\text{mL}}$ $= 10.58\ \text{mmol HCl}$
2. The balanced equation shows a 2:1 mole ratio between the reacting species.	$\text{mmol } Sr(OH)_2 = 10.58\ \text{mmol HCl} \times \dfrac{1\ \text{mmol } Sr(OH)_2}{2\ \text{mmol HCl}}$ $= 5.290\ \text{mmol } Sr(OH)_2$
3. Express the final answer to three significant figures.	$pOH = 14.000 - 13.500 = 0.500$ $[OH^-] = 10^{-0.500} = 0.3162\ M$ $[Sr(OH)_2] = \dfrac{[OH^-]}{2} = 0.1581\ M = 0.1581\ \dfrac{\text{mmol}}{\text{mL}}$ $\text{Volume } Sr(OH)_2 \text{ solution} =$ $5.290\ \text{mmol } Sr(OH)_2 \times \dfrac{1\ \text{mL}}{0.1581\ \text{mmol}} = 33.4\ \text{mL}$ (3 sig. figures)

Practice Problems — Calculating Solution Volume

1. How many milliliters of a 0.215 M KOH solution are required to neutralize 15.0 mL of a 0.173 M H_2SO_4 solution?

2. A solution of HCl is standardized and found to have a pH of 0.432. What volume of this solution must be added to 25.0 mL of a 0.285 M $Sr(OH)_2$ solution to reach the equivalence point?

3. A 5.60 L sample of NH_3 gas, measured at STP, is dissolved in enough water to produce 500.0 mL of solution. A 20.0 mL sample of this solution is titrated with a 0.368 M HNO_3 solution. What volume of standard solution is required to reach the equivalence point?

Calculating Molar Mass

The molar mass of an unknown acid (or base) can be determined from a titration as long as we know if that acid (or base) is monoprotic or diprotic, etc. This tells us the molar ratio in the neutralization reaction that occurs. This in turn allows us to calculate the moles of the unknown compound that react during the titration. Depending on how the information is provided, we can then choose to calculate the molar mass in one of two ways, as shown in the following sample problems.

Sample Problem — Calculating Molar Mass 1

A 0.328 g sample of an unknown monoprotic acid, HA, is dissolved in water and titrated with a standardized 0.1261 M NaOH solution. If 28.10 mL of the basic solution is required to reach the equivalence point, calculate the molar mass of the acid.

What to Think About	How to Do It
1. The mole ratio in the balanced equation is 1:1 so the mol of NaOH reacted = the mol of HA present in 0.328 g.	$NaOH(aq) + HA(aq) \rightarrow NaA(aq) + H_2O(l)$ $\text{mmol NaOH} = 28.10 \text{ mL} \times \dfrac{0.1261 \text{ mmol}}{\text{mL}} = 3.543 \text{ mmol}$
2. The mass of the unknown acid divided by the moles present equals the molar mass.	$\text{mmol HA} = 3.543 \text{ mmol NaOH} \times \dfrac{1 \text{ mmol HA}}{\text{mmol NaOH}}$ $= 3.543 \text{ mmol HA} = 0.003543 \text{ mol HA}$ $\text{molar mass of HA} = \dfrac{0.328 \text{ g HA}}{0.003543 \text{ mol HA}} = 92.6 \text{ g/mol}$ (3 sig. figures)

Sample Problem — Calculating Molar Mass 2

A 2.73 g sample of an unknown diprotic acid is placed in a volumetric flask and then diluted to 500.0 mL. A 25.0 mL sample of this solution requires 30.5 mL of a 0.1112 M KOH solution to completely neutralize the acid in a titration. Calculate the molar mass of the acid.

What to Think About	How to Do It
1. Two moles of KOH are required to neutralize each mole of diprotic acid, H_2A.	$2 KOH(aq) + H_2A(aq) \rightarrow K_2A(aq) + 2 H_2O(l)$ $\text{mol KOH} = 0.0305 \text{ L} \times \dfrac{0.1112 \text{ mol}}{L} = 0.003416 \text{ mol}$
2. Calculate the concentration of the acid solution and use the volume of the original solution to determine the moles of H_2A present. This will allow you to determine the molar mass using the mass of the original acid sample.	$\text{mol } H_2A = 0.003416 \text{ mol KOH} \times \dfrac{1 \text{ mol } H_2A}{2 \text{ mol KOH}} = 0.001708 \text{ mol}$ $[H_2A] = \dfrac{0.001708 \text{ mol } H_2A}{0.0250 \text{ L}} = 0.06832 \text{ M}$ $\text{mol } H_2A \text{ in original 500.0 mL} = \dfrac{0.06832 \text{ mol}}{L} \times 0.5000 \text{ L}$ $= 0.03416 \text{ mol } H_2A$ $\text{molar mass } H_2A = \dfrac{2.73 \text{ g } H_2A}{0.03416 \text{ mol}} = 79.9 \text{ g/mol}$ (3 sig. figures)

© Edvantage Interactive 2016

Practice Problems — Calculating Molar Mass

1. A 3.648 g sample of an unknown monoprotic acid is dissolved in enough water to produce 750.0 mL of solution. When a 25.0 mL sample of this solution is titrated to the equivalence point, 12.50 mL of a 0.1104 M NaOH solution is required. Calculate the molar mass of the acid.

2. A 0.375 g sample of an unknown diprotic acid is dissolved in water and titrated using 0.2115 M NaOH. The volumes of standard solution required to neutralize the acid in three separate trials are given below.

Titration Trial	Volume of NaOH Solution
1	37.48 mL
2	37.36 mL
3	37.34 mL

Calculate the molar mass of the acid.

3. A 2.552 g sample of a monoprotic base is diluted to 250.0 mL in a volumetric flask. A 25.0 mL sample of this solution is titrated with a standardized solution of 0.05115 M HCl. If 17.49 mL of the acid solution is required to reach the equivalence point, calculate the molar mass of the base.

Calculating Percent Purity

If a solid sample of an impure acid or base is dissolved in solution and titrated against a standard solution, the actual number of moles of the pure solute can be determined. Depending on how the information is presented, this allows percent purity to be calculated. For example, we may be told that a small mass of an impure solid is dissolved in enough water to form the solution that is titrated directly. In this case, the percent purity can be calculated by dividing the *actual mass of pure solute* present in the sample, as determined by the titration, by the *given mass of the impure sample*.

$$\text{percent purity} = \frac{\text{actual mass of pure solute (from titration)}}{\text{given mass of impure solute}} \times 100\%$$

We may also be told that a mass of impure solid is dissolved in a given volume of solution, and then a portion of that solution is withdrawn and analyzed in the titration. In this case, we can choose to calculate the percent purity by dividing the *actual solution concentration*, as determined by the titration, by the *expected concentration* in the original solution if the sample had been pure.

$$\text{percent purity} = \frac{\text{actual concentration (from titration)}}{\text{expected concentration (from original mass)}} \times 100\%$$

There are other possible approaches, but each uses a true value provided by the titration and compares it to a given value to determine percent purity.

Sample Problem — Calculating Percent Purity 1

A 0.3470 g sample of impure $NaHSO_3$ is dissolved in water and titrated with a 0.1481 M NaOH solution. If 20.26 mL of the standard solution is required, calculate the percent purity of the $NaHSO_3$ sample.

What to Think About

1. The mole ratio in the balanced equation is 1:1.

2. The titration will allow you to calculate the actual number of moles of $NaHSO_3$ in the sample from which you can obtain percent purity.

How to Do It

$$NaOH(aq) + NaHSO_3(aq) \rightarrow Na_2SO_3(aq) + H_2O(l)$$

$$\text{mol NaOH} = 0.02026\ \cancel{L} \times \frac{0.1481\ mol}{\cancel{L}} = 0.003000\ mol$$

$$\text{mol pure } NaHSO_3 = \text{mol NaOH} = 0.003000\ mol$$

$$\text{actual mass pure } NaHSO_3 = 0.003000\ \cancel{mol} \times \frac{104.1\ g\ NaHSO_3}{\cancel{mol}}$$

$$= 0.3123\ g\ NaHSO_3$$

$$\% \text{ purity} = \frac{\text{actual mass pure } NaHSO_3}{\text{given mass impure } NaHSO_3} \times 100\%$$

$$= \frac{0.3123\ \cancel{g}}{0.3470\ \cancel{g}} \times 100\% = 90.00\% \text{ (4 sig. figures)}$$

Sample Problem — Calculating Percent Purity 2

A 2.70 g sample of impure $Sr(OH)_2$ is diluted to 250.0 mL in a volumetric flask. A 25.0 mL portion of this solution is then neutralized in a titration using 31.39 mL of 0.131 M HCl. Calculate the percent purity of the $Sr(OH)_2$.

What to Think About

1. The balanced equation shows a 2:1 mole ratio for the reactants.

2. Compare the actual concentration of the solution to the expected concentration to determine percent purity.

3. Round the answer to three significant figures.

How to Do It

$$2\ HCl(aq) + Sr(OH)_2(aq) \rightarrow SrCl_2(aq) + 2\ H_2O(l)$$

$$\text{mmol HCl} = 31.39\ \cancel{mL} \times \frac{0.131\ mmol}{\cancel{mL}} = 4.112\ mmol$$

$$\text{mmol } Sr(OH)_2 = 4.112\ \cancel{mmol\ HCl} \times \frac{1\ mmol\ Sr(OH)_2}{2\ \cancel{mmol\ HCl}}$$

$$= 2.056\ mmol\ Sr(OH)_2$$

$$\text{actual } [Sr(OH)_2] = \frac{2.056\ mmol\ Sr(OH)_2}{25.0\ mL} = 0.08224\ M$$

$$\text{expected } [Sr(OH)_2] = \frac{2.70\ g\ \cancel{Sr(OH)_2}}{0.2500\ L} \times \frac{1\ mol\ Sr(OH)_2}{126.1\ \cancel{g}}$$

$$= 0.08565\ M$$

$$\% \text{ purity} = \frac{\text{actual } [Sr(OH)_2]}{\text{expected } [Sr(OH)_2]} \times 100\%$$

$$= \frac{0.08224\ \cancel{M}}{0.08565\ \cancel{M}} \times 100\% = 96.0\% \text{ (3 sig. figures)}$$

© Edvantage Interactive 2016

Practice Problems — Calculating Percent Purity

1. Benzoic acid, C_6H_5COOH, is a white crystalline solid. It is among the most common food preservatives and is also used as an antifungal skin treatment. A 0.3265 g sample of impure benzoic acid is dissolved in enough water to form 25.0 mL of solution. In a titration, 23.76 mL of a 0.1052 M NaOH solution is required to reach the equivalence point. Calculate the percent purity of the acid.

2. A 1.309 g sample of impure $Ca(OH)_2$ is dissolved in water to produce 750.0 mL of solution. A 25.0 mL sample of this solution is titrated against a standard solution of 0.0615 M HCl. If 17.72 mL of the acid solution is required in the titration, calculate the percent purity of the $Ca(OH)_2$.

3. Nicotinic acid, C_5H_4NCOOH, (also known as niacin or vitamin B_3) is considered an essential human nutrient and is available in a variety of food sources such as chicken, salmon, eggs, carrots, and avocados. A 1.361 g sample of impure nicotinic acid is dissolved in water to form 30.00 mL of solution. The acid solution requires 20.96 mL of 0.501 M NaOH to reach the equivalence point. Calculate the percent purity of the acid.

5.3 Activity: Titration Experimental Design

Question
Can you identify the equipment and procedures associated with a typical titration and then employ them in designing a titration?

Background
As you have learned in this section, a titration is one of the most valuable analytical procedures employed by chemists. This activity is intended to review the equipment and reagents involved in a titration and then present you with the task of designing such an investigation.

Procedure
1. What is the function of each the following in a titration?
   (a) burette

   (b) volumetric pipette

   (c) Erlenmeyer flask

   (d) indicator

   (e) standard solution

   (f) acidic or basic primary standard

2. Why must every titration be repeated?

3. The concentration of a solution of acetylsalicylic acid, $C_8H_7O_2COOH$, must be determined very accurately for a clinical trial. The equipment and chemical reagents available to you to accomplish this are listed below. Using all of them, describe in point form and in order the laboratory procedures you would use.

Equipment	Reagents
• analytical balance • 100 mL beaker • 2 funnels • wash bottle • 250 mL volumetric flask • two 125 mL Erlenmeyer flasks • 50 mL burette • two 25 mL pipettes with suction bulbs • ring stand • burette clamp • safety goggles • lab apron	• pure oxalic acid dihydrate crystals • NaOH solution (approximately 0.1 M) • ASA solution (approximately 0.1 M) • phenolphthalein indicator solution

Titration Procedure

Results and Discussion

1. Write the balanced equation for the reaction that occurs during standardization of the basic solution and for the titration of the ASA solution.

2. (a) What salt solution exists at the equivalence point of the ASA titration?

   (b) Would you expect the pH of the solution at the equivalence point to be 7? Why or why not?

3. What concentration might be appropriate for the oxalic acid solution that you prepare?

4. Identify at least three possible sources of error and their impact on the experimental results.

5.3 Review Questions

1. A student intends to titrate two 25.0 mL acidic solutions, each with a known concentration of approximately 0.1 M. One solution is hydrochloric acid and the other solution is acetic acid. He expects to require more of a standard NaOH solution to reach the equivalence point when titrating the HCl solution because it is a strong acid with a higher $[H_3O^+]$. Do you agree or disagree with the prediction? Explain your answer.

2. During a titration, a student adds water from a wash bottle to wash down some reactant solution that has splashed up in the Erlenmeyer flask. Although this changes the volume of the solution in the flask, she is confident that the accuracy of the titration will not be affected. Do you agree or disagree? Explain your answer.

3. A student must titrate a 25.0 mL sample of acetic acid solution whose concentration is known to be approximately 0.2 M. After adding a small amount of phenolphthalein indicator to the reaction flask, the student fills a 50 mL burette with a standardized 0.0650 M solution of NaOH and prepares to begin the titration. His lab partner insists that the titration cannot succeed. Do you agree or disagree with the lab partner? Explain your answer.

4. A student requires a standard solution of NaOH for a titration with a concentration as close as possible to 0.500 M. Using a digital balance, she carefully measures 20.00 g of NaOH. She quantitatively transfers it to a 1 L volumetric flask and adds the precise amount of water. She then calculates the concentration of the resulting solution to be 0.500 M and prepares to fill a burette and begin the titration. Her lab partner insists that the concentration is inaccurate. Do you agree or disagree with the lab partner? Would you expect the calculated concentration to be too high or too low? Explain your answer.

5. A student standardizing a solution of NaOH finds that 25.24 mL of that solution is required to neutralize a solution containing 0.835 g of KHP. Calculate the [NaOH].

© Edvantage Interactive 2016

6. A 21.56 mL solution of NaOH is standardized and found to have a concentration of 0.125 M. What mass of oxalic acid dihydrate would be required to standardize this solution?

7. A solution of NaOH is standardized and found to have a pH of 13.440. What volume of this solution must be added to 25.0 mL of a 0.156 M $H_2C_2O_4$ solution in a titration to neutralize the acid?

8. A 4.48 L sample of HCl gas, measured at STP, is dissolved in enough water to produce 400.0 mL of solution. A 25.0 mL sample of this solution is titrated with a 0.227 M $Sr(OH)_2$ solution. What volume of standard solution is required to reach the equivalence point?

9. A 0.665 g sample of an unknown monoprotic acid, HA, is dissolved in water and titrated with a standardized 0.2055 M KOH solution. If 26.51 mL of the basic solution is required to reach the equivalence point, calculate the molar mass of the acid.

10. A 5.47 g sample of an unknown diprotic acid is placed in a volumetric flask and then diluted to 250.0 mL. A 25.0 mL sample of this solution requires 23.6 mL of a 0.2231 M $Sr(OH)_2$ solution to completely neutralize the acid in a titration. Calculate the molar mass of the acid.

11. Tartaric acid, $C_4H_6O_6$, is a white crystalline diprotic organic acid. It occurs naturally in many plants, such as grapes and bananas, is often added to foods to give them a sour taste, and is one of the main acids found in wine. A 7.36 g sample of impure tartaric acid is diluted to 250.0 mL in a volumetric flask. A 25.0 mL portion of this solution is transferred to an Erlenmeyer flask and titrated against a 0.223 M standardized NaOH solution. If 40.31 mL of the basic solution is required to neutralize the acid, calculate the percent purity of the tartaric acid.

12. Sorbic acid, C_5H_7COOH, is a monoprotic organic acid that was first isolated from the berries of the mountain ash tree in 1859. It is a white crystalline solid used primarily as a food preservative. A 0.570 g sample of impure sorbic acid is dissolved in water to form 25.00 mL of solution. The acid solution requires 27.34 mL of 0.178 M KOH to reach the equivalence point. Calculate the percent purity of the sorbic acid.

13. Phenylacetic acid, C_7H_7COOH, is used in some perfumes and possesses a honey-like odor in low concentrations. A 0.992 g sample of impure phenylacetic acid dissolved in solution is titrated against a 0.105 M standard $Sr(OH)_2$ solution. If 31.07 mL of the standard solution is required to reach the equivalence point, calculate the percent purity of the acid.

14. Why is a titration considered to be a "volumetric" analysis?

© Edvantage Interactive 2016

5.4 A Closer Look at Titrations

Warm Up

Consider each pair of reactants in the three titrations below.

	Titration 1	Titration 2	Titration 3
Solution in burette	0.100 M NaOH	0.100 M NaOH	0.100 M HCl
Solution in flask	0.100 M HCl	0.100 M CH₃COOH	0.100 M NH₃

1. Write the formula equation for each titration.

   Titration 1:

   Titration 2:

   Titration 3:

2. What salt solution exists in each reaction flask at each of the equivalence points?

   Titration 1: _____

   Titration 2: _____

   Titration 3: _____

3. Indicate whether you would expect the pH of each solution at the equivalence point to be below, equal to, or above 7, and explain your decision.

   Titration 1:

   _____

   Titration 2:

   _____

   Titration 3:

   _____

Measuring pH with Acid-Base Indicators

In section 5.3 we described titrations as a form of volumetric chemical analysis. We will now take a closer look at the procedure by monitoring the pH changes in the reaction mixture during several types of titrations. In doing so, we'll also see how the principles of hydrolysis and buffer chemistry apply to and give us a better understanding of the titration process.

Usually we measure pH using either an acid-base indicator or a pH meter. Let's begin by describing the behavior and role of an acid-base indicator in a titration. Acid-base indicators are weak (usually monoprotic) organic acids whose conjugate pairs display different and normally intense colors. Those intense colors mean that only a small amount of an indicator is needed for a titration. If the appropriate indicator has been chosen, the change from one color to another will signal when the equivalence point has been reached.

Acid-base indicators are complex organic molecules and so we normally represent their formulas as simply "HIn." A typical indicator is a weak acid as shown in the aqueous equilibrium below.

$$\textbf{HIn}(aq) \quad + \quad H_2O(l) \quad \rightleftharpoons \quad \textbf{In}^-(aq) \quad + \quad H_3O^+(aq)$$

Acidic form and color predominate when $[H_3O^+]$ is relatively high and the equilibrium favors the reactant side.

Basic form and color predominate when $[H_3O^+]$ is relatively low and the equilibrium favors the product side.

If a small amount of the indicator is placed in a solution where the hydronium concentration is relatively high, this equilibrium will favor the reactant side. Thus, the acidic form of the indicator, **HIn**, and its color will predominate. In a basic solution, where the hydronium concentration is low, the equilibrium will favor the product side and so the basic form, **In⁻**, and its color will be prominent. For example, Figure 5.4.1 shows the acidic and basic forms of bromthymol blue.

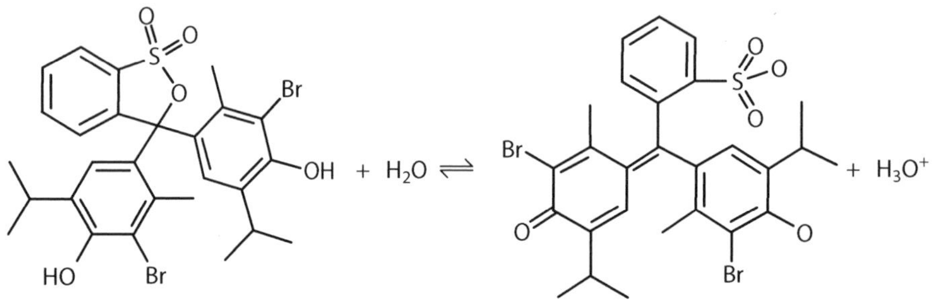

Acidic (yellow) form of bromthymol blue predominates in an acidic solution with a pH below **6.0**.

Basic (blue) form of bromthymol blue predominates in an alkaline solution with a pH above **7.6**.

Figure 5.4.1 *The acidic and basic forms of bromthymol blue*

A table of Acid-Base Indicators tells us that changes in indicator colors occur over a *range* of pH values rather than instantly at one pH. This is because our eyes are limited in their ability to perceive slight changes in shades of color. Normally during a titration, about *one tenth* of the initial form of an indicator must be converted to the other form (its conjugate) for us to notice a color change.

It is useful to follow the progress of a typical titration in terms of the position of the indicator equilibrium and the relative amount of each member of the conjugate pair present in the reaction flask as the titrant is added.

For example, in a flask containing an indicator in an acidic solution, the acid form of the indicator, HIn, predominates. If we now begin adding a basic solution from a burette, the OH⁻ ions reduce the $[H_3O^+]$ in the flask and the position of the $[In^-]/[HIn]$ equilibrium begins to shift towards In⁻ according to Le Châtelier's principle. As the [HIn] decreases and the [In⁻] increases, we eventually reach a point where the $[In^-]/[HIn]$ ratio = 0.10. Here, we notice *the first color change*.

As the addition of OH⁻ ions continues to reduce the $[H_3O^+]$, the ratio continues to increase until the [HIn] = [In⁻]. An equal concentration of each form of the indicator will now combine to produce an *intermediate color* in the solution. The point at which we see this intermediate color, where the indicator is *half-way through its color change*, is called the **transition point** or **end point** of the indicator. At the transition point, as [HIn] = [In⁻], then

$$K_a = \frac{[H_3O^+][\cancel{In^-}]}{[\cancel{HIn}]} \quad \text{reduces to: } \boldsymbol{K_a = [H_3O^+]}$$

This tells us that the $[H_3O^+]$ at the transition point equals the value of the K_a for the indicator (sometimes called K_{In}).

> If we take the negative logarithm of both sides of the above equation, we see that:
> the pK_a of an indicator = the pH at its transition point

When you refer to a table of acid-base indicators, you will notice that different indicators change colors at different pH values. Those pH values reflect the pK_a values for each indicator.

As we continue adding base, we would see the indicator's color change complete when only about *one-tenth* of the initial acid form HIn remains in the flask, that is, when $[In^-]/[HIn]$ = 10. We can summarize this progression in Table 5.4.1 beginning with the first detectable color change as the basic solution is added and ending when the color change is seen to be complete.

Table 5.4.1 *Indicator Color Change During the Titration of an Acid with a Base*

Indicator Color Change First Seen	Indicator Transition Point Occurs	Indicator Color Change Complete
$\dfrac{[In^-]}{[HIn]} = \dfrac{1}{10}$	$\dfrac{[In^-]}{[HIn]} = 1$	$\dfrac{[In^-]}{[HIn]} = \dfrac{10}{1}$
so $K_a = [H_3O^+](0.1)$	so $K_a = [H_3O^+]$	so $K_a = [H_3O^+](10)$
and $pK_a = pH + -\log(0.1)$	and $pK_a = pH$	and $pK_a = pH + -\log(10)$
or $pK_a = pH + 1$	or	or $pK_a = pH - 1$
so	$\mathbf{pH = pK_a}$	so
$\mathbf{pH = pK_a - 1}$		$\mathbf{pH = pK_a + 1}$
The first color change is seen when the pH of the solution is about one pH unit below the pK_a of the indicator.	The transition point and intermediate color occur when the pH of the solution equals the pK_a of the indicator.	The color change is complete when the pH of the solution is about one pH unit above the pK_a of the indicator.

We see from the above table that the range over which an indicator's color changes is normally about two pH units extending from approximately one pH unit below to one pH unit above the indicator's pK_a. This corresponds to a 100-fold change in the $[In^-]/[HIn]$ ratio and tells us that the useful pH range for an indicator in a titration is usually given by $\mathbf{pK_a \pm 1}$.

As we will discuss later in this section, depending on the reagents used in a titration, the pH at the equivalence point can be quite different. We normally attempt to choose an indicator whose pK_a is within one unit of the pH at the equivalence point.

Had we applied the above discussion to bromthymol blue, we would have noticed the indicator's yellow color begin to change at pH = 6 and continue changing until it appears completely blue at about pH = 7.6. Halfway through that change, at an *average of the two pH values*, the transition point pH of 6.8 is reached, which equals the indicator pK_a. At the transition point, bromthymol blue displays an intermediate green color.

> An indicator's transition point pH and pK_a value can be estimated by averaging the two pH values associated with the range over which the indicator changes color.

Look again at the table of acid-base indicators (Table A6) and consider the order that those indicators appear top-to-bottom. Notice that the pH values over which the color changes occur increase as we move down the table from the acidic end of the pH scale to the basic end. This means that the pK_a values of those indicators must also increase.

As an increase in pK_a corresponds to a *decrease in K_a*, this tells us that the indicator acid strength decreases as we move down a table in the same way as it does showing the relative strengths of a table of Brønsted-Lowry acids and bases.

Combining Acid-Base Indicators — A Universal Indicator

Several different indicators that each go through a different color change over a different pH range can be combined into a single indicator solution. This solution will display different colors over a wide range of pH values. A universal indicator solution can also be added to absorbent strips of paper so that when the solvents evaporate, the individual test strips can be dipped into solutions to estimate pH values.

In a universal indicator, the colors of the component indicators at each pH combine to display virtually all the colors of the visible spectrum. Commercially available universal indicators are often composed of the indicator combination shown in Table 5.4.2. The indicator colors combine over the entire range of the pH scale to produce the results shown in Table 5.4.3. The original universal indicator recipe was patented by the Japanese chemist Yamada in 1923.

Table 5.4.2 *Indicators That Make up a Typical Universal Indicator*

Indicator	pK_a Value	Color of Acid Form	Color of Base Form
Thymol blue*	2.0 (pK_{a1})	red	yellow
Methyl red	5.6	red	yellow
Bromthymol blue	6.8	yellow	blue
Thymol blue*	8.8 (pK_{a2})	yellow	blue
Phenolphthalein	9.1	colorless	pink

Table 5.4.3 *Indicator Colors When Combined in a Universal Indicator*

Indicator	pH < 2	pH 3–4	pH 5-6	pH 7-8	pH 9-11	pH >12
Thymol Blue*	red/orange	yellow	yellow	yellow	green/blue	blue
Methyl Red	red	red	orange/yellow	yellow	yellow	yellow
Bromthymol Blue	yellow	yellow	yellow	green/blue	blue	blue
Phenolphthalein	colorless	colorless	colorless	colorless	pink	pink
Combined color	*red/orange*	*orange/yellow*	*yellow*	*yellow/green*	*green/blue*	*purple*

* Note. Thymol blue undergoes a *color change over two different pH ranges*. What does this tell us about the chemical nature of this acid?

© Edvantage Interactive 2016

Sample Problem — Estimating Indicator K_a and pK_a values

Eight acid-base indicators listed on a acid-base indicators table display an orange color at their transition points. Identify which of those has a $K_a = 5 \times 10^{-8}$.

What to Think About	How to Do It
1. Calculate the pK_a value from the given K_a.	$pK_a = -\log (5 \times 10^{-8}) = 7.3$
2. That pK_a represents the average of one of the pair of pH values listed for indicators on the table. Focus on the middle of the indicator table.	Phenol red undergoes its color change from yellow to red between pH 6.6 and 8.0. The intermediate color is orange.
3. Once you calculate it, immediately focus on a particular region of the table to find the appropriate indicator.	Averaging the two pH values, we obtain: $\frac{6.6 + 8.0}{2} = 7.3$ The indicator is phenol red.

Sample Problem — Estimating Solution pH

Samples of a solution were tested with three different indicators. Determine the pH range of the solution given the results shown below.

Indicator	Color
thymolphthalein	colorless
bromthymol blue	blue
thymol blue	Yellow

What to Think About	How to Do It
1. Use each data entry to identify a range of possible pH values for the solution.	First data entry: pH $\leq$ 9.4 Second data entry: pH $\geq$ 7.6 Third data entry: pH $\leq$ 8
2. Give the final answer as a narrow pH range rather than an exact value.	The pH range of the solution is given by: $7.6 \leq pH \leq 8.0$

Practice Problems — Acid-Base Indicators

1. The indicator bromphenol blue appears yellow below pH = 3.0 and blue above pH = 4.5. Estimate the pK_a and K_a of the indicator and determine the color it will display in a 1.8×10^{-4} M HCl solution.

2. Estimate the $[H_3O^+]$ in a solution given the following data:

Indicator	Color
Phenol red	red
Phenolphthalein	colorless

Continued on next page

Practice Problems (*Continued*)

3. A few drops of alizarin yellow are added to 25.0 mL of a 0.0010 M NaOH solution. What color should the indicator display? Explain your answer by showing the work.

4. Like thymol blue, the indicator alizarin also undergoes a color change over two different pH ranges. Use the table below to estimate the K_{a1} and K_{a2} values for alizarin.

	Below pH 5.6	Above pH 7.3	Below pH 11.0	Above pH 12.4
Alizarin color	yellow	red	red	purple

5. The following 0.10 M salt solutions have had their labels removed: $NaHSO_4$, Na_2CO_3, NaH_2PO_4, and NH_4CH_3COO. The solutions are tested with three indicators and the following results were observed.

	Bromthymol Blue	Methyl Orange	Phenolphthalein
Solution A	blue	yellow	pink
Solution B	green	yellow	colorless
Solution C	yellow	yellow	colorless
Solution D	yellow	red	colorless

Identify each solution: A _____   B _____

C _____   D _____

Acid-Base Titration Curves

We now begin a more detailed discussion of acid-base titrations by focusing on the pH changes that occur in the reaction flask as the titrant is added from the burette. We will look at three different types of titrations and apply our knowledge of indicators in each case.

An efficient way to monitor the progress of an acid-base titration is to plot the pH of the solution being analyzed as a function of the volume of titrant added. Such a diagram is called a titration curve.

> A **titration curve** is a plot of the pH of the solution being analyzed versus the volume of titrant added.

Each of the three types of titrations we will consider has a different net ionic equation, a different titration curve with a characteristic shape and features, and a different equivalence point pH requiring selection of a suitable indicator.

We will begin by considering the titration of the strong acid HCl(*aq*) with the strong base NaOH(*aq*). The formula and net ionic equations for the titration are given below:

$$HCl(aq) + NaOH(aq) \rightarrow NaCl(aq) + H_2O(l)$$

$$H_3O^+(aq) + OH^-(aq) \rightarrow 2\,H_2O(l)$$

The titration curve for the titration of a 25.00 mL solution of 0.100 M HCl with a 0.100 M NaOH solution is shown in Figure 5.4.2. An analysis of the curve reveals several important features.

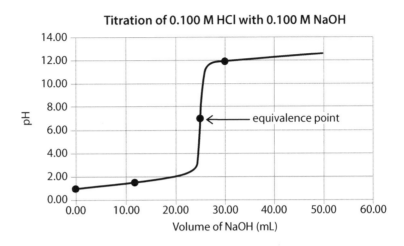

Titration of 0.100 M HCl with 0.100 M NaOH

Figure 5.4.2 *Titration curve for a 25.00 mL solution of 0.100 M HCl titrated with a 0.100 M NaOH solution*

1. Because the acid is strong and therefore the initial $[H_3O^+]$ is high, *the pH starts out low.* As the titration proceeds, as long as there is *excess strong acid* in the flask, the pH will remain low and increase only very slowly as the NaOH is added.

2. The slow increase in pH continues until the moles of NaOH added almost equal the moles of H_3O^+ initially present in the acid. Then, when the titration is within one or two drops of the equivalence point, the slope of the curve increases dramatically. The next drop of titrant neutralizes the last of the acid at the equivalence point and then introduces a tiny excess of OH^- ions into the flask. When this occurs, *the line becomes almost vertical and the pH rises by six to eight units almost immediately.*

3. Following the steep rise in pH at the equivalence point, the pH then increases slowly as excess OH^- is added.

Look at the titration curve above in Figure 5.4.2. Four points have been placed on the curve, representing key stages during the titration. Let us consider the chemical species present in the reaction flask and *calculate the pH at these four key stages.*

Stage 1: *The pH prior to the addition of any titrant*
Before any NaOH has been added, the reaction flask contains 25.00 mL of
0.100 M HCl(*aq*). As HCl is a strong acid, the [HCl] = $[H_3O^+]$ = 0.100 M. Therefore the
pH = – log (0.100) = 1.000.
(Note the location of the *first* point on the above titration curve.)

Stage 2: *The pH approximately halfway to the equivalence point*
Once we begin adding NaOH, two changes occur in the solution in the flask that influence its pH: some of the acid has been neutralized by the added base, and the volume has increased.
Calculating the pH at this stage is similar to the process discussed in section 5.4 when a strong acid was mixed with a strong base. Recall that the calculation involves determining the diluted concentrations of H_3O^+ and OH^- (designated as $[H_3O^+]_{ST}$ and $[OH^-]_{ST}$) before the reaction and then subtracting the lesser concentration from the greater concentration to determine the concentration of

the ion in excess. Although this method will work again in this situation, as we move forward through this and the other types of titration calculations, you will learn another approach.

This method allows us to organize and manage information efficiently when solutions are mixed and involve limiting and excess reactants. The process involves the use of an **ICF** table, which is a variation on the ICE table you are already familiar with. The "**I**" and the "**C**" still represent the "**I**nitial" and "**C**hange" in reagent concentrations, but because titration reactions go to completion, the "**E**" has been replaced with an "**F**" representing the "**F**inal" concentrations present when the reaction is complete. Let's use this method to calculate the pH of the solution present in the flask at stage 2, following the addition of 12.50 mL of the 0.100 M NaOH to the 25.00 mL of 0.100 M HCl in the flask — that is *halfway* to the equivalence point. Consider the Sample Problem below.

Sample Problem — Calculating pH Halfway to the Equivalence Point

Calculate the pH of the solution produced in the reaction flask during a titration following the addition of 12.50 mL of 0.100 M NaOH to 25.00 mL of 0.100 M HCl.

What to Think About

1. Determine the diluted [HCl] and [NaOH] before the neutralization reaction. Enter these into the "Initial" row on the table as "$[HCl]_{IN}$" and "$[NaOH]_{IN}$."

2. In step 2, construct and complete an ICF table underneath the balanced equation using the $[HCl]_{IN}$ and $[NaOH]_{IN}$ determined in step 1. Notice that the *NaOH is the limiting reactant*. Omit the states (*aq*) and (*l*) in the table.

3. Use the species present in the reaction flask when the reaction is complete to determine the pH.

4. As the reactant acid and base are both strong, *neither of the ions in the product salt* can react with water to affect the pH of the solution. The product salt is therefore *neutral*.

How to Do It

$$[HCl]_{IN} = 0.100 \text{ M} \times \frac{25.00 \text{ mL}}{37.50 \text{ mL}} = 0.06667 \text{ M}$$

$$[NaOH]_{IN} = 0.100 \text{ M} \times \frac{12.50 \text{ mL}}{37.50 \text{ mL}} = 0.03333 \text{ M}$$

	HCl	+ NaOH	→ NaCl	+ H$_2$O
I	0.06667	0.03333	0	
C	− 0.03333	− 0.03333	+ 0.03333	
F	0.03334	≈ 0	0.03333	

Although the [OH$^-$] cannot actually be zero (recall that [H$_3$O$^+$][OH$^-$] must = 10^{-14}), as the excess HCl is the major species present, the [OH$^-$] is insignificant.

final [HCl] = final [H$_3$O$^+$]

pH = − log (0.03334) = 1.477 (3 sig. figures)

(Note the location of the *second* point on the curve.)

Stage 3: *The pH at the equivalence point*

After 25.00 mL of 0.100 M NaOH has been added to the original 25.00 mL of 0.100 M HCl, the equivalence point is reached. At this point, the total number of moles of H$_3$O$^+$ from the acid now equals the total number of moles of OH$^-$ from the base. Consider Sample Problem 6.4.2(b) on the next page.

© Edvantage Interactive 2016

Sample Problem — Calculating pH at the Equivalence Point

Determine the pH of the solution produced in the reaction flask when 25.00 mL of 0.100 M NaOH has been added to 25.00 mL of 0.100 M HCl.

What to Think About

1. Approach this problem in the same way as the problem above.

2. The $[HCl]_{IN}$ and $[NaOH]_{IN}$ are equal to each other and so neither will be in excess following the reaction.

3. At the equivalence point, the reaction flask will contain only water and NaCl(aq). As *neither ion is capable of hydrolysis, the solution in the flask will be neutral.*

How to Do It

$$[HCl]_{IN} = 0.100 \text{ M} \times \frac{25.00 \text{ mL}}{50.00 \text{ mL}} = 0.05000 \text{ M}$$

$$[NaOH]_{IN} = 0.100 \text{ M} \times \frac{25.00 \text{ mL}}{50.00 \text{ mL}} = 0.05000 \text{ M}$$

	HCl	+ NaOH	→ NaCl	+ H_2O
I	0.05000	0.05000	0	
C	− 0.05000	− 0.05000	+ 0.05000	
F	≈ 0	≈ 0	0.05000	

Neither the $[H_3O^+]$ nor the $[OH^-]$ can be zero because their product must equal 10^{-14}. However, neither is in excess so final $[H_3O^+]$ = final $[OH^-]$ = 1.00×10^{-7} M and pH = $-\log (1.00 \times 10^{-7}$ M$) = 7.000$.

(Note the location of the *third point* on the curve.)

As mentioned above, as neither ion in the product salt is capable of reacting with water, the pH of the solution at the equivalence point is 7.

> The titration of a strong monoprotic acid by a strong base will produce a solution with a pH of 7 at the equivalence point because neither of the ions present in the product salt can undergo hydrolysis to affect the pH.

As discussed, the appropriate indicator for a titration should ideally have a pK_a value that is as close as possible to the equivalence point (normally within about one pH unit). For a strong acid–strong base titration, however, the *large jump in pH* that occurs with the addition of a single drop of titrant at the equivalence point means that we have more flexibility in our choice of indicators. The table of acid-base indicators (Table A6) shows us that several indicators undergo their color change over the steep portion of the curve. Therefore, the indicators with transition points as low as pH 5 and as high as pH 9 (from methyl red to phenolphthalein) on the table are suitable for such a titration.

Stage 4: *The pH beyond the equivalence point*

After all of the acid has been neutralized, the solution now becomes increasingly basic as excess OH⁻ ions are added from the burette. We will use the ICF table below to calculate the pH of the solution in the reaction flask after 30.00 mL of the NaOH solution has been added.

Quick Check

1. Write the net ionic equation for a strong acid–strong base titration.

2. Although we have a choice of several indicators for such a titration, phenolphthalein is often chosen for practical reasons. Why?

    _____

3. Why is the pH at the equivalence point of a strong acid–strong base titration equal to 7?

    _____

A Reverse Scenario

Now let's consider the reverse scenario in which a 0.100 M NaOH solution is titrated with a 0.100 M HCl solution. The titration curve is effectively inverted compared to a strong acid titrated with a strong base, but the net ionic equation, general shape, and important features are the same. Note the inclusion of the same points at the four key stages of this titration on the curve in Figure 5.4.3.

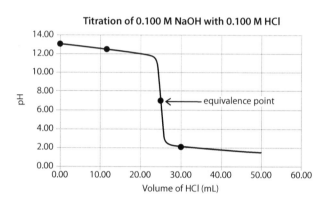

Figure 5.4.3 *Titration curve for a 0.100 M NaOH solution is titrated with a 0.100 M HCl solution*

Sample Problem — Calculating pH beyond the Equivalence Point

Calculate the pH of the solution produced in the reaction flask when 30.00 mL of 0.100 M NaOH has been added to 25.00 mL of 0.100 M HCl.

What to Think About

1. The $[NaOH]_{IN}$ will exceed the $[HCl]_{IN}$ because the equivalence point has been passed by 5.00 mL. We therefore expect the pH to be well above 7.

2. As [NaOH] will be in excess, the final [HCl] will appear as zero on the table. Although the $[H_3O^+]$ cannot actually be zero, its final concentration is insignificant.

3. The subtraction yielding the final $[OH^-]$ gives an answer to two significant figures.

How to Do It

$$[HCl]_{IN} = 0.100\ M \times \frac{25.00\ mL}{55.00\ mL} = 0.04545\ M$$

$$[NaOH]_{IN} = 0.100\ M \times \frac{30.00\ mL}{55.00\ mL} = 0.05454\ M$$

	HCl	+ NaOH	→ NaCl	+ H_2O
I	0.04545	0.05454	0	
C	−0.04545	−0.04545	+0.04545	
F	≈ 0	0.00909	0.04545	

final $[OH^-]$ = final [NaOH] = 0.00909 M

pOH = −log (0.00909) = 2.041

pH = 14.000 − 2.041 = 11.96 (2 sig. figures)

(Note the location of the *fourth point* on the curve.)

Practice Problems — Strong Acid–Strong Base Titration Curves

1. Consider the titration described above in the sample problems. Use an ICF table to calculate the pH of the solution in the reaction flask after 24.95 mL of 0.100 M NaOH has been added to the 25.00 mL of 0.100 M HCl. (This corresponds to about *1 drop before the equivalence point.*)

2. Use an ICF table to calculate the pH of the solution in the same flask after 25.05 mL of 0.100 M NaOH has been added to the 25.00 mL of 0.100 M HCl. (This corresponds to about *1 drop beyond the equivalence point.*)

3. Would you expect the complete neutralization of sulfuric acid by a sodium hydroxide solution in a titration to produce a neutral solution at the equivalence point? Why or why not? (Begin your answer by writing the balanced formula equation for the reaction.)

II. Weak Acid–Strong Base Titration Curves

Let's now consider the titration of the *weak acid* $CH_3COOH(aq)$ with the strong base $NaOH(aq)$. The formula and net ionic equations for the reaction are shown below:

$$CH_3COOH(aq) + NaOH(aq) \rightarrow NaCH_3COO(aq) + H_2O(l)$$

$$CH_3COOH(aq) + OH^-(aq) \rightarrow CH_3COO^-(aq) + H_2O(l)$$

Note that the acid is weak so it ionizes only to a small extent. Therefore, the predominant species reacting with the hydroxide ion from the strong base is the intact molecular acid. The diagram in Figure 7.4.4 shows the curve obtained when we titrate 25.0 mL of a 0.100 M CH_3COOH solution with 25.0 mL of a 0.100 M NaOH solution. Once again, we can identify a number of important features.

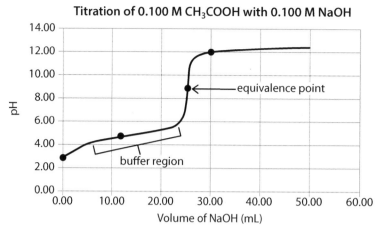

Titration of 0.100 M CH₃COOH with 0.100 M NaOH

Figure 5.4.4 *Titration curve for 25.0 mL of a 0.100 M CH₃COOH solution titrated with 25.0 mL of a 0.100 M NaOH solution*

Important Features of a Weak Acid–Strong Base Titration Curve

1. Because the acid is weak and thus ionizes only to a slight extent, the initial $[H_3O^+]$ is lower and so *the initial pH is higher* than for a strong acid.

2. There is an initial small jump in pH, but then the pH increases more slowly over a portion of the curve called the *buffer region* (labeled above) just before the steep rise to the equivalence point. However, *the pH in this region still changes more quickly than it does during a strong acid–strong base titration*. The buffer region occurs because large enough quantities of both the weak acid and its conjugate base exist in the reaction flask. This will be discussed in detail below.

3. The steep rise to the equivalence point occurs *over a smaller pH range* than when a strong acid is titrated with a strong base and *the pH at the equivalence point is greater than 7*. The solution at the equivalence point contains the anion from a weak acid (CH_3COO^-) and the cation from a strong base (Na^+). Although the cation can't react with water, the anion is a weak base and will therefore *accept protons from water, producing OH⁻ ions*. Hence the pH is greater than 7.

4. Beyond the equivalence point, the pH once again increases slowly as excess OH⁻ is added.

Note that we have again placed points on the curve at the same four key stages as we discussed in the strong acid–strong base titration. Let's once again consider the chemical species present in the reaction flask and calculate the pH at those four key stages. The calculations are different because of the minimal ionization of the weak acid and the hydrolysis reaction of its conjugate base with water.

Stage 1: *The pH prior to the addition of any titrant*
You may recognize this calculation as the first type of weak acid calculation we discussed in section 5.5, namely calculating the pH of a weak acid solution given the initial concentration and the K_a value. Recall that the minimal ionization (less than 5%) of the acid allowed us to assume that its initial and equilibrium concentrations were approximately equal. Using the same approach here, the initial concentration of 0.100 M and the K_a for acetic acid of 1.8×10^{-5} allows us to perform the calculation below.

Let $x = [H_3O^+]_{eq}$
Assume $0.100 - x \approx 0.100$

$$CH_3COOH \ + \ H_2O \ \rightleftharpoons \ CH_3COO^- + H_3O^+$$

I	0.100		0	0
C	$-x$		$+x$	$+x$
E	$0.100 - x$		x	x

© Edvantage Interactive 2016

$$K_a = \frac{[CH_3COO^-][H_3O^+]}{[CH_3COOH]} = \frac{x^2}{0.100} = 1.8 \times 10^{-5}$$

$$x = \sqrt{(1.8 \times 10^{-5})(0.100)} = 1.342 \times 10^{-3} \text{ M}$$

So pH $= -\log(1.342 \times 10^{-3} \text{ M}) = 2.87$ (2 sig. figures)

(Note the location of the *first point* on the titration curve in Figure 7.4.4.)

Stage 2: *The pH approximately halfway to the equivalence point*
As we begin adding NaOH from the burette, the OH^- ions react with the CH_3COOH in the flask to produce CH_3COO^- and H_2O. Therefore, from the beginning of the titration until the equivalence point is reached, the flask will contain *a mixture of a weak acid and its conjugate base*. This means that, for most of that time, the reaction mixture will qualify as a buffer solution. When you look at the titration curve, you can see that the *buffer region* represents the interval over which there are sufficient quantities of both CH_3COOH and CH_3COO^- for the solution to be a buffer.

To calculate the pH of the reaction mixture at about halfway to the equivalence point, we can use the same sequence of calculations with the ICF table as for a strong acid–strong base titration. Consider Sample Problem below.

Sample Problem — Calculating pH Just before Halfway to the Equivalence Point

Calculate the pH of the solution produced in the reaction flask *just prior to halfway to the equivalence point* when 12.00 mL of 0.100 M NaOH has been added to 25.00 mL of 0.100 M CH_3COOH.

What to Think About

1. Once again calculate the diluted concentrations of reactant acid and base before the reaction.

2. The final concentrations of CH_3COOH and CH_3COO^- in the solution are significant and thus constitute a buffer.

3. Therefore calculate the pH either by manipulating the K_a expression for acetic acid or, by way of extension, using the Henderson-Hasselbalch equation (see below).

How to Do It

$$[CH_3COOH]_{IN} = 0.100 \text{ M} \times \frac{25.00 \text{ mL}}{37.00 \text{ mL}} = 0.06757 \text{ M}$$

$$[NaOH]_{IN} = 0.100 \text{ M} \times \frac{12.00 \text{ mL}}{37.00 \text{ mL}} = 0.03243 \text{ M}$$

$$CH_3COOH + NaOH \rightarrow NaCH_3COO + H_2O$$

	CH_3COOH	$NaOH$	$NaCH_3COO$	
I	0.06757	0.03243	0	
C	−0.03243	−0.03243	+0.03243	
F	0.03514	≈ 0	0.03243	

$$K_a = \frac{[H_3O^+][CH_3COO^-]}{[CH_3COOH]}, \text{ so } [H_3O^+] = \frac{K_a[CH_3COOH]}{[CH_3COO^-]}$$

$$[H_3O^+] = \frac{(1.8 \times 10^{-5})(0.03514)}{(0.03243)} = 1.95 \times 10^{-5} \text{ M}$$

so pH $= -\log(1.95 \times 10^{-5}) = 4.71$ (2 sig. figures)

(Note the location of the *second point* on the curve.)

Using the Henderson-Hasselbalch Equation (Extension)

Because a buffer solution exists in the reaction flask, we could have also chosen to solve the above problem using the Henderson-Hasselbalch equation as follows:

$$pH = pK_a + \log\left[\frac{[CH_3COO^-]}{[CH_3COOH]}\right] = 4.745 + \log\left[\frac{(0.03243)}{(0.03514)}\right] = 4.745 + (-0.0348) = 4.71$$

The above methods show us that just before halfway to the equivalence point in the titration, *the log of the ratio is negative* because the [base]/[acid] ratio is less than one. This means that *just before halfway to the equivalence point, the solution pH is always less than the pK_a.*

Note that *exactly halfway to the equivalence point*, half of the acid has been converted to its conjugate base, so [CH$_3$COOH] = [CH$_3$COO$^-$]. We therefore see that:

$$[H_3O^+] = \frac{K_a[\cancel{CH_3COOH}]}{[\cancel{CH_3COO^-}]} \qquad \text{and} \qquad pH = pK_a + \log\frac{[\cancel{CH_3COO^-}]}{[\cancel{CH_3COOH}]}$$

$$\text{so} \quad [H_3O^+] = K_a = 1.8 \times 10^{-5} \qquad\qquad \text{so} \quad pH = pK_a + \log 1$$

$$\mathbf{pH = pK_a = 4.74}$$

The fact that the pH of the solution halfway to the equivalence point equals the pK_a of the weak acid being titrated is a useful relationship. This allows us to determine the K_a of a weak acid by titrating it with a strong base and noting the pH of the solution exactly halfway to the equivalence point on the titration curve.

Sample Problem — Calculating pH Just beyond Halfway to the Equivalence Point

Calculate the pH of the solution produced in the reaction flask *just beyond halfway to the equivalence point* when 13.00 mL of 0.100 M NaOH has been added to 25.00 mL of 0.100 M CH$_3$COOH.

What to Think About

1. Calculate the diluted concentrations and enter them into the ICF table.

2. The solution in the reaction flask once again qualifies as a buffer.

3. Use the final concentrations of CH$_3$COOH and CH$_3$COO$^-$ to calculate the pH of the solution in two ways as in the previous example.

How to Do It

$$[CH_3COOH]_{IN} = 0.100\ M \times \frac{25.00\ \cancel{mL}}{38.00\ \cancel{mL}} = 0.06579\ M$$

$$[NaOH]_{IN} = 0.100\ M \times \frac{13.00\ \cancel{mL}}{38.00\ \cancel{mL}} = 0.03421\ M$$

$$CH_3COOH + NaOH \rightarrow NaCH_3COO + H_2O$$

I	0.06579	0.03421	0
C	− 0.03421	− 0.03421	+ 0.03421
F	0.03158	0	0.03421

$$K_a = \frac{[H_3O^+][CH_3COO^-]}{[CH_3COOH]} \qquad \text{so} \qquad [H_3O^+] = \frac{K_a[CH_3COOH]}{[CH_3COO^-]}$$

$$[H_3O^+] = \frac{(1.8 \times 10^{-5})(0.03158)}{(0.03421)} = 1.66 \times 10^{-5}\ M$$

so pH = − log (1.66 × 10^{-5}) = 4.78 (2 sig. figures)

Using the Henderson-Hasselbalch Equation (Extension)

Once again, we could have chosen to solve the above problem using the Henderson-Hasselbalch equation as follows:

$$pH = pK_a + \log\left[\frac{[CH_3COO^-]}{[CH_3COOH]}\right] = 4.745 + \log\left[\frac{(0.03421)}{(0.03158)}\right] = 4.74 + (0.0347) = 4.78$$

We can therefore see that beyond halfway to the equivalence point in the titration, *the log of the ratio is positive* because the [base]/[acid] is greater than one. This means that *beyond halfway to the equivalence point, the solution pH is always greater than the pK_a.*

© Edvantage Interactive 2016

During the titration of a weak acid with strong base:

- prior to halfway to the equivalence point: $[H_3O^+] > K_a$ and so $pH < pK_a$
- halfway to the equivalence point: $[H_3O^+] = K_a$ and so $pH = pK_a$
- beyond halfway and prior to the equivalence point: $[H_3O^+] < K_a$ and so $pH > pK_a$

Stage 3: *The pH at the equivalence point*

If you look again at the weak acid–strong base titration curve (Figure 5.4.4), you'll notice that the volume of 0.100 M NaOH required to neutralize 25.00 mL of 0.100 M CH_3COOH at the equivalence point is *exactly the same* as that required to neutralize the same volume of 0.100 M HCl. This reminds us that the strength of an acid has *no bearing* on the volume of base required to neutralize it in a titration.

At the equivalence point, all of the acid originally present has reacted with the added NaOH. The reaction flask therefore contains an aqueous solution of the salt produced from a weak acid and a strong base, namely $NaCH_3COO$. As noted above, although the Na^+ ion cannot react with water, the CH_3COO^- ion from a weak acid is itself a weak base and will therefore accept protons from water, producing OH^- ions. This means that the pH at the equivalence point will be above 7 due to the presence of a basic salt.

> The titration of a weak acid by a strong base will produce a basic solution with a pH greater than 7 at the equivalence point because the anion present in the product salt will undergo hydrolysis to produce OH^- ions and the cation will not hydrolyze.

To correctly calculate the pH at the equivalence point, we must first consider the initial reaction that *goes to completion*. This requires the use of the IC**F** table. We must then use the IC**E** table to manage the hydrolysis reaction of the acetate anion with water, which involves an *equilibrium*. This is illustrated in Sample Problem below.

Sample Problem — Calculating pH at the Equivalence Point

Calculate the pH of the solution produced in the reaction flask when 25.00 mL of 0.100 M NaOH has been added to 25.00 mL of 0.100 M CH_3COOH

What to Think About	**How to Do It**
1. Once again dilute the acid and base and then enter those values into the ICF table for the reaction that goes to completion.	**Part 1** $[CH_3COOH]_{IN} = 0.100 \text{ M} \times \dfrac{25.00 \text{ mL}}{50.00 \text{ mL}} = 0.0500 \text{ M}$ $[NaOH]_{IN} = 0.100 \text{ M} \times \dfrac{25.00 \text{ mL}}{50.00 \text{ mL}} = 0.0500 \text{ M}$
2. Examine the bottom line of the ICF table. It reveals that a 0.0500 M solution of $NaCH_3COO$ exists in the reaction flask at the equivalence point.	$CH_3COOH + NaOH \rightarrow NaCH_3COO + H_2O$

$$CH_3COOH + NaOH \rightarrow NaCH_3COO + H_2O$$

I	0.0500	0.0500	0	✕
C	− 0.0500	− 0.0500	+ 0.0500	✕
F	≈ 0	≈ 0	0.0500	✕

Continued on next page

Sample Problem (Continued)

What to Think About

3. The anion of the dissociated salt is the conjugate base of a weak acid and is thus capable of accepting protons from water in a hydrolysis reaction.

4. For the second part of the calculation, enter the 0.0500 M CH_3COO^- in the Initial row of the ICE table for the hydrolysis equilibrium.

5. Calculate the pH of the solution resulting from the anionic hydrolysis of the acetate ion.

How to Do It

Part 2

Let $x = [OH^-]_{eq}$

$$CH_3COO^- + H_2O \rightleftharpoons CH_3COOH + OH^-$$

	CH_3COO^-		CH_3COOH	OH^-
I	0.0500		0	0
C	$-x$		$+x$	$+x$
E	$0.0500 - x$		x	x

Assume $0.0500 - x \approx 0.0500$

$$K_b = \frac{[CH_3COOH][OH^-]}{[CH_3COO^-]} = \frac{K_w}{K_a} = \frac{1.0 \times 10^{-14})}{1.8 \times 10^{-5}} = 5.6 \times 10^{-10}$$

$$\frac{x^2}{0.0500} = 5.6 \times 10^{-10} \quad so \quad x = \sqrt{(0.0500)(5.6 \times 10^{-10})}$$

$$x = [OH^-] = 5.29 \times 10^{-6} \, M \quad so \quad pOH = -\log(5.292 \times 10^{-6})$$

$$pOH = 5.27 \quad and \quad so \quad pH = 14.000 - 5.27 = 8.72$$

(2 sig. figures)

(Note the location of the *third point* on the curve.)

Choosing the Right Indicator

Because the vertical region on the titration curve around the equivalence point is shorter than for a strong acid–strong base titration, we are more limited when choosing the proper indicator. The table of acid-base indicators (Table A6) shows us that either phenolphthalein or thymol blue (based on its second transition point) would be an appropriate indicator in this case. Methyl red would not.

Stage 4: *The pH beyond the equivalence point*
After all of the acid has been neutralized, the solution again becomes increasingly basic with the addition of excess OH^- ions. Although a relatively high concentration of the weakly basic acetate ion remains in the reaction flask beyond the equivalence point, the presence of excess hydroxide ions in the flask is far more significant in determining the pH. The excess NaOH is a *strong base* and the increasing $[OH^-]$ from that base forces the weak base hydrolysis equilibrium even further to the left.

$$CH_3COO^-(aq) + H_2O(l) \rightleftharpoons CH_3COOH(aq) + \mathbf{OH^-}(aq)$$

The result is that we can safely ignore any contribution to the $[OH^-]$ in the flask by the acetate ion and thus use only the ICF table to calculate the pH. Consider Sample Problem 7.4.3(d) below.

Sample Problem — Calculating pH beyond the Equivalence Point Calculate

the pH of the solution produced in the reaction flask when 30.00 mL of 0.100 M NaOH has been added to 25.00 mL of 0.100 M CH$_3$COOH.

What to Think About

1. Because the equivalence point has been passed by 5.00 mL, once again expect the pH to be well above 7.

2. As [NaOH] will be in excess, ignore the final [CH$_3$COO$^-$] when calculating pH.

3. The subtraction yielding the final [OH$^-$] gives an answer to three significant figures. This specifies the decimal places in the final pH.

How to Do It

$$[CH_3COOH]_{IN} = 0.100\ M \times \frac{25.00\ \text{mL}}{55.00\ \text{mL}} = 0.04545\ M$$

$$[NaOH]_{IN} = 0.100\ M \times \frac{30.00\ \text{mL}}{55.00\ \text{mL}} = 0.05454\ M$$

$$CH_3COOH + NaOH \rightarrow NaCH_3COO + H_2O$$

I	0.04545	0.05454	0	
C	− 0.04545	− 0.04545	+ 0.04545	
F	≈ 0	0.00909	0.04545	

$$final\ [OH^-] = final\ [NaOH] = 0.00909\ M$$
$$pOH = -log\ (0.00909) = 2.041$$
$$pH = 14.000 - 2.041 = 11.959\ (3\ sig.\ figures)$$

(Note the location of the *fourth point* on the curve.)

Comparing Titration Curves

Note that the pH at this *final stage* is the same as for the titration of 0.100 M HCl by 0.100 M NaOH, although the pH values at *the first three stages are different*.

Figure 5.4.5 compares the two titration curves. Note the position of the weak acid–strong base titration curve relative to the strong acid–strong base curve *before the equivalence point*. As the strength of the acid being titrated decreases, the portion of the titration curve before the equivalence point will shift farther and farther up so that each of the first three stages we have discussed will be associated with higher and higher pH values during the titration. Yet despite the acid's strengths being different, the volume of base required to reach equivalence remains the same!

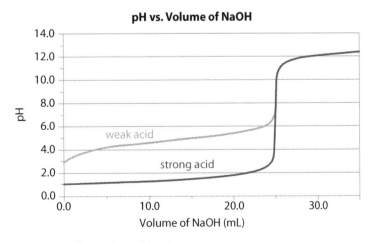

pH vs. Volume of NaOH

Figure 5.4.5 *Comparison of titration curves*

Quick Check

1. Why do we label a region of a weak acid–strong base titration curve before the equivalence point as a "buffer region"?

   _____

2. Why is the pH at the equivalence point of a weak acid–strong base titration higher than 7?

   _____

3. When titrating acetic acid with sodium hydroxide, why can we ignore any contribution to the $[OH^-]$ by the acetate anion beyond the equivalence point when calculating pH?

   _____

4. *On Figure 8.4.5 above,* sketch the titration curve for the titration of 25.0 mL 0.100 M hypochlorous acid, HClO, with a solution of 0.100 M NaOH, given the following information:

Initial pH of HClO Solution	pH Halfway to Equivalence Point	pH at Equivalence Point
4.27	7.54	10.12

Practice Problems — Weak Acid–Strong Base Titration Curves

1. (a) Calculate the pH of the solution produced when 9.00 mL of 0.200 M NaOH has been added to 20.0 mL of 0.200 M HCOOH. Is this value less than or greater than the pK_a of HCOOH?

   (b) Calculate the pH at the equivalence point of this titration.

2. A student titrates an unknown weak monoprotic acid with a standard solution of KOH and draws a titration curve. Halfway to the equivalence point, the pH of the solution is identified to be 4.187. Identify the acid.

3. (a) A 20.0 mL sample of 0.450 M HNO_2 is titrated with a 0.500 M NaOH solution. What $[H_3O^+]$ will exist in the reaction flask exactly halfway to the equivalence point?

   (b) The equivalence point is reached when 18.00 mL of the basic solution has been added to the original nitrous acid solution. Calculate the pH at the equivalence point.

© Edvantage Interactive 2016

The third type of titration we will discuss can be considered the opposite of the previous type — namely, the titration of a *weak base* by a *strong* acid. Recall that the curve for a strong base titrated with a strong acid is the *same shape* as a strong acid titrated with a strong base, but is *inverted*. The same is true of the titration curve for a weak base titrated with a strong acid compared with the curve for a weak acid titrated with a strong base: *the shape is the same but inverted.*

Let's investigate the titration of a 0.100 M NH_3 solution with a 0.100 M HCl. The formula and net ionic equations for the reaction are shown below:

$$NH_3(aq) + HCl(aq) \quad \rightarrow \quad NH_4^+(aq) + Cl^-(aq)$$

$$NH_3(aq) + H_3O^+(aq) \quad \rightarrow \quad NH_4^+(aq) + H_2O(l)$$

If we compare the titration curve for the above reaction to that for a *strong base* titrated with a strong acid, we can once again identify a number of important features. Consider those two curves in Figure 5.4.6 below.

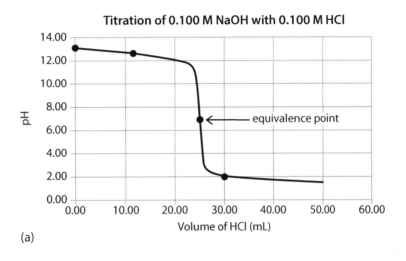

(a)

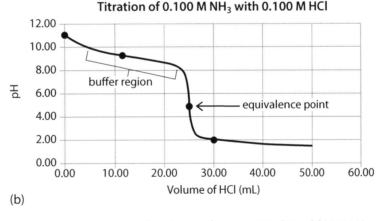

(b)

Figure 5.4.6 *Titration curves for solutions of (a) 0.100 M NaOH and (b) 0.100 M NH_3 titrated with 0.100 M HCl*

1. Because the solution we begin with is a *weak* base, we expect the initial pH to be above 7, but *lower* than if we were starting with a *strong base*.

2. There is an initial small drop in pH as the titration begins, but then the pH decreases more slowly over a *buffer region* during which significant amounts of the weak base (NH_3) and its conjugate acid (NH_4^+) are present in the flask. However, the pH in this region still changes *more quickly* than it does during a strong base–strong acid titration. The buffer region ends just before the steep drop in pH associated with the equivalence point.

3. The steep drop at the equivalence point occurs *over a smaller pH range* than when a *strong base* is titrated with a strong acid and *the pH at the equivalence point is below 7*. The solution at the equivalence point contains the anion from a strong acid (Cl^-) and the cation from a weak base (NH_4^+). Although the anion can't accept protons from water, *the cation is a weak acid and will therefore donate protons to water, producing H_3O^+ ions*. Hence the pH is below 7.

4. Beyond the equivalence point, the pH decreases slowly as excess H_3O^+ is added.

The four points have once again been placed at the same key stages of the titration. And once again, by considering the species present in the reaction flask at these stages, we can calculate the pH of the solution. The calculations are similar to the previous titration type in that they reflect, in this case, the minimal ionization of the weak base and the hydrolysis reaction of its conjugate with water.

Stage 1: *The pH before the addition of any titrant*
This calculation is the first type we discussed for weak bases in section 5.5: the pH of a weak base solution is determined given the initial concentration and the K_b value. The slight ionization of the NH_3 allows us to assume that its initial and equilibrium concentrations are approximately equal. Consider the following pH calculation:

$$K_b \text{ for } NH_3 = \frac{K_w}{K_a \text{ for } NH_4^+} = \frac{1.00 \times 10^{-14}}{5.6 \times 10^{-10}} = 1.8 \times 10^{-5}$$

Let $x = [OH^-]_{eq}$
Assume $0.100 - x \approx 0.100$

	NH_3	$+$ $H_2O \rightleftharpoons$	NH_4^+	$+$	OH^-
I	0.100		0		0
C	$-x$		$+x$		$+x$
E	$0.100 - x$		x		x

$$K_b = \frac{[NH_4^+][OH^-]}{[NH_3]} = \frac{x^2}{0.100} = 1.8 \times 10^{-5}$$

$x = \sqrt{(1.8 \times 10^{-5})(0.100)} = 1.34 \times 10^{-3} \text{ M} = [OH^-]$

so $pOH = -\log(1.34 \times 10^{-3}) = 2.872$ and

$pH = 14.000 - 2.872 = 11.13$

(Note the location of the *first point* on the curve.)

Stage 2: *The pH approximately halfway to the equivalence point*
As the titration begins and HCl is added to the flask, the H_3O^+ ions react with the NH_3 to produce NH_4^+ and H_2O. Thus, from the beginning of the titration until the equivalence point is reached, the flask will contain *a mixture of a weak base and its conjugate acid*. This means once again that, for most of that time, the reaction mixture will qualify as a buffer solution. If you look at the titration curve, you can see that the *buffer region* represents the interval over which there are significant quantities of both NH_3 and NH_4^+ in the solution.

The use of the ICF table will again allow us to efficiently organize and manage the information provided in the question.

Sample Problem — Calculating pH before Halfway to the Equivalence Point

Calculate the pH of the solution produced during a titration following the addition of 12.00 mL of 0.100 M HCl to 25.00 mL of 0.100 M NH_3. This is almost *halfway* to the equivalence point.

What to Think About	**How to Do It**
1. Once again determine the diluted concentrations and enter those values into the ICF table.	$[NH_3]_{IN} = 0.100 \text{ M} \times \dfrac{25.00 \text{ mL}}{37.00 \text{ mL}} = 0.06757$ M $[HCl]_{IN} = 0.100 \text{ M} \times \dfrac{12.00 \text{ mL}}{37.00 \text{ mL}} = 0.03243$ M

2. Use the final concentrations at the completion of the reaction to determine the pH.

3. As we are almost halfway to the equivalence point, the $[NH_3]$ and $[NH_4^+]$ are sufficient to constitute a buffer.

4. The $[Cl^-]$ cannot react with water and so will not affect the pH of the solution.

	NH_3	$+$ HCl	$\rightarrow$ NH_4^+	$+$ Cl^-
I	0.06757	0.03243	0	0
C	-0.03243	-0.03243	$+0.03243$	$+0.03243$
F	0.03514	≈ 0	0.03243	0.03243

$$K_b = \frac{[NH_4^+][OH^-]}{[NH_3]}, \text{ so } [OH^-] = \frac{K_b[NH_3]}{[NH_4^+]}$$

$$[OH^-] = \frac{(1.8 \times 10^{-5})(0.03514)}{(0.03243)} = 1.95 \times 10^{-5} \text{ M}$$

$$pOH = -\log(1.95 \times 10^{-5}) = 4.710$$

$$\text{so } pH = 14.000 - 4.710 = 9.29 \text{ (2 sig. figures)}$$

(Note the location of the *second point* on the curve.)

Using the Henderson-Hasselbalch Equation (Extension)

Because a buffer solution exists in the reaction flask, we could have again chosen to solve the above problem using the Henderson-Hasselbalch equation. In the equation, we use the pK_a for the conjugate acid of NH_3. The pK_a for $NH_4^+ = -\log(5.6 \times 10^{-10}) = 9.252$.

$$pH = pK_a + \log\left[\frac{[NH_3]}{[NH_4^+]}\right] = 9.252 + \log\left[\frac{[0.03514]}{[0.03243]}\right] = 9.252 + (0.0349) = 9.29$$

Note that, because the [base]/[acid] ratio is greater than 1, *the log of the ratio is positive*. This means that just prior to halfway to the equivalence point, *the pH is greater than the pK_a*

$pOH = pK_b$ of Weak Base at Halfway Point

Note that *exactly halfway to the equivalence point* half of the base has been converted to its conjugate acid. Therefore $[NH_3] = [NH_4^+]$. This means that:

$$[OH^-] = \frac{K_b[NH_3]}{[NH_4^+]} \qquad\qquad pOH = pK_b + \log\frac{[NH_3]}{[NH_4^+]}$$

so $\quad [OH^-] = K_b = 1.8 \times 10^{-5}$ $\qquad\qquad$ so $\quad pOH = pK_b + \log 1$

and $\quad [H_3O^+] = \dfrac{1.00 \times 10^{-14}}{1.8 \times 10^{-5}} = 5.6 \times 10^{-10}$ $\qquad$ **$pOH = pK_b = 4.745$**

$\qquad [H_3O^+] = K_a$ (for NH_4^+) $\qquad\qquad\qquad$ **$pH = pK_a$ (for NH_4^+) $= 9.25$**

The fact that the pOH of the solution halfway to the equivalence point equals the pK_b of the weak base is a similar scenario to that of a *weak acid–strong base* titration. In this case, we can determine the K_b of a weak base by titrating it with a strong acid and noting the pOH of the solution exactly halfway to the equivalence point on the titration curve. (Had we chosen to use the Henderson-Hasselbalch equation, we would have calculated the same pH value.)

Stage 3: *The pH at the equivalence point*
At the equivalence point, all of the base initially present in the flask has reacted with the added HCl. The flask therefore contains an aqueous solution of the salt produced from a strong acid and a weak base — in this case, NH_4Cl. We noted above that the Cl^- ion cannot react with water, but the NH_4^+ is weakly acidic and will therefore react with water to produce H_3O^+ ions. This means that the pH at the equivalence point will be below 7 due to the presence of an acidic salt.

> The titration of a weak base by a strong acid will produce an acidic solution with a pH below 7 at the equivalence point because the cation present in the product salt will undergo hydrolysis to produce H_3O^+ ions and the anion will not hydrolyze.

To calculate the pH at the equivalence point, we must once again consider the initial reaction that *goes to completion*, and then the hydrolysis reaction of the ammonium anion with water that involves an *equilibrium*. Consider Sample Problem 6.4.4(b) on the next page.

Sample Problem — Calculating pH at the Equivalence Point

Calculate the pH of the solution produced in the reaction flask when 25.00 mL of 0.100 M HCl has been added to 25.00 mL of 0.100 M NH_3.

What to Think About

1. Dilute the acid and base and enter those values into the ICF table for the reaction that goes to completion.

2. Examine the bottom line of the ICF table. It shows that a 0.0500 M NH_4Cl solution exists in the reaction flask at the equivalence point.

3. The cation of the dissociated salt is weakly acidic and is thus capable of donating protons to water in a hydrolysis reaction.

4. For the second part of the calculation, enter the 0.05000 M NH_4^+ into the Initial row of the ICE table for the hydrolysis equilibrium.

5. Calculate the pH of the solution resulting from the cationic hydrolysis of the ammonium ion.

How to Do It

Part 1

$$[NH_3]_{IN} = 0.100\ M \times \frac{25.00\ mL}{50.00\ mL} = 0.0500\ M$$

$$[HCl]_{IN} = 0.100\ M \times \frac{25.00\ mL}{50.00\ mL} = 0.0500\ M$$

	NH_3 +	HCl →	NH_4^+ +	Cl^-
I	0.0500	0.0500	0	0
C	− 0.0500	− 0.0500	+ 0.0500	+ 0.0500
F	≈ 0	≈ 0	0.0500	0.0500

Part 2

Let $x = [H_3O^+]_{eq}$

	NH_4^+ +	H_2O ⇌	NH_3 +	H_3O^+
I	0.0500		0	0
C	− x		+ x	+ x
E	0.0500 − x		x	x

Assume $0.0500 - x \approx 0.0500$

$$K_a = \frac{[NH_3][H_3O^+]}{[NH_4^+]} = 5.6 \times 10^{-10}$$

$$\frac{x^2}{0.0500} = 5.6 \times 10^{-10} \quad so \quad x = \sqrt{(0.0500)(5.6 \times 10^{-10})}$$

$$x = 5.292 \times 10^{-6}\ M \quad so\ pH = -log\ (5.292 \times 10^{-6}) = 5.28$$

(Note the location of the *third point* on the curve.)

The relatively short vertical section of the curve near the pH at the equivalence point of 5.28 suggests that an appropriate indicator for this titration would be methyl red. The pK_a for methyl red is 5.4.

Stage 4: *The pH beyond the equivalence point*

After all of the base has been neutralized, the solution again becomes increasingly acidic with the addition of excess H_3O^+ ions. Although a relatively high concentration of the weakly acidic ammonium ion remains in the reaction flask beyond the equivalence point, its presence is insignificant in determining pH in the same way that excess acetate ions were insignificant beyond the equivalence point in the weak acid–strong base titration. In this case, the presence of excess H_3O^+ in the flask is the only significant factor in determining the pH. The excess HCl is a *strong acid* and the increasing $[H_3O^+]$ from that acid forces the weak acid hydrolysis equilibrium even further to the left.

$$NH_4^+(aq) + H_2O(l) \rightleftharpoons NH_3(aq) + \mathbf{H_3O^+}(aq)$$

The result is that we can safely ignore any contribution to the $[H_3O^+]$ in the flask by the ammonium ion and so need only use the ICF table to calculate the pH. Consider Sample below.

Sample Problem — Calculating pH beyond the Equivalence Point

Calculate the pH of the solution produced in the reaction flask when 30.00 mL of 0.100 M HCl has been added to 25.00 mL of 0.100 M NH_3

What to Think About

1. Because the equivalence point has been passed by 5.00 mL, expect the pH to be well below 7.

2. As [HCl] will be in excess, ignore the final $[NH_4^+]$ when calculating pH. Also ignore the $[Cl^-]$.

3. The subtraction yielding the final $[H_3O^+]$ gives an answer to three significant figures. This determines the decimal places in the final pH.

How to Do It

$$[NH_3]_{IN} = 0.100\ M \times \frac{25.00\ mL}{55.00\ mL} = 0.04545\ M$$

$$[HCl]_{IN} = 0.100\ M \times \frac{30.00\ mL}{55.00\ mL} = 0.05454\ M$$

	NH_3	+ HCl	→ NH_4^+	+ Cl^-
I	0.04545	0.05454	0	0
C	− 0.04545	− 0.04545	+ 0.04545	+ 0.04545
F	≈ 0	0.00909	0.04545	0.04545

$$\text{final } [HCl] = \text{final } [H_3O^+] = 0.00909\ M$$

$$pH = -\log(0.00909) = 2.04\ (2\ \text{sig. figures})$$

(Note the location of the *fourth point* on the curve.)

Practice Problems — Weak Base–Strong Acid Titration Curves

1. Calculate the pH of the solution produced during the titration described above after 13.0 mL of 0.100 M HCl has been added to 25.0 mL of 0.100 M NH_3. (This is just beyond halfway to the equivalence point). Should your answer be greater than or less than the pK_a of NH_4^+?

2. Explain how the titration curve for a weak base titrated by a strong acid can be used to determine the K_b of the weak base.

3. Calculate the pH of the solution produced in the titration described above after 40.0 mL of 0.100 M HCl has been added to 25.0 mL of 0.100 M NH_3. Does the pH value you calculate agree with the titration curve?

Quick Check

1. Why is the pH at the equivalence point of a weak base–strong acid titration lower than 7?

   _____

2. Phenolphthalein is an appropriate indicator for the first two types of titrations we discussed in this section. Why is phenolphthalein a poor indicator choice for the titration of a weak base with a strong acid?

   _____

3. When titrating aqueous ammonia with hydrochloric acid, why can we ignore any contribution to the $[H_3O^+]$ by the ammonium cation beyond the equivalence point when calculating pH?

   _____

A Titration Curve Summary Table

Strong Acid + Strong Base	Weak Acid + Strong Base	Weak Base + Strong Acid
Net Ionic Equation	Net Ionic Equation	Net Ionic Equation
Sketch of Titration Curve	Sketch of Titration Curve	Sketch of Titration Curve
Reason for Equivalence Point pH Value	Reason for Equivalence Point pH Value	Reason for Equivalence Point pH Value
Hydrolysis Reaction (if any)	Hydrolysis Reaction (if any)	Hydrolysis Reaction (if any)

Results and Discussion

1. The volume of titrant required to reach the equivalence point in each titration should be exactly the same. Explain why.

2. Explain how each of the two "weak–strong" titration curves can be used to determine one of either a K_a or a K_b value.

5.4 Review Questions

1. Consider the following for a hypothetical indicator: $K_a = \dfrac{[H_3O^+][In^-]}{[HIn]} = 1.0 \times 10^{-7}$

So, given that $\dfrac{K_a}{[H_3O^+]} = \dfrac{[In^-]}{[HIn]}$

Complete the following table for three different solutions given that HIn is *yellow* and In⁻ is *blue*.

Solution	[In⁻]/[HIn] Ratio in Solution	Solution Color
0.0010 M HCl		
Pure water		
0.0010 M NaOH		

2. Equal concentrations of an indicator, HIn, and one of three different acids are placed in three separate flasks and the following data was obtained for each pair of compounds:

Solution →	0.1 M HNO₃	0.1 M HA1	0.1 M HA2
0.1 M HIn color	red	yellow	red

Use the above data to list the three acids, HA1, HA2, and HIn, in order of increasing strength and explain your reasoning.

_____ < _____ < _____

3. You are given four 0.10 M solutions without labels and told they are HCl, NaOH, FeCl₃, and NaCN. You are also told to choose only three indicators that will positively identify each solution. Complete the table below showing your choice of indicators and their colors in each solution.

Solution →	0.10 M HCl	0.10 M NaOH	0.10 M FeCl₃	0.10 M NaCN
Indicator 1:				
Indicator 2:				
Indicator 3:				

4. Complete the table below showing the reactants in three different titrations.
   (a) State if the pH at the equivalence point of each titration will be below, equal to, or above 7.
   (b) Select an appropriate indicator from a table of acid-base indicators for each titration. (There may be more than one correct choice for each titration.)

	HNO₃ + KOH	NaOH + HCOOH	HBr + NH₃
pH at equivalence pt.			
Indicator			

© Edvantage Interactive 2016

5. Bromcresol purple undergoes its color change from yellow to purple as pH increases from 5.2 through to 6.8.
   (a) Is bromcresol purple a stronger or a weaker acid than acetic acid? Explain your answer.

   (b) Would bromcresol purple be a good indicator to indicate that acetic acid is acidic? Why or why not?

6. The following 0.10 M solutions have had their labels removed: NaCl, K_3PO_4, LiHCOO, CH_3COOH, and HIO_3. The solutions are tested with three indicators and the results in the table below were observed.

	Bromthymol Blue	Methyl Orange	Thymolphthalein
Solution A	yellow	red	colorless
Solution B	green	yellow	colorless
Solution C	blue	yellow	blue
Solution D	yellow	yellow	colorless
Solution E	blue	yellow	colorless

Identify each solution:

A _____ B _____ C _____ D _____ E _____

7. Complete the following table:

Indicator	pK_a	K_a	Color in Pure Water	Color Displayed in 0.010 M NaOH	Color Displayed in 0.010 M HCl
Phenol red					
Methyl orange					
Alizarin yellow					

8. Complete each of the following statements relating to weak–strong titrations by placing the words "lower" or "higher" in each of the blank spaces in each statement.
   (a) In a weak acid–strong base titration, the weaker the acid being titrated, the _____ (lower or higher) the initial pH of the solution will be, and the _____ (lower or higher) the pH at the equivalence point will be.
   (b) In a weak base–strong acid titration, the weaker the base being titrated, the _____ (lower or higher) the initial pH of the solution will be, and the _____ (lower or higher) the pH at the equivalence point will be.

9. The chemistry of buffers and the hydrolysis of salts must both be considered when calculating the pH at different stages during the final two types of titrations we have discussed in this section. For each type of titration below, explain why in the appropriate space in the table:

	Calculating pH Halfway to the Equivalence Point (Chemistry of Buffers)	Calculating pH at the Equivalence Point (Hydrolysis of Salts)
Titration of a weak acid by a strong base		
Titration of a weak base by a strong acid		

10. Explain why the calculation of pH at the equivalence point for each of the titration types in question 8 above requires a *two-step* process.

11. A titration is performed in which a standard 0.200 M solution of NaOH is added to a 20.0 mL sample of a 0.250 M HCOOH solution.
    (a) Determine the pH halfway to the equivalence point.

    (b) Calculate the volume of standard solution required to reach the equivalence point.

    (c) Calculate the pH at the equivalence point.

12. A student titrates a solution of a weak monoprotic acid with a standardized NaOH solution. She monitors the pH with a pH meter and draws the titration curve. The curve reveals that, halfway to the equivalence point, the pH of the reaction mixture was 3.456. Identify the weak acid.

13. A solution of the weak base ethanolamine, $HOCH_2CH_2NH_2$, is titrated with a standard HCl solution. The pH is monitored with a pH meter and the titration curve is drawn. The curve reveals that, halfway to the equivalence point, the pH of the reaction mixture was 9.50. Calculate the K_b for ethanolamine.

14. The curve below shows the titration of a 0.10 M NaOH solution with a 0.10 M HCl solution. On the *same set of axes below*:
    (a) Sketch the titration curve for a 0.20 M NaOH solution being titrated with the same acid. Choose an appropriate indicator.

    (b) Sketch the titration curve for a 0.10 M NH₃ solution being titrated with the same acid. Choose an appropriate indicator.

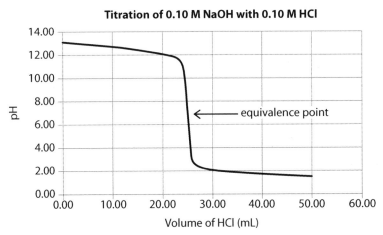

15. The curves we have discussed for the titration of both strong and weak acids have been limited to monoprotic acids. What do you think the titration curve might look like if the titration involved the titration of a weak *diprotic* acid with a strong base?

    (a) Sketch your suggested curve below:

    (b) What would you need to consider when selecting an indicator for such a titration?

6 Solubility Equilibrium

By the end of this chapter, you should be able to do the following:

- Determine the solubility of a compound in aqueous solution
- Describe a saturated solution as an equilibrium system
- Determine the concentration of ions in a solution
- Determine the relative solubility of a substance, given solubility tables
- Apply solubility rules to analyze the composition of solutions
- Formulate equilibrium constant expressions for various saturated solutions
- Perform calculations involving solubility equilibrium concepts
- Devise a method for determining the concentration of a specific ion

By the end of this chapter, you should know the meaning of these **key terms**:

- aqueous solution
- common ion
- complete ionic equation
- dissociation equation
- electrical conductivity
- formula equation
- hard water
- ionic solution
- K_{sp}
- molecular solution
- net ionic equation
- precipitate
- relative solubility
- saturated solution
- solubility equilibrium

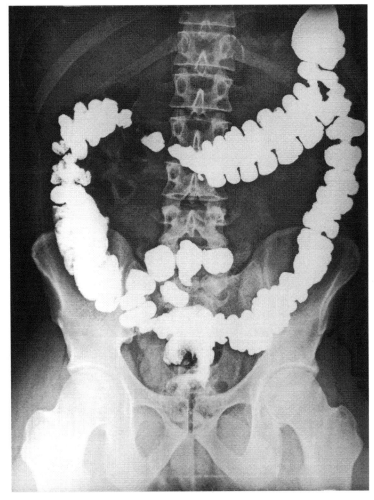

A patient must ingest a solution of barium sulfate for the large intestine (shown here) to be visible on an X-ray. The small solubility product, or K_{sp}, of $BaSO_4$ means humans can safely ingest the suspension.

6.1 The Concept of Solubility Review Questions

1. Give three examples for each of the following:
    (a) strong electrolytes

    (b) non-electrolytes

2. Compare the electrical conductivity of 1.0 M $HClO_4$ to that of 1.0 M H_3PO_4. Explain your reasoning.

3. Write dissociation equations for the following in aqueous solution. Ensure that your equations are balanced for both number of atoms and charge.

    (a) magnesium perchlorate

    (b) calcium dichromate

    (c) copper(II) acetate

    (d) manganese(II) thiocyanate

    (e) aluminum binoxalate

    (f) barium hydroxide octahydrate

4. Barium sulfate is used in medicine as a radiopaque contrast material. Patients drink a suspension of barium sulfate to coat their gastrointestinal tract. The surface of the tissue being studied is then highly visible under X-ray or CT scan. Radiologists can better see disease or trauma internally using this method. What is the molar solubility of barium sulfate if a saturated solution contains 0.0012 g dissolved in 500. mL of solution?

5. Calcium carbonate is used to treat calcium deficiencies in the body. Your body needs calcium to build and maintain healthy bones. What mass of calcium carbonate is required to produce 250. mL of solution with a calcium ion concentration of 7.1×10^{-5} M ?

6. Sodium dichromate is used in the production of chromic acid; a common etching agent. Calculate the concentration of each ion in a solution of sodium dichromate prepared by dissolving 0.50 g in 150. mL of solution.

7. Solutions of magnesium chloride and sodium chloride are mixed to make brine commonly used to keep roads from becoming slippery because of ice. The brine solution lowers the freezing point of water by up to 10°C. A brine solution is made by mixing 60. L of 5.0 M sodium chloride with 30. L of 2.4 M magnesium chloride. Calculate the concentration of each ion in this solution.

8. Describe how you would prepare 1.0 L of a saturated solution of sodium chloride.

9. Write the equation for the equilibrium present in saturated solutions of the following:
   (a) silver bromate

   (b) aluminum chromate

   (c) magnesium hydroxide

   (d) lead(II) sulfate

   (e) copper(II) phosphate

6.2 Qualitative Analysis — Identifying Unknown Ions Review Questions

1. Classify the following solutes as soluble or low solubility according to a solubility table:
   (a) Rb_2SO_3

   (b) Al_2S_3

   (c) CuI

   (d) ammonium sulfate

   (e) chromium(III) nitrate

   (f) potassium oxalate

2. According to the solubility table, silver sulfate has a low solubility. In a saturated solution of silver sulfate, are silver and sulfate ions present in solution? Explain.

3. The solubility of silver acetate is 11.1 g/L at 25°C. According to the solubility table, would silver acetate be classified as being soluble or of low solubility?

4. Describe the difference between a formula equation, a complete ionic equation, and a net ionic equation. How are they similar? Different?

5. What is a spectator ion? Give an example of a cation and an anion that are common spectator ions in precipitate reactions.

6. Write a balanced formula equation, complete ionic equation, and net ionic equation for each of the following reactions:

   (a) $(NH_4)_2S(aq) + FeSO_4(aq) \rightarrow$

   (b) $H_2SO_3(aq) + CaCl_2(aq) \rightarrow$

   (c) copper(II) sulfate and calcium sulfide $\rightarrow$

© Edvantage Interactive 2016

7. Explain why it would be difficult to separate the ions Na^+ and K^+ in solution using precipitation.

8. A solution contains Cr^{3+}, Ca^{2+}, and Mg^{2+} ions. Describe a method to remove each ion individually from solution. Be sure to state the compound you would add and how you would remove the precipitate from solution. For each reaction that occurs, write a net ionic equation.

9. A solution contains PO_4^{3-}, Cl^-, and S^{2-} ions. Describe a method to remove each ion individually from solution. Be sure to state the compound you would add and how you would remove the precipitate from solution. For each reaction that occurs, write a net ionic equation.

10. Why are compounds containing nitrates used to test for anions?

11. Give two examples where re-dissolving is necessary to separate two precipitates.

12. A solution of Na_2CO_3 is added to a solution of $AgNO_3$.
    (a) Write the net ionic equation for this reaction.

    (b) Two different reagents will dissolve the precipitate formed. Write a net ionic equation for each reaction in which the precipitate dissolves.

13. (a) Define *hard water* and *scale*.

    (b) Scale can be removed by adding a solution of HCl to the water. Write a formula equation, complete ionic equation, and net ionic equation for this reaction.

    (c) Suggest a substance that could be added to water to remove both Ca^{2+} and Mg^{2+} from solution.

    (d) Explain why adding a water softener to your washing machine when doing laundry improves the cleaning job on your clothes.

© Edvantage Interactive 2016

6.3 The Solubility Product Constant K_{sp}

Warm Up

1. Define each of the following terms:
   (a) solubility

   _____

   (b) product (the mathematical definition)

   _____

   (c) constant

   _____

2. The solubility of lead(II) chloride is 4.4 g/L at a particular temperature.
   (a) Write a balanced dissociation equation for lead(II) chloride.

   (b) Calculate the molar solubility of lead(II) chloride at this temperature.

   (c) Calculate the concentration of each ion in a saturated solution of lead(II) chloride.

The Solubility Product Constant

Recall from chapter 5 that some chemical systems establish an equilibrium. For such systems, you learned how to write an equilibrium constant expression, K_{eq}.

In a saturated solution, an equilibrium is established between the dissolving and recrystallization of a salt. Consider a saturated solution of $PbCl_2$. We can represent this equilibrium using the following dissociation equation:

$$PbCl_2(s) \rightleftharpoons Pb^{2+}(aq) + 2\ Cl^-(aq)$$

Notice that the solid appears on the reactant side of the equation and the ions on the product side. Recalling that solids do not appear in the K_{eq} expression, for this equilibrium

$$K_{eq} = [Pb^{2+}][Cl^-]^2$$

This is a special type of equilibrium, so it is given its own equilibrium constant type: K_{sp}.

$$K_{sp} = [Pb^{2+}][Cl^-]^2 \quad \text{where } K_{sp} \text{ stands for the } \textbf{solubility product constant}$$

In the Warm Up at the beginning of this section, you defined solubility as the maximum amount of solute that can be dissolved in a particular volume of solution. You defined a product as a mathematical answer derived from multiplication. Therefore, the *solubility product* is the value obtained when the maximum concentrations of ions are multiplied together. This is different from simply the solubility. As solubility depends on temperature, so does the value of K_{sp}.

> The molar solubility of a substance is the molar concentration of solute in a saturated solution.
>
> The solubility product constant (K_{sp}) is the *product* of the ion concentrations in a saturated solution raised to the power of the coefficients in the equilibrium.

Obviously, as the solubility of a substance increases, so does the concentration of ions. It follows that the value of K_{sp} also increases.

Quick Check

1. Write an equation to represent the equilibrium present in saturated solutions of the following:
   (a) strontium carbonate

   (b) magnesium hydroxide

   (c) calcium phosphate

2. For each of the equilibria above, write the corresponding K_{sp} expression next to it.

3. Explain the difference between the solubility and the solubility product constant of strontium carbonate.

   _____

   _____

Calculating the K_{sp} From Solubility

The solubility of a substance differs from its solubility product constant, but they are related, and we can calculate one from the other. *When solving any K_{sp} type problem, it is wise to start by writing the equilibrium equation for the saturated solution and then the K_{sp} expression.*

Sample Problem — Calculating K_{sp} from Solubility

The molar solubility of $CaSO_4$ is 8.4×10^{-3} M at a particular temperature. Calculate its K_{sp}.

What to Think About	How to Do It
1. Write an equation representing the equilibrium in a saturated solution.	$CaSO_4(s) \rightleftharpoons Ca^{2+}(aq) + SO_4^{2-}(aq)$ 8.4×10^{-3} M $\quad 8.4 \times 10^{-3}$ M $\quad 8.4 \times 10^{-3}$ M
2. Write the corresponding K_{sp} expression.	$K_{sp} = [Ca^{2+}][SO_4^{2-}]$
3. The solubility of $CaSO_4$ is given in mol/L. Fill in the concentrations of each ion in the equation.	
4. Substitute the concentrations of ions into the K_{sp} expression.	$K_{sp} = [8.4 \times 10^{-3}][8.4 \times 10^{-3}]$ $\quad\ = 7.1 \times 10^{-5}$

Sample Problem — Calculating K_{sp} from Solubility

The solubility of lead(II) chloride is 4.4 g/L at a particular temperature. Calculate its K_{sp}.

What to Think About	How to Do It
1. The formula is $PbCl_2$. Write an equation representing the equilibrium present in a saturated solution.	$PbCl_2(s) \rightleftharpoons Pb^{2+}(aq) + 2\,Cl^-(aq)$
2. Write the corresponding K_{sp} expression.	$K_{sp} = [Pb^{2+}][Cl^-]^2$
3. In order to calculate K_{sp}, the molarities of Pb^{2+} and Cl^- must be known. Calculate the concentration of each ion from the solubility given.	$[PbCl_2] = \dfrac{4.4\ \cancel{g}}{1\ L} \times \dfrac{1\ mol}{278.3\ \cancel{g}} = 0.016$ M so $[Pb^{2+}] = 0.016$ M and $[Cl^-] = 0.032$ M
4. Substitute the concentrations of ions into the K_{sp} expression.	$K_{sp} = [0.016][0.032]^2$ $\quad\ = 1.6 \times 10^{-5}$

Practice Problems — Calculating K_{sp} from Solubility

1. Calculate the K_{sp} for each of the following.
   (a) $CaCO_3$ has a solubility of 6.1×10^{-5} M.

   (b) $Mn(OH)_2$ has a solubility of 3.6×10^{-5} M.

   (c) The solubility of barium chromate is 2.8×10^{-3} g/L.

   (d) The solubility of silver oxalate is 0.033 g/L.

2. A student prepares a saturated solution by dissolving 5.5×10^{-5} mol of $Mg(OH)_2$ in 500. mL of solution. Calculate the K_{sp} of $Mg(OH)_2$.

3. A student evaporated 150. mL of a saturated solution of MgC_2O_4. If 0.16 g of solute remains, calculate the K_{sp}.

© Edvantage Interactive 2016

Chemists can calculate the solubility of a substance from its K_{sp}. The K_{sp} values of some salts are listed in Table 6.3.1. Note that these values are for saturated solutions at 25°C.

It is very important to understand that the K_{sp} value is NOT a concentration. It is the *product* of the ion concentrations in a saturated solution raised to the power of their coefficients from the balanced dissociation equation.

Table 6.3.1 *Solubility Product Constants at 25°C*

Name	Formula	K_{sp}
Barium carbonate	$BaCO_3$	2.6×10^{-9}
Barium chromate	$BaCrO_4$	1.2×10^{-10}
Barium sulfate	$BaSO_4$	1.1×10^{-10}
Calcium carbonate	$CaCO_3$	5.0×10^{-9}
Calcium oxalate	CaC_2O_4	2.3×10^{-9}
Calcium sulfate	$CaSO_4$	7.1×10^{-5}
Copper(I) iodide	CuI	1.3×10^{-12}
Copper(II) iodate	$Cu(IO_3)_2$	6.9×10^{-8}
Copper(II) sulfide	CuS	6.0×10^{-37}
Iron(II) hydroxide	$Fe(OH)_2$	4.9×10^{-17}
Iron(II) sulfide	FeS	6.0×10^{-19}
Iron(III) hydroxide	$Fe(OH)_3$	2.6×10^{-39}
Lead(II) bromide	$PbBr_2$	6.6×10^{-6}
Lead(II) chloride	$PbCl_2$	1.2×10^{-5}
Lead(II) iodate	$Pb(IO_3)_2$	3.7×10^{-13}
Lead(II) iodide	PbI_2	8.5×10^{-9}
Lead(II) sulfate	$PbSO_4$	1.8×10^{-8}
Magnesium carbonate	$MgCO_3$	6.8×10^{-6}
Magnesium hydroxide	$Mg(OH)_2$	5.6×10^{-12}
Silver bromate	$AgBrO_3$	5.3×10^{-5}
Silver bromide	$AgBr$	5.4×10^{-13}
Silver carbonate	Ag_2CO_3	8.5×10^{-12}
Silver chloride	$AgCl$	1.8×10^{-10}
Silver chromate	Ag_2CrO_4	1.1×10^{-12}
Silver iodate	$AgIO_3$	3.2×10^{-8}
Silver iodide	AgI	8.5×10^{-17}
Strontium carbonate	$SrCO_3$	5.6×10^{-10}
Strontium fluoride	SrF_2	4.3×10^{-9}
Strontium sulfate	$SrSO_4$	3.4×10^{-7}
Zinc sulfide	ZnS	2.0×10^{-25}

Sample Problem — Calculating Solubility from K_{sp}

Calculate the molar solubility of iron(II) hydroxide from its K_{sp}.

What to Think About	How to Do It
1. The formula is $Fe(OH)_2$. Write an equation representing the equilibrium present in a saturated solution.	$$Fe(OH)_2(s) \rightleftharpoons Fe^{2+}(aq) + 2\,OH^-(aq)$$ $$ s \qquad\quad s \qquad\qquad 2s$$
2. Let s be the molar solubility of $Fe(OH)_2$. The concentrations of Fe^{2+} and OH^- are then s and $2s$ respectively.	
3. Write the corresponding K_{sp} expression.	$$K_{sp} = [Fe^{2+}][OH^-]^2$$
4. Look up the K_{sp} value for $Fe(OH)_2$ and substitute in the concentrations of ions.	$$4.9 \times 10^{-17} = (s)(2s)^2$$ $$4.9 \times 10^{-17} = 4s^3$$
5. Simplify and solve.	$$s = \sqrt[3]{4.9 \times 10^{-17}/4}$$ $$= 2.3 \times 10^{-6}\ M$$

Sample Problem — Calculating Solubility from K_{sp}

What mass is dissolved in 275 mL of saturated silver bromate?

What to Think About	How to Do It
1. The formula is $AgBrO_3$. Write an equation representing the equilibrium present in a saturated solution.	$$AgBrO_3(s) \rightleftharpoons Ag^+(aq) + BrO_3^-(aq)$$ $$ s \qquad\quad s \qquad\qquad s$$
2. Let s be the molar solubility of $AgBrO_3$. The concentrations of Ag^+ and BrO_3^- are then both s.	
3. Write the corresponding K_{sp} expression.	$$K_{sp} = [Ag^+][BrO_3^-]$$
4. Look up the K_{sp} value for $AgBrO_3$ and substitute in the concentrations of ions.	$$5.3 \times 10^{-5} = (s)(s)$$ $$= s^2$$
5. Solve for the molar solubility.	$$s = 7.3 \times 10^{-3}\ M$$
6. To calculate the mass, use the molar mass of $AgBrO_3$ and the given volume of solution.	$$mass = 0.275\ L \times \frac{7.3 \times 10^{-3}\ mol}{1\ L} \times \frac{235.8\ g}{1\ mol}$$ $$= 0.47\ g$$

© Edvantage Interactive 2016

Practice Problems — Calculating Solubility from K_{sp}

1. Calculate the solubility of the following:
   (a) silver chloride in mol/L

   (b) iron (II) sulfide in g/mL

   (c) lead(II) iodate in M

   (d) strontium fluoride in g/L

2. What is the concentration of hydroxide in a saturated solution of iron(III) hydroxide? Hint: Write out the dissociation equation and K_{sp} expression first. This example is different than the ones shown.

3. What mass of calcium oxalate is dissolved in 650. mL of saturated solution?

Types of Salts

To summarize, we have introduced two types of salts: AB (such as AgCl) and AB_2 (such as $PbCl_2$) salts.

For AB salts, $K_{sp} = (\text{solubility})^2$

For AB_2 or A_2B salts, $K_{sp} = 4(\text{solubility})^3$

6.3 Review Questions

1. Write equilibrium equations and the corresponding K_{sp} expressions for each of the following solutes in saturated aqueous solution.

   (a) $Al(OH)_3$

   (b) $Cd_3(AsO_4)_2$

   (c) $BaMoO_4$

   (d) calcium sulfate

   (e) lead(II) iodate

   (f) silver carbonate

2. Consider a saturated solution of $BaSO_3$.
   (a) Write the equation that represents the equilibrium in the solution.

   (b) Explain the difference between the solubility and the solubility product constant of $BaSO_3$.

3. A saturated solution of $ZnCO_3$ was prepared by adding excess solid $ZnCO_3$ to water. The solution was analyzed and found to contain $[Zn^{2+}] = 1.1 \times 10^{-5}$ M. What is the K_{sp} for $ZnCO_3$?

4. When a student evaporated 250. mL of a saturated solution of silver phosphate, 0.0045 g of solute remained. Calculate the K_{sp} for silver phosphate.

© Edvantage Interactive 2016

5. Gypsum is used in drywall and plaster, and occurs naturally in alabaster. It has the formula $CaSO_4 \cdot 2\,H_2O$ and its K_{sp} is 9.1×10^{-6}. What mass of gypsum is present in 500. mL of saturated solution?

6. Naturally occurring limestone contains two forms of $CaCO_3$ called calcite and aragonite. They differ in their crystal structure. High-grade calcite crystals were used in World War II for gun sights, especially in anti-aircraft weaponry. Aragonite is used in jewelry and glassmaking. Using the following K_{sp} values, calculate the solubility of each in g/L.
   (a) K_{sp} calcite $= 3.4 \times 10^{-9}$

   (b) K_{sp} aragonite $= 6.0 \times 10^{-9}$

7. Lead(II) arsenate, $Pb_3(AsO_4)_2$, was commonly used as an insecticide, especially against codling moths. Because of the toxic nature of lead compounds, it was banned in the 1980s. It has a solubility of 3.0×10^{-5} g/L. Calculate the K_{sp} for lead(II) arsenate.

8. A student compares the K_{sp} values of cadmium carbonate ($K_{sp} = 1.0 \times 10^{-12}$) and cadmium hydroxide ($K_{sp} = 7.2 \times 10^{-15}$) and concludes that the solubility of cadmium carbonate is greater than the solubility of cadmium hydroxide. Do you agree or disagree? Support your answer with appropriate calculations.

9. A titration was carried out to determine the unknown concentration of Cl^- ion in solution. The standard solution was $AgNO3$ and an indicator of K_2CrO_4 was used. The equivalence point was reached when the solution turned the red color of Ag_2CrO_4, signaling that virtually all of the Cl^- ions had been used up. Explain why a precipitate of AgCl formed before a precipitate of Ag_2CrO_4. Use data from the K_{sp} table provided in this section.

10. Silver carbonate is used as an antibacterial agent in the production of concrete. What mass of silver carbonate must be dissolved to produce 2.5 L of saturated solution?

© **Edvantage Interactive 2016**

6.4 Precipitation Formation and the Solubility Product K_{sp}

Warm Up

1. Describe how to make a saturated solution of silver chloride, given solid silver chloride and pure water. How does the concentration of Ag^+ compare to the concentration of Cl^-?

_____

_____

2. A student mixed 25 mL of 0.10 M silver nitrate with 15 mL of 0.085 M sodium chloride.
   (a) Calculate the $[Ag^+]$ and $[Cl^-]$ before a reaction occurred in the mixed solution.

   (b) How does the $[Ag^+]$ compare with the $[Cl^-]$ before the reaction? Explain why they are not equal.

   _____

   (c) Write a net ionic equation for this reaction.

Precipitates That Form When Solutions Are Mixed Together

In section 6.3, we investigated saturated solutions formed by attempting to dissolve an excess of solute in water. In such a case, the concentrations of the ions are directly related to one another. For example, if we attempt to dissolve excess AgCl in water, the $[Ag^+]$ equals the $[Cl^-]$. Similarly, if we use an excess of $PbCl_2$, the $[Cl^-]$ is double the $[Pb^{2+}]$.

In this section, we will be examining situations in which the ions forming the precipitate do not come from the same solute. Because of this, the concentrations of the ions in solution are not related to one another, but instead depend on the concentrations and the volumes of the solutions being combined. When determining ion concentrations, it is always important to *consider the source* of each ion.

Predicting Whether a Precipitate Will Form

When two solutions are mixed, we can predict whether a precipitate will form. The K_{sp} value represents the maximum product of the ion concentrations in a saturated solution. If the product of the ion concentrations present exceeds this value, the ions will not remain dissolved in solution and a precipitate will form. On the other hand, if the product of the ion concentrations is less than the value of K_{sp}, the ions remain dissolved in solution, and no precipitate forms.

The concentrations in a K_{sp} expression are the *equilibrium* concentrations of ions in a saturated solution. If an equilibrium is not present in solution, then we calculate a **trial ion product (TIP)**, also called a trial K_{sp} value or reaction quotient (Q).

If the TIP > K_{sp}, a precipitate forms.

If the TIP < K_{sp}, no precipitate forms.

If the TIP = K_{sp}, the solution is saturated.

Sample Problem — Predicting Whether a Precipitate Will Form

Will a precipitate form when 23 mL of 0.020 M Na_2CO_3 is added to 12 mL of 0.010 M $MgCl_2$?

What to Think About	How to Do It
1. Determine the precipitate that will potentially form using the solubility table. Then write an equation representing the equilibrium present in a saturated solution.	$Na_2CO_3 + MgCl_2 \rightarrow MgCO_3(s) + 2\ NaCl$ $MgCO_3(s) \rightleftharpoons Mg^{2+}(aq) + CO_3^{2-}(aq)$
2. Write the corresponding K_{sp} expression and its value.	$K_{sp} = [Mg^{2+}][CO_3^{2-}] = 6.8 \times 10^{-6}$
3. When one solution is added to another, *both* are diluted. Calculate the concentration of each solution before the reaction occurs.	$[Na_2CO_3] = \dfrac{0.020\ mol}{1\ L} \times \dfrac{0.023\ L}{0.035L}$ $= 0.013\ M$
4. Determine the $[Mg^{2+}]$ and $[CO_3^{2-}]$ in the diluted solutions. Be sure to consider the source of the ions to determine whether these concentrations should be multiplied by a whole number.	$[MgCl_2] = \dfrac{0.010\ mol}{1\ L} \times \dfrac{0.012\ L}{0.035\ L}$ $= 0.0034\ M$ $[CO_3^{2-}] = 0.013\ M$
5. Calculate the value of TIP.	$[Mg^{2+}] = 0.0034\ M$
6. Compare the TIP with the real K_{sp}.	$\begin{aligned} TIP &= [Mg^{2+}][CO_3^{2-}] \\ &= (0.013)(0.0034) \\ &= 4.4 \times 10^{-5} \end{aligned}$ $TIP > K_{sp}$ so a precipitate forms.

Practice Problems — Predicting Whether a Precipitate Will Form

1. Will a precipitate form when 8.5 mL of 6.3×10^{-2} M lead(II) nitrate is added to 1.0 L of 1.2×10^{-3} M sodium iodate?

2. Will a precipitate form when 1.5 mL of 4.5×10^{-3} M ammonium bromate is added to 120.5 mL of 2.5×10^{-3} M silver nitrate?

3. No precipitate forms when 24 mL of 0.17 M sodium fluoride is added to 55 mL of 0.22 M cadmium nitrate. From this information, what can you conclude about the numerical value for the K_{sp} of CdF_2? (State the K_{sp} value as a range.)

© Edvantage Interactive 2016

Using K_{sp} to Calculate the Concentration of Ions in Solution

These problems are very similar to the ones you analyzed earlier, except that the ions that form the precipitate are from different stock reagent sources. First, determine the concentrations of any ions present in the solution. Once another solution is added, consider the potential precipitate that might form. Then, as always, you should write an equation for the equilibrium present in a saturated solution (the dissociation of the precipitate) and then the K_{sp} expression.

Consider a solution of 0.025 M $Pb(NO_3)_2$. By writing a dissociation equation for lead(II) nitrate, we can calculate the concentration of each ion in solution:

$$Pb(NO_3)_2(aq) \rightarrow Pb^{2+}(aq) + 2\ NO_3^-(aq)$$
$$0.025\ M \qquad\qquad 0.025\ M \qquad\quad 0.050\ M$$

If a solution of NaCl is added, the precipitate that may form is $PbCl_2(s)$. If a precipitate forms, then a saturated solution of $PbCl_2$ is present and is governed by its K_{sp}.

$$PbCl_2(s) \rightleftharpoons Pb^{2+}(aq) + 2\ Cl^-(aq)$$

$$K_{sp} = [Pb^{2+}][Cl^-]^2$$

Note that the original $[Pb^{2+}]$ and $[Cl^-]$ are unrelated to each other because they came from *different* sources. The maximum concentration of Cl^- that can exist in this solution can be calculated from the K_{sp} and the concentration of Pb^{2+} provided by the $Pb(NO_3)_2$ source. From the concentration of chloride, the mass of solute required can be calculated using its molar mass.

$$1.2 \times 10^{-5} = (0.025)\ [Cl^-]^2$$
$$[Cl^-] = 0.022\ M = [NaCl]$$

Sample Problem — Forming a Precipitate in a Solution

What mass of sodium sulfate is required to start precipitation in 500. mL of 0.030 M calcium chloride? (Assume the volume remains constant.)

What to Think About	How to Do It
1. Determine the precipitate that will form using the solubility table. Then write an equation representing the equilibrium present in a saturated solution.	$Na_2SO_4(aq) + CaCl_2(aq) \rightarrow CaSO_4(s) + 2\ NaCl(aq)$ $CaSO_4(s) \rightleftharpoons Ca^{2+}(aq) + SO_4^{2-}(aq)$
2. Write the corresponding K_{sp} expression.	$K_{sp} = [Ca^{2+}][SO_4^{2-}]$
3. The calcium ions came from the 0.030 M $CaCl_2$ solution, and the sulfate ions came from $Na_2SO_4(s)$. The chloride ions and sodium ions are spectators. Calculate the concentration of Ca^{2+} in the $CaCl_2$ solution.	$CaCl_2(aq) \rightarrow Ca^{2+}(aq) + 2\ Cl^-(aq)$ $0.030\ M \qquad\quad 0.030\ M$
4. Substitute the value of K_{sp} (from the K_{sp} table, Table 4.3.1) and the known ion concentration to solve for the unknown $[SO_4^{2-}] = [Na_2SO_4]$.	$7.1 \times 10^{-5} = (0.030)\ [SO_4^{2-}]$ $[SO_4^{2-}] = 2.4 \times 10^{-3}\ M$
5. Calculate the mass of solid sodium sulfate required to be dissolved in 500. mL of solution from $[SO_4^{2-}]$ and the molar mass of sodium sulfate.	$mass\ Na_2SO_4 = 0.500\ L \times \dfrac{2.4 \times 10^{-3}\ mol}{1\ L} \times \dfrac{142.1\ g}{1\ mol}$ $= 0.17\ g$

Sample Problem — Forming a Precipitate in Solution What is the maximum $[SO_4^{2-}]$ that can exist in a saturated solution of $CaCO_3$?

What to Think About	How to Do It
1. Calculate the $[Ca^{2+}]$ in a saturated solution of $CaCO_3$.	$CaCO_3(s) \rightleftharpoons Ca^{2+}(aq) + CO_3^{2-}(aq)$ $\qquad\qquad\qquad\quad S \qquad\qquad S$ $K_{sp} = [Ca^{2+}][CO_3^{2-}]$ $5.0 \times 10^{-9} = s^2$
2. The calcium ions form a precipitate with the sulfate ions. Write the equation for the equilibrium present in the saturated solution of $CaSO_4$.	$s = 7.1 \times 10^{-5}\ M = [Ca^{2+}]$ $CaSO_4(s) \rightleftharpoons Ca^{2+}(aq) + SO_4^{2-}(aq)$
3. Substitute the value of K_{sp} for $CaSO_4$ and the known $[Ca^{2+}]$ and solve for the $[SO_4^{2-}]$.	$K_{sp} = [Ca^{2+}][SO_4^{2-}]$ $7.1 \times 10^{-5} = (7.1 \times 10^{-5})[SO_4^{2-}]$ $[SO_4^{2-}] = 1.0\ M$

Practice Problems — Forming a Precipitate In Solution

1. Calculate the maximum $[Sr^{2+}]$ that can exist in solutions of the following:
   (a) 0.045 M sodium fluoride (Remember to consider the source of the fluoride ion.)

   (b) 2.3×10^{-4} M lithium carbonate

   (c) 0.011 M sulfuric acid

2. Sodium carbonate may be added to hard water to remove the Mg^{2+} ions. What mass of sodium carbonate is required to soften 10.0 L of hard water containing 3.2×10^{-3} M Mg^{2+}? (Assume no volume change occurs.)

3. What is the maximum $[Ag^+]$ that can exist in a saturated solution of PbI_2?

© Edvantage Interactive 2016

The Common Ion Effect

We defined the solubility of a substance as the maximum amount of solute that will dissolve in a given volume of solvent at a specific temperature. You know that solubility depends on temperature, but it also depends on the solvent's identity. Up to now, we have only considered pure water as the solvent. The presence of other ions in the solvent also has an effect on the solubility of a solute.

> The solubility of a substance depends on the presence of other ions in solution and the temperature. The K_{sp} of a substance depends on temperature only.

Consider a saturated solution of Ag_2CO_3:

$$Ag_2CO_3(s) \rightleftharpoons 2\,Ag^+(aq) + CO_3^{2-}(aq)$$

At a given temperature, the amount of Ag^+ and CO_3^{2-} in solution is governed by the K_{sp}. If the solvent already contained Ag^+ ions, the $[Ag^+]$ is increased. To maintain the value of K_{sp}, the $[CO_3^{2-}]$ must decrease. According to Le Châtelier's principle, an increase in $[Ag^+]$ causes the equilibrium to shift left. This shift causes the $[CO_3^{2-}]$ to decrease and the amount of solid Ag_2CO_3 to increase. The presence of silver ions in the solvent effectively decreases the solubility of Ag_2CO_3. This is called the *common ion effect* because the solubility of Ag_2CO_3 is decreased due to the common ion Ag^+ in the solvent. The presence of CO_3^{2-} in the solvent would cause a similar effect and resulting decrease in the solubility.

$$Ag_2CO_3(s) \rightleftharpoons 2\,Ag^+(aq) + CO_3^{2-}(aq)$$

Adding Ag^+ or CO_3^{2-} causes the equilibrium to shift left, so the solubility of Ag_2CO_3 decreases.

> The solubility of a solute is decreased by the presence of a second solute in a solvent containing a common ion.

According to Le Châtelier's principle, the solubility of Ag_2CO_3 may be increased by removing the Ag^+ or CO_3^{2-} ions. This would cause the equilibrium to shift right. An example of this would be the presence of HCl in the solvent. Carbonates dissolve in acid solutions. The presence of H_3O^+ from the acid causes the $[CO_3^{2-}]$ to decrease, which in turn causes more $Ag_2CO_3(s)$ to dissolve. Additionally, the chloride ion from the acid precipitates the silver ion from the solution. The removal of the silver ion causes a further right shift, increasing the solubility of silver carbonate even further.

© Edvantage Interactive 2016

Quick Check

1. Consider a saturated solution of AgCl.
   (a) How can you change the K_{sp} for AgCl?

   (b) How can you change the solubility of AgCl?

2. List two substances that would decrease the solubility of $Mg(OH)_2$. Use Le Châtelier's principle to explain each.

3. List two substances that would increase the solubility of $Mg(OH)_2$. Use Le Châtelier's principle and a K_{sp} expression to explain each.

**Calculating Solubility
With a Common Ion
Present (Extension)**

The presence of a common ion in the solvent decreases the solubility of a solute. Let's compare the solubility of $Mg(OH)_2$ in water to its solubility in 0.10 M $MgCl_2$.

© Edvantage Interactive 2016

Sample Problem — Calculating Solubility With a Common Ion Present

What is the solubility of $Mg(OH)_2$ in (a) water? (b) 0.10 M $MgCl_2$?

What to Think About	How to Do It
(a) in water	
1. Write the equilibrium for a saturated solution of $Mg(OH)_2$.	$Mg(OH)_2(s) \rightleftharpoons Mg^{2+}(aq) + 2\,OH^-(aq)$ $ S 2S$
2. Write the corresponding K_{sp} expression.	$K_{sp} = [Mg^{2+}][OH^-]^2$
3. Look up the value for K_{sp} on the K_{sp} table and solve for the solubility.	$5.6 \times 10^{-12} = (s)(2s)^2 = 4s^3$ $s = 1.1 \times 10^{-4}\,M =$ solubility of $Mg(OH)_2$
(b) in 0.10 M $MgCl_2$	
1. Write the equilibrium for a saturated solution of $Mg(OH)_2$.	$Mg(OH)_2(s) \rightleftharpoons Mg^{2+}(aq) + 2\,OH^-(aq)$
2. The equilibrium for the saturated solution is shifted on the addition of the common ion Mg^{2+} from the $MgCl_2$. Use an ICE table. In the $MgCl_2$, there is initially 0.10 M Mg^{2+}. The amount of $Mg(OH)_2$ that dissolves will increase the $[Mg^{2+}]$ and $[OH^-]$ by x and $2x$ respectively.	$Mg(OH)_2(s) \rightleftharpoons Mg^{2+}(aq) + 2\,OH^-(aq)$ I — 0.10 0 C — +x +2x E — 0.10 +x 2x
3. The amount of Mg^{2+} that dissolves from the $Mg(OH)_2$ (represented by x) is very small compared to the amount of Mg^{2+} in solution from the $MgCl_2$ (0.10 M). Assume that $[Mg^{2+}] = 0.10 + x = 0.10$.	
4. Substitute $[Mg^{2+}]$ and $[OH^-]$ at equilibrium into a K_{sp} expression.	$K_{sp} = [Mg^{2+}][OH^-]^2$ $5.6 \times 10^{-12} = (0.10)(2x)^2$
5. Solve for the solubility, x.	$5.6 \times 10^{-11} = (2x)^2 = 4x^2$ $x = 3.7 \times 10^{-6}\,M$

Practice Problems — Calculating Solubility With a Common Ion Present

1. Calculate the molar solubility of silver iodate in 0.12 M sodium iodate.

2. Calculate the molar solubility of lead(II) iodide in 0.10 M KI.

3. Calculate the solubility (in g/L) of barium sulfate in 0.050 M barium nitrate.

6.4 Activity: Experimentally Determining the K_{sp} Of Copper(II) Iodate

Question
What is the approximate value of K_{sp} for copper(II) iodate?

Background
A TIP calculation can be used to determine if a precipitate will form. If TIP > K_{sp}, a precipitate forms. If TIP < K_{sp}, no precipitate forms. Five different dilutions of copper(II) nitrate and sodium iodate were prepared and mixed together. By observing which mixed solutions contained a precipitate, information about the K_{sp} can be deduced.

Procedure:
1. Five different dilutions of copper(II) nitrate and sodium iodate were prepared as shown in the data table below. The given volume of each solution was mixed together with water and the formation of a precipitate was noted. Answer the questions below.

	Mixture 1	Mixture 2	Mixture 3	Mixture 4	Mixture 5
Volume 0.010 M $Cu(NO_3)_2$ (mL)	10.0	8.0	6.0	4.0	2.0
Volume 0.020 M $NaIO_3$ (mL)	10.0	8.0	6.0	4.0	2.0
Volume water added (mL)	0.0	4.0	8.0	12.0	16.0
Observation	precipitate	precipitate	precipitate	no precipitate	no precipitate

Results and Discussion
1. Write balanced formula, complete ionic, and net ionic equations for this reaction.

2. Calculate the $[Cu^{2+}]$ in each of the mixtures.

3. Calculate the $[IO_3^-]$ in each of the mixtures.

4. Write the equation for the equilibrium involving the precipitate, and the K_{sp} expression.

© Edvantage Interactive 2016

5. Calculate a TIP value for each mixture.

6. State the K_{sp} as a range of values from this data.

7. Compare your range to the stated K_{sp} value on the K_{sp} table.

6.4 Review Questions

1. The following solutions were mixed together. Write the equilibrium equation for the precipitate that forms and its K_{sp} expression.
   (a) $FeCl_2$ and Na_2S

   (b) $Sr(OH)_2$ and $MgBr_2$

   (c) silver nitrate and ammonium chromate

2. A student mixed equal volumes of 0.2 M solutions of sulfuric acid and calcium chloride together.
   (a) What precipitate forms?

   (b) Write an equation for the equilibrium present and the K_{sp} expression.

   (c) In the resulting solution, does $[SO_4^{2-}] = [Ca^{2+}]$? Explain.

3. What is the maximum $[Pb^{2+}]$ that can exist in 0.015 M $CuSO_4$?

4. Kidney stones are crystals of calcium oxalate that form in the kidney, ureter, or bladder. Small kidney stones are passed out of the body easily, but larger kidney stones may block the ureter causing severe pain. If the $[Ca^{2+}]$ in blood plasma is 5×10^{-3} M, what $[C_2O_4^{2-}]$ must be present to form a kidney stone?

5. What is the maximum $[CO_3^{2-}]$ that can exist in a saturated solution of AgBr?

6. A 100.0 mL sample of seawater was tested by adding one drop (0.2 mL) of 0.20 M silver nitrate. What mass of NaCl is present in the seawater to form a precipitate?

© Edvantage Interactive 2016

7. Does a precipitate form when 2.5 mL of 0.055 M $Sr(NO_3)_2$ is added to 1.5 L of 0.011 M $ZnSO_4$? Justify your answer with calculations.

8. Does a precipitate form when 0.068 g of lead(II) nitrate is added to 2.0 L of 0.080 M NaCl? Justify your answer with calculations. (Assume no volume change.)

9. In section 4.2, you learned that the addition of Ag^+ to a solution containing Cl^- and I^- will cause precipitates of both AgCl and AgI to form. Because AgCl and AgI have quite different K_{sp} values, you can use this information to separate Cl^- from I^- in solution by carefully manipulating the $[Ag^+]$ so that only one of Cl^- or I^- precipitates at a time. Consider a solution containing 0.020 M Cl^- and 0.020 M I^-. Solid silver nitrate is slowly added without changing the overall volume of solution.

   (a) Write the equilibrium equation for each precipitate that forms.

   (b) Beside each equilibrium equation, write the corresponding K_{sp} expression and value from your K_{sp} table.

   (c) Based on the K_{sp} values, which precipitate will form first?

   (d) Calculate the $[Ag^+]$ required just to start precipitation of the first precipitate.

   (e) Calculate the $[Ag^+]$ required just to start precipitation of the second precipitate.

   (f) State the range of $[Ag^+]$ required to precipitate I^- but not Cl^-.

   (g) What $[I^-]$ remains in solution just before the formation of AgCl?

   (h) What percentage of I^- is precipitated out before the AgCl starts to precipitate?

10. Washing soda, $Na_2CO_3 \cdot 10\ H_2O$ is used to treat hard water containing Ca^{2+} and Mg^{2+}. A 1.0 L sample contained 12 mg of Mg^{2+}. What mass of washing soda is required to precipitate out the Mg^{2+}?

11. List two substances that, when added to water, that would decrease the solubility of lead(II) iodate. Explain each.

12. Explain why $BaSO_4$ is less soluble in a solution of Na_2SO_4 than in water.

13. Is iron(III) hydroxide more or less soluble in water than in 0.1 M HCl? Explain.

Extension

14. An aqueous suspension of $BaSO_4$ is used as a contrast agent to improve the quality of intestinal X-rays. The patient drinks a suspension of $BaSO_4$. However, Ba^{2+} is toxic, so the $BaSO_4$ is dissolved in a solution of 0.10 M Na_2SO_4.
    (a) Calculate the maximum mass of $BaSO_4$ that can be dissolved in 200. mL of water. (Assume no volume change.)

    (b) Calculate the maximum mass of $BaSO_4$ that can be dissolved in 200. mL of 0.10 M Na_2SO_4 without forming a precipitate.

 © Edvantage Interactive 2016

7 Organic Chemistry

By the end of this chapter, you should be able to do the following:

- Describe characteristic features and common applications of organic chemistry
- Demonstrate knowledge of the various ways that carbon and hydrogen can combine to form a wide range of compounds
- Generate names and structures for simple organic compounds
- Differentiate the various types of bonding between carbon atoms
- Identify common functional groups
- Perform a simple organic preparation

By the end of the chapter you should know the meaning of these **key terms:**

- alcohol
- aldehyde
- alkane
- alkene
- alkyne
- amide
- amine
- aromatic
- benzene ring
- bromo-
- chloro-
- cyclic
- ester
- ether
- ethyl-
- fluoro-
- hydrocarbon
- ketone
- methyl-
- organic acid
- organic chemistry
- substituent groups

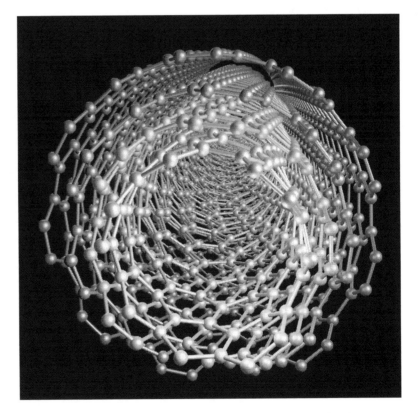

A model of a multi-walled carbon nanotube: sheets of one-atom thick carbon atoms in a hexagonal arrangement and curved into tubes. Wider tubes have narrower tubes inside them.

7.1 Simple Hydrocarbons and Isomerism

Warm Up

1. Draw the Lewis dot structure for carbon.

2. How many valence electrons does a carbon atom have? _____

3. Classify the following compounds as ionic or covalent:

   (a) Na_2CO_3 _____

   (b) C_2H_6 _____

   (c) CO_2 _____

   (d) CaC_2 _____

   (e) C_2H_5OH _____

Organic Compounds

Chemical compounds can be classified as belonging to one of two very large groups: organic compounds or inorganic compounds. Organic compounds contain carbon atoms, usually bonded to other carbon atoms and hydrogen atoms. They may also contain other elements such as halogens, nitrogen, oxygen, phosphorus, and sulfur. Note that some compounds such as carbonates, carbides, and oxides of carbon contain carbon but are not classified as organic compounds. For example, in the question 3 above, C_2H_6 and C_2H_5OH are organic. The remaining compounds in question 3 are inorganic: Na_2CO_3, CO_2, and CaC_2.

Chemists have been distinguishing organic and inorganic compounds for hundreds of years. Organic compounds were called "organic" because it was believed that these compounds could only be made from living things such as plants or animals. Scientists thought that organic compounds contained a "life force" or "vitality." Friedrich Wohler proved that this belief was inaccurate in 1828 when he heated an inorganic salt, ammonium cyanate [$NH_4(NCO)$] and produced urea [$(NH_2)_2CO$], an organic compound (Figure 7.1.1). Urea is a waste product of protein metabolism and, up to that time, was thought to be produced only from living things.

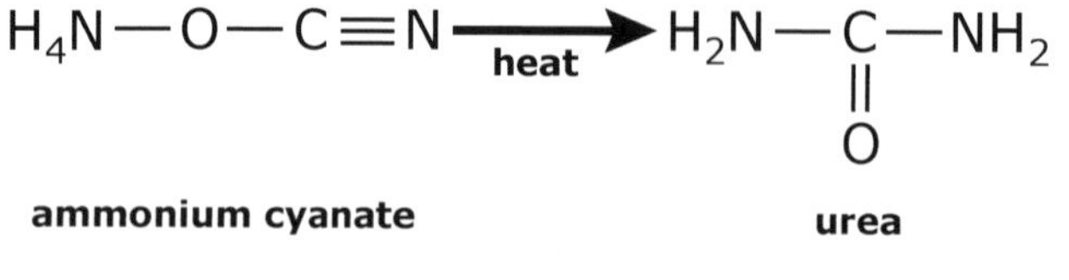

$$H_4N-O-C\equiv N \xrightarrow{\text{heat}} H_2N-\overset{\displaystyle \underset{\displaystyle O}{\|}}{C}-NH_2$$

ammonium cyanate   **urea**

Figure 7.1.1 *Heating ammonium cyanate produces urea.*

Once scientists learned that organic compounds could be made in the lab, a whole new branch of chemistry was born: **organic chemistry**. Even though we now know that not all organic compounds come from living organisms, we still use the word "organic" to describe many carbon compounds.

Recall that a carbon atom has four valence electrons. Because of this, carbon can share electrons with other atoms to complete its outermost electron shell. Each carbon atom can form four covalent bonds. A carbon atom may bond to other carbon atoms in a chain using single, double, or triple bonds, and carbon chains may link to form carbon rings or cages.

With so many different ways that carbon can bond, there are millions of known organic compounds. Every day, you use organic products such as foods, cosmetics, plastics, clothing fibres, pharmaceuticals, and fuels.

Sample Problem — Using Structural Formulas to Represent Organic Compounds

Butane is a fuel used in lighters. It has the formula C_4H_{10} and has four carbon atoms attached to each other in a chain with only single bonds. Draw a structural formula for butane.

What to Think about

1. The four carbon atoms are bonded to each other in a chain, so draw four carbon atoms attached to one another in a line.

2. Each carbon atom can form four covalent bonds. The first carbon atom has one bond to the carbon atom beside it. It can therefore bond with three hydrogen atoms.

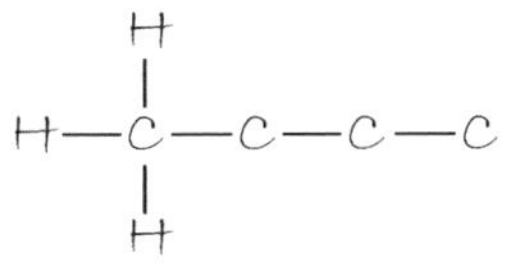

3. The next two carbon atoms have two other carbon atoms already covalently bonded to them. They can only bond with two hydrogen atoms each.

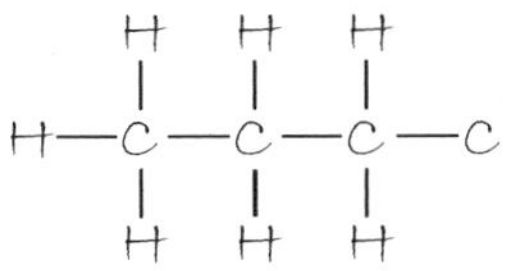

4. The last carbon atom is already bonded to one other carbon atom. It can form three bonds with hydrogen. The formula shown on the right is called a structural formula.

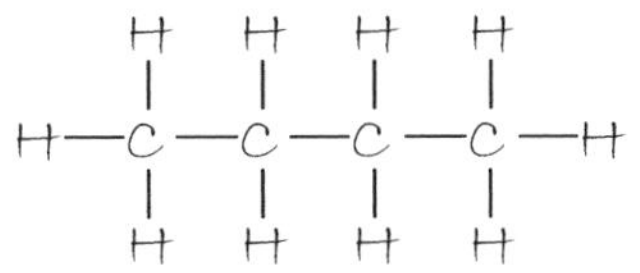

5. Condense this structural formula by writing the number of hydrogen atoms bonded to each carbon.

6. To condense this formula even more, use a line to represent each carbon bond. Do not show the carbon or hydrogen atoms at all. Notice that the lines will not be attached in a straight line. Organic molecules are not linear. At the end of each line segment is a carbon atom not shown. Hydrogen atoms are also not shown in this formula.

How to Do It

$$C - C - C - C$$

Structural Formula:

Condensed Structural Formula:
$$CH_3 - CH_2 - CH_2 - CH_3$$

Carbon Skeleton Formula:

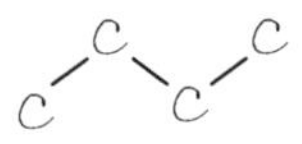

becomes

Practice Problems—Using Structural Formulas to Represent Organic Compounds

1. Octane, a constituent of gasoline, has the molecular formula C_8H_{18}. Draw a structural formula, condensed structural formula, and carbon skeletal formula for octane. Assume that the carbons are all bonded in a single chain to each other.

2. Draw a structural formula, condensed structural formula, and carbon skeletal formula for C_6H_{12}. Arrange the carbon atoms in a closed ring shape so that each carbon atom is bonded to two other carbon atoms.

3. The carbon skeleton formula for an organic compound is shown below. Draw the structural and condensed structural formula. What is its molecular formula?

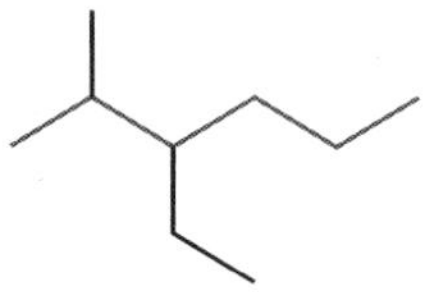

Hydrocarbons

Hydrocarbons are the simplest types of organic compounds. **Hydrocarbons** are compounds that contain only carbon and hydrogen atoms. We will examine five types of hydrocarbons: alkanes, cycloalkanes, alkenes, alkynes, and aromatic hydrocarbons.

Table 7.1.1 *Greek Prefixes*

No. of C Atoms	Prefix
1	*meth-*
2	*eth-*
3	*prop-*
4	*but-*
5	*pent-*
6	*hex-*
7	*hept-*
8	*oct-*
9	*non-*
10	*dec-*

Alkanes

Alkanes are hydrocarbons containing only single bonds. They are **saturated**, meaning that there is no room for other atoms to bond to the carbon skeleton. They have the general formula $C_nH_{(2n+2)}$. Table 7.1.2 on the next page lists the first 10 straight-chain alkanes that you need to know.

How to Name Alkanes

Notice in Table 7.1.2 that each alkane name ends in "-ane." You will need to memorize the prefixes that have been italicized in the table. The prefix indicates the number of carbon atoms bonded together in the chain. For example, hexane means six carbons bonded in a chain. *Hex* is the Greek word for six. Table 9.1.1 lists the prefixes.

Not only do carbon atoms bond together to make chains, but often branches of carbon atoms are connected to the carbon atoms of the main chain. These branches are called **substituent groups**. Rules for naming branched alkanes are on the page after Table 7.1.2.

Table 7.1.2 *10 Straight-Chain Alkanes You Need to Know*

Name	Molecular formula	Structural formula	Ball and stick model	Space filling model
*meth*ane	CH_4			
*eth*ane	C_2H_6			
*prop*ane	C_3H_8			
*but*ane	C_4H_{10}			
*pent*ane	C_5H_{12}			
*hex*ane	C_6H_{14}			
*hept*ane	C_7H_{16}			
*oct*ane	C_8H_{18}			
*non*ane	C_9H_{20}			
*dec*ane	$C_{10}H_{22}$			

Naming Branched Alkanes

To name a branched alkane, there are a few rules:

1. Find the longest continuous chain of carbon atoms. It does not have to be in a straight line. This is the "parent" chain. State the number of carbon atoms using the appropriate prefix and the ending "ane."
2. Number the carbon atoms in the parent chain starting at the end closest to the branches. Branches are called "alkyl" groups. The carbon atom's number becomes like the "address" of the branch off the parent chain.
3. Name each branch with a prefix according to the number of carbon atoms it contains. Branch names end in "yl" instead of "ane." For example, a branch containing one carbon atom is called a **methyl** branch. If the branch contains two carbon atoms, it is called an **ethyl** branch. List the branches in alphabetical order. Then, if two, three, or four branches have the same number of carbon atoms, use the prefixes "di" (two), "tri" (three), and tetra" (four). For example, if there are two branches each with three carbons, they are called "dipropyl."
4. State the name of the alkane by first listing the "address" of each branch, then naming the branches, then naming the parent. Use commas between numbers and hyphens between a number and a branch name.

Figure 7.1.2 shows an example of a branched alkane correctly named and incorrectly named. Note that the carbon atoms in the parent chain must be numbered starting at the end closest to the branch.

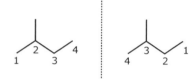

2-methyl-butane   **3-methyl-butane**

Correct: Incorrect
Branch has the
lowest number.

Figure 7.1.2 *Example of how to name a branched alkane*

Sample Problem — Naming Simple Alkanes

Name the simple alkane shown here.

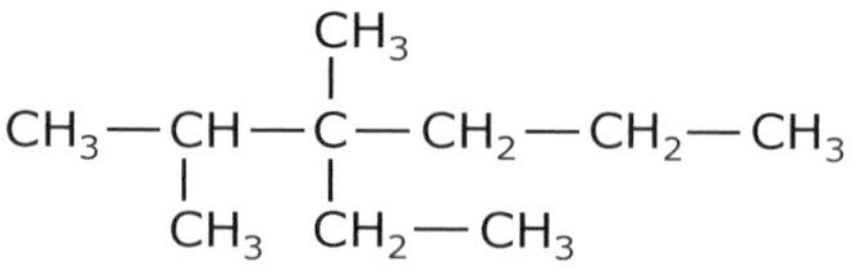

$$CH_3 - CH - C - CH_2 - CH_2 - CH_3$$
(with CH_3 above the C, and CH_3 and $CH_2 - CH_3$ below the CH and C)

What to Think about

1. The longest chain of carbon atoms is six and the prefix for six is "hex." Name the parent chain.

2. The parent chain carbons are numbered from the left, because the branches start closer to the left. The branch addresses from left to right would be 2, 3, 3. There is a methyl group attached to the second and also the third carbon atom in the parent chain.

3. There is an ethyl group attached to the third carbon in the parent chain.

4. The name states the address then the branch names alphabetically, then the parent chain. Alphabetically, "ethyl" will be listed before "methyl." We do not consider the prefixes "di" and "tri" etc. when listing alphabetically.

How to Do It

hexane

2,3-dimethyl

3-ethyl

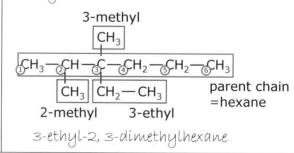

3-methyl

2-methyl   3-ethyl

parent chain
=hexane

3-ethyl-2, 3-dimethylhexane

                                    © Edvantage Interactive 2016

Practice Problems—Naming Simple Alkanes

Name the following alkanes:

1. (a) _____

   (b) _____

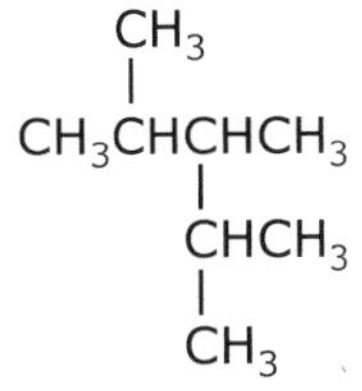

$$CH_3$$
$$|$$
$$CH_3CHCHCH_3$$
$$|$$
$$CHCH_3$$
$$|$$
$$CH_3$$

(a)

$$CH_3$$
$$|$$
$$CH_3CCH_2CHCH_3$$
$$|\ \ \ \ \ |$$
$$CH_3\ \ CH_3$$

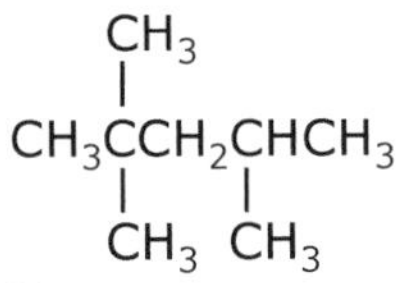

(b)

2. Draw the condensed structural formula for 4-ethyl-2,3-dimethyl-5-propyloctane.

3. Draw the condensed structural formula for 3,4,4,5- tetramethyldecane.

Structural Isomers

Consider Table 7.1.2 below. What do you notice about the molecular formulas of the two substances in the table? Pentane and 2-methybutane are different compounds with different chemical properties, and yet they have the same molecular formula. These are called **structural isomers**. There is one more structural isomer of C_5H_{12}. Can you figure it out? Read on to find out how.

Table 7.1.2 *Examples of structural isomers*

Name	Structural Formula	Molecular Formula
pentane	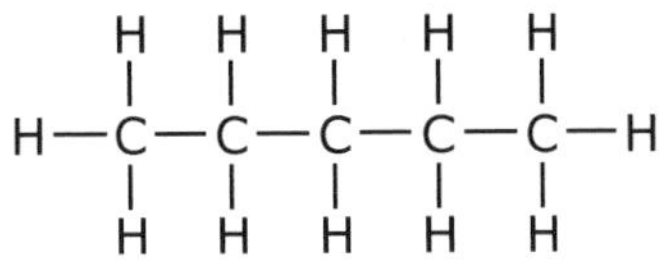 H—C—C—C—C—C—H (with H's)	C_5H_{12}
2-methylbutane	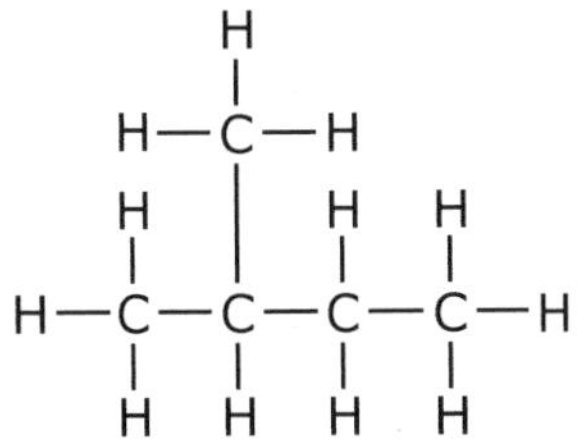 H—C—H / H—C—C—C—C—H (with H's)	C_5H_{12}

You need to be methodical when drawing isomers of a compound. For example, the compound pentane has 5 carbon atoms and 12 hydrogen atoms. Let's focus on the carbon skeleton. The most obvious way to arrange five carbon atoms is in a single chain:

$$CH_3 — CH_2 — CH_2 — CH_2 — CH_3$$

We can also arrange four carbon atoms in a chain and have the fifth carbon atom as a methyl branch. Note that the branch cannot go on either end of the carbon chain because then it would be a part of the parent chain, giving us pentane again. We can put the methyl branch on the second carbon in the parent chain, as shown in Figure 9.1.3.

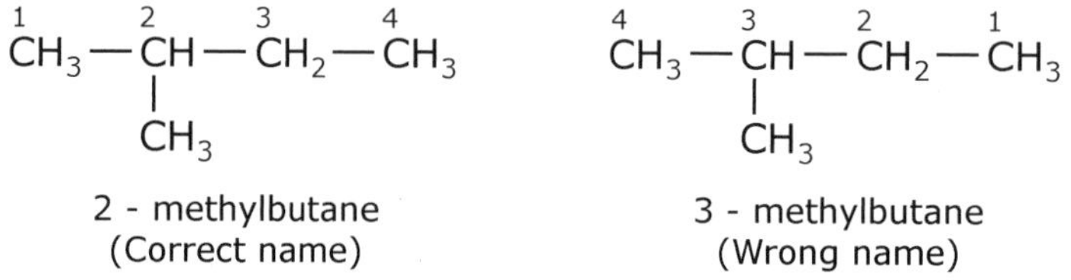

$$\overset{1}{C}H_3 - \overset{2}{C}H - \overset{3}{C}H_2 - \overset{4}{C}H_3 \qquad \overset{4}{C}H_3 - \overset{3}{C}H - \overset{2}{C}H_2 - \overset{1}{C}H_3$$
$$| \qquad\qquad\qquad\qquad |$$
$$CH_3 \qquad\qquad\qquad\qquad CH_3$$

2 - methylbutane   3 - methylbutane
(Correct name)   (Wrong name)

Figure 7.1.3 *2-methylbutane*

Why is there not a molecule called 3-methylbutane? It depends on numbering the carbon atoms in the parent chain. Remember to always number the carbons in the parent chain starting from the end closest to the branch. The "address" of the branches must be the lowest numbers.

Finally, we can arrange three carbon atoms in the parent chain and have two methyl branches on the second carbon, as shown in Figure 7.1.4.

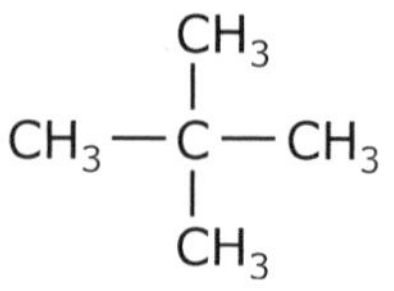

$$CH_3$$
$$|$$
$$CH_3 - C - CH_3$$
$$|$$
$$CH_3$$

Figure 7.1.4 *2,2-dimethylpropane*

There are three structural isomers for C_5H_{12}. As the number of carbon atoms in a molecule increases, the number of possible isomers increases dramatically.

- C_5H_{12} has three structural isomers.
- C_6H_{14} has five structural isomers.
- C_7H_{16} has nine structural isomers.
- $C_{20}H_{42}$ has more than 300 000 structural isomers.

Quick Check

1. What is the molecular formula for an alkane that has 12 carbon atoms? _____

2. Why is simply knowing the molecular formula of an alkane not enough to draw a structural formula for that alkane?

   _____

3. Draw condensed structural formulas for three of the structural isomers of C_7H_{16}.

4. Name the three structural isomers you drew in question 3.

   _____

© Edvantage Interactive 2016

Cycloalkanes

Carbon atoms may bond to each other and form a **cyclic** structure called a ring, like the one in the diagram below. The hormones testosterone and progesterone are examples of compounds that contain ring structures.

Consider the molecule shown in Figure 7.1.4(a). This compound has the formula C_5H_{10}. Alkanes have the general formula $C_nH_{(2n+2)}$. The general formula for a cycloalkane like the one in the diagram is $C_nH_{(2n)}$. The carbon skeleton formula for this compound is shown in Figure 7.1.4(b).

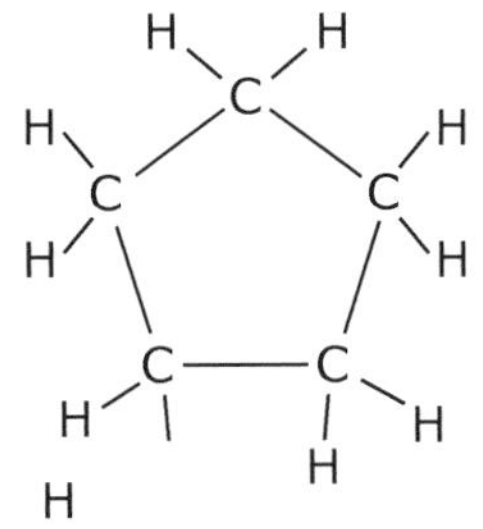

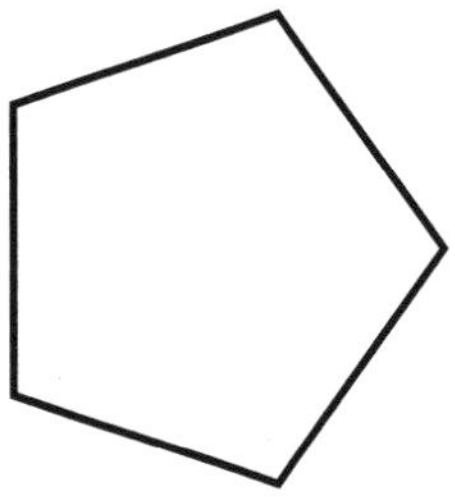

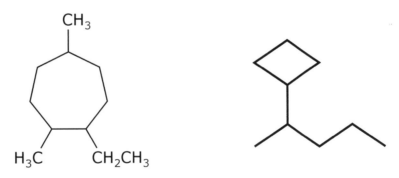

Figure 7.1.4 *(a) C_5H_{10} (b) the carbon skeleton formula for C_5H_{10}*

When naming an alkane that contains a ring structure, the same rules apply as for a chain alkane. See Figure 7.1.5 for examples.

1. The ring that contains the greater number of carbon atoms is the parent chain. The prefix "cyclo" is placed before the parent chain name.

2. The carbon atoms in the parent ring are numbered either clockwise or counterclockwise so that the lowest numbers are used to identify the placement of the branches.

3. If the ring structure is not the longest continuous carbon chain, then it is named as a branch with the prefix "cyclo" and ends in "yl."

(a) 1-ethyl-2,5-dimethylcycloheptane   (b) 2-cyclobutylpentane

Figure 7.1.5 *Example of alkanes that contain ring structures*

Alkenes

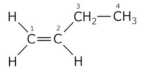

Figure 7.1.6 *An example of an alkene: 1-butene*

Alkenes are hydrocarbons containing double bonds. They are **unsaturated**. This means that the double bond is a reactive site where other atoms could attach to the carbon skeleton. They have the general formula C_nH_{2n}. As you saw above, cycloalkanes have the same general formula as alkenes. Molecules with this general formula contain either one alkane ring or one double bond.

The rules for naming alkenes are the same as for alkanes except that an alkene's parent chain name ends in "ene." See Figure 7.1.6 for an example.

- The parent chain must contain the double bond.
- The position of the double bond is indicated in the name by stating the number of the carbon atom in the parent chain that the double bond follows.
- The parent chain carbon atoms are numbered starting at the end closest to the double bond.

In some cases, the groups attached to the double-bonded carbon atoms provide for a new type of isomerism, as shown in Figure 7.1.7. **Geometric isomers** are alkenes that have the same structure, but the orientation of the groups across the double bond are different. Geometric isomers are also called *cis-trans* **isomers**.

For example, *cis*-2-butene has two hydrogen atoms bonded to the double-bonded carbon atoms on the same side of the double bond. Both hydrogen atoms are below the double bond. *Trans*-2-butene has the groups bonded to the double-bonded carbon atoms on opposite sides of the double bond. One hydrogen is above the double bond, and the other hydrogen is below the double bond.

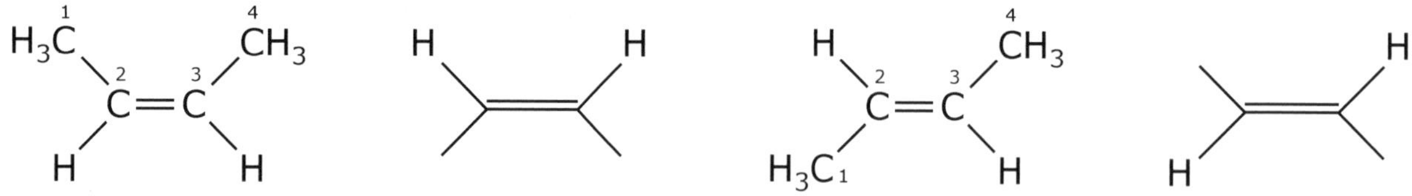

cis-2-butene   trans-2-butene

Figure 7.1.7 *Examples of cis-trans isomers*

Quick Check

1. What is the molecular formula for an alkene containing one double bond and seven carbon atoms?

2. Draw a cycloalkane containing seven carbon atoms. What is its molecular formula?

3. Name the compound shown here.

_____

4. Draw cyclohexane and write its molecular formula. Beside it, draw the 2 geometric isomers of 2-hexene, and write their molecular formulas. Classify each molecule as saturated or unsaturated.

© Edvantage Interactive 2016

Alkynes

Alkynes are hydrocarbons containing triple bonds. They are also unsaturated. They have the general formula $C_nH_{(2n-2)}$.

The rules for naming alkynes are the same as for alkanes except the parent chain name ends in "yne." See Figure 9.1.8 for an example.

- The parent chain must contain the triple bond.
- The position of the triple bond is indicated in the name by stating the number of the carbon atom in the parent chain that the triple bond follows.
- The parent chain carbon atoms are numbered starting at the end closest to the triple bond.

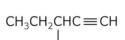

$$CH_3CH_2CHC \equiv CH$$
$$|$$
$$CH_3$$

Figure 9.1.8 *3-methyl-1-pentyne*

Aromatic Hydrocarbons

Benzene is a hydrocarbon with six carbon atoms in a ring. This structure is called a **benzene ring**. It has the molecular formula C_6H_6. The bonds between each carbon atom are slightly longer than a double bond, but slightly shorter than a single bond. The electrons in the benzene molecule are *delocalized*, meaning that they are spread across more than one atom. In other words, there is more than one way to draw its Lewis structure. Equivalent Lewis structures are called **resonance structures**. We can represent benzene using the resonance structure shown in Figure 7.1.9(a). It can also be represented as shown in Figure 7.1.9(b).

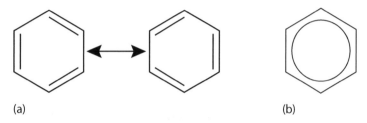

(a)   (b)

Figure 7.1.9 *Examples of resonance structures for benzene*

Aromatic hydrocarbons always contain at least one benzene ring. When one of the hydrogen atoms in a benzene ring is replaced by another atom or group, we call it a monosubstituted benzene. Monosubstituted benzenes are named by simply using the name of the substituted group as a prefix attached to "benzene."

If more than one hydrogen atom in a benzene has been replaced, we call it a polysubstituted benzene. For polysubstituted benzenes, branches are named and their "address" on the benzene ring is indicated in a similar way to that used for cycloalkanes. We label the first substituted carbon as 1 and proceed either clockwise or counterclockwise in such a way as to give the lowest combination of numbers of substituted carbons.

For benzenes where only two branches exist on the ring, the three possible 1,2-, 1,3-, and 1,4- positions can also be indicated using the prefixes "ortho," "meta," and "para" respectively. These prefixes describe how close the branches are to each other on the benzene ring (Figure 9.1.10). A benzene ring with one methyl branch is commonly called toluene. A benzene ring with two methyl branches is commonly called xylene.

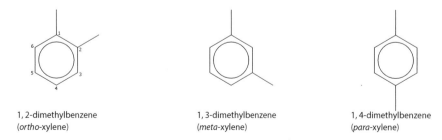

1, 2-dimethylbenzene   1, 3-dimethylbenzene   1, 4-dimethylbenzene
(*ortho*-xylene)   (*meta*-xylene)   (*para*-xylene)

Figure 7.1.10 *Examples of prefixes used to describe the branches on a benzene ring*

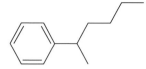

Some organic compounds have benzene as a branch. If this is the case, the branch name is "phenyl" (Figure 7.1.11).

Figure 7.1.12 shows the structures and names of some common aromatic compounds.

Figure 7.1.11 *2-phenylhexane*

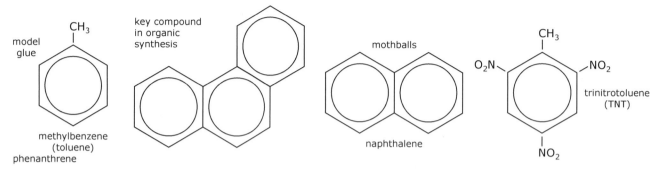

Figure 7.1.12 *Examples of common aromatic compounds*

Quick Check

1. What is the molecular formula for an alkyne containing one triple bond and 8 carbon atoms in a chain?

2. Do alkynes exhibit *cis* and *trans* isomerism? Explain.

3. Draw the condensed structural formula for 3,4-dimethyl-1-hexyne.

4. Draw the structural formula for benzene.

© Edvantage Interactive 2016

7.1 Activity: Building and Naming Structural Isomers

Question

How many structural isomers are there for hexane?

Background

Structural isomers have the same molecular formula, but are different arrangements of the same atoms. The general formula for an alkane is $C_nH_{(2n+2)}$.

Procedure

1. You will need one organic chemistry model kit to share with your partner. Working together, construct and name the structural isomers of C_6H_{14}.

Results and Discussion

1. Draw the condensed structural formula for hexane.

2. Using your model kit, build hexane.

3. Build the different structural isomers of C_6H_{14}. Draw the condensed structural formula for each isomer you build. Write the name of each isomer under its condensed structural formula.

4. How many structural isomers are there for hexane? _____

5. Build 3-hexene. Draw the condensed structural formula for the two geometric isomers of 3-hexene, and write the name of each one under its formula.

7.1 Review Questions

1. How is a condensed structural formula different from a carbon skeleton formula? Use an example.

2. Draw carbon skeleton structural formulas for all of the isomers of the alkane with seven carbon atoms. Under each diagram, write the isomer's name.

3. What is the difference between a structural isomer and a geometric isomer? Use an example in your answer.

4. Draw 1-pentene. Does this molecule exhibit *cis-trans* isomerism? Explain.

5. Classify the following as being *cis* or *trans* isomers:

(a)

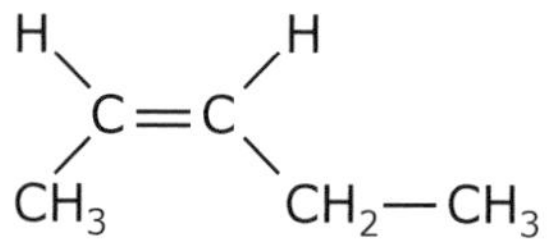

(b)

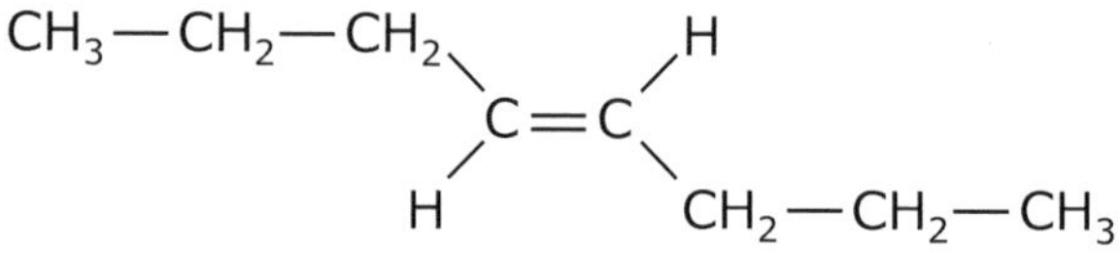

(c)

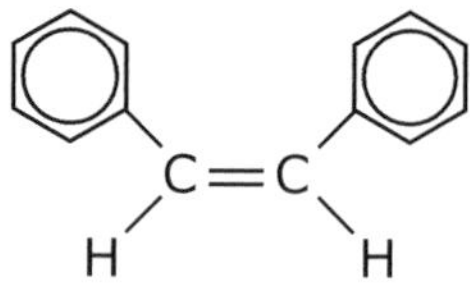

6. An important nutrient for your body is fat. Infants require a diet high in fat for brain development. Your body needs fats for energy and to dissolve certain vitamins. Fats in foods are classified as saturated, unsaturated, and polyunsaturated. Animal products contain a high level of saturated fats. What is meant by the term "saturated"?

7. (a) Unsaturated fats are generally a liquid at room temperature. What is meant by the term "unsaturated"?

(b) Which of the following are unsaturated: alkanes, alkenes, alkynes, cycloalkanes, aromatics?

8. Classify the following as alkane, alkene, alkyne, cycloalkane, or aromatic without drawing the structure. Some may have more than one classification.
(a) C_5H_{10} _____
(b) $C_{15}H_{32}$ _____
(c) C_9H_{16} _____
(d) C_6H_6 _____

9. Name the following compounds.

(a)

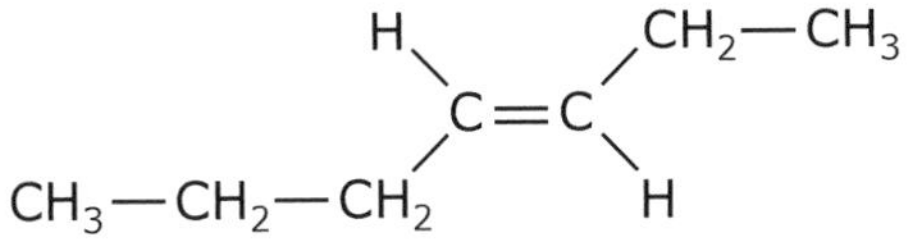

(b)

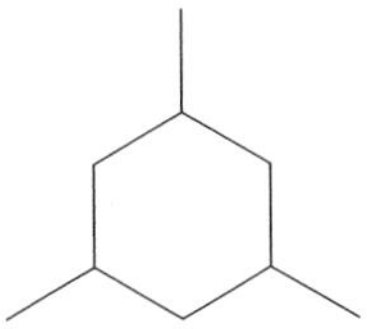

(c)

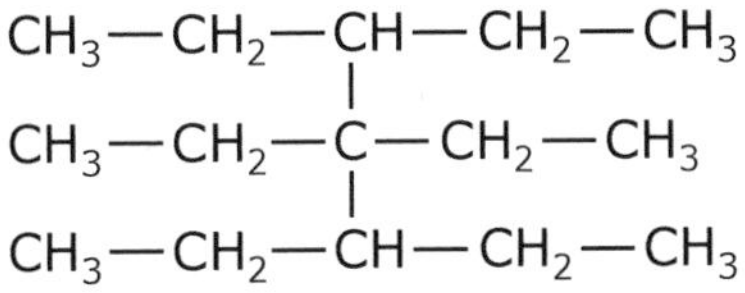

$$CH_3-CH_2-CH-CH_2-CH_3$$
$$CH_3-CH_2-C-CH_2-CH_3$$
$$CH_3-CH_2-CH-CH_2-CH_3$$

(d)

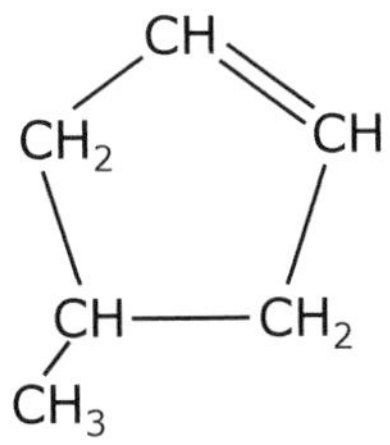

(e)

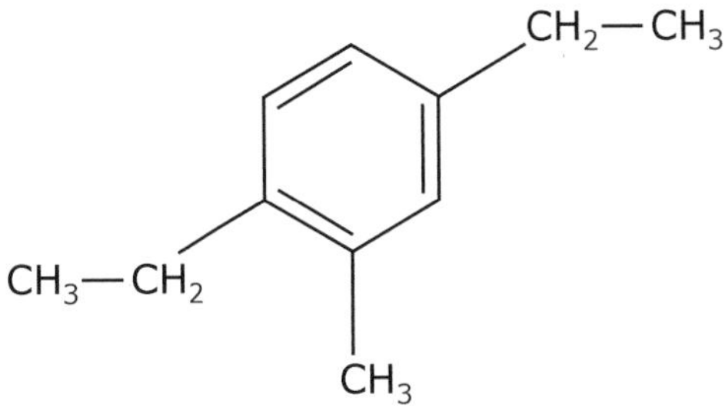

(f)

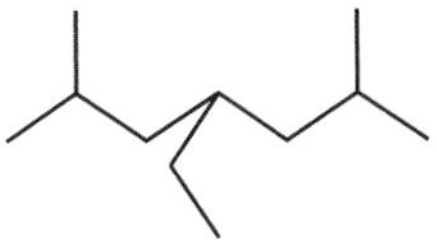

(g)

(h)

$$CH\equiv C-CH-CH-CH_3$$
$$CH_3-CH_2 \quad CH_2-CH_3$$

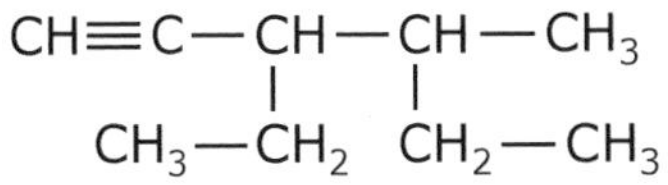

10. Draw condensed structural formulas for the following compounds.

(a) 4-ethyl-3,5-dimethylnonane

(b) 5,6-dimethyl-3-heptyne

(c) *trans*-2-heptene

(d) 1,3-dimethyl-2-propylcycloheptane

(e) 4,5,5-trimethyl-2-heptyne

(f) ethylcyclohexane

(g) 4-ethyl-3,3-dimethyloctane

(h) 3-cyclopentyl-5,5-dimethyl-1-hexene

7.2 Functional Groups

Warm Up

Every day, you use products that contain organic compounds.
In the list below, place a checkmark beside each product that you have in your home.

Product		Product	
☐	vanilla flavouring	☐	fuels (gasoline, for example)
☐	nail polish remover	☐	cosmetics
☐	insecticide	☐	glue
☐	acetaminophen (Tylenol)	☐	asphalt
☐	antifreeze	☐	nylon
☐	wax	☐	Teflon
☐	plastics	☐	paint thinner

Functional Groups

Earlier in this chapter, you learned about organic compounds containing carbon and hydrogen atoms. The number of isomers possible for large hydrocarbons is enormous. Now imagine how many more isomers would be possible if we included atoms of oxygen, nitrogen, sulfur, or other elements! If you look into reference books such as the *Handbook of Chemistry and Physics*, you will see that organic compounds greatly outnumber inorganic compounds. All of the products listed in the Warm Up above contain organic compounds. You are surrounded by organic chemistry!

In section 7.1, you learned about the structures of alkenes, alkynes, and aromatic hydrocarbons, such as benzene. Groups of organic compounds like these are called functional groups. A **functional group** is an atom, group of atoms, or organization of bonds in an organic molecule that react in a characteristic manner. Organic compounds with the same functional group react in a similar manner

Functional groups are identified by the placement of certain atoms in a molecule.

Chemists use a shorthand to represent carbon and hydrogen atoms that are not part of the functional group. We use the symbol **R** to represent the hydrocarbon fragment of the organic molecule not involved in the functional group. **R'** (called "r prime") may be used for a different hydrocarbon fragment in the same molecule.

You need to be able to identify the functional group. Naming rules will be given for the types of organic compounds you should be able to name.

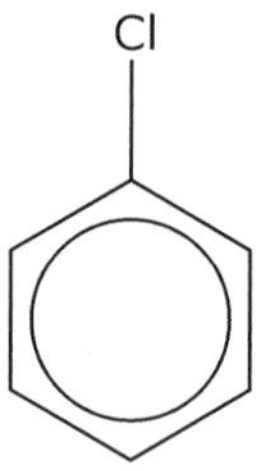

Alkyl Halides: R-X (where X = F, Cl, I, or Br)

Organic compounds containing halogens are called alkyl halides (Figure 7.2.1). They are named using the same rules you learned in section 7.1 except that the halogen atom is named as a branch group. It is treated the same way as an alkyl group was in section 7.1. The prefixes to use for each element are:

F = **fluoro**   Cl = **chloro**   Br = **bromo**   I = **iodo**

Alcohols: R-OH

Organic compounds containing a **hydroxyl** (–OH) group attached to a carbon atom are called **alcohols**. Do not confuse a hydroxyl group with a hydroxide ion. Compounds with a hydroxide ion are bases and are ionic. Alcohols are covalent compounds that do not readily release the –OH group. Here are the rules for naming alcohols:

1. The parent chain must contain an atom attached to the –OH group. Number the carbon atoms in the parent chain such that the –OH group is given the lowest number.
2. The name of the parent chain ends with "–ol" instead of "–e."
3. Name and identify positions of the branches as usual.

(a) chlorobenzene

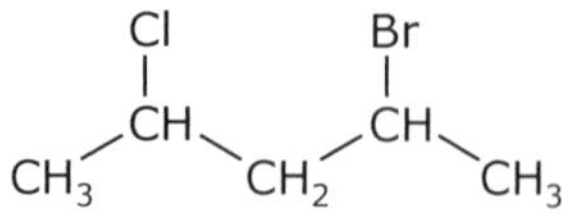

(b) 2-bromo-4-chloropentane

Figure 7.2.1 *Examples of alkyl halides*

Table 7.2.1 shows examples of how these rules are used. The first example, ethanol, is the alcohol consumed in alcoholic beverages. While all alcohols are toxic to humans, ethanol is somewhat less so, although large quantities consumed in a short period of time can cause death. Ethanol is also an important additive to fuels and is used as a solvent for flavourings, colourings, and pharmaceuticals.

Table 7.2.1 *Examples of how to name alcohols*

Alcohol Name	Structure
Ethanol (commonly called ethyl alcohol) • Notice that a number is not required to indicate the position of the hydroxyl group as it must be at the end of a two-carbon chain.	$CH_3 — CH_2 — OH$
3-methyl-1-butanol	CH_3 | $CH_3 — CH — CH_2 — CH_2 — OH$
2-propanol (commonly called isopropanol or isopropyl alcohol) • The name "isopropyl" refers to the branch of three carbons (recall from Table 9.1.1 in section 9.1 that "prop-" means three). The branch is attached at the second carbon atom in the chain of three carbon atoms. • Isopropyl alcohol is used as a cleaner for electronics, and for sterilizing solutions.	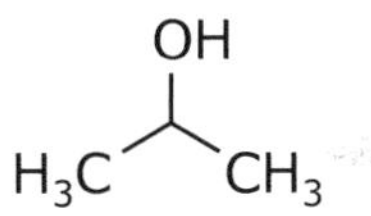

Quick Check

1. Draw full structural formulas for the following compounds:
   (a) 3,3-dichloropentane   (b) *cis*-1,2-dichloroethene   (c) 4,4-dimethyl-3-hexanol

2. Name the following compounds:

   (a) $CH_3 — OH$ _____

   (b) $CH_3 — CH_2 — CH_2 — CH_2 — Br$ _____

3. There are two isomers of C_3H_7OH that are alcohols. One of them, 2-propanol is shown in Table 9.2.1 above. Draw the other isomer and name it.

4. Ethanol poisoning occurs when the body cannot metabolize alcohol fast enough. What kinds of products are commonly consumed that lead to ethanol poisoning?

   _____

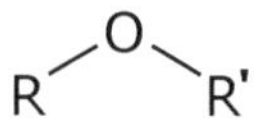

Ethers

Ethers are organic compounds in which two hydrocarbon fragments are attached by an oxygen atom. Table 7.2.2 shows examples of ethers.

Table 7.2.2 *Examples of Ethers and Their Applications*

Ether Name	Application	Structure
Methoxymethane (commonly called dimethyl ether)	aerosol spray propellant	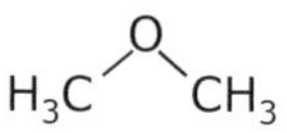 H_3C—O—CH_3
Ethoxyethane (commonly called diethyl ether)	early anesthetic	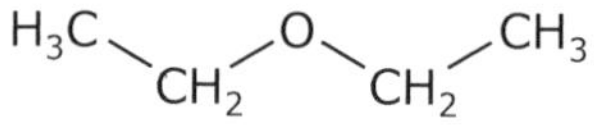 H_3C—CH_2—O—CH_2—CH_3
Methoxybenzene (commonly called methylphenyl ether)	anise (licorice) flavoring	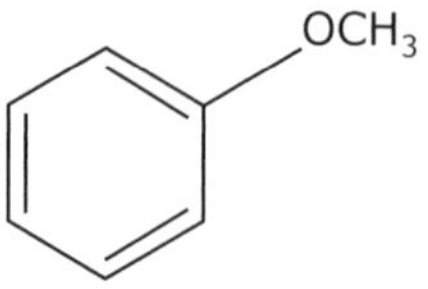 benzene ring—OCH_3

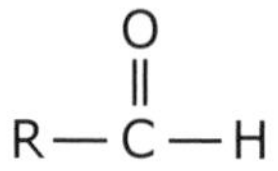

Aldehyde

An **aldehyde** is an organic compound containing a carbonyl group at the end of a carbon chain. A **carbonyl** group is a carbon atom double bonded to an oxygen atom. Aldehydes are used to produce dyes and organic acids. You may be familiar with formaldehyde, which is used as a biological preservative. Almond extract and some perfumes contain benzaldehyde. Figure 7.2.2 shows two examples of aldehydes.

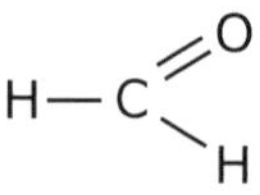

(a) methanal (commonly called formaldehyde)

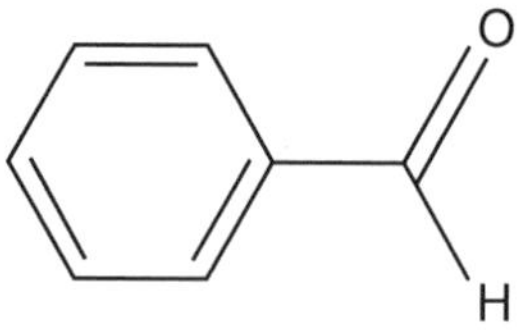

(b) benzaldehyde

Figure 7.2.2 *Examples of aldehydes*

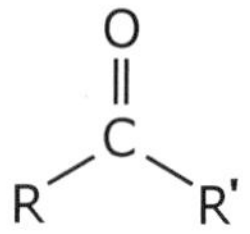

Ketone

A ketone is an organic compound also containing a carbonyl group, but unlike an aldehyde, the carbonyl group of a ketone is not at the end of the carbon chain. Nail polish remover is a ketone commonly called acetone. Ketones are used as solvents and to make polymers and pharmaceuticals. A **polymer** is a very large molecule that is produced by linking together many smaller molecules. We will explore polymers in the next section. Figure 7.2.3 shows two examples of ketones.

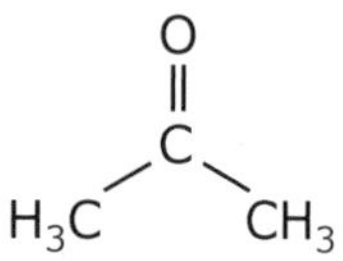

(a) propanone (commonly called acetone)

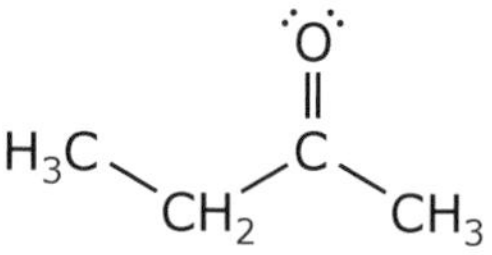

(b) 2-butanone (commonly called ethylmethylketone)

Figure 7.2.3 *Examples of ketones*

© Edvantage Interactive 2016

Quick Check

1. What is a carbonyl group?

   _____

2. Consider the following classes of organic compounds: alkyl halide, alcohol, ether, aldehyde and ketone. Circle the ones that contain a carbonyl group.

3. (a) Describe how an ether and a ketone are similar and how they are different.

   _____

   _____

   (b) Describe how an aldehyde and a ketone are similar and how they are different.

   _____

   _____

4. Estrogen is a steroid and the primary female sex hormone. On the diagram of estrogen below, circle and label the functional groups.

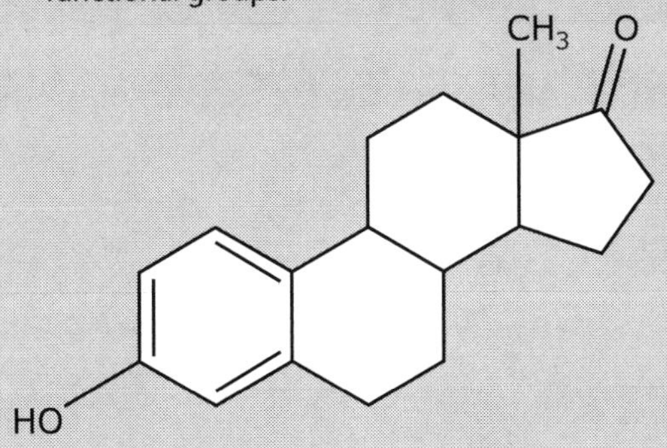

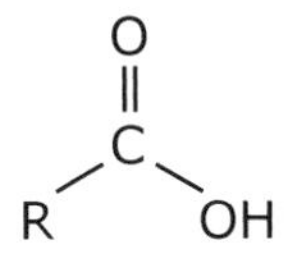

Carboxylic Acid

A carboxylic acid is an organic compound containing a **carboxyl** (–COOH) group. These are sometimes called organic acids and are commonly found as food preservatives. White vinegar is a 5% solution of ethanoic acid, commonly called acetic acid. Methanoic acid (commonly called formic acid) is the compound responsible for the sting of bee or red ant bites. Carboxylic acids usually have unpleasant odours. In section 7.3, you will learn how to name a carboxylic acid for a specific type of reaction. Figure 7.2.4 shows two examples of carboxylic acids.

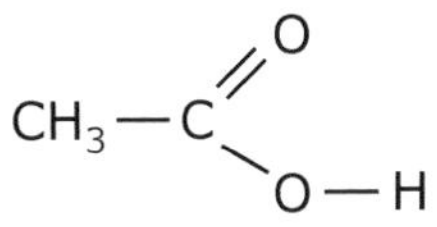

(a) ethanoic acid (commonly called acetic acid)

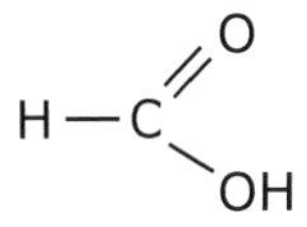

(b) methanoic acid (commonly called formic acid)

Figure 7.2.4 *Examples of carboxylic acids*

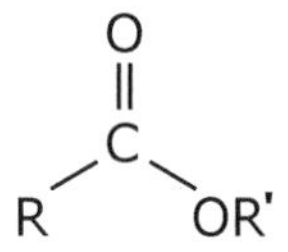

Ester

An ester is an organic compound in which a –COO– group connects two other hydrocarbon fragments. Many esters have strong fruity odors and are used in perfumes and flavorings. DNA and some plastics and explosives contain ester groups. Figure 7.2.5 shows two examples of esters.

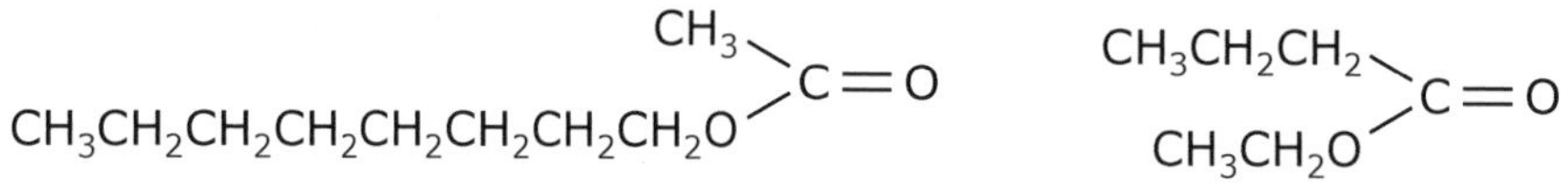

$CH_3CH_2CH_2CH_2CH_2CH_2CH_2CH_2O$ — CH_3 — $C=O$

(a) octyl ethanoate (orange flavouring)

$CH_3CH_2CH_2$ — CH_3CH_2O — $C=O$

(b) ethyl butanoate (pineapple flavouring)

Figure 7.2.5 *Examples of esters*

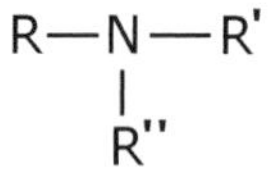

Amines: R-NH$_2$ or R-NH-R' or as in the diagram to the left

Amines are organic compounds containing only single bonds and nitrogen atoms attached to a carbon atom. Amines are used to produce dyes and drugs. For example, chlorpheniramine is used as an antihistamine. Ephedrine and phenylephrine are decongestants. Figure 7.2.6 shows two examples of amines.

CH_3 — NH_2

(a) methylamine

H_3C — N — CH_3 / H

(b) dimethylamine

Figure 7.2.6 *Examples of amines*

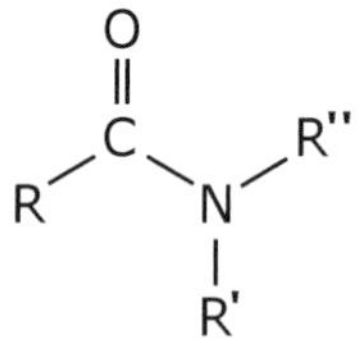

Amides

Organic compounds containing a nitrogen atom bonded to a carbonyl group are called amides. Amides are found in plastics, rubber, inks, and cosmetics. Amides are also used to make nylon and Kevlar. The pain killer acetaminophen is an amide. An amide group links amino acids together in the peptide chains that make up proteins. Figure 7.2.7 shows two examples of amides.

CH_3C — O — NH_2

(a) ethanamide (ethylamide)

CH_3 — CH_2 — CH_2 — C — O — NH_2

(b) butanamide

Figure 7.2.7 *Examples of amides*

Quick Check

1. What is a carboxyl group?

   _____

2. How are a carboxylic acid and ester similar and how are they different?

   _____

3. How are an amine and an amide similar and how are they different?

   _____

4. (a) Aspirin is a common pain reliever. On the structure of aspirin shown below, circle and name the functional groups.

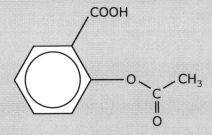

   (b) Cocaine is an addictive stimulant for the central nervous system. On the structure of cocaine shown below, circle and name the functional groups.

Table 7.2.3 summarizes what you have learned about the functional groups described in this section.

Table 7.2.3 *Functional groups*

Functional Group	Classification of Organic Compound
H H | | —C=C—	alkene
—C≡C—	alkyne
(aromatic ring structure)	aromatic hydrocarbon
X | —C—	alkyl halide
OH | —C—	alcohol
| | —C—O—C— | |	ether
O || —C—H	aldehyde
O || —C—	ketone
O || —C—OH	carboxylic acid
O || —C—O—C— |	ester
NH₂ | —C—	amine
O || —C—NH₂	amide

© Edvantage Interactive 2016

7.2 Activity: Recognizing Functional Groups

Question
Can you classify an organic compound according to its functional group?

Background
The reactivity of an organic compound depends largely on the presence of its functional group. You can classify organic compounds by their functional group by carefully examining which groups of atoms are present on a molecule. You should be able to recognize the following types of functional groups in the following organic compounds: alkane, alkene, alkyne, cycloalkane, aromatic, alkyl halide, alcohol, ether, amine, amide, aldehyde, ketone, carboxylic acid, and ester.

Procedure
1. Work with a partner.
2. Copy the following structure diagrams onto a piece of paper.

1.	2.
3. $HC\equiv C-CH_3$	4.
5.	6.
7.	8.
9.	10.

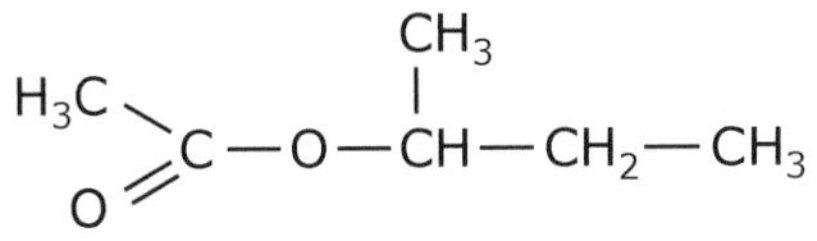

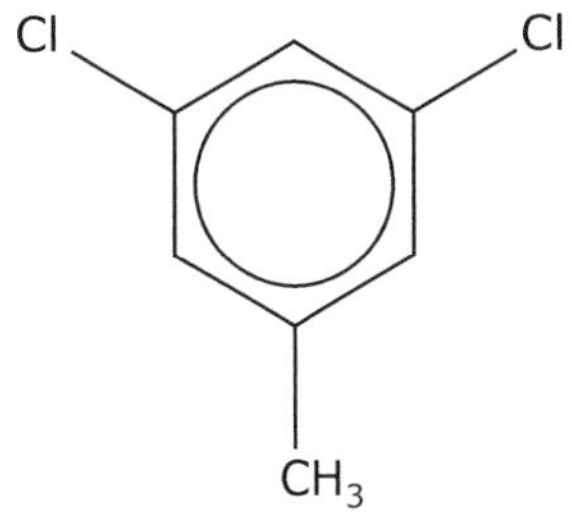

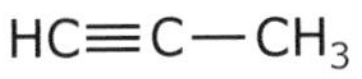

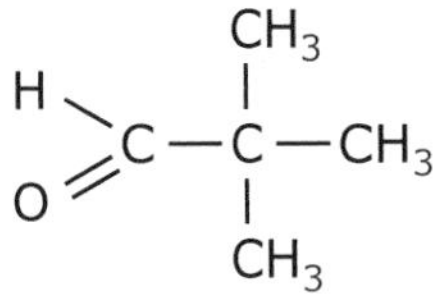

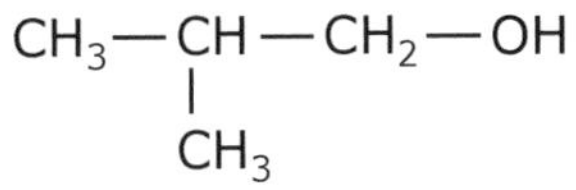

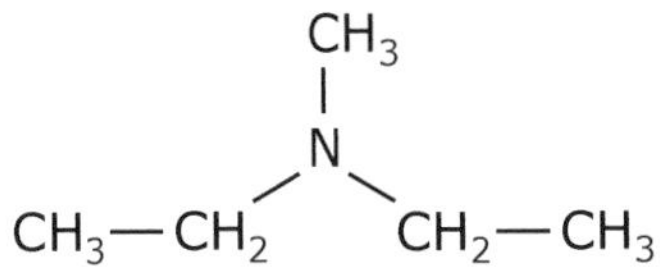

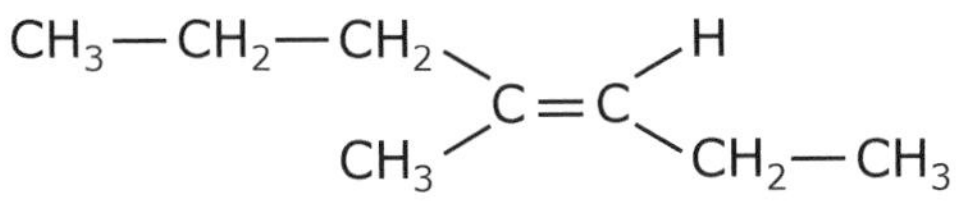

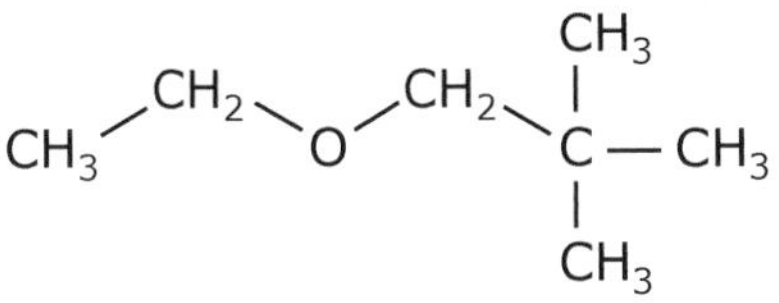

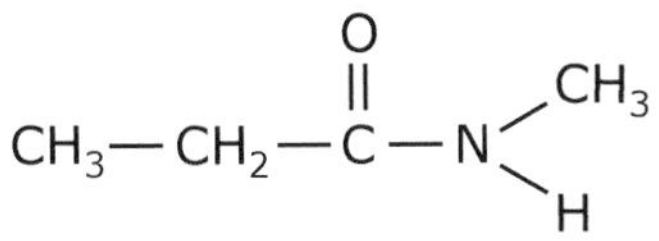

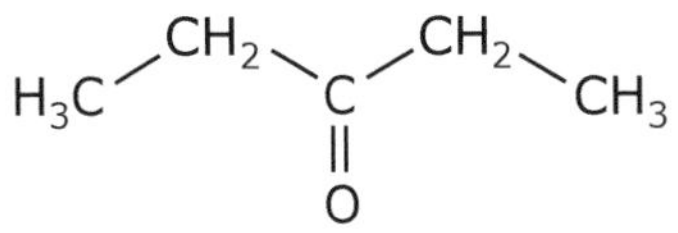

Continued on next page

© Edvantage Interactive 2016

3. Cut the paper into 10 squares and place each square face down on the table.

4. Take turns with your partner. Turn over one piece of paper, and state which functional groups are represented. Some examples may include more that one functional group. If your partner agrees, you get to keep that piece of paper. If your partner disagrees, place that piece of paper to the side.

Results and Discussion

1. Once you have completed all 10 squares, count how many questions you answered correctly. _____

2. For questions where you disagreed, re-examine the question and try to come to an agreement about the functional group. If you cannot agree, ask a nearby pair of students.

3. You know how to name some of these compounds. List the names below of as many as you can and compare your answers to those of a nearby pair of students.

7.2 Review Questions

1. What elements other than carbon and hydrogen commonly appear in organic molecules?

2. What is a functional group? Give two examples of a functional group.

3. Alkyl halides contain one or more of which family of elements?

4. Complete the following table:

Name of group	Atoms and their arrangement
hydroxyl	
carbonyl	
carboxyl	

5. Name the following compounds:

(a)

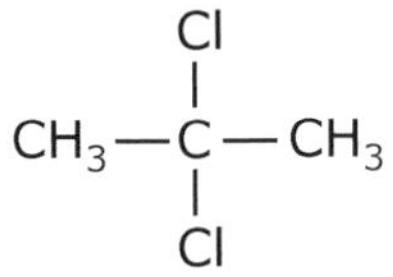

$$CH_3 - \overset{\overset{\displaystyle Cl}{|}}{\underset{\underset{\displaystyle Cl}{|}}{C}} - CH_3$$

(b)

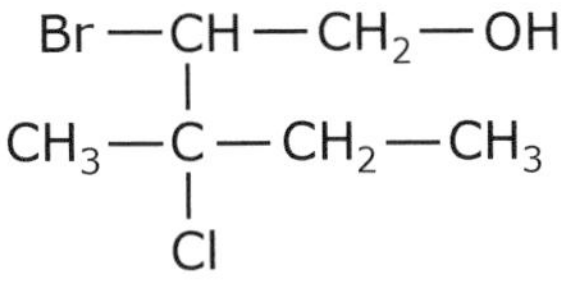

$$Br - CH - CH_2 - OH$$
$$CH_3 - \overset{\overset{\displaystyle |}{}}{\underset{\underset{\displaystyle Cl}{|}}{C}} - CH_2 - CH_3$$

(c)

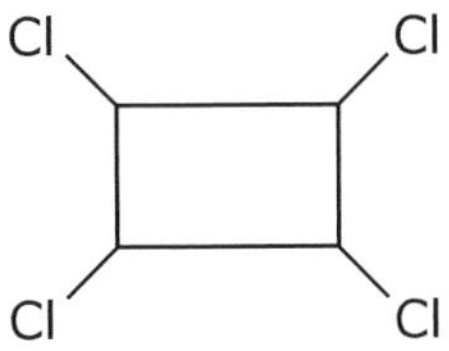

(d)

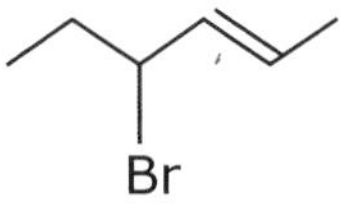

(e)

$$CH_3 - CH_2 - CH_2 - CH_2 - C \overset{\displaystyle O}{\underset{\displaystyle OH}{}}$$

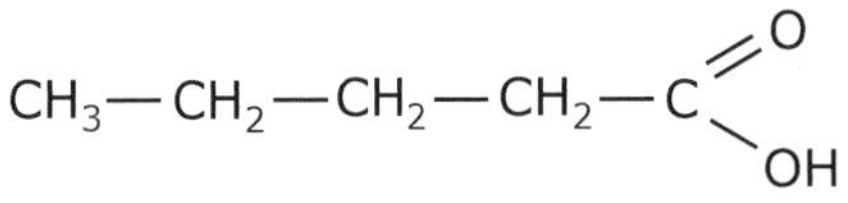

(f)

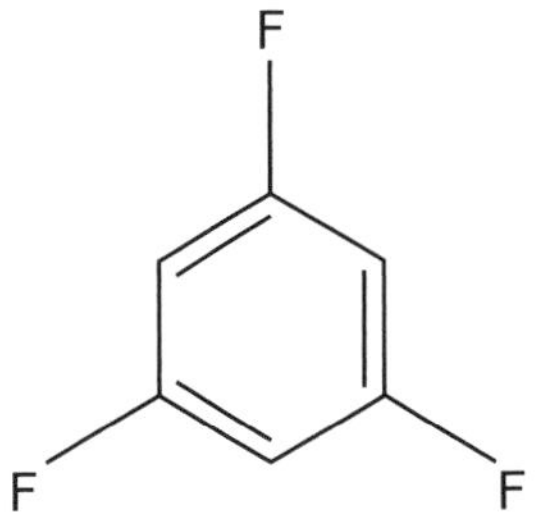

6. Draw condensed structural formulae for each compound below.

(a) cyclopentanol

(b) 1,1-dichloroethene

(c) 2-methyl-3-pentanol

(d) 2-chloropropane

(e) 1,1-dichloro-3,3-dimethyl-2-hexanol

(f) 2,3,5-tribromocyclohexanol

7. Both organic and inorganic compounds may contain an –OH group. In an ionic compound, what is the name of the –OH group? In an organic compound?

8. Which functional groups contain only the following?
   (a) single bonded oxygen atoms

   (b) double bonded oxygen atoms

   (c) both single and double bonded oxygen atoms

9. How is an amide different than a carboxylic acid? How are they similar?

10. For each of the following compounds named, classify the compound according to its functional group. For some compounds, more than one functional group may be used. Draw condensed structural formulas for as many of these as you can.
    (a) 2,3-dichloropentane

    (b) 2-decyne

    (c) *trans*-3-hexene

    (d) 1,2-dimethylbenzene

    (e) 2-chloro-2-pentanol

    (f) 3-methylbutanamide

    (g) propanal

    (h) pentanoic acid

11. Classify the following molecules according to their functional group.

    (a)

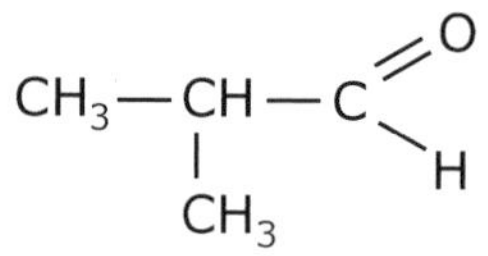

    $CH_3-CH-C\begin{smallmatrix}O\\H\end{smallmatrix}$
    |
    CH_3

    (b)

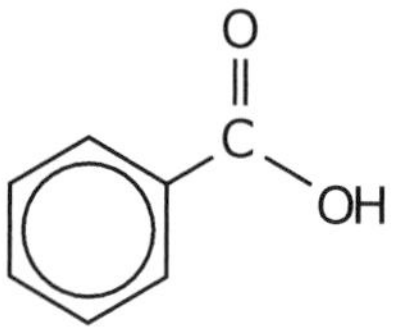

    (c)

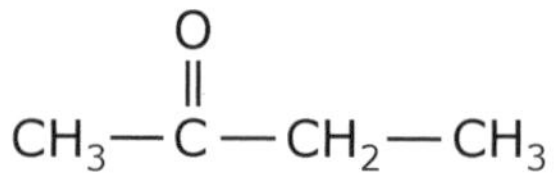

    $CH_3-\overset{\overset{O}{\|}}{C}-CH_2-CH_3$

    (d)

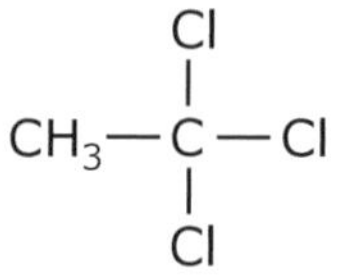

    $CH_3-\overset{\overset{Cl}{|}}{\underset{\underset{Cl}{|}}{C}}-Cl$

    (e)

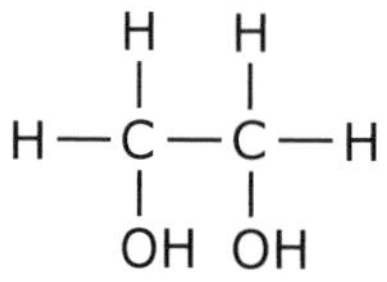

    $H-\overset{\overset{H}{|}}{\underset{\underset{OH}{|}}{C}}-\overset{\overset{H}{|}}{\underset{\underset{OH}{|}}{C}}-H$

    (f)

    $C_{17}H_{35}C\begin{smallmatrix}O\\O-C_2H_5\end{smallmatrix}$

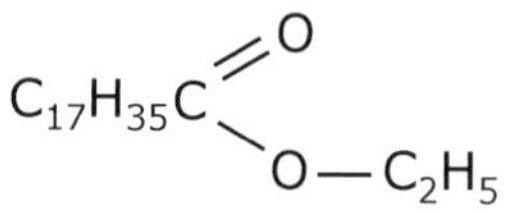

    (g)

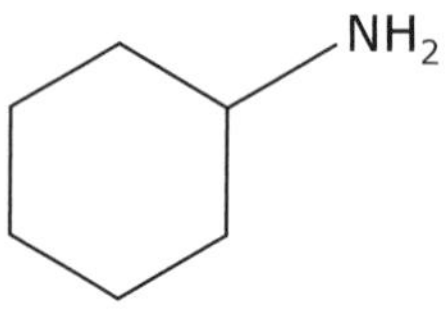

    (h)

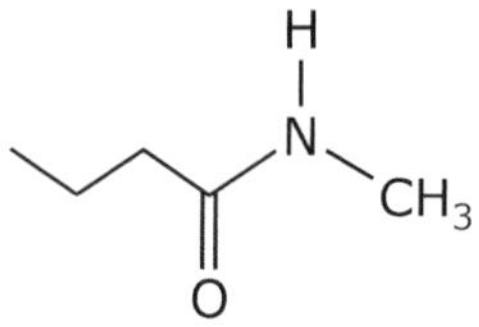

12. The following molecules are common organic compounds. For each molecule, circle and identify each functional group present. These molecules contain more than one functional group.
    (a) vanillin (a food flavoring)

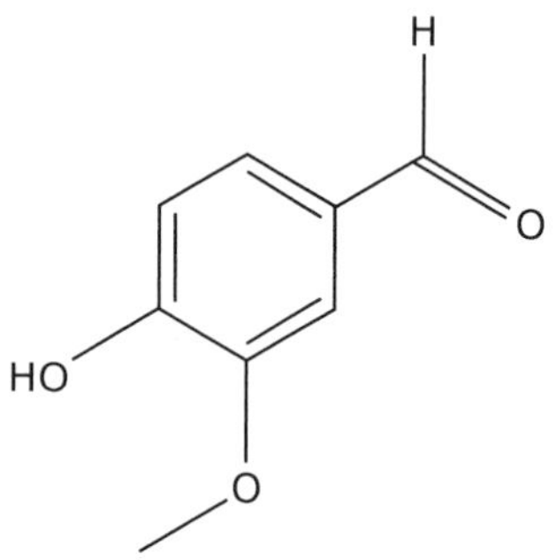

(b) morphine (a painkiller) Note that, in this diagram, the thicker black line represents a chain containing two carbon atoms coming out of the page towards you. This chain attaches the nitrogen atom to the carbon atom in the flat chain.

(c) ibuprofen (a painkiller)

(d) capsaicin (the molecule that makes chili peppers "hot"; used in pepper spray)

(e) penicillin G (an antibiotic)

(f) caffeine (the active ingredient in coffee that keeps chemistry students awake while studying)

(g) theobromine (found in chocolate)

7.3 Reactions of Organic Molecules

Warm Up

1. Unsaturated fats such as those found in olive oils and avocados are healthier than saturated fats found in coconut oil and butter. What do the words "unsaturated" and "saturated" mean in terms of organic molecular structure?

   _____

2. Earlier in this book you learned about the types of chemical reactions. What are the products of the combustion of a hydrocarbon or carbohydrate?

   _____

3. The chemical reactivity of an organic compound largely depends on the type of organic compound involved. Match the functional group in the column on the left to the correct description from the column on the right. Draw lines to connect each pair.

(a) alcohol	(i) contains a carboxyl group
(b) alkyne	(ii) contains a halogen
(c) carboxylic acid	(iii) contains a hydroxyl group
(d) alkyl halide	(iv) contains a double bond between two carbon atoms
(e) alkene	(v) contains a –COOR group
(f) ester	(vi) contains a triple bond between two carbon atoms

Simple Organic Reactions

Countless organic reactions are happening in your body as you read this. In a living organism, the reactions between organic compounds are the basis for the functioning of systems such as respiration, reproduction, digestion, and circulation. The production of proteins, carbohydrates, and nucleic acids, such as DNA and RNA, involves reactions of organic molecules. Not only is organic chemistry within you, it surrounds you. An enormous variety of organic molecules exists. Many of the products we use daily are made from organic compounds such as fabrics, building materials, food products, drugs, paints, fuels, greases, perfumes, explosives, plastics, dyes, and soaps. A large number of these products are synthesized in a lab.

This chapter began by introducing the work of Friedrich Wohler. He was the first chemist to recognize that an organic compound could be produced in a lab. In this section, we will focus on some simple reactions of organic molecules that occur in nature and in the lab.

Combustion Reactions

The fuel for your car is a mixture of hydrocarbons that react with oxygen in a combustion reaction to produce energy. This is a type of oxidation reaction. It's also an exothermic reaction. Earlier, you learned that the products of hydrocarbon combustion are water and carbon dioxide. The example below shows the reaction of octane (C_8H_{18}) and oxygen.

$$2\ C_8H_{18}(l) + 25\ O_2(g) \rightarrow 16\ CO_2(g) + 18\ H_2O(g) + energy$$
$$\text{octane} + \text{oxygen} \rightarrow \text{carbon dioxide} + \text{water} + \text{energy}$$

This equation represents the complete combustion of octane, which occurs when there is an excess of oxygen. The flame appears a clean blue or yellow.

Incomplete combustion may occur when there is a limited amount of oxygen. In that case, products may be carbon monoxide or carbon and water. The solid carbon is the sooty material that you see in blackened smoke. Carbon monoxide is a colourless, odorless, and very poisonous gas. Your home may have a carbon monoxide detector. It will sound an alarm if the fuels heating your home are undergoing incomplete combustion. Your car exhaust contains carbon monoxide as well. It is dangerous to run your car in an enclosed space such as a garage. Every year, people die from carbon monoxide poisoning.

Here is another example of complete and incomplete combustion, this time using methane (CH_4):

Complete combustion: $CH_4(g) + 2 O_2(g) \rightarrow CO_2(g) + 2 H_2O(g) + energy$

Incomplete combustion: $CH_4(g) + O_2(g) \rightarrow C(s) + 2 H_2O(g) + energy$
Or $\quad 2 CH_4(g) + 3 O_2(g) \rightarrow 2 CO(g) + 4 H_2O(g) + energy$

Quick Check

1. Some cars are powered by propane. Write the balanced chemical equation for the complete combustion of propane.

   _____

2. Find out if your home has a carbon monoxide detector. Why might a carbon monoxide detector be a good idea?

   _____

3. Write a balanced chemical equation to represent the incomplete combustion of propane.

   _____

Types of Reactions

You have learned about many types of reactions. Organic compounds undergo different types of reactions. In this section, we will look at some simple reactions called substitution, addition, and elimination reactions.

Substitution Reactions

In a substitution reaction, an atom or group of atoms from a reactant takes the place of an atom or group of atoms on the organic molecule. For example, methane reacts with chlorine when exposed to ultraviolet light to produce chloromethane, as shown in Figure 7.3.1.

Figure 7.3.1 *Reaction of methane with chlorine*

One of the chlorine atoms is substituted for a hydrogen atom. Notice that the number of atoms that the central carbon atom bonds to does not change. It is bonded to four atoms in both the reactants and products. This reaction can go further with another chlorine atom replacing a hydrogen atom, which produces dichloromethane:

$CH_3Cl + Cl_2 \rightarrow CH_2Cl_2 + HCl$

Aromatic compounds can undergo substitution reactions many times. In the example in Figure 7.3.2, benzene reacts with chlorine to produce chlorobenzene and hydrochloric acid. Chlorobenzene will further react with Cl_2 to form dichlorobenzene (Figure 7.3.3).

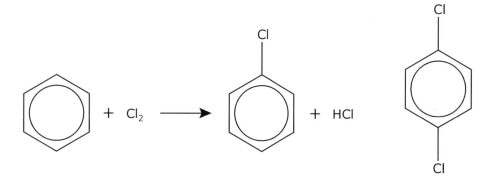

Figure 7.3.2 *Reaction of benzene with chlorine*

Figure 7.3.3 *Dichlorobenzene*

Addition Reactions

An addition reaction occurs when an unsaturated compound becomes saturated. In an addition reaction, electrons in the double or triple bond are shared with a reactant molecule. A triple bond may become a double bond or a double bond may become a single bond. It can be represented in general terms as shown in Figure 7.3.4.

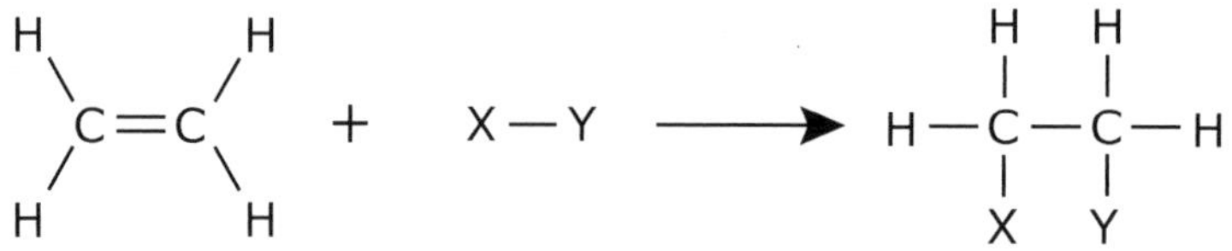

Figure 7.3.4 *An addition reaction*

Halogens are particularly reactive with alkenes and alkynes. When an addition reaction occurs, a halogen atom is added to each of the carbon atoms involved in the multiple bond. This may be called a **halogenation** reaction (Figure 7.3.5). Notice that the number of atoms each carbon atom is bonded to has increased. In the reactants, each carbon atom is bonded to three other atoms. In the products, each carbon atom is bonded to four other atoms.

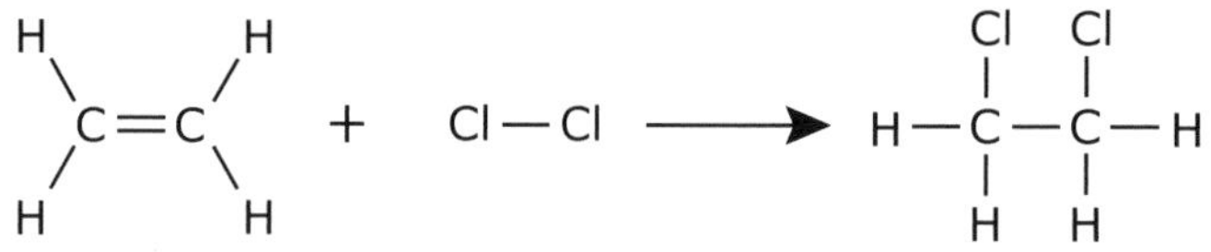

Figure 7.3.5 *A halogenation reaction*

Ethanol is a common additive to gasoline and is produced synthetically by the addition reaction between ethene (ethylene) and water (Figure 9.3.6). The acids H_3PO_4 or H_2SO_4 act as a catalyst to speed up the rate of this reaction.

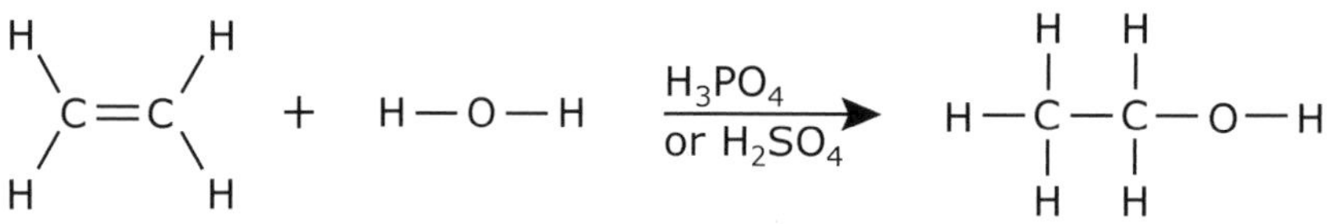

Figure 7.3.6 *Production of ethanol*

© Edvantage Interactive 2016

When the atoms being added to the unsaturated site are hydrogen atoms, the reaction can also be called **hydrogenation** (Figure 7.3.7).

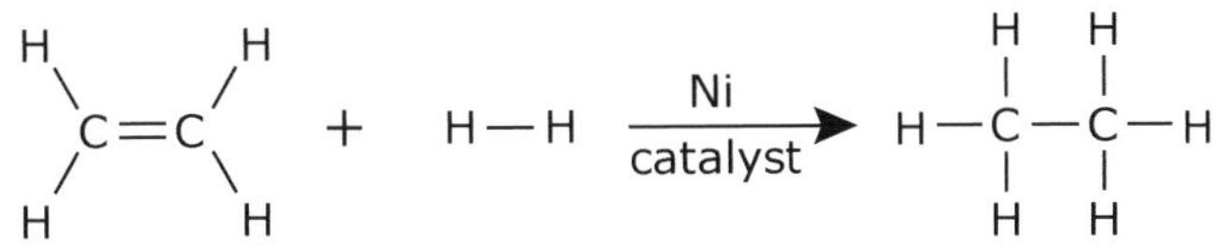

Figure 7.3.7 *A hydrogenation reaction*

Alkynes can also undergo addition reactions (Figure 7.3.8).

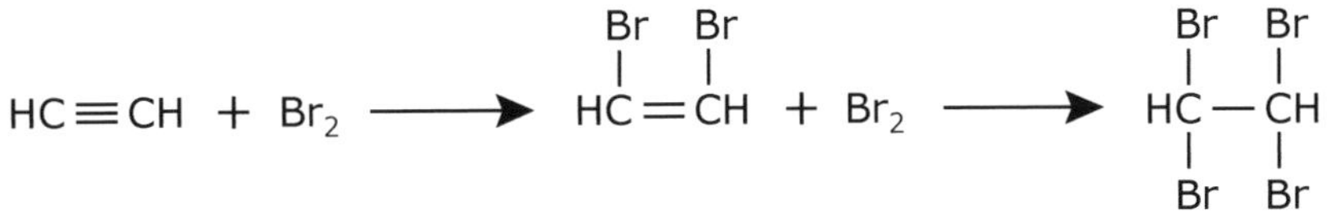

Figure 7.3.8 *Alkyne addition reaction*

Quick Check

1. How can the number of atoms bonded to the carbon assist your classification of a reaction as addition or substitution?

    _____

2. Classify the following as substitution or addition reactions:

    (a) _____

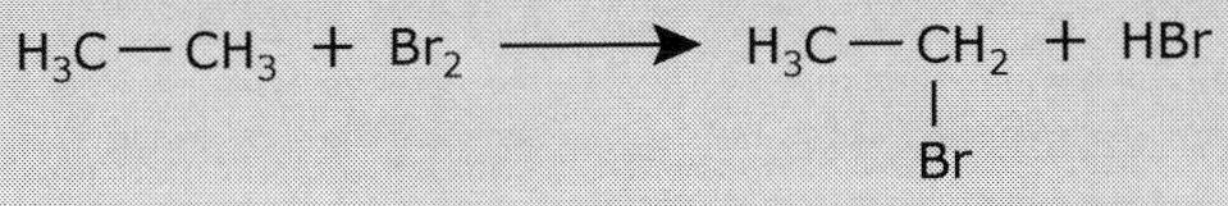

    (b) _____

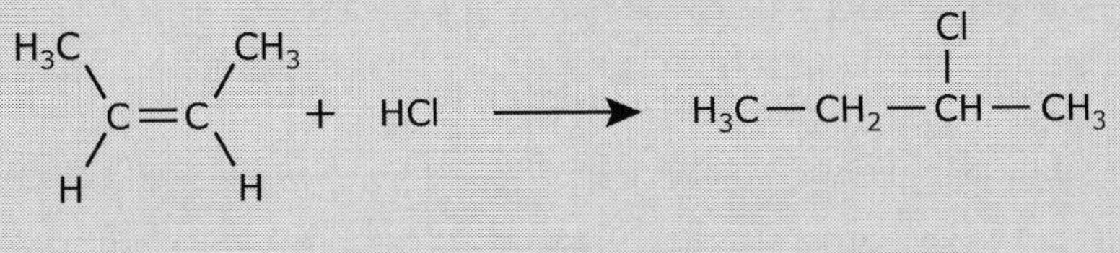

3. Using structural formulas, draw reactions showing the following. For each reaction, write the name of the reactants and products under the appropriate molecule.
    (a) formation of bromoethane

    (b) reaction between trichloromethane and fluorine

4. Can an alkane undergo an addition reaction? Explain.

    _____

© Edvantage Interactive 2016

Elimination Reactions

An elimination reaction is the opposite of an addition reaction. A small molecule such as H_2O or HX is eliminated, as shown in Figure 7.3.9.

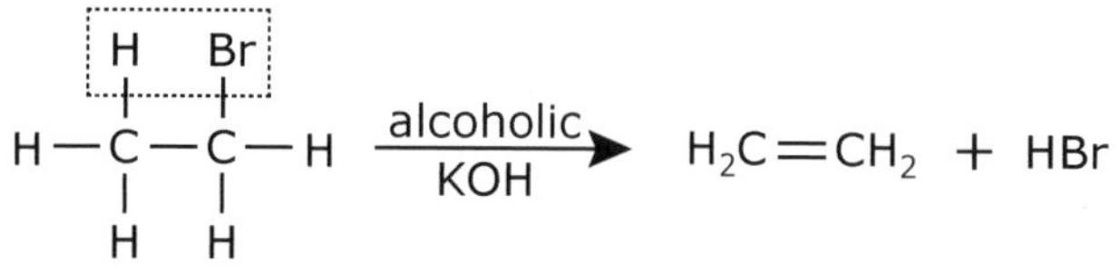

$$H-\overset{\overset{\displaystyle H}{|}}{\underset{\underset{\displaystyle H}{|}}{C}}-\overset{\overset{\displaystyle Br}{|}}{\underset{\underset{\displaystyle H}{|}}{C}}-H \xrightarrow{\text{alcoholic KOH}} H_2C=CH_2 \ + \ HBr$$

(H and Br are eliminated)

Figure 7.3.9 *An elimination reaction*

Notice that in an elimination reaction, the number of atoms that a carbon atom is bonded to decreases. Each carbon atom in the reactant is bonded to four other atoms. In the products, each carbon atom is only bonded to three other atoms.

If water is eliminated, the reaction can also be called **dehydration** or **condensation** (Figure 7.3.10).

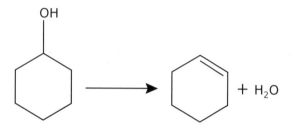

Figure 7.3.10 *Dehydration or condensation*

Esterification is the process of reacting an organic acid and an alcohol to produce an ester. Esters have a sweet, often fruity, scent. Esterification is a type of dehydration or elimination reaction.

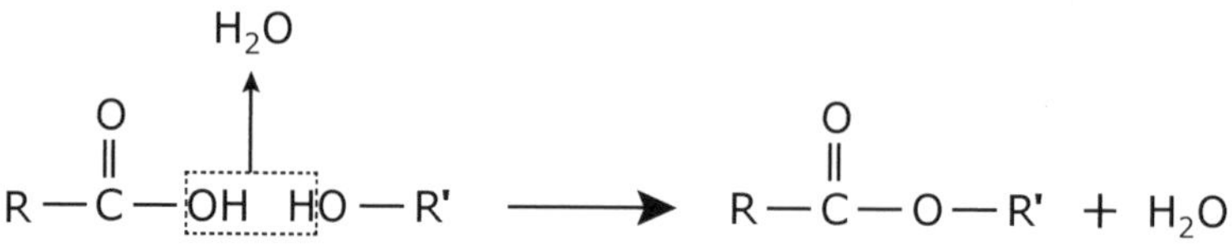

$$R-\overset{\overset{\displaystyle O}{\|}}{C}-OH \quad HO-R' \longrightarrow R-\overset{\overset{\displaystyle O}{\|}}{C}-O-R' \ + \ H_2O$$

Figure 7.3.10 *Esterification*

The –OH group on the carboxylic acid combines with the H atom from the alcohol group to make water. The name of the ester is derived from the names of the alcohol and carboxylic acid. The first part of the name of an ester comes from the alcohol. The alcohol portion of the ester is named by removing the "-ol" ending and changing it to "-yl." The name of the carboxylic acid part is changed by dropping the "-oic acid" part and adding "-oate."

An example of an ester is ethyl butanoate, which has the sweet smell of pineapple. It is produced when ethanol and butanoic acid are reacted, as shown below and in Figure 7.3.11:

butanoic acid + ethanol → ethyl butanoate + water

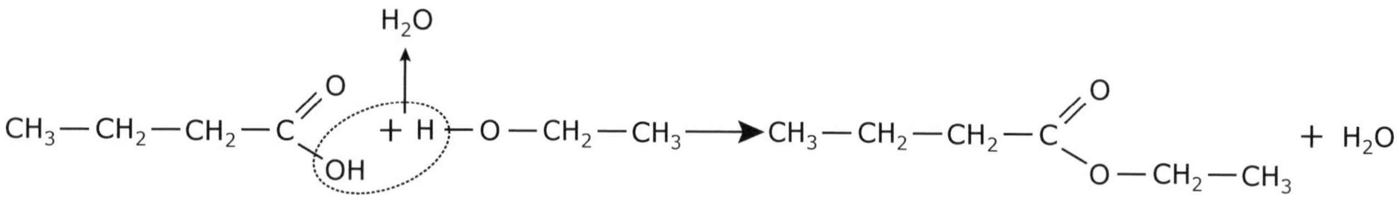

$$CH_3-CH_2-CH_2-\overset{\overset{\displaystyle O}{\diagup\!\!\diagup}}{C}\underset{\displaystyle OH}{} + H-O-CH_2-CH_3 \longrightarrow CH_3-CH_2-CH_2-\overset{\overset{\displaystyle O}{\diagup\!\!\diagup}}{C}\underset{\displaystyle O-CH_2-CH_3}{} + H_2O$$

Figure 7.3.11 *Formation of ethyl butanoate*

Animal and vegetable fats and oils are esters. The fat in Figure 7.3.12 is made from octadecanoic acid, commonly called stearic acid, and propane-1,2,3-triol, commonly called glycerol. Its real name is propane-1,2,3-triyl trioctadecanoate, but it is better known as glyceryl tristearate.

$$CH_3(CH_2)_{16}COOCH_2$$
$$|$$
$$CH_3(CH_2)_{16}COOCH$$
$$|$$
$$CH_3(CH_2)_{16}COOCH_2$$

Figure 7.3.12 *Glyceryl tristearate*

Saturated fats are molecules where the organic acid part of the carbon chain does not contain any double bonds. An unsaturated fat contains double bonds in the carbon parent chain of the organic acid section. Fats are an important nutrient for your body. They supply your body with energy and help in the absorption of fat-soluble vitamins. People on a Mediterranean diet, consisting of fruits, vegetables, fish, and whole grains, consume more unsaturated fats than saturated fats. This is believed to be one reason why people on this diet have healthier lives.

Sample Problem — Writing Equations for Simple Organic Reactions

Using structural diagrams, represent the reaction between methanol and ethanoic acid. Name the product, a solvent common in products like airplane glue.

What to Think about	How to Do It
1. Methanol is an alcohol, and ethanoic acid is a carboxylic acid. When these react, an ester is formed.	Methanol $CH_3 - OH$ Ethanoic acid
2. The carboxylic acid loses the –OH group, and the alcohol loses the –H atom.	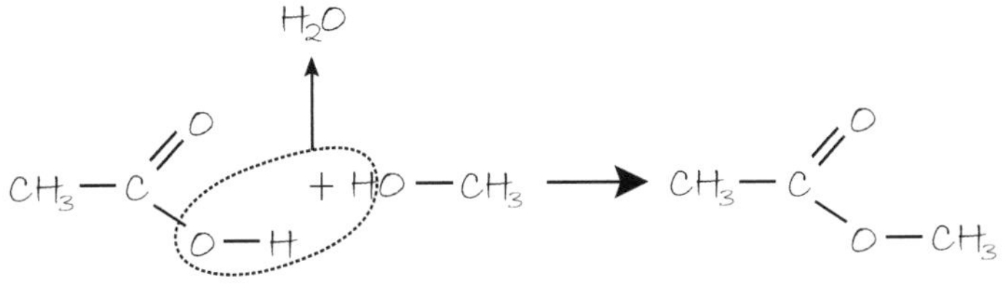
3. To name the ester: • methanol becomes "methyl" • ethanoic acid becomes "ethanoate"	 The ester is called methyl ethanoate.

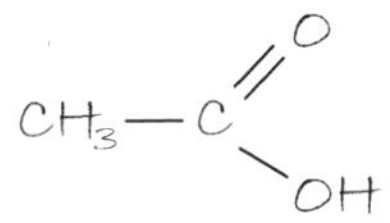

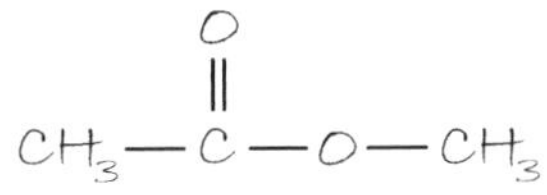

Practice Problems — Writing Equations for Simple Organic Reactions

1. Oil of wintergreen contains the ester formed when methanol and salicylic acid react. What is the name of the ester responsible for this pleasant odor?

   _____

2. Ethyl heptanoate smells like apricots. Draw structural diagrams to represent the reaction that produces ethyl heptanoate.

3. Chlorofluorocarbons (CFCs) in the stratosphere are molecules that use up Earth's protective ozone layer. Ozone molecules at this level absorb harmful UV-B and UV- C radiation. One such CFC is called chlorodifluoromethane. Draw structural diagrams to represent how this CFC is produced. Assume that methane reacts with chlorine, and then the product reacts with excess fluorine. What type of reactions are these?

Polymerization

You have learned how to calculate the molar mass of a compound. The molecules that we have been discussing in this text so far have been relatively small. The chemical formulas of these molecules contain relatively few atoms. In the 1920s, a chemist named Hermann Staudinger proposed that some natural compounds such as rubber and cellulose were composed of very, very large molecules containing tens of thousands of atoms each. He called these "macromolecules." These compounds have molar masses greater than a few thousand.

The word "polymer" means "many parts." Polymers are really long molecules made by stringing together smaller parts called "monomers." The word "monomer" means "one part." A polymer might look like Figure 7.3.13. There are many types of monomers that can be linked together, so imagine how many types of polymers exist!

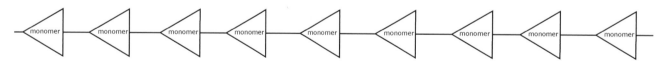

Figure 7.3.13 *A polymer model*

Polymers are found in nature and in many useful materials made synthetically. In your body, examples of polymers include DNA, starch, and proteins. Polymers we use every day include rubber, silk, plastics, nylon, Styrofoam, pharmaceuticals, Teflon, paints, and Plexiglas.

The name of a polymer depends on the monomer that it was made from. If the repeating unit is only one monomer, it is called a homopolymer (Figure 7.3.14). A copolymer contains a mixture of repeating units (Figure 7.3.15). In Figure 7.3.14, the monomer is shown on the left. When monomers are linked together to produce a polymer, the polymer is represented by showing the monomer in brackets, with the n representing some large number of repeat units.

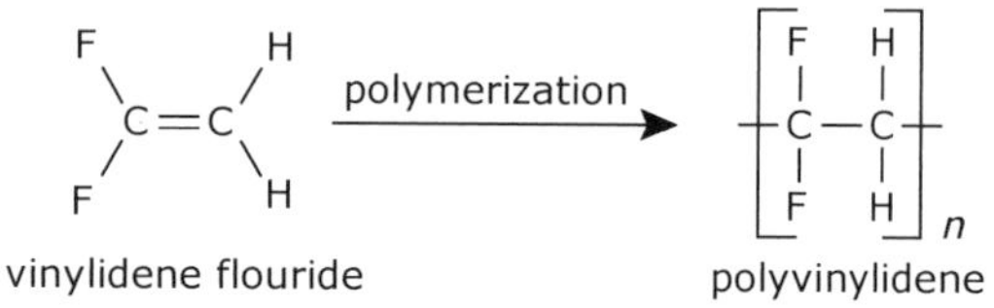

vinylidene flouride

polyvinylidene

Figure 7.3.14 *A homopolymer*

© Edvantage Interactive 2016

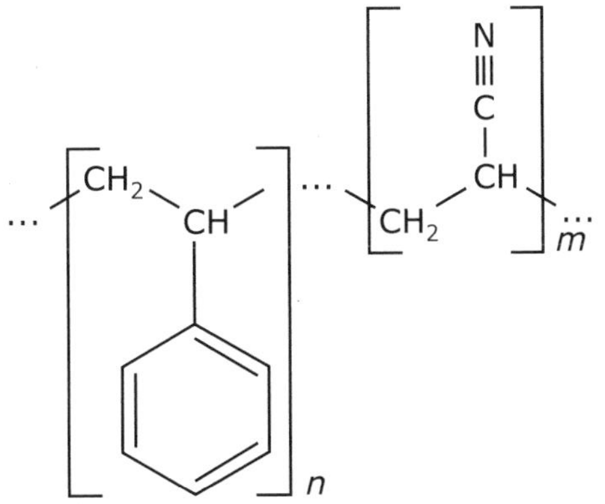

Figure 7.3.15 *A copolymer*

Addition Polymerization

You may have heard of polyethylene, one of the most common plastics. It is a polymer made up of repeating units of ethane. To make polyethylene, thousands of ethene molecules are reacted together in a huge addition reaction called "addition polymerization" (Figure 7.3.16).

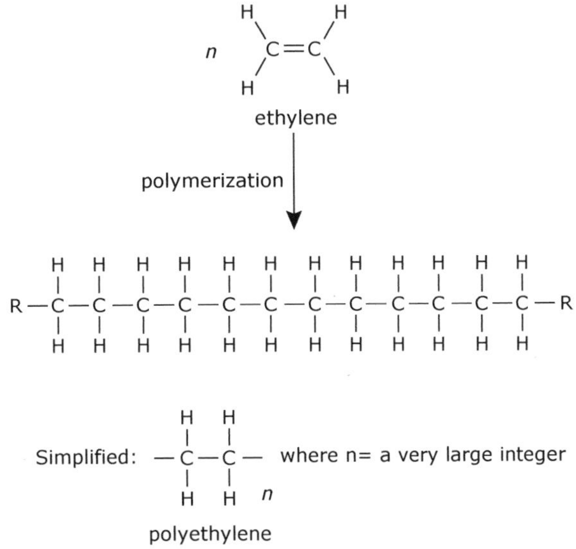

Figure 7.3.16 *Formation of polyethylene*

When the carbon backbone in the molecule is linear with few branches, we call it "high-density polyethylene" or HDPE. Long strands of these molecules can fit close together. If the carbon backbone of the molecule has many polyethylene branches, we call it "low-density polyethylene" or LDPE because the long chains of polymer cannot be packed tightly together. HDPE is much stronger and stiffer than LDPE, but LDPE is less expensive to make (Figure 7.3.17). Products made of HDPE include milk jugs, plastic garbage cans, shampoo bottles, and water pipes. LDPE products include plastic films, food wrap, and garbage bags.

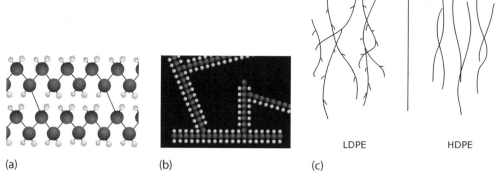

(a)   (b)   (c)   LDPE   HDPE

Figure 7.3.17 *(a) High-density polyethylene; (b) Low-density polyethylene; (c) LDPE and HDPE fibres*

Polyethylene macromolecules have molecular weights in the hundreds of thousands. Ultra-high molecular weight polyethylenes (UHMWPEs) are used in bulletproof vests and artificial joints and have molecular weights in the millions!

Polyethylene is called a thermoplastic because it can be melted and molded into other shapes. Because of this property, many of these plastics can be recycled. Polyethylene does not biodegrade, so it contributes to the problem of putting these plastics in landfills.

Other Examples of Polymers

Addition reactions are one common way to produce many different polymers. Other polymers made by addition reactions include those shown in Table 7.3.1.

Table 7.3.1 *Examples of Polymers Formed by Addition Reactions*

Name	Formula	Monomer	Applications
Polypropylene (PP) different grades	$-[CH_2-CH(CH_3)]_n-$	propylene $CH_2=CHCH_3$	Indoor/outdoor carpeting, plastic bottles, upholstery
Poly(vinyl chloride) (PVC)	$-(CH_2-CHCl)_n-$	vinyl chloride $CH_2=CHCl$	Pipes, siding, flooring
Polystyrene (PS)	$-[CH_2-CH(C_6H_5)]_n-$	styrene $CH_2=CHC_6H_5$	Insulation, furniture, packing materials
Polytetrafluoroethylene (PTFE, Teflon)	$-(CF_2-CF_2)_n-$	tetrafluoroethylene $CF_2=CF_2$	Non-stick surfaces on cooking utensils, lining in engines, electrical insulation
Polychloroprene (cis + trans) (Neoprene)	$-[CH_2-CH=CCl-CH_2]_n-$	chloroprene $CH_2=CH-CCl=CH_2$	Synthetic rubber products for wetsuits, insulation

Quick Check

1. Polytetrafluoroethylene, commonly called Teflon, is a non-stick substance used in kitchen products, the aerospace industry, electronics, and communications. It is a polymer that can be represented by the diagram below.

   Is this a homopolymer or a copolymer? _____

   Circle the repeating unit on the diagram.

```
     F   F    F    F    F    F    F    F    F    F    F    F    F    F
     |   |    |    |    |    |    |    |    |    |    |    |    |    |
 ... C — C — C — C — C — C — C — C — C — C — C — C — C — C ...
     |   |    |    |    |    |    |    |    |    |    |    |    |    |
     F   F    F    F    F    F    F    F    F    F    F    F    F    F
```

   segment of Teflon polymer

2. On a molecular level, how does HDPE differ from LDPE?

   _____

3. Many plastic pipes, siding, and flooring are made of polyvinyl chloride or PVC. The reaction for its formation is shown below. What type of reaction is this? On the diagram above, circle the repeat unit in this polymer.

   _____

```
  Cl          H    Cl          H    Cl          H
    \        /       \        /       \        /
     C = C            C = C            C = C
    /        \       /        \       /        \
  H           H    H           H    H           H
```

                              ↓

```
     Cl   H    Cl   H    Cl   H
     |    |    |    |    |    |
   — C — C — C — C — C — C —
     |    |    |    |    |    |
     H    H    H    H    H    H
```

4. The symbols shown here are used to distinguish HDPE from LDPE. List two products in your home that are made up of HDPE and two products made of LDPE.

HDPE

LDPE

Condensation Reactions

Another way to make polymers is through a **condensation reaction**. One such polymer is nylon. It is produced when hexamethylenediamine reacts with adipic acid. For each amine that reacts with a carboxylic acid, a water molecule is eliminated. The monomer in nylon-66 has been circled in Figure 7.3.18.

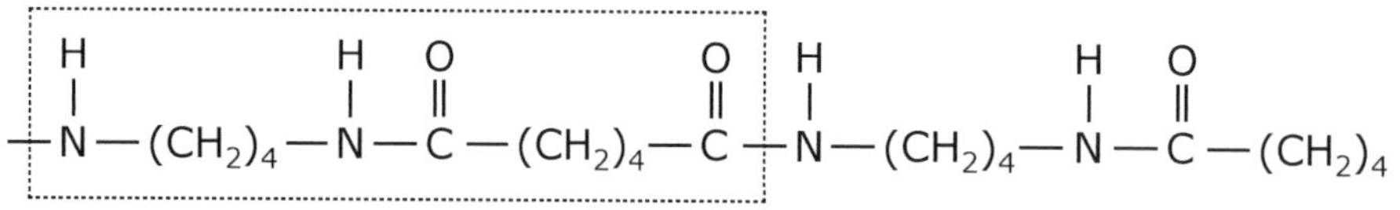

monomer

Figure 7.3.18 *Nylon*

Another example of a condensation reaction is found in your body in the process of protein production. The building blocks of proteins are amino acids. An amino acid is an organic molecule containing at least one amino group ($-NH_2$) and one carboxyl group ($-COOH$). There are 20 different amino acids in your body used to produce various proteins. The amino group on one amino acid reacts with the carboxyl group on another amino acid. When two amino acids combine, they form a dipeptide and water as shown in the reaction below and in Figure 7.3.19.

amino acid + amino acid $\dashrightarrow$ dipeptide + water

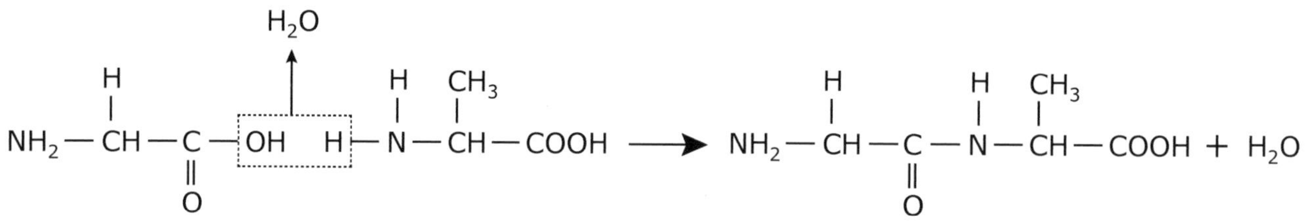

Figure 7.3.19 *Formation of a dipeptide*

When many amino acids combine, the structure is called a polypeptide or a protein. One water molecule is eliminated with the formation of each new peptide bond. A protein chain may contain from 50 to thousands of amino acid fragments. A protein is a natural polymer (Figure 7.3.20). Other important polymer molecules in your body include nucleic acids such as DNA and RNA. Deoxyribonucleic acid is one of the largest molecules known, and has a molecular weight of up to several billion amu.

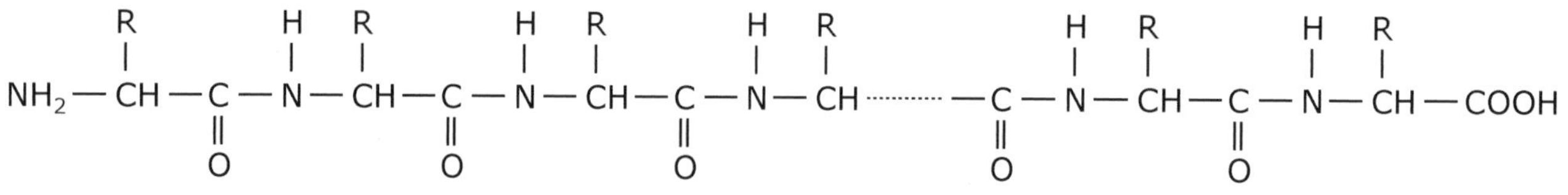

Figure 7.3.20 *A protein polymer*

© Edvantage Interactive 2016

7.3 Review Questions

1. What is the difference between complete combustion and incomplete combustion? Compare and contrast the reaction conditions and products for each.

2. (a) Which types of reactions do alkanes typically undergo?

   (b) Which types of reactions do alkenes and alkynes typically undergo?

3. In an elimination reaction, state two molecules commonly eliminated.

4. What happens to the number of atoms bonded to the carbon atom in the skeleton during an addition reaction?

   A substitution reaction?

5. What happens during a hydrogenation reaction?

   A condensation reaction?

   A dehydration reaction?

6. Describe the difference between a monomer and a polymer.

7. Salicylic acid is both an acid and an alcohol. It can undergo two different esterification reactions.
   (a) When reacted with ethanoic acid (commonly called acetic acid) the common painkiller acetylsalicylic acid (ASA) is formed. This is the active ingredient in Aspirin. In this reaction, the hydroxyl group on salicylic acid reacts with the carboxyl group on the acetic acid. Using the structures shown above and below, draw structural formulas to represent this reaction. Write the name of each molecule underneath each structure.

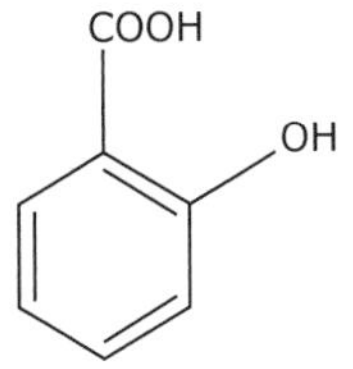

salycylic acid

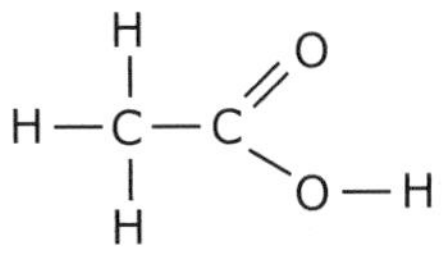

ethanoic acid

(b) When reacted with methanol, the carboxylic acid part of salicylic acid reacts with the hydroxyl group on the methanol. In this reaction, methyl salicylate is formed, commonly known as oil of wintergreen. Using the structures shown above and below, draw structural formulas to represent this reaction. Write the name of each molecule next to each structure.

COOH

OH

salicylic acid

$$H-\overset{\overset{\displaystyle H}{|}}{\underset{\underset{\displaystyle H}{|}}{C}}-O-H$$

methanol

8. Represent the following reactions by drawing skeletal formulas, then state the type of reaction involved.
(a) propene + oxygen

(b) cyclohexane + chlorine

(c) cyclohexene + hydrogen

(d) 1-octanol + ethanoic acid

(e) propyne + hydrogen bromide

9. What is addition polymerization? Give an example of a polymer produced by addition polymerization.

10. What is condensation polymerization. Give an example of a polymer produced by condensation polymerization.

11. Name three naturally occurring polymers.

12. For the following polymers, circle the repeating unit.

(a) polystyrene (Styrofoam)

$$-CH_2-CH-CH_2-CH-CH_2-CH-CH_2-CH-CH_2-CH-CH_2-CH-$$

(b) cellulose (component of cell walls in plant cells)

(c) natural rubber

(d) polyvinyl chloride (PVC)

© Edvantage Interactive 2016

8 Structure and Properties of Matter

By the end of this chapter, you should be able to do the following:

- Explain the concept of chemical equilibrium with reference to reacting systems
- Predict, with reference to entropy and enthalpy, whether reacting systems will reach equilibrium
- Apply Le Châtelier's principle to the shifting of equilibrium
- Apply the concept of equilibrium to a commercial or industrial process
- Draw conclusions from the equilibrium constant expression
- Perform calculations to evaluate the changes in the value of K_{eq} and in concentrations of substances within an equilibrium system

By the end of this chapter, you should know the meaning of these **key terms**:

- chemical equilibrium
- closed system
- dynamic equilibrium
- enthalpy
- entropy
- equilibrium concentration
- equilibrium constant expression
- equilibrium shift
- Haber process

- heterogeneous reaction
- homogeneous reaction
- ICE table
- K_{eq}
- Le Châtelier's principle
- macroscopic properties
- open system
- PE diagram

When the number of shoppers travelling between the two floors on the escalators is equal, the crowd has reached equilibrium.

8.1 Describing Chemical Bonding

Warm Up

1. What term do we give to an atom's outer electrons that take part in chemical bonding?

   _____

2. Define electronegativity.

   _____

3. In which region of the periodic table are elements located that tend to
   (a) lose outer electrons most easily during chemical changes?

   _____

   (b) gain outer electrons most easily during chemical changes?

   _____

An Introduction to Chemical Bonding

All matter is composed of atoms, and those individual atoms are far too small to see. From that, it seems reasonable to conclude that matter must be made up of large numbers of atoms connected or bonded together. In this section, we will investigate the nature of the bonds between atoms and how those bonds determine important properties in compounds.

Atoms are electrical species with a negative cloud of electrons surrounding and attracted to a positive nucleus. As you have learned, the electrostatic forces of attraction and repulsion within atoms influence properties such as atomic size, ionization energy, and electronegativity. Those same forces and properties also play a role whenever atoms bond together.

When two atoms approach each other, all of the electrostatic interactions associated with equally and oppositely charged particles occur. The negative electron clouds of the atoms exert repulsive forces on each other, as do the positive nuclei of each atom. This repulsion slows the approaching atoms and converts some of their kinetic energy to potential energy. In addition, each nucleus also begins to attract the approaching atom's outer electron cloud. These attractive forces are most intense in the region of space where the electron clouds "overlap" between the adjacent nuclei. If the attractive forces between the atoms are stronger than the repulsive forces, the two atoms together are in a state of lower energy than when they were apart. Thus, a chemical bond forms between them.

Types of Chemical Bonds

The events described above apply to the formation of all chemical bonds. But recall that we have classified elements as metals and non-metals based on a number of physical and chemical properties that correlate to different positions on the periodic table. These properties and the three possible ways that these two varieties of elements can combine give rise to three different *types* of chemical bonds, which are listed in Table 8.1.1. In this course, we will cover ionic and covalent bonds.

Table 8.1.1 *Types of Chemical Bonds*

Atoms Involved in Chemical Bond	Type of Chemical Bond
1. metal bonded to non-metal	ionic bond
2. non-metal bonded to non-metal	covalent bond
3. metal bonded to metal	metallic bond

Table 8.1.1 is a simplified summary of chemical bonds because the bonds between atoms in most chemical compounds have varying proportions of both ionic and covalent characteristics. We will begin with clear examples of each type of bond to introduce the concepts involved.

Ionic Bonds

Ionic bonds form between two atoms with large differences in their ionization energies and electronegativities. Recall that such combinations typically occur when relatively large metal atoms located on the far left side of the periodic table in groups 1 or 2 combine with smaller non-metal atoms on the far right side of the table belonging to groups 16 or 17.

Look again at the electronegativities on your periodic table. Imagine a "collision," for example, between an alkali metal atom such as sodium and a halogen atom such as chlorine. These elements are located at opposite ends of the 3rd period of the periodic table and therefore exhibit significant differences in size, ionization energy, and electronegativity.

Compared to an atom of sodium, a chlorine atom is smaller with a higher ionization energy and electronegativity. As a result, when the outer electron clouds of these two atoms encounter each other, sodium's lone valence electron will be closer to chlorine's nucleus than to its own. It will therefore feel a stronger attraction from chlorine's nucleus than from its own. In fact, because the difference in the electronegativities of these two elements is *greater than 1.7*, the probability of finding sodium's outer electron near chlorine's nucleus is so great that the sodium atom can be considered to *transfer* that valence electron to the chlorine atom. Electronegativity difference is often abbreviated as **ΔEN**.

The large sodium atom, having lost the only electron in its 3rd energy level, is now a much smaller positively charged sodium cation (Na^+). The relatively small chlorine atom, having gained an extra electron, becomes a larger negatively charged chloride anion (Cl^-). These two oppositely charged ions are now bound together by an electrostatic attraction called an **ionic bond**.

> An **ionic bond** is the electrostatic attractive force between the oppositely charged ions produced when a metal atom transfers one or more electrons to a non-metal atom.

The electron transfer from sodium to chlorine and the resulting ionic bond is shown in Figure 8.1.1. These diagrams are **Bohr model** diagrams, showing the number of electrons in the shells surrounding the nuclei of the atoms and ions.

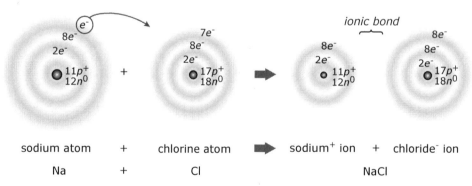

sodium atom   +   chlorine atom   ➡   sodium$^+$ ion   +   chloride$^-$ ion

Na   +   Cl   NaCl

Figure 8.1.1 *An electron transfers from sodium atom to a chlorine atom, resulting in the formation of an ionic bond between the ions.*

The Ionic Crystal Lattice

Obviously, when any macroscopic sample of chlorine gas and sodium metal react together, countless atoms will transfer electrons to form countless oppositely charged ions. These oppositely charged species being produced in close proximity are drawn together into an ordered, solid, three-dimensional array of cations and anions called a **crystal lattice** (Figure 8.1.2). The smallest whole number cation-to-anion ratio in this structure represents the chemical formula for the ionic compound, in this case, NaCl.

Figure 8.1.2 *NaCl crystal lattice*

The vast number of interionic forces present in a crystal lattice locks all of the ions into place. This helps explain why all ionic compounds are solids with high melting temperatures (e.g., sodium chloride melts at 801°C.)

Ionic compounds form a number of different crystal structures depending on the relative sizes and ratios of their ions. Those ratios in turn depend on the charges on the ions in the compound.

Recall that the representative elements in groups 1, 2, 13, 15, 16, and 17 of the periodic table tend to form stable ions by losing or gaining sufficient electrons to become isoelectronic with the nearest noble gas. This results in the common ion charges shown in Table 8.1.2 for those groups.

Table 8.1.2 *Common Ion Charges in Groups 1, 2, 13, 15, 16, and 17*

Group Number	1	2	13	15	16	17
Most Common Ion Charge	1+	2+	3+	3-	2–	1–

We can think of ionic bond formation as a case of *extremely unequal electron sharing*. Both metal and non-metal nuclei attract the valence electrons between them when their atoms meet. However, the non-metal pulls those electrons so close to its own nucleus that it effectively captures the metal's valence electrons and forms the metal cation and non-metal anion. An accurate analogy might be a grossly mismatched tug-of-war, except that in this case, the smallest competitor wins.

Several important points should be mentioned when summarizing ionic bonding:

1. Ionic compounds form between metals and non-metals whose ΔEN exceed 1.7. They typically form when metals from groups 1 or 2 react with non-metals from groups 16 or 17 of the periodic table.

2. During the formation of an ionic bond, metal atoms will transfer one or more valence electrons to the more electronegative non-metal atoms. This occurs because of the metal's relatively low ionization energies and electronegativities. In the process, metal cations and non-metal anions form and are attracted to each other by ionic bonds.

3. Ionic compounds form structures known as crystal lattices. The vast number of attractive forces present in such lattices account for the high melting temperatures of ionic compounds.

4. The formulas for ionic compounds represent the smallest whole number ratios of cations-to-anions that are electrically neutral.

Quick Check

1. What event occurs when atoms of metals and non-metals react to become cations and anions?

   _____

2. Identify the three types of chemical bonds based on the different elements involved.

   _____

   _____

   _____

3. Which chemical families in the periodic table are typically associated with ionic bond formation?

   _____

Sample Problem — Ionic Bond Formation

Write formulas for the compounds formed when the following elements combine and justify that the bonds present are ionic by determining the ΔEN in each case.

(a) Ca and Br   (b) Al and O   (c) Be and O   (d) Rb and N   (e) Ba and Cl

What to Think about	How to Do It
1. Write the element symbols with their charges and criss-cross the numbers. 2. Reduce formulas to smallest whole number ratios 3. Determine ΔEN values using the table above. Values above 1.7 represent ionic bonds.	(a) Ca^{2+} Br^- → $CaBr_2$ ΔEN = 1.8 (ionic bond) (b) Al^{3+} O^{2-} → Al_2O_3 ΔEN = 2.0 (ionic bond) (c) Be^{2+} O^{2-} → BeO ΔEN = 2.0 (ionic bond) (d) Rb^+ N^{3-} → Rb_3N ΔEN = 2.2 (ionic bond) (e) Ba^{2+} Cl^- → $BaCl_2$ ΔEN = 2.1 (ionic bond)

Practice Problems — Ionic Compounds

1. Write formulas for the ionic compounds formed when the following elements combine:

   (a) Ba and Br   (d) Mg and Cl

   (b) Be and O   (e) Fr and F

   (c) Sr and N

2. Justify that the bonds in the following compounds are ionic by calculating the ΔEN values for each.

   (a) RbF   (c) KBr

   (b) $RaCl_2$ (d) Na_2O

3. Write formulas for the ionic compounds formed when the following elements combine. Using the ΔEN values, arrange the compounds in order of the increasing ionic character of the bonds in each compound.

   (a) Na and N   (b) Sr and Br   (c) Li and Cl   (d) Cs and F   (e) Rb and O

Covalent Bonds

Now let's look at the formation of a bond between two atoms of the same non-metal element, such as hydrogen (Figure 8.1.3). Obviously, the electronegativities of these or any two identical atoms would be the same.

As mentioned above, bond formation begins with atoms "colliding." As the two hydrogen atoms approach each other, their kinetic energy increases as each electron cloud is attracted to the other's approaching positive nucleus. The two atoms continue moving together until the repulsive forces of the two negative electron clouds and the two positive nuclei slow the atoms and convert their kinetic energy into potential energy.

As the atoms get close to each other, their electron clouds may overlap enough to cause attractive forces to exceed repulsive ones. The two valence electrons will move into the region of space between the adjacent nuclei because this is where they experience the most attractive force from those two centres of positive charge. The two atoms will settle into a position next to each other with the pair of valence electrons in a cloud of negative charge between the two nuclei. As the electron clouds of each hydrogen atom overlap, the two valence electrons experience the maximum attractive force between the two adjacent nuclei. This force of attraction of a pair of valence electrons between two adjacent nuclei constitutes a single **covalent bond**. In our example, the result of this covalent bond is a molecule of hydrogen, H_2

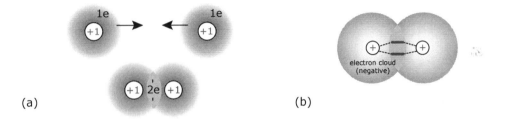

(a)   (b)

Figure 8.1.3 *(a) Two hydrogen atoms collide and two valence electrons move into the space between the nuclei. (b) The valence electrons experience a force of attraction from the two nuclei. This attraction holds the two atoms together to form H_2.*

Because this bond has formed between two atoms of hydrogen, the electronegativity difference associated with the atoms in the bond must be zero. This tells us that, on average, the pair of bonded electrons will spend the majority of their time equidistant between the two hydrogen nuclei. Stated another way, this means that the density of the electron charge cloud is greatest in the region of space halfway between the two adjacent nuclei. This is true whenever two atoms of the same element form covalent bonds. The "equal sharing" of valence electrons is sometimes referred to as a "pure covalent" or non-polar covalent bond.

Although both ionic and covalent bond formation involves only valence electrons, there are several important differences between the two events:

1. Covalent bonds typically form between two non-metal atoms rather than between metal atoms and non-metal atoms.

2. Because no electron transfer occurs and no ions form, all of the species prior to and following covalent bond formation between two atoms are electrically neutral.

3. The force of attraction in a covalent bond is between a pair of electrons and two adjacent positive nuclei, rather than between a cation and an anion as in an ionic bond. Electrons in covalent bonds are *always associated into pairs*.

4. Covalent compounds often exist as independent molecules rather than large crystal structures.

Polar Covalent Bonds

Table 8.1.3 *Relationship of ΔEN and Bond Designation*

ΔEN	Bond Designation
0	non-polar covalent
< 0.4	mostly covalent
0.4 – 1.7	polar covalent
> 1.7	ionic

We have discussed above the two extreme cases of bonding: complete electron transfer and completely equal electron sharing. Between these extremes are covalent bonds involving *unequal* electron sharing.

When atoms with different electronegativities form covalent bonds, those ΔEN values may be minimal or significant. If ΔEN is less than 0.4, the bonding electrons between the two atoms spend no more of their time nearer one nucleus than the other. Such bonds are designated as being mostly covalent because ΔEN appears to be insignificant. Another way to characterize this is to say that these bonds have very little "ionic character."

However, as ΔEN increases beyond 0.4, the pair of bonding electrons will be drawn closer and closer to the nucleus of the atom with the higher electronegativity. This unequal distribution of electron density will give that end of the bond a partially negative "pole" and the other a partially positive "pole." A bond "dipole" is said to exist and the bond itself is known as a **polar covalent bond**.

As the ΔEN increases and the bonds become more and more polar, we could say that the amount of ionic character in those bonds increases (Table 8.1.3).

Let's look at an example of a polar covalent bond. When a hydrogen atom having an electronegativity of 2.1 bonds to a chlorine atom with an electronegativity of 3.0, the ΔEN = 0.9. The electron density will be concentrated near chlorine giving that end of the bond a partial negative charge and leaving the hydrogen end with a partial positive charge. The bond dipole is said to be in the direction of chlorine and we can designate this polar covalent bond in several ways. Two are shown in Figure 8.1.4. The lower case Greek deltas (δ) indicate that there are slight or *partial* charges associated with each end of the HCl molecule. Note also that more electron density is associated with chlorine. Another depiction of this polar covalent bond simply shows the hydrogen chloride bond as a straight line between the element symbols. Beneath this is an arrow facing in the direction of the highest electron density or the negative end of the bond dipole.

Figure 8.1.4 *Polar covalent bond depictions. The bond dipole is in the direction of the chlorine.*

Atoms That Form More Than One Bond

So far we have considered the formation of only one bond per atom in two different molecules, namely H_2 and HCl. Notice that hydrogen and chlorine each require a single electron to become isoelectronic with their nearest noble gas. In hydrogen's case, one more electron will complete its first energy level. When chlorine acquires another electron it achieves a stable octet in its valence shell.

In each example, the sharing of a pair of valence electrons, whether equal or not, gives each atom in the bond the benefit of that extra electron in its valence shell. The bond also allows both atoms to have *all of their valence electrons paired,* which is a very stable configuration from a quantum mechanical perspective.

Of course, non-metals sometimes require more than one electron to achieve a stable outer electron shell and have all of their valence electrons paired. Consider several non-metals in groups 14, 15, and 16. To achieve a stable octet containing four electron pairs in each of their valence shells, carbon requires four electrons, nitrogen needs three, and oxygen needs two.

> This tells us that the number of electrons required by an atom to achieve the stable outer electron configuration of the nearest noble gas also represents the number of covalent bonds that the atom must form.

We can use Table 8.1.4 to predict formulas for compounds formed between elements in these families. For example, when phosphorus and chlorine react together, phosphorus requires three electrons to complete its octet, while chlorine requires only one.

© Edvantage Interactive 2016

Table 8.1.4 *Electrons Needed to Achieve a Stable Octet for Non-metals*

Periodic Table Group Number	14	15	16	17
Electrons Needed to Achieve Stable Octet	4	3	2	1

The element with the lower electronegativity, in this case phosphorus, normally requires the most electrons and is written first in a chemical formula. Place the number of electrons it requires above its symbol on the right (similar to a charge without the sign). Then do the same for chlorine as follows: P^3 Cl^1 Now criss-cross those numbers to give the formula: PCl_3.

The process is similar to writing ionic formulas except no charges exist and you don't always reduce the formula to the smallest ratio of atoms. This is because a covalent formula does not represent a ratio. Rather, it tells us the actual number of atoms that exist in the molecule. Assume at this point, however, that you *can* reduce covalent formulas unless told otherwise by your teacher.

There are also numerous examples where more than one pair of electrons is shared between the same two atoms. Two pairs of shared valence electrons results in a double covalent bond and three pairs will produce a triple covalent bond. We will discuss multiple bonds in detail in the next section. For now, we will only mention that as the number of electron pairs shared between two adjacent nuclei increases, so does the strength of the covalent bond.

Sample Problem — Covalent Bond Formation

Predict the formulas for the compounds formed when the following elements combine and determine whether the bonds present are non-polar covalent or polar covalent.

(a) N and F   (b) C and H   (c) Si and N   (d) C and S   (e) O and O

What to Think about	How to Do It
1. Determine how many electrons each atom requires to complete its valence shell and write that number above the symbol. 2. Criss-cross those numbers and reduce ratios if possible (for now). 3. Determine the ΔEN for each and classify the bonds present.	(a) $N^3 F^1 \rightarrow NF_3$ $\Delta EN = 1.0$ (polar covalent) (b) $C^4 H^1 \rightarrow CH_4$ $\Delta EN = 0.4$ (polar covalent) (c) $Si^4 N^3 \rightarrow Si_3N_4$ $\Delta EN = 1.2$ (polar covalent) (d) $C^4 S^2 \rightarrow CS_2$ $\Delta EN = 0$ (non-polar covalent) (e) $O^2 O^2 \rightarrow O_2$ $\Delta EN = 0$ (non-polar covalent)

Practice Problems — Comparing Types of Chemical Bonds

1. Consider the ΔEN values and pair up the elements Al, Cl, N, and Na to write the formula for the types of compounds identified below. Justify each choice by showing the appropriate ΔEN value next to each formula.

   (a) A compound with an ionic bond

   (b) A compound with a polar covalent bond

   (c) A compound with a non-polar covalent bond

2. Calculate the ΔEN values for the bonds in the following compounds. Then arrange the compounds in order from those containing bonds in which the electrons are shared most equally to those in which the electrons are shared most unequally.

   (a) H_2O (b) PCl_3 (c) Cl_4 (d) SiO_2 (e) AlN

3. Complete the following table:

Elements Present	Formula	ΔEN Value	Nature of Bonds	Atom Possessing Greater Electron Density
C and S				
B and Cl				
Al and O				
N and I				
Ca and F				

The Strength of Ionic vs. Covalent Bonds

Remember that ionic compounds are solids at room temperature and have high melting points. This results from the vast number of interionic forces locking all of the ions together in place in the crystal lattice. As mentioned earlier, the common ionic compound NaCl melts at 801°C.

Covalent compounds, however, usually exist as individual molecules and in any of the three states of matter: solid, liquid, or gas. We shouldn't conclude from this, however, that covalent bonds are any weaker than ionic bonds. Consider, for example, the molecule methane, CH_4, the main component of natural gas.

Although the melting point of methane (–182°C) is very low compared to sodium chloride, this physical property does not reflect the strength of the C – H bonds in methane or indicate that the bonds are weak compared to those in NaCl.

This is because no chemical bonds are broken when methane or any molecular covalent compound melts. Instead, weak intermolecular forces *between* the molecules are overcome. The result is that molecules are separated *from each other* rather than breaking the bonds between the atoms within those molecules.

The energy required to separate the bonded carbon and hydrogen atoms within the molecules from each other is far more than that required to simply pull the molecules apart. In the final section

© Edvantage Interactive 2016

of this chapter, we will discuss the different forces that hold molecules together. Although some of those forces are stronger than others, *none are as strong as chemical bonds*.

Compelling evidence of the strength of covalent bonds can be seen by studying compounds called **network covalent solids**. Rather than consisting of individual molecules, these substances are held together by covalent bonds that extend throughout the entire sample. In the same way that melting an ionic solid requires overcoming all of the attractive forces between the oppositely charged ions in the crystal lattice, melting a network covalent solid involves breaking all of the covalent bonds within what is effectively a giant molecule literally as big as the sample.

Consider quartz, for example, which is a network covalent solid having the formula SiO_2 (Figure 8.1.5). The fact that no separate molecules exist in a quartz crystal means that the melting point is very high: 1550°C. The melting point does reflect the strength of the bonds in the compound. It shows us that covalent bonds can be as strong as ionic bonds.

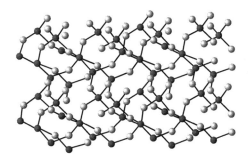

Figure 8.1.5 *A quartz crystal*

8.1 Activity: The Colors of Chemical Bonds

Question
Can one primary color blending into another be used to depict the transition from pure covalent bonding to ionic bonding?

Materials
Either blue, green, and yellow colored pencils or blue, green, and yellow watercolor paint and brushes.

Procedure
1. Use the three grids below, (A), (B), and (C). In each of the blank spaces, write the correct formula for the compound resulting from the combination of the two elements that intersect at that space. Remember to write the least electronegative atom symbol first.

2. Consult the electronegativities of the elements on your periodic table. Determine the electronegativity difference for each pair of elements to determine the type of bonds present in those compounds. Then shade in the spaces around each formula according to these directions: Shade in the spaces around the compounds containing ionic bonds yellow, covalent bonds blue and polar covalent bonds green.

(A)

	Li	Be	B	C	N	O	F
F							

(B)

	Na	Mg	Al	Si	P	S	Cl
Cl							

(C)

	K	Ca	Ga	Ge	As	Se	Br
Br							

Results and Discussion
1. Does every metal-non-metal combination result in an ionic bond?

© Edvantage Interactive 2016

8.1 Review Questions

1. (a) For a chemical bond to form between two atoms, how must the energy associated with the bonded atoms compare to the energy when the atoms are apart?

   (b) What does this tell us about the attractive forces compared to the repulsive forces between them?

2. What is an ionic crystal lattice and how does it explain the high melting points of ionic compounds?

3. Use your answer to question 2 to explain why formulas for ionic compounds do not represent neutral independent molecules of those compounds.

4. Identify the attractive forces associated with
   (a) ionic bonds

   (b) covalent bonds

5. (a) Identify two similarities between ionic and covalent bonds.

   (b) Identify two differences between ionic and covalent bonds.

6. Complete the following table by writing in the formulas of the compounds formed from the pairs of elements. Determine the ΔEN value for each and then classify the bonds as non-polar covalent, polar covalent, or ionic.

Elements	Compound Formula	ΔEN Value	Nature of Bonds Present
(a) rubidium and oxygen			
(b) strontium and bromine			
(c) carbon and sulfur			
(d) silicon and chlorine			

7. Magnesium is a metal and sulfur is a non-metal. Compare the ΔEN value for these elements in the compound MgS to the ΔEN value for the non-metals hydrogen and oxygen in water, H_2O. Which of the two compounds possesses a greater amount of ionic character in its bonds?

8. Glucose is a covalent compound with the molecular formula $C_6H_{12}O_6$. This and many other covalent formulas aren't reduced to the smallest whole-number ratios of atoms in the compound. Why not?

9. Many covalent compounds have much lower melting points than ionic compounds. Why does this not mean that covalent bonds are weaker than ionic bonds?

10. Diamond is a form of pure carbon containing only covalent bonds. It is the hardest substance known and has a melting point of about 3550°C. What name do we give to this type of covalent substance? Suggest a reason for its very high melting point.

11. Consider the nature of the covalent bonds present in HCl and in N_2. Which substance would you expect to have the higher melting point? Give a reason for your answer.

© Edvantage Interactive 2016

8.2 Lewis Structure Diagrams

Warm Up

1. Why do elements in the same chemical family display similar chemical behaviour?

_____

2. How can you determine the number of valence electrons in each of the representative or main group elements?

_____

3. Define the term "stable octet."

_____

Depicting Atoms, Ions, and Molecules in Two Dimensions

As you learned earlier, an atom's valence electrons are the outermost electrons. These are the electrons involved in chemical bonding. This means that, in chemical behaviour, the valence electrons of an atom are really the only electrons that matter.

In 1916, the American chemist Gilbert N. Lewis devised a system of representing the atoms of the elements based on the number of valence electrons they possess. This notation system uses each element symbol to represent the nucleus and all of the inner electrons of an atom (Lewis called this the "kernel" of an atom). It then surrounds that symbol with a series of dots representing that atom's valence electrons. These **electron dot diagrams** are called **Lewis structures**.

The notation is a simple and useful way to represent atoms and serves as a foundation to help us understand and predict chemical behaviours and compound structures without the need for sophisticated bonding theories. Our discussion of Lewis structures and diagrams will be confined to the representative or main group elements in the periodic table, that is, groups 1, 2, 13, 14, 15, 16, 17, and 18.

We will begin by discussing Lewis structures for individual atoms and ions, and then expand that discussion to include Lewis diagrams for molecular compounds and polyatomic ions.

Lewis Structures for Atoms

To write a Lewis structure for an atom, you need only determine the number of an atom's valence electrons. Recall from our discussion of the periodic table that this process is straightforward for the main group elements. For any period, beginning at the alkali metals, we see that atoms of this family have one valence electron. As we move across the period, each main group family has atoms with one additional valence electron up to the stable octet of four electron pairs present in each noble gas (except helium) (Table 8.2.1).

Table 8.2.1 *Valence Electrons in Main Group Atoms*

Main Group Number	1	2	13	14	15	16	17	18
Valence Electrons	1	2	3	4	5	6	7	8
Valence Electron Configuration	ns^1	ns^2	$ns^2 np^1$	$ns^2 np^2$	$ns^2 np^3$	$ns^2 np^4$	$ns^2 np^5$	$ns^2 np^6$

To write Lewis structures for the atoms, follow these steps:

1. Write the element symbol.
2. For hydrogen place a single dot next to the symbol. For helium place a pair of dots.
3. For 2nd period elements and beyond: for each valence electron present, place one dot around that symbol at one of the four positions of the compass: west, east, north, or south.
4. If more than four valence electrons are present, begin pairing the dots only after the four compass positions are filled.

The relative placement of the paired and unpaired dots is not as important as how many of each is present. Figure 8.2.1 shows the Lewis structures for the main group elements of the first three periods.

Group Number	1	2	13	14	15	16	17	18
	H·							He:
	Li·	Be·	B·	·C·	·N:	·O:	·F:	:Ne:
	Na·	Mg·	Al·	·Si·	·P:	·S:	·Cl:	:Ar:

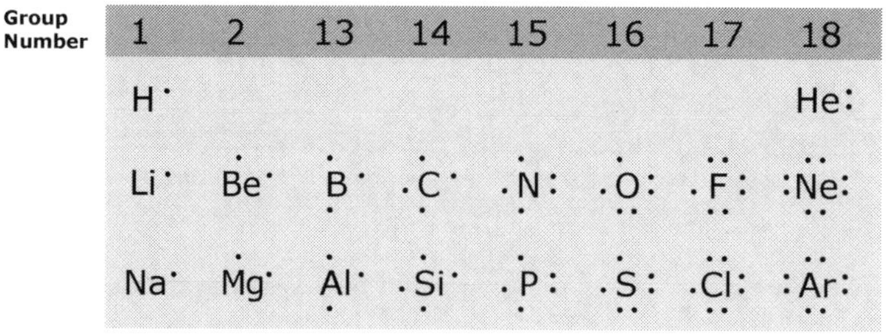

Figure 8.2.1 *Lewis structures for main group elements of the first three periods*

As you view Figure 8.2.1, consider the following important points:

1. As each element in a family has the same number of valence electrons, the Lewis structure for those elements has the same number of dots.

2. For the metals, the *total number of dots* represents the number of electrons that each atom loses when forming a cation.

3. In a correctly drawn Lewis structure for a non-metal, the number of *unpaired* dots shown represents either the number of electrons that atom *must gain* when forming an anion, or the number the electrons the atom *must share* to complete its octet when forming covalent bonds.

Lewis Structures for Monatomic Ions

From points 2 and 3 above, we can see that writing Lewis structures for monatomic ions is straightforward.

For the metals in groups 1, 2, and 13, the Lewis structure for their *stable ions* does not include any dots. The element symbol is usually enclosed in square brackets with the cation's charge written outside the brackets on the upper right. The magnitude of that positive charge simply equals the number of dots (which represent electrons) that were removed from the neutral atom's Lewis structure. Remember that because the number of protons in the nucleus has not changed, a loss of any number of electrons will result in that amount of positive charge on the cation.

For the non-metals in groups 15, 16, and 17, the Lewis structures for their anions all include four pairs of dots surrounding the element symbol enclosed in square brackets with the appropriate negative charge written outside the brackets on the upper right. The magnitude of the negative charge written outside the brackets equals the number of *unpaired* dots that were originally present in the parent atom's Lewis structure. This also equals how many electrons were required to generate the four pairs resulting in a stable octet.

The Lewis structures are shown for the sodium and chloride ions in Figure 8.2.2. Note that the chlorine atom originally had one unpaired dot. This required one electron for four pairs resulting in the charge of 1– on the anion. The sodium has had its one dot removed to form a 1+ cation.

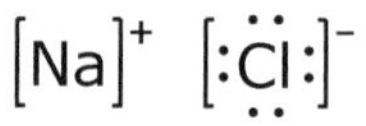

$$[\text{Na}]^+ \quad [:\ddot{\text{Cl}}:]^-$$

Figure 8.2.2 *Lewis structures for sodium ions and chloride ions*

© Edvantage Interactive 2016

Quick Check

1. What do the "dots" in a Lewis structure for an atom or an ion represent?

   _____

2. What do the total number of dots present in the Lewis structures for the metals in groups 1, 2, and 13 tell us about the cations these atoms will form during a chemical change?

   _____

3. The Lewis structures for nitrogen, phosphorus, and antimony include one pair of dots and three unpaired dots. How many electrons do these atoms require to form a stable octet?

   _____

Sample Problem — Drawing Lewis Structures

Draw the Lewis structures for the representative elements belonging to period 4 of the periodic table.

What to Think about	How to Do It
1. Elements in the same chemical family have the same number of valence electrons.	
2. Those electrons are represented by placing dots around each element symbol.	
3. Consider Figure 6.4.1. Begin at group 1 and give potassium 1 valence electron. Continue to the right placing the same number of dots around each symbol in the same way that the dots appear for the other members of each group.	**Group Number**

$$\begin{array}{ccccccccc} 1 & 2 & & 13 & 14 & 15 & 16 & 17 & 18 \\ K\cdot & Ca\cdot & & Ga\cdot & \cdot Ge\cdot & \cdot \ddot{A}s\colon & \cdot \ddot{S}e\colon & \colon \ddot{B}r\colon & \colon \ddot{K}r\colon \end{array}$$

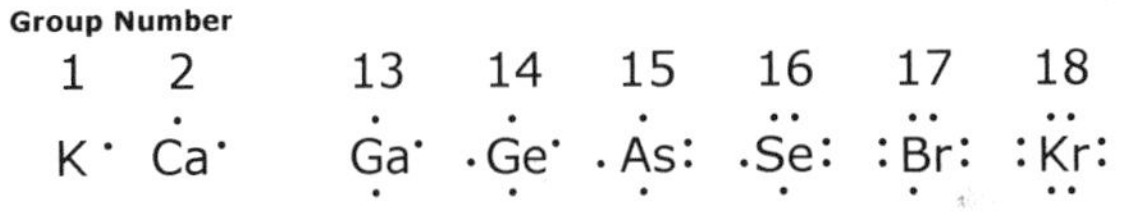

Practice Problems — Building Lewis Structures

1. Write the Lewis structures for the main group elements in period 5 of the periodic table.

2. Write the Lewis structures for the following atoms and ions.

   (a) Ba   (b) Al^{3+} (c) Bi   (d) I^- (e) Te

3. Convert the following atomic symbols to the Lewis structures for the ions of those elements:

   (a) Ca   (b) Se   (c) Ga   (d) As

Lewis Structures for Molecules

$$:\!\ddot{C}l\!-\!\ddot{C}l\!:$$

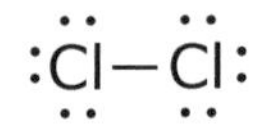

Figure 8.2.3 *Lewis structure of Cl_2*

Each of the pages in this book is a flat surface and any diagrams or images that you see on these pages can only be two-dimensional representations of the real three-dimensional world. Of course, the ionic and molecular compounds that make up that world are also three-dimensional. Understanding their shapes is a very important part of explaining and predicting their behaviour.

Recall that ionic compounds normally exist as ordered, three-dimensional arrays of cations and anions called crystal lattices. The arrangement of ions in these crystals maximizes the attractions between the oppositely charged ions within the lattices and minimizes the repulsions between ions with the same charges.

When molecules form, their three-dimensional shapes are also governed by the attractive and repulsive forces that exist within them. The first step toward visualizing the three-dimensional shape of a molecule is to convert its molecular formula into a two-dimensional Lewis structure.

One of the simplest examples of a Lewis structure is a diatomic halogen molecule such as Cl_2 (Figure 8.2.3). The single line between the atoms represents one pair of shared electrons. The other pairs of electrons are referred to as non-bonding or **lone pairs** of electrons. Note that all 14 of the valence electrons possessed by the 2 chlorine atoms are accounted for in the Lewis structure. Note also that each chlorine atom now has the benefit of an extra valence electron and thus has a stable octet.

As with any new procedure, learning to draw Lewis diagrams for molecules is easier if you follow a series of steps. Let's begin with a simple example: the Lewis structure for a molecule of nitrogen trichloride, NCl_3.

Step 1: Determine the total number of valence electrons in the molecule.
A correctly drawn Lewis structure must account for all of the valence electrons present. In this case, nitrogen has five valence electrons and each chlorine atom has seven. Therefore the total number of valence electrons is given by: $5 + (3 \times 7) = 26$.

Note that this is an even number, which will be true for all of the examples you will see. There are a few cases where odd numbers of electrons exist, but the vast majority of molecules (and polyatomic ions) possess even numbers of valence electrons. All bonding electrons exist in pairs.

Step 2: Construct the "skeleton" of the molecule using lines to indicate single covalent bonds between the atoms.

To generate the most likely skeleton of the molecule, the following set of guidelines will be of great help. The guidelines are based on numerous empirical observations and hold true for the vast majority of molecules. They also correspond to what we would expect given the electron configurations and electronegativities of the atoms involved. They may seem difficult to remember at first, but you won't need to use all of them for every molecule you draw. As with any new skill, the steps will become more familiar with practice.

Guidelines for Generating Molecule "Skeletons"

1. If the general formula for the compound is of the form "AX_n," then the central atom "A" will be the one with the lower group number, which also usually corresponds to the lower electronegativity. Obviously, if only two atoms exist in the molecule, then no central atom exists.
2. Hydrogen atoms form only one bond and so do not achieve an octet of electrons.
3. Fluorine atoms always form only one bond, and the other halogen atoms *usually* form only one bond. Exceptions to this occur if those halogens are central atoms and are bonded to other smaller halogens or to oxygen.
4. (a) Oxygen atoms normally form two bonds and don't often bond to each other in compounds with other elements. (An exception to this is hydrogen peroxide.)
    (b) Nitrogen atoms normally form three bonds.
    (c) Carbon atoms normally form four bonds.
5. Avoid creating rings or cyclic structures when you draw skeletons.

© Edvantage Interactive 2016

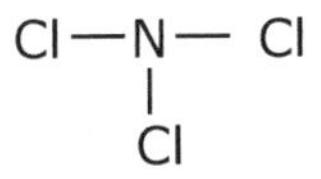

Figure 8.2.4 *Molecular skeleton for NCl_3*

Using the above rules, we see that a central atom exists and that nitrogen is most likely that central atom. We can therefore sketch the molecular skeleton for NCl_3 shown in Figure 8.2.4. The relative orientation of each chlorine atom around the nitrogen atom isn't that important because Lewis structures do not depict shape or 3-D geometry. All the matters at this stage is that nitrogen is in the centre and each chlorine atom is a peripheral or surrounding atom.

Step 3: Subtract the number of valence electrons used to construct the skeleton from the total number of valence electrons available from step 1 to determine the number of valence electrons remaining.

Consider that each line drawn in the skeleton represents a pair of bonding valence electrons, so, in this case, the number of valence electrons remaining is:
$26 - (3 \times 2) = 20$.

Step 4: Assume that all of the atoms in the molecule obey the octet rule (except hydrogen). Determine the number of additional valence electrons required (beyond those already present as a result of the bonds drawn) to give all of those atoms the required eight valence electrons.

In this case, because each peripheral chlorine atom has one bond and is therefore associated with two valence electrons, each chlorine atom needs six more electrons to complete its octet. The central nitrogen has three bonds and so has the benefit of six valence electrons. This means that the nitrogen atom needs only two more valence electrons to complete its octet. The calculation to determine the total number of required valence electrons is: $(3 \times 6) + 2 = 20$

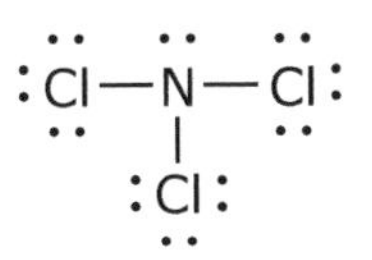

Figure 8.2.5 *Lewis structure for NCl_3*

Step 5: Compare the number of valence electrons available (from step 3) to the number of valence electrons needed to complete the octets of the atoms (from step 4). If those two numbers match, pair up the electrons. Beginning with the peripheral atoms and ending with the central atom, place those electron pairs where they're needed to satisfy the octets. In this case, the two numbers do indeed match and so the resulting Lewis structure is shown in Figure 8.2.5. If the numbers don't match, there is a procedure we'll discuss later.

At this point, consider the following:

Criteria Governing the Octet Rule in a Lewis Structure

(a) A peripheral or surrounding atom must not violate the octet rule in a Lewis structure. If an atom does violate the octet rule, then it must be a central atom in the molecule. This doesn't apply to hydrogen, which is associated with only two electrons in molecules.

(b) *Exception (i)* Atoms belonging to the second period in the periodic table will not have expanded octets in Lewis structures. An expanded octet (more than eight valence electrons) is only possible for elements belonging to the 3rd period or higher because only those atoms have access to d orbital electrons. These electrons are unavailable below the third energy level.

Exception (ii) The atoms Be, B, and Al will often have incomplete octets such that only two or three pairs of valence electrons will be associated with these central atoms in Lewis structures for molecules.

Step 6: If the numbers in step 5 above agree, then as a final step, check that the total number of valence electrons represented in the diagram matches the total number of valence electrons you began with in step 1.

In this example, the number of valence electrons in the diagram matches the number in the molecule.

Quick Check

1. Suggest a reason why the elements Be, B, and Al are not able to achieve a valence octet when they form covalent compounds.

   _____

2. Hydrogen sulfide, H_2S, is a poisonous, foul-smelling, and flammable gas. Why is the molecular skeleton "S – H – H" incorrect for this molecule?

   _____

3. Determine the total number of valence electrons present in each of the following molecules:

   (a) H_2Se _____   (b) CCl_4 _____   (c) NF_3 _____   (d) PCl_5 _____   (e) SF_6 _____

Sample Problem — Drawing a Lewis Structure for a Molecule

Draw the Lewis structure for a molecule of water, H_2O.

What to Think about

1. Each hydrogen atom will form one bond and the oxygen will form two. The oxygen must therefore be the central atom even though it has a higher electronegativity than hydrogen. Oxygen has six valence electrons and hydrogen has one.

2. Use the steps listed above:

   Step 1: Determine the total number of valence electrons in the molecule.

   Step 2: Construct the "skeleton" of the molecule.

   Step 3: Determine the number of valence electrons remaining.

   Step 4: Assume that all of the atoms in the molecule obey the octet rule (except hydrogen).

   Step 5: Compare the number of valence electrons available to the number of valence electrons needed to complete the octets of the atoms. Pair up remaining electrons and place them where needed to satisfy oxygen's octet.

   Step 6: Available electrons match electrons in the diagram. Note that in the final structure, oxygen is associated with two bonding pairs and two non-bonding (or lone pairs).

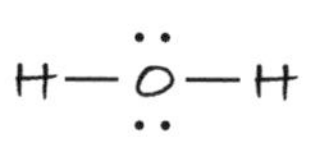

How to Do It

$6 + (2 \times 1) = 8$ valence electrons present in molecule

H – O – H

Electrons available: 8
Electrons used in skeleton: 4
Electrons remaining: $8 - 4 = 4$

Electrons required to complete oxygen's octet: 4

H—Ö—H

© Edvantage Interactive 2016

Practice Problems – Drawing Lewis Structures for Molecules

1. Construct the Lewis structure for a molecule of carbon tetrachloride, CCl_4.

2. (a) Draw the Lewis structure for a molecule of ammonia, NH_3.

    (b) When you're finished drawing the structure, determine how many bonding pairs and how many lone pairs of electrons are associated with the central atom.

3. (a) Draw the Lewis structure for a molecule of boron trichloride, BCl_3.

    (b) Consider the central atom in your structure. Does it possess a stable octet of eight electrons?

Drawing Lewis Structures for Molecules Containing Multiple Bonds

We have seen that one pair of valence electrons shared between two adjacent nuclei constitutes a single covalent bond. There are also many cases where the covalent bonds between two atoms involve more than one pair of shared electrons. These are known as **multiple bonds**. If two pairs of electrons are shared between the same two atoms, the bond is called a double bond and if three pairs exist, the bond is a triple bond.

As you might expect, as multiple bonds involve more attractive forces between two atoms than single bonds do, multiple bonds are stronger. Bond strengths are usually measured by the amount of energy required to break a mole of those bonds and are thus represented by the unit kJ/mol. The greater attraction between the atoms in a multiple bond also draws those bonded atoms closer together, which means that multiple bonds are also shorter than single bonds. Table 8.2.2 compares some single and multiple bond strengths and lengths.

Table 8.2.2 *Single and Multiple Bond Strengths and Lengths*

Bond	Bond Energy (kJ/mol)	Bond Length (pm)
C – C	347	154
C = C	614	134
C ≡ C	839	120
N – N	160	145
N = N	418	125
N ≡ N	941	110
C – O	358	143
C = O	799	123
C ≡ O	1072	113

Let's follow the steps outlined above to draw the Lewis structure for a molecule that contains double bonds, such as carbon dioxide, CO_2.

Step 1: The total number of valence electrons is given by: $4 + (2 \times 6) = 16$

Step 2: Carbon has the lower group number and electronegativity, and oxygen doesn't usually bond to itself in compounds with other elements. Therefore the following skeleton is likely:

O – C – O

Step 3: As four electrons were used to construct the above skeleton, 12 of the original 16 electrons remain to complete each atom's octet.

Step 4: Each of the oxygens in the skeleton requires six electrons and the carbon atom requires four electrons to complete their valence shells. This gives a total of:
$(2 \times 6) + 4 = 16$ electrons.

Step 5: Notice that 16 electrons are required but only 12 electrons are available to complete the octets of the atoms. We are therefore lacking four electrons. This means that we must return to step 2 and re-draw the molecular skeleton such that we incorporate one *multiple bond* for each pair of electrons that we lack to complete the octets._

Because we are four electrons short, we can consider either of the following modified skeletons:

skeleton 1:   **O = C = O**   or   skeleton 2:   **O ≡ C – O**

Although both skeletons above show carbon forming a total of 4 bonds, as oxygen normally forms two bonds, we would choose skeleton 1, showing each oxygen atom participating in a double bond as being the most likely skeleton. Note also the symmetry associated with this choice as opposed to skeleton 2. Molecules will often possess a high degree of symmetry and that also makes this choice more likely: **O = C = O**

Now we again return to following the steps:

Step 3: Each line in the skeleton represents a pair of shared electrons, so each double bond indicates two electron pairs or four electrons. Therefore eight electrons have been used in constructing the skeleton, so the number of electrons remaining is given by: $16 - (2 \times 4) = 8$

Step 4: The two oxygen atoms each need four more electrons to complete their octets, but the carbon atom now has the benefit of eight valence electrons and so requires no more. This means that only eight electrons are needed to complete the octets of the atoms in the skeleton.

Step 5: As the number of electrons we need now matches the number available, we pair up those electrons to give the Lewis structure for carbon dioxide. Figure 8.2.6 shows two possible ways of representing that structure.

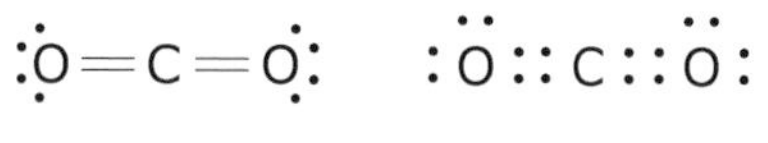

$$:\!\overset{..}{O}\!=\!C\!=\!\overset{..}{O}\!: \qquad :\overset{..}{O}::C::\overset{..}{O}:$$

Figure 8.2.6 *Lewis structures for CO₂*

As a final step we see that all 16 valence electrons have been accounted for in the Lewis structure. The construction of this molecule can be understood by considering how the valence electrons present in each individual atom are reorganized as the two double bonds form:

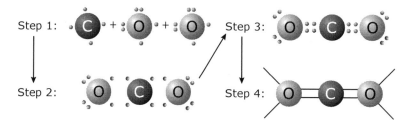

Figure 8.2.7 *Constructing the molecule from the Lewis structures*

Drawing Lewis Structures Containing Atoms With Expanded Octets

Sometimes we discover that fewer electrons are available than needed to complete the octets of the atoms in a molecule. At other times, we might encounter situations where more electrons are available than needed. This normally results in **expanded octets** associated with the central atom in a Lewis structure. Remember that an expanded octet is only possible for an atom if d orbital electrons are available. That is only possible for elements belonging to period 4 or higher in the periodic table.

Let's investigate this by drawing the Lewis structure for one of the few compounds involving noble gases, namely XeF_4. To do this, we follow the steps below:

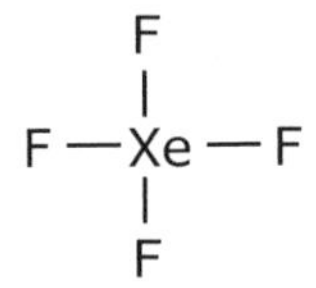

Step 1: Total number of valence electrons = 8 + (4 × 7) = 36

Step 2: Molecular skeleton: See Figure 6.5.8.

Step 3: Electrons used in skeleton: 4 × 2 = 8
Electrons remaining: 36 – 8 = 28

Step 4: Electrons required to complete octets: 4 × 6 = 24
Note that xenon needs no electrons but each fluorine atom needs six electrons to complete its octet.

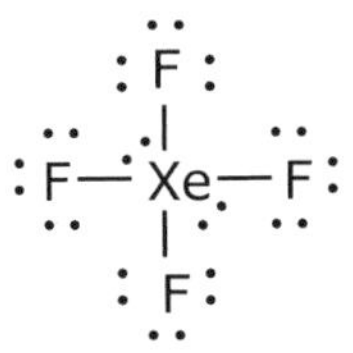

Step 5: We have 28 electrons available but only need 24. At this point, we first place the 24 electrons where they're needed in pairs around each peripheral fluorine atom. We then place the remaining two pairs of electrons around the central xenon. The orientation of the lone pairs on the central atom is not important. Simply placing two pairs at any two locations available on xenon is all that matters. Note that xenon has an "expanded octet" of 12 valence electrons.

Step 6: All 36 valence electrons are accounted for in the Lewis structure (Figure 8.7.9).

Figure 8.2.8 *Molecular skeleton for XeF4*

Figure 8.2.9 *Lewis structure for XeF$_4$*

Sample Problem — Drawing a Lewis Structure Containing a Multiple Bond

Draw the Lewis structure for a molecule of hydrogen cyanide, HCN.

What to Think about	How to Do It
1. Calculate the total valence electrons present in the molecule.	Total of 10 valence electrons available
2. Determine the most likely molecular skeleton.	H – C – N
3. Determine electrons used in skeleton and those remaining.	4 electrons used to construct the skeleton, 6 electrons remaining.
4. Determine electrons needed to complete octets.	The carbon needs 4 more electrons and the nitrogen needs 6 to complete their respective octets.
5. Compare the number of valence electrons available to the number of valence electrons needed to complete the octets of the atoms.	Only 6 electrons are left: 4 electrons short
6. The original skeleton must be changed to incorporate multiple bonds.	
7. Hydrogen only forms one bond and so cannot be the central atom. The two extra bonds must be added between the nitrogen and carbon atoms in the form of a triple bond.	
Of the remaining two atoms, carbon has the lower group number and electronegativity. Carbon is therefore the most likely central atom.	H – C ≡ N
Carbon normally forms four bonds and nitrogen forms three.	
8. We see that 8 valence electrons (4 × 2) have been used in this new skeleton, leaving only 2 of the original 10. Pair up those final 2 electrons and place them on nitrogen.	
As carbon's octet is now satisfied and nitrogen only needs 2 more electrons, the number of available electrons matches the number required.	H — C ≡ N :
9. A final check shows us that all 10 valence electrons are accounted for.	

Practice Problems – Lewis Structures Containing Multiple Bonds and Expanded Octets

1. Formaldehyde is used as a disinfectant, an embalming agent, and as a component in many organic synthesis reactions. Draw the Lewis structure for a molecule of formaldehyde, CH_2O. (Hint: Carbon is the central atom.)

2. Carbon monoxide is an invisible, odorless, and toxic gas that renders hemoglobin unable to transport oxygen to body tissues. Draw the Lewis structure for a molecule of CO.

3. Bromine trifluoride is a very reactive and toxic liquid that explodes on contact with water and organic compounds. Draw the Lewis structure for a molecule of BrF_3.

© Edvantage Interactive 2016

Drawing Lewis Structures for Polyatomic Ions

$$\left[\begin{array}{c} H \\ | \\ H - N - H \\ | \\ H \end{array} \right]^{+}$$

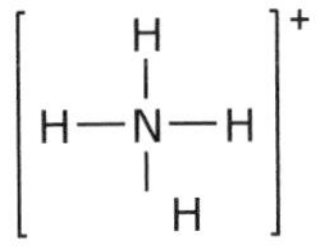

Figure 8.2.10 *Lewis structure for the ammonium cation, NH_4^+*

Many polyatomic ions contain non-metal atoms bonded covalently to each other. To draw a Lewis diagram for a polyatomic ion, we follow the same steps discussed above but must be careful to count the correct number of valence electrons present when we begin. Remember that the magnitude of the charge on a cation equals the number of valence electrons *removed* from the original neutral species. The amount of negative charge on an anion represents the number of electrons *added*.

Consider the ammonium cation, NH_4^+. The positive charge tells us that one valence electron has been removed from the total number of valence electrons possessed by the five neutral atoms. To begin this Lewis structure, we therefore count a total of $5 + (4 \times 1) - 1 = 8$ valence electrons. Following the above steps, we eventually arrive at the Lewis structure in in Figure 8.2.10. We normally enclose Lewis structures for both monatomic and polyatomic ions in square brackets, as shown.

The Curious Case of Resonance

$$\left[\begin{array}{c} \overset{..}{\underset{}{O}} \\ || \\ :\overset{..}{O} - C - \overset{..}{O}: \\ .. \qquad .. \end{array} \right]^{2-}$$

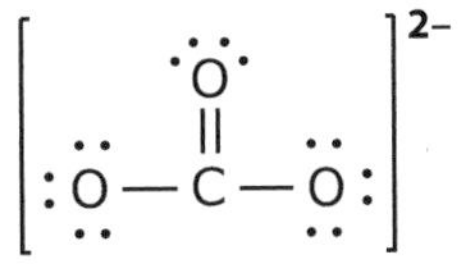

Figure 8.2.11 *Lewis structure for the carbonate anion, CO_3^{2-}*

When a molecule or ion contains double bonds next to single bonds, there are often several different and equally correct Lewis structures that we can draw. Consider the case of the carbonate anion, CO_3^{2-}. This ion has a total of: $4 + (3 \times 6) + 2 = 24$ valence electrons. (Note the extra two electrons due to the charge.)

Following the steps learned earlier, we realize that we are short two electrons when completing the octets of all the atoms. We therefore incorporate one double bond into the skeleton. The final Lewis structure therefore becomes the one shown in Figure 8.2.11.

If this represented the actual structure, we would expect that the two single carbon – oxygen bonds would prove to be longer and weaker than the double bond. Experimental data indicates, however, that all three bonds are equal in strength and length. They appear to be stronger than a single C – O bond, but weaker than a double bond. They are also slightly shorter than a single bond, but slightly longer than a double bond. It is as if the two electrons in the multiple bond have been shared equally or "averaged" between the central carbon and each of the three oxygen atoms.

Chemists call these electrons "delocalized" because they're not associated with any one pair of bonded atoms, but are rather "spread out" equally between all three pairs. Lewis structures cannot properly show delocalized electrons. They represent this phenomenon by depicting the double bond in each of the possible locations in a series of diagrams and connecting each diagram with a set of double arrows. The diagrams are called **resonance structures**. It must be emphasized, however, that the pair of electrons *does not* move around between pairs of atoms as the diagrams might suggest. The three diagrams in Figure 8.2.12 are simply the only way to depict delocalized bonding electrons using Lewis structures. The phenomenon of resonance is evident in an important organic compound called benzene.

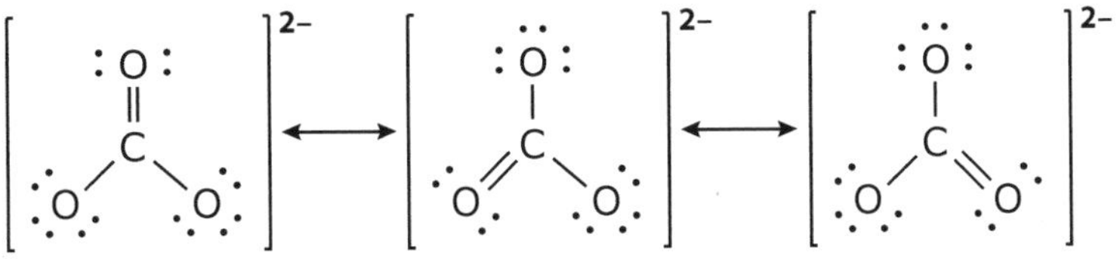

Figure 8.2.12 *Resonance structures for a carbonate ion*

Lewis Structures for Molecules with More than One Central Atom

Molecules and ions can be much more complicated than we have discussed above. Lewis structures are not often used to depict such species, but we can still employ the process when several central atoms exist in relatively simple molecules and ions. In these examples, you will be given the basic skeleton and can then proceed with the remaining steps to generate the correct Lewis structure.

Consider a simple organic acid called formic acid whose formula is CH_2O_2 (or HCOOH). Recall that carbon, oxygen, and hydrogen normally form four bonds, two bonds, and one bond respectively. In Figure 8.2.13, note that both a carbon atom and an oxygen atom are between other atoms in different locations in the structure.

You should now be able to complete the diagram following the remaining steps. The final Lewis structure you arrive at should be the one shown in Figure 8.2.14. You will encounter many such molecules when discussing organic chemistry.

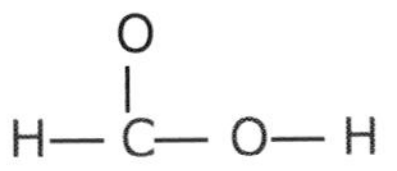

$$\begin{array}{c} O \\ | \\ H - C - O - H \end{array}$$

Figure 8.2.13 *Skeleton for formic acid, CH_2O_2 (or HCOOH)*

$$\begin{array}{c} :\overset{..}{O}: \\ || \\ H - C - \overset{..}{\underset{..}{O}} - H \end{array}$$

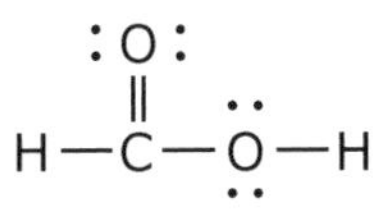

Figure 8.2.14 *Lewis structure for formic acid, CH_2O_2 (or HCOOH)*

8.2 Activity: Making the Leap to Three Dimensions

Question
How can we use Lewis structures to predict the three-dimensional shapes of molecules or polyatomic ions?

Materials
modelling clay
Popsicle® sticks or wooden splints

Procedure
1. Consider the Lewis structures discussed in this section: NCl_3, H_2O, CO_2, NH_4^+, XeF_4, and CO_3^{2-}. Review each as you fill in the following table. The first one is done for you.

1. Chemical Formula	2. Number of Atoms Bonded to Central Atom	3. Number of Lone Pairs on Central Atom	4. Sum of Columns 2 and 3
NCl_3	3	1	3 + 1 = 4
H_2O			
CO_2			
NH_4^+			
XeF_4			
CO_3^{2-}			

2. Obtain some modeling clay and wooden splints or Popsicle® sticks. Using the clay, make a small sphere about the size of a lemon. This will represent the central atom in each of the above species.

    In any chemical species, each pair of bonding or lone pair of electrons represents regions of negative charge. It follows, then, that when these are attached to a central atom in a molecule or polyatomic ion, they will attempt to minimize the repulsive forces between them. They accomplish this by assuming positions in three-dimensional space around the central atom such that they are as far away from each other as possible, while still remaining bonded to that central atom.

3. To represent this, consider each molecule and ion listed above. Look at the total number in column 4 for each species and select that number of sticks. Now insert them into the clay such that they are all as far away from each other as possible in three-dimensional space.

Continued

© Edvantage Interactive 2016

4. Sketch the shapes that you construct for each species in the appropriate space in the table below.

Chemical Formula	Sketch of 3-D Shape
NCl_3	
H_2O	
CO_2	
NH_4^+	
XeF_4	
CO_3^{2-}	

5. Are all of the shapes different? If not, which ones look similar? How do the numbers in column 4 compare for those shapes that might look similar?

8.2 Review Questions

1. Consider the following list of elements. Place each in the appropriate column in the table below depending on whether it obeys the octet rule, likely has an incomplete octet, or could potentially have an expanded octet in a Lewis structure.

   H, Be, B, C, N, O, F, Al, Si, P, S, Cl

Incomplete Valence Octet	Valence Octet	Expanded Valence Octet

2. Helium and neon are in the same chemical family but yet have different numbers of dots in their Lewis structures. What is the reason for this? Explain why neither element ever forms chemical compounds.

4. The molecule tetrafluoroethene is a building block of the synthetic material known as Teflon®. Tetrafluoroethene has the formula C_2F_4. Consider the following molecular skeletons for this molecule. Complete the Lewis structure for the most likely skeleton.

5. Draw Lewis structures for each of the following molecules in the space provided.

   OF_2

   H_2S

3. Consider the following pairs of elements in the table below. If each pair was part of a molecule or polyatomic ion, which of the two would most likely be the central atom and which would be the peripheral or surrounding atom? Place each element of each pair in the appropriate column in the table.

Element Pair	Probable Central Atom	Probable Peripheral Atom
(a) phosphorus and chlorine		
(b) nitrogen and oxygen		
(c) carbon and sulfur		
(d) nitrogen and hydrogen		
(e) oxygen and fluorine		

© Edvantage Interactive 2016

PCl$_3$

CCl$_2$F$_2$

6. Draw Lewis structures for each of the polyatomic ions in the space provided.

OH$^-$

AlH$_4^-$

CN$^-$

7. Draw Lewis structures for each of the following. Each central atom in the molecules or ions has an expanded octet.

SF$_6$

PCl$_5$

ICl$_4^-$

SeBr$_4$

8. Draw Lewis structures for each of the following containing multiple bonds.

CS$_2$

SCO (C is central)

O$_3$ (Draw two resonance structures)

NO$_3^-$ (Draw three resonance structures)

9. Convert the following molecular skeletons into complete Lewis structures.

H—C—C—H

H—O—O—H

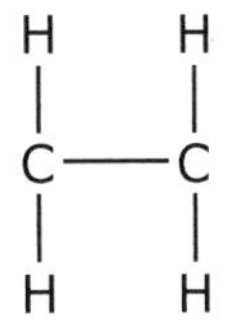

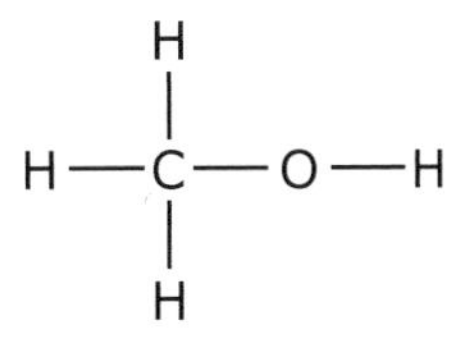

```
 H      H
 |      |
 C  —  C
 |      |
 H      H
```

```
        H
        |
 H  —  C  —  O  —  H
        |
        H
```

8.3 The Shape and Behaviour of Molecules

Warm Up

1. What does an element's electronegativity tell us?

   _____

2. Use your answer to question 1 to define the term "polar covalent bond."

   _____

3. If a substance contains polar *molecules*, how might that affect its melting and boiling points?

   _____

Converting Lewis Structures into Three Dimensions — VSEPR Theory

Drawing Lewis structures serves an important purpose beyond indicating connectivity of atoms in molecules and polyatomic ions. The two-dimensional collections of symbols, lines, and dots often allow us to deduce the three-dimensional shapes of the chemical species they represent. Determining the shapes of those chemical species is an essential part of understanding and predicting their physical and chemical behaviour.

The process of inferring a three-dimensional shape from a Lewis structure is based on a very simple premise: Valence electrons represent regions of negative charge that repel each other.

> Any group of valence electrons associated with a central atom will tend to orient themselves in three-dimensional space around that atom so as to minimize the repulsion between them. Examples of such groups of valence electrons include a lone pair, bonding pair, or multiple pairs involved in a double or triple bond.

In short, while remaining attached to the central atom, these groups of electrons will position themselves as far away from each other as possible. This is the fundamental principle behind the **valence shell electron pair repulsion (VSEPR) theory,** which chemists use whenever they convert Lewis structures into molecular shapes.

Let's imagine a central atom in three-dimensional space and apply the above principle to distribute two, three, four, five, and six electron groups around that centre. When we do, we discover that a different spatial arrangement results for each number of electron groups. Each arrangement minimizes the repulsive forces between the groups by occupying the maximum amount of space around the central atom.

We can show these five arrangements using balloons attached together to represent the electron groups. Just as the balloons will fill up all the available space around their centre of attachment, so too will electron groups fill up the available space around a central atom (Figure 283.1).

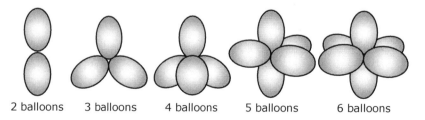

2 balloons   3 balloons   4 balloons   5 balloons   6 balloons

Figure 8.3.1 *Balloons in different arrangements around a central attachment*

If the electron groups are *bonding electrons*, then the peripheral atoms they bind to the central atom adopt that same arrangement and produce a *molecular shape*.

Several experimental tools exist that allow us to determine molecular geometry. X-ray crystallography as well as neutron and electron diffraction are employed for compounds in the solid phase. For molecules in the gaseous phase, gas electron diffraction is used.

Electron groups and their repulsive effects ultimately determine where and how the nuclei of the atoms in a molecule or polyatomic ion arrange themselves in three-dimensional space. And it's the resulting *shapes of those species* that we really care about.

We will consider each of the five electron group arrangements separately. Let's begin by assuming that each electron group is a bonding group connecting the central atom (with single or multiple bonds) to the peripheral atoms. We'll then expand our discussion to include lone-pair electron groups on the central atom. As a general notation, the central atom is "**A**," a peripheral or surrounding atom is "**X**," and a lone-pair of electrons on the central atom is "**E**."

Two-Bonding Electron Groups: AX₂

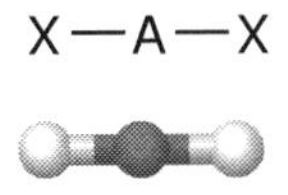

X — A — X

Figure 8.3.2 *The shape of two-bonding electron groups is linear.*

When two groups of bonding electrons connect the central atom to two peripheral atoms, the notation "**AX₂**" applies. The surrounding atoms are as far as possible from each other on opposite sides of the central atom. The shape is *linear* with the X–A–X bond angle being 180° (Figure 8.3.2).

The shape is the same whether the two-bonding groups are the shared electrons in two single bonds, two double bonds, or a single and a triple bond. For example, consider the following three molecules. Note that all are AX₂ molecules with the same linear shape and that any lone-pairs attached to the surrounding atoms do not affect their orientation around the central atom.

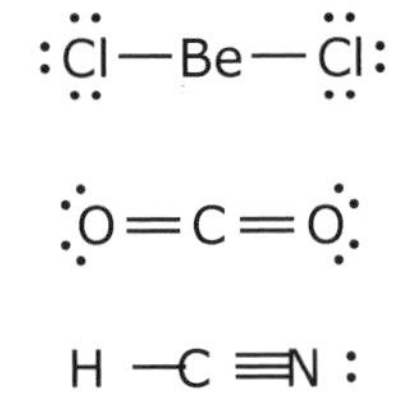

$$\overset{..}{\underset{..}{:Cl}} - Be - \overset{..}{\underset{..}{Cl:}}$$

$$\overset{..}{\underset{..}{:O}} = C = \overset{..}{\underset{..}{O:}}$$

$$H - C \equiv N:$$

Figure 8.3.3 *AX₂ molecules have the same linear shape whether the shared electrons form two single bonds, two double bonds, or a single and a triple bond.*

Three-Electron Groups: AX₃ and AX₂E

When three groups of electrons orient around a central atom, two shapes are possible. If all the electron groups are bonding, then an **AX₃** arrangement gives rise to a *trigonal planar* (or flat triangle) molecule with X–A–X bond angles of 120°. The bonding electron group interactions are called "*bond-pair – bond-pair*" (BP-BP) interactions.

If one of the three electron groups is a lone-pair rather than a bonding pair, we use the notation **AX₂E**. The molecule that we see is *bent* or *angular* with the lone-pair occupying one of the three corners of the triangle. As lone-pair electrons are attracted to only one atomic nucleus, they are held less tightly than bonding electron groups. Their electron clouds therefore occupy more space and exert more repulsive force on bonding electron groups than those groups exert on each other. These more intense "*lone-pair – bond-pair*" (LP-BP) interactions force the bonded atoms closer together in an AX₂E molecule and so reduce the X–A–X bond angle to less than 120°.

Similar to lone-pairs, we would also expect that larger peripheral atoms would exert *more repulsive forces* than smaller ones, and thus affect bond angles in a molecule. In Table 8.3.1, a solid triangle represents an atom or lone electron pair projecting out of the page, while a dashed line means the atom or lone-pair goes into the page.

Table 8.3.1 *Shapes of Three-Electron Groups: AX₃ and AX₂E*

AXₘEₙ Notation	Molecular Shape	Sample Lewis Structure
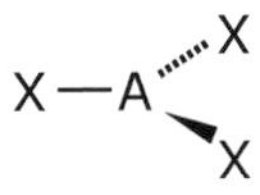 AX₃	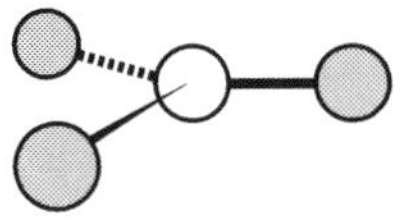 trigonal planar	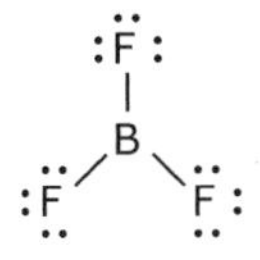 boron trifluoride
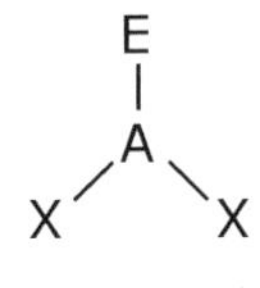 AX₂E	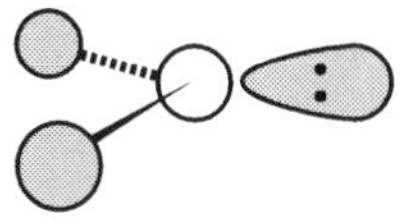 bent or angular	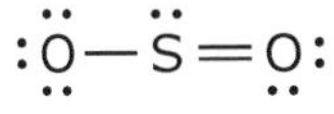 sulfur dioxide (1 of 2 resonance structures)

Four electron groups will occupy the four corners of a regular tetrahedron and may result in three different molecular shapes. If all the electron groups are bonding, then the molecule is labeled as **AX_4** and adopts a tetrahedral (four-sided or four-faced) shape with each of the X–A–X bond angles at 109.5°. An example of this is methane gas, CH_4.

If one of the four electron groups is non-bonding, the molecule is considered **AX_3E** and the lone-pair occupies one of the four corners of the tetrahedron. The molecule we see is called a trigonal pyramid. Once again, the more intense LP-BP interactions will push the bonded atoms closer together than they would be in an AX_4 molecule. Evidence of this is seen in an AX_3E molecule such as ammonia in which the H–N–H bond angles are only 107° rather than 109.5°.

When two of the four groups of electrons are lone-pairs, the designation **AX_2E_2** applies. Two of the four corners will be occupied by the two bonded atoms and the remaining two corners by the lone-pairs. The molecule will be an angular shape similar to AX_2E, although the X–A–X bond angle will be smaller. In such an arrangement, not only will each of the two lone-pairs force the bonded atoms closer together via LP-BP interactions, but they will also exert a repulsive force on each other called a *lone-pair – lone-pair* (LP-LP) interaction. This is the most intense of the electron group repulsive interactions. The combined result of the additional repulsive forces is an even smaller X–A–X bond angle. In water, for example, the H–O–H bond angle is found to be only 104.5°. Table 8.3.2 below shows the molecular shapes of four-electron groups.

Table 8.3.2 *Shapes of Four-Electron Groups: AX_4, AX_3E, and AX_2E_2*

AX_mE_n Notation	Molecular Shape	Sample Lewis Structure
AX_4	tetrahedral	methane
AX_3E	trigonal pyramidal	ammonia
AX_2E_2	bent or angular	water

If more than four electron groups surround a central atom, that atom will have an expanded octet so it must belong to period 3 or higher in the periodic table. Expanded octets are only possible if d orbitals are available and none exist below the third energy level.

When five electron groups are present, two distinct sets of positions are occupied by those groups. One set of three positions lies in a trigonal plane, and the electron groups are referred to as *equatorial groups*. A second set of two positions places each group of electrons above and below the trigonal plane. These are called *axial groups*. The equatorial electron groups are separated by 120° bond angles, and the axial and equatorial groups are separated by 90°. Once again, LP-BP and LP-LP interactions play a role in reducing X–A–X bond angles as the number of lone-pairs attached to the central atom increases. Table 8.3.3 shows the molecular shapes of five-electron group systems.

Table 8.3.3 *Shapes of Five-Electron Groups: AX₅, AX₄E, AX₃E₂ and AX₂E₃*

AX$_m$E$_n$ Notation	Molecular Shape	Sample Lewis Structure
AX₅	trigonal bipyramidal	phosphorus pentachloride
AX₄E	seesaw	sulfur tetrafluoride
AX₃E₂	T-Shaped	chlorine trifluoride
AX₂E₃	linear	xenon difluoride

The final major electron group arrangement has six electron groups around the central atom. Unlike the five-electron group system, all six vertices are equivalent and point towards the corners of an octahedron as shown in Table 8.3.4.

If all of the electron groups are bonding, then the molecule is labeled as **AX$_6$**. The shape adopted by the molecule is octahedral (eight-faced) and all of the X–A–X bond angles are 90°.

When one of the six-electron groups is a non-bonding pair, it doesn't matter which of the six locations that lone-pair occupies around the central atom because all locations are identical. The molecule is classified as **AX$_5$E** and the molecular shape is square pyramidal. The lone pair is directed downward at the bottom centre of the four-based pyramid as Table 8.3.4 shows.

If two of the six-electron groups are lone-pairs, there are two orientations available in an octahedral shape. They could lie adjacent to each other with a separation of 90°, or lie opposite each other separated by 180°. As the diagram shows below, the two lone-pairs will always be as far away from each other as possible and separated by 180°. This minimizes the significant LP-LP repulsive interaction between them.

Table 8.3.4 *Shapes of Six-Electron Groups: AX$_6$, AX$_5$E, and AX$_4$E$_2$*

AX$_m$E$_n$ Notation	Molecular Shape	Sample Lewis Structure
 AX$_6$	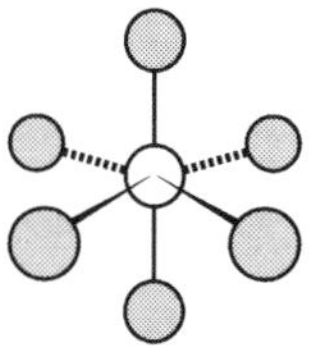 octahedral	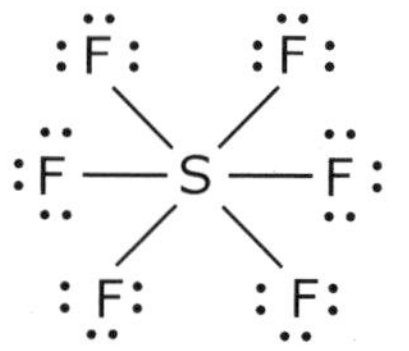 sulfur hexafluoride
 AX$_5$E	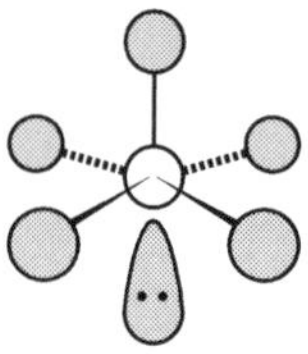 square pyramidal	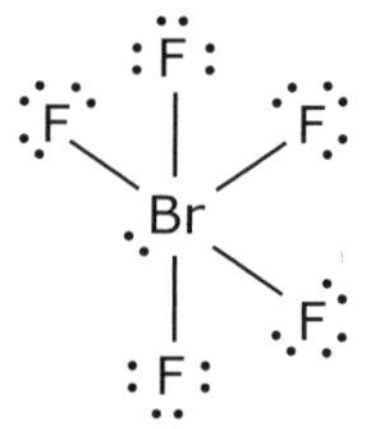 bromine pentafluoride
 AX$_4$E$_2$	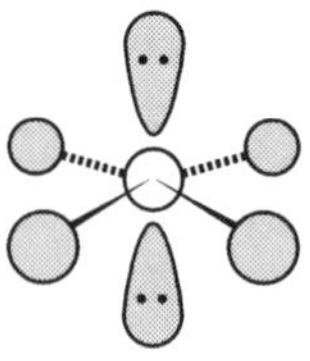 square planar	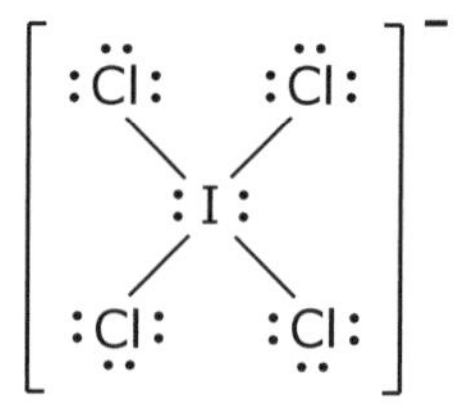 tetrachloroiodate ion

Quick Check

1. What is the fundamental principle associated with VSEPR Theory?

   _____

2. Consider the electron group interactions: LP-BP, BP-BP, and LP-LP. Arrange these in order from least intense to most intense.

   _____

3. Although methane, ammonia, and water each have four electron groups associated with the central atom, the bond angles between the atoms in each molecule are 109.5°, 107°, and 104.5° respectively. Explain why.

   _____

© Edvantage Interactive 2016

Molecular Formulas to Molecular Shapes

We are now in a position to combine the information from this and the previous section to predict molecular shapes starting with a molecular formula. The steps will guide you through this process:

Step 1: Beginning with the formula, determine the Lewis structure.

Step 2: Consider the central atom in the completed Lewis structure. Note the number of bonded atoms and lone pairs associated with that atom.

Step 3: Assign an AX_mE_n notation to the molecule or polyatomic ion. (Note any bond angles affected by the presence of one or more lone pairs.)

Step 4: Refer to the appropriate electron group arrangement category given in the tables above to determine the shape of the molecule.

(You're done!)

Sample Problem – Deducing a Molecular Shape

Determine the shape of the molecule tellurium tetrachloride, $TeCl_4$

What to Think about	How to Do It
1. Refer to the steps listed in section 6.4 to determine the Lewis structure for the molecule.	
2. Tellurium has the lower electronegativity and so is the central atom. All of the chlorine atoms will therefore obey the octet rule and form only one bond. Note that tellurium is a member of the 5th period in the periodic table and is therefore capable of having an expanded octet.	
3. There are five electron groups around the central atom. Four are bonding groups and one is a lone-pair of electrons. The molecule is therefore classified as AX_4E. An AX_4E molecule will have a "seesaw" shape.	

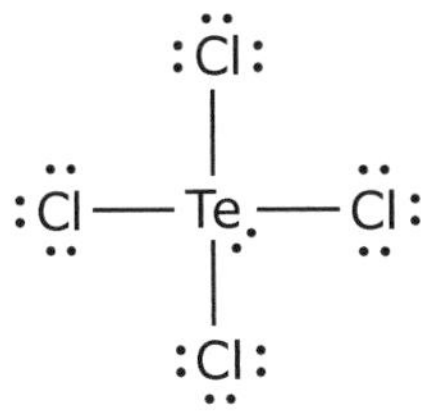

Practice Problems

1. Complete the following table for each of the chemical species.

Lewis Structure	AX$_m$E$_n$ Notation	Molecular Shape (Name and Diagram)
(a)		
(b)		

2. Complete the following table for each of the chemical species.

Chemical Formula	Lewis Structure	AX$_m$E$_n$ Notation	Molecular Shape (Name and Diagram)
(a) CCl_4			
(b) PF_3			
(c) SCl_2			

© Edvantage Interactive 2016

Below is a table of electronegativity values.

Increasing EN

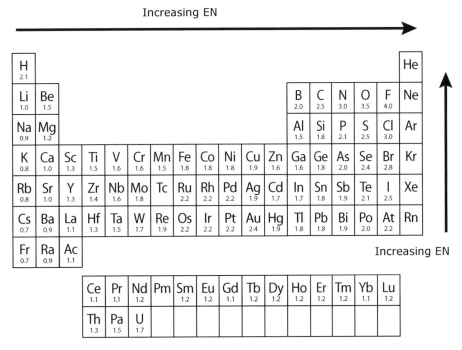

Figure 8.3.4 *Periodic table showing electronegativity values*

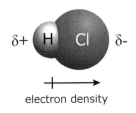

electron density

Figure 8.3.5 *HCl is a diatomic molecule containing a polar bond.*

As stated at the beginning of this section, an essential part of understanding and predicting the chemical and physical properties of substances is determining the shapes of their molecules. Among the most *significant consequences* of molecular shape is the *polarity of molecules.*

Molecular polarity not only affects physical properties such as melting point, boiling point, and solubility, but also influences a substance's chemical reactivity in both synthetic and biological processes.

Recall that a chemical bond is considered to be polar if electron-sharing in the bond is unequal enough due to the electronegativity differences of the atoms involved. If a diatomic molecule contains a polar bond, then the *molecule itself* must also be polar, as in a compound such as HCl (Figure 8.3.5).

However, if a molecule contains *more than two atoms*, the shape of the molecule as well as the polarity of its bonds will play a role in determining if the entire molecule will be polar. Stated another way, if the bonds within the molecule are polar, the molecule itself may or may not be, depending on its shape. Let's consider an example of each.

In carbon dioxide, each of the two C=O double bonds is quite polar because the two atoms have a $\Delta EN = 1.0$. However, because the molecule itself is AX_2 and therefore linear, each of those identical bond dipoles is pointing in a direction exactly opposite to the other because of the 180° O – C – O bond angle. This means that the molecular shape is such that the bond dipoles *effectively cancel each other out* resulting in a non-polar molecule. You can compare this to two evenly matched tug-of-war teams pulling in opposite directions on a rope — neither team wins because they are equally strong.

In water, just as in CO_2, a central atom is bonded between two identical peripheral atoms and each of those two bonds has a significant and identical dipole. However, because H_2O qualifies as an AX_2E_2 molecule, it is bent or V-shaped. This means that the molecular shape is such that the bond dipoles point in the same general direction and so reinforce each other. This results in a polar molecule.

Chemists can detect and measure a molecule's polarity in an electric field. They assign a magnitude to that polarity expressed as a "dipole moment." Water is very polar and has a significant dipole moment, but the dipole moment of non-polar carbon dioxide is zero. As Figure 8.3.6 shows, the water molecule has a net dipole, while the carbon dioxide molecule does not. The importance of the polarity of water molecules cannot be overstated as we will soon see.

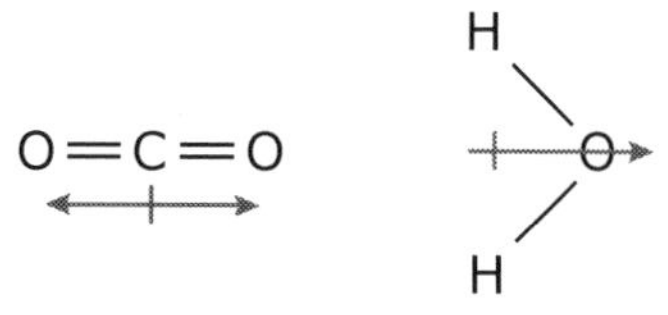

$$O=C=O$$

non-polar   polar

Figure 8.3.6 *The V-shape of a water molecule results in a significant dipole moment.*

In the above example, two *different molecular shapes* were the reason that bond dipoles in one molecule cancelled out, but didn't cancel in another molecule. There is also a possibility that two molecules having the *same shape* and containing polar bonds could be either polar or non-polar. We can use two AX_4 molecules to demonstrate this.

In Figure 8.3.7, carbon tetrachloride on the left is a symmetric molecule with four chlorines situated at the corners of a tetrahedron. Each C – Cl bond is polar in the direction of chlorine because carbon and chlorine have electronegativities of 2.5 and 3.0 respectively. The four bond dipoles, however, cancel out as they point in opposite directions in the symmetric molecule and so the molecule itself is non-polar. Carbon tetrachloride is a liquid used as a solvent for other non-polar substances. As you will soon see, one non-polar substance will usually mix well with another.

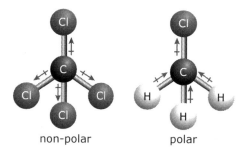

non-polar   polar

Figure 8.3.7 *Two molecules having the same shape can have different polarities. Carbon tetrachloride, on the left, is non-polar; chloromethane, on the right, is polar.*

The molecule on the right in Figure 8.3.7 is called chloromethane. All of its bond dipoles point in the same general direction. Each C – H bond is polar towards the carbon due to carbon's higher EN value (2.5 vs. 2.1), and the C – Cl bond polarity points in a similar direction towards chlorine. Now, as was the case with water above, the bond dipoles reinforce each other and so the entire molecule is polar.

In this example, molecular composition rather than molecular shape determined whether a molecule was polar or non-polar. In all cases, however, the key question is the same.

> Does the molecule contain polar bonds and, if so, do the bond dipoles cancel each other or not?

If bond dipoles exist but cancel each other, then the molecule is non-polar. If bond dipoles don't cancel or if they reinforce each other, then the molecule is polar. Answering this question often involves attempting to visualize and even manipulate a three-dimensional shape based on a diagram drawn on a flat page. Although that might seem difficult at first, it will become easier with practice. Remembering the simple guidelines below will also help.

© Edvantage Interactive 2016

Guidelines for Determining If a Molecule Is Non-polar or Polar

1. When the peripheral atoms in a molecule are identical and arranged symmetrically around a central atom, any bond dipoles that exist will cancel out and the molecule will be non-polar.

2. When the molecule is asymmetric (not symmetric) either due to its shape or its composition, any bond dipoles that exist will usually not cancel out and the molecule will be polar.

If you review all the shapes listed in the tables given earlier, you will notice that several shapes have the peripheral atoms arranged *symmetrically* around the central atom. "Symmetrical" means balanced or evenly arranged.

In most cases, symmetrical molecules are AX_m molecules in which no lone pairs exist on the central atom. All such molecules containing identical peripheral atoms will be non-polar, regardless of the bond dipoles that exist.

Can you discover any shapes where lone pairs *do exist* on the central atoms that include symmetrically arranged peripheral atoms? If so, then those molecules will also prove to be non-polar as long as the peripheral atoms are all the same.

Sample Problem

Consider the Lewis structure shown here for the compound chlorine trifluoride:
Determine the shape of the molecule and if the molecule is polar.

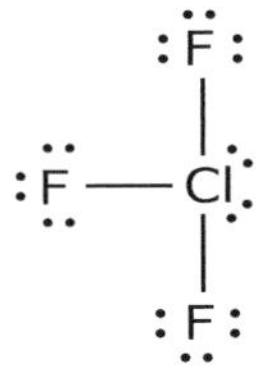

What to Think about

1. To determine if the bonds are polar, find the ΔEN from the electronegativity table.
   The bonds are therefore polar in the direction of fluorine.

2. To determine if the molecule is polar, assign an AX_mE_n label and find the molecular shape.
   The molecule has an AX_3E_2 designation and so adopts a "T-shaped" structure.

3. Considering the molecular shape, decide if the molecule is symmetric or asymmetric and therefore either polar or non-polar.
   The bond dipoles therefore do not cancel and so the molecule is polar.

How to Do It

$$\Delta EN = 4.0 - 3.0 = 1.0$$

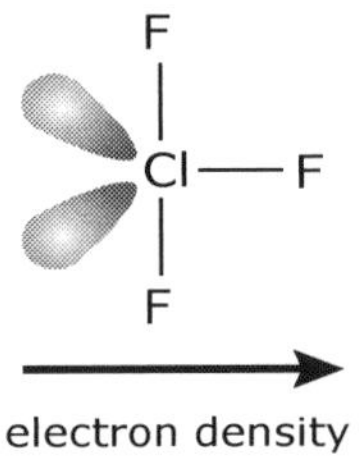

electron density

Practice Problems

1. Complete the following table by listing the AX_mE_n notations and their shapes in the appropriate columns for all the symmetric and asymmetric molecules that you can find. Assume that all the peripheral atoms in the molecules are the same. The first entries are done for you.

Symmetric Molecules		Asymmetric Molecules	
AX_mE_n Notation	Shape of Molecule	AX_mE_n Notation	Shape of Molecule
AX_2	linear	AX_2E	bent or angular

2. Complete the following table.

Lewis Structure	AX_mE_n Notation	Molecular Shape (Name and Diagram)	Polar Molecule? (Yes / No)
(a) H‒C=O (with H above C)			
(b) H‒N‒H (with H below N)			
(c) Cl‒P with 4 surrounding Cl			

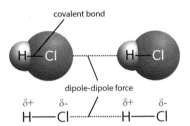

We have seen that opposite charges are ultimately responsible for all chemical bonds. Electron-deficient positive ions are attracted to electron-abundant negative ions in ionic bonds. Pairs of negative electrons are attracted to adjacent positive nuclei in covalent bonds.

> The chemical bonds within molecules are called **intramolecular** forces. ("Intra" means "within.") Attractive forces between molecules and between ions and molecules are called **intermolecular forces.**

Intermolecular forces are as dependent on electrostatic attraction as intramolecular forces are. However, because they typically involve smaller charges and/or greater distances between the chemical species, they aren't as strong as chemical bonds. Yet these forces are so important that without them, life itself could never exist on this tiny "blue marble" in space we call Earth.

Our final discussion of this chapter will focus on the various types of intermolecular forces that exist. We will begin with the forces that act between neutral molecules, and then consider a force that acts between molecules and ions. Let's start where our previous discussion ended by revisiting polar molecules.

Dipole-Dipole Forces — Attractions Between Polar Molecules

Within any substance containing polar molecules, each molecule has a positive and a negative pole — a **molecular dipole**. Because of these partial charges, the molecules in the liquid and solid phases will naturally orient themselves so that the positive pole of one molecule will be next to and attract the negative pole of an adjacent molecule. This force of attraction is called a **dipole-dipole force**. This network of dipole-dipole forces will result in higher melting and boiling points because more energy will be required to overcome the attractions between the molecules.

The more polar those molecules are, the stronger the dipole-dipole forces. Figure 8.3.8 shows two depictions of polar HCl molecules with the dipole-dipole force acting between them.

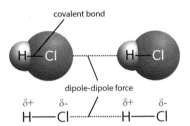

Figure 8.3.8 *One way to show dipole-dipole forces is to draw the actual molecule shapes (top diagram). Another way is to use the element symbols only (bottom diagram.*

Hydrogen Bonds — Special Dipole-Dipole Forces

A much stronger example of a dipole-dipole force exists between polar molecules that contain a hydrogen atom bonded to either nitrogen, oxygen, or fluorine. The atoms of these 2nd period elements are each small, highly electronegative, and have lone electron pairs. All of these properties are significant.

The H – **N**, H – **O**, and H – **F** bonds in each of these molecules will be *very polar* due to hydrogen's low electronegativity resulting in a large ΔEN. This means that a significant amount of electron density will be removed from hydrogen, leaving it with a large partial positive charge. This will also leave its nucleus almost unshielded because hydrogen has no core electrons. The other end of the molecule will gain that electron density and thus acquire a large partial negative charge.

The partially positive hydrogen in one molecule will then be attracted to the lone electron pair of the partially negative atom of another molecule. That attractive force will be particularly strong not only because of the extremely polar bonds within the molecules, but also because *all of the atoms involved are small.* This allows the tiny electropositive hydrogen to get very close to the lone pairs on the partially negative nitrogen, oxygen, or fluorine atoms of the other molecules. This intense intermolecular force is known as a **hydrogen bond**.

It is not an exaggeration to state that hydrogen bonds make life on Earth possible. For example, consider that most of our Earth and most of our bodies are composed of water. Water molecules have a relatively low mass and the vast majority of substances composed of such molecules have very low boiling points, even if those molecules are polar. Look at Figure 8.3.9 showing the boiling points of the binary (two element) hydrides of groups 14 to 17 of the periodic table.

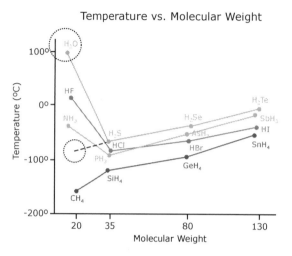

Figure 8.3.9 *Boiling points of binary hydrides of groups 14 to 17*

The group 14 hydrides are all symmetric AX_4 molecules and non-polar, so we would expect those substances (SnH_4, GeH_4, SiH_4, and CH_4) to have low boiling points, and they do. Note that the boiling points of these compounds decrease with decreasing molar mass. The binary hydrides of the remaining groups, however, are asymmetric polar molecules. Their dipole-dipole forces contribute to higher boiling points than seen in group 14.

Something very interesting occurs, however, with the lightest hydrides in groups 15, 16, and 17. Look at how the boiling points change for these substances as we move up each group. Consider the group 16 binary hydrides for example: H_2Te, H_2Se, H_2S, and finally H_2O (water). As the mass of each polar AX_2E_2 molecule decreases, the boiling point drops, but not consistently. After H_2S, if the trend were consistent, we would expect water to have a boiling point of approximately –90°C (see dashed line in Figure 8.3.9). The fact that the actual boiling point is almost 200°C higher than that is clear evidence of the strength of the hydrogen bonds in water (Figure 8.3.10a). Life as we know it would be very unlikely if water became a gas at –90°C! Even the fact that ice floats is due to hydrogen bonding. That characteristic of water is of great importance to aquatic life during cold temperatures.

The significance of hydrogen bonds is further demonstrated by the fact that the three-dimensional structure of many proteins and even the base-pairing in the double helix of DNA molecules depend on the existence of these essential forces. These are hydrogen bonds involving an oxygen or nitrogen atom (Figure 8.3.10b).

© Edvantage Interactive 2016

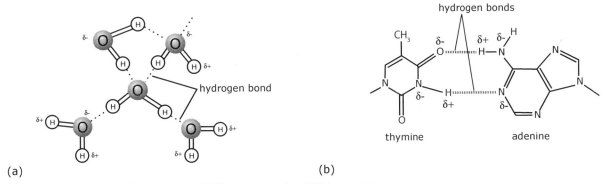

(a)   (b)

Figure 8.3.10 *(a) Hydrogen bonds in water; (b) Hydrogen bonds in DNA base-pairing*

Dispersion (London) Forces — A Growing Attraction

For a molecular substance to exist as a liquid or solid, the molecules must be close together. This means some kind of intermolecular attractive force must exist between those molecules.

So far, we have discussed two of these intermolecular forces. Dipole-dipole forces and hydrogen bonds act to cause polar molecules to "stick" together and maintain a molecular substance in the liquid or solid state of matter.

However, we might expect that substances composed of non-polar molecules might never exist as liquids or solids since they have no particular reason to attract each other. That is definitely not the case. Many molecular substances composed of non-polar molecules exist as liquids or even solids at room temperatures. Those that don't can usually be condensed or solidified under the right conditions. The obvious question would be: What intermolecular force would cause non-polar molecules to attract each other?

The explanation of this force relies on the quantum mechanical description of the atom and the force itself is named for the physicist, Fritz London, who used quantum mechanics to explain the basis of the attraction. We'll use a non-polar molecule as an example.

Consider a sample of chlorine gas, Cl_2. As the $\Delta EN = 0$, the molecules are non-polar and the electron density in the negative cloud surrounding this diatomic molecule is evenly distributed. This means that *on average*, the electrons will spend no more of their time nearer one chlorine nucleus than the other, and so the probability distribution is even throughout the orbital cloud.

However, at any instant, there is a *possibility* that there may be more electron density on one side of the molecule than the other, resulting in an instantaneous molecular dipole. This dipole will have little effect on any other Cl_2 molecules that are far away. But if those molecules are in close proximity, even a short-lived dipole in one molecule will distort or polarize the electron cloud of a neighbouring molecule. This happens because the negative pole of the instantaneous dipole will repel electron density in the nearby electron cloud to the opposite side of that molecule. As well, the positive pole will pull electron density to the near side of another neighbouring molecule. Each induced dipole results in an intermolecular attraction between the newly polarized molecules and induces more dipoles in surrounding molecules. As a result, the dipoles *disperse* throughout the sample, causing the molecules to attract each other. These intermolecular forces of attraction are called **dispersion forces** or **London dispersion forces**.

Figure 8.3.11 shows an instantaneous dipole in the non-polar molecule on the left inducing a dipole in the neighbouring molecule on the right. The dispersion force then exists between the two molecules.

Although London forces are the *only* forces acting between non-polar molecules, they exist between the particles of *all* substances. Except in the case of strong hydrogen bonds, they may be the dominant intermolecular force even for polar molecules.

The strength of dispersion forces will increase as the size of the molecules involved increases. This is because large electron clouds are more loosely held than smaller clouds. Thus they are more easily deformed or polarized by a nearby dipole than compact tightly held clouds are.

Even molecular shape can play a role in dispersion forces. Molecules with more surface area

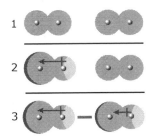

Figure 8.3.11 *An instantaneous dipole in the non-polar molecule on the left (2 induces a dipole in its neighbouring molecule on the right 3).*

have electron clouds that are spread out and so are more easily distorted by neighboring dipoles.

Consider the melting and boiling points of diatomic halogens of group 17. The higher temperatures required for these phase changes as we descend the group is evidence of the increasing strength of the London forces between the molecules.

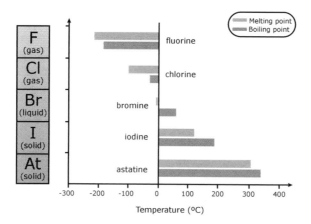

Figure 8.3.12 *Melting and boiling points of diatomic halogens of group 17*

Ion-Dipole Forces — Surround and Separate

We will conclude our discussion of intermolecular forces by focusing on an important interaction that occurs when an ionic compound dissolves in water.

The ionic bonds holding a crystal lattice together are strong. However, when the surface of that lattice is in contact with water, each ion on that surface will attract the oppositely charged end of polar water molecules near them. That attraction between an ion and a polar molecule is called an **ion-dipole force.** These attractive forces soon overcome those between the ions themselves, so the crystal structure begins to break down. As the ions move away from the lattice surface, they immediately become surrounded or enclosed in what chemists call a **hydration shell.**

At the centre of one type of hydration shell, the negative oxygen ends of water molecules orient themselves next to and surround a cation. At the centre of another shell, an anion is engulfed by water molecules oriented with their positive hydrogens next to the ion's negative charge. Figure 8.3.13 shows the ion-dipole forces acting between water and Na^+ and Cl^- ions in an aqueous solution. Ion-dipole forces are the primary force responsible for the solubility of ionic compounds in water and aqueous solutions of some ionic compounds are almost as necessary for life as water itself.

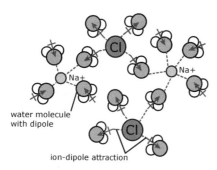

Figure 8.3.13 *Ion-dipole forces between water molecules and Na^+ and Cl^- ions in an aqueous solution*

Valence Bond Theory — The Hybridization of Atomic Orbitals and the Concept of Formal Charge

G.N. Lewis's dot structures provide useful models of the arrangement of atoms in covalent molecules. By evaluating the total number of valence electrons in a molecule and the formal charge on the atoms, Lewis structures provide a way to represent whether covalent molecules contain single or multiple bonds. The repulsion that occurs between bonding and/or non-bonding pairs of electrons can be used to predict molecular shape. This is the VSEPR theory. Consideration of the electronegativity of atoms within a molecule's Lewis structure provides a way to deduce whether a molecular dipole exists. The strength of the intermolecular forces (IMFs) in molecules is determined by

© Edvantage Interactive 2016

a combination of London dispersion forces and dipole forces. Intermolecular forces influence all of the physical and chemical characteristics of these molecules.

There are some limitations and over simplifications associated with the Lewis structure model of covalent molecules. For example, we know that electrons are not accurately represented as pairs of dots in a region of space between two atoms that produce a bond. The quantum mechanical model explains that electrons actually exhibit particle-wave duality in atoms and that they are located in orbitals.

Valence bond theory describes the location of bonding and non-bonding, lone electrons in quantum-mechanical orbitals, created by overlap of the standard s, p, d, and f orbitals. **Hybridization** is a mathematical process in which these standard atomic orbitals are combined to form new atomic orbitals called **hybrid orbitals**. Hybrid orbitals are located on individual atoms, but their shapes and energies differ from those of standard atomic orbitals. Hybrid orbitals are more stable than standard atomic orbitals. They *minimize* the energy of the molecule by *maximizing* the orbital overlap in a bond. The mathematical equations involved in hybridization are very complex; however, the following statements help describe it.

- The sum of the number of standard atomic orbitals is equal to the number of hybrid orbitals formed.
- The combinations of standard atomic orbitals determine the number and energies of the hybrid orbitals formed.
- The type of hybridization that occurs is the one with the lowest overall potential energy.
- We can use the electron geometry determined by the VSEPR theory to predict the type of hybridization.

sp³ Hybridization

This is the most common type of hybridization as it is found in molecules whose central atom is surrounded by a stable octet. Methane, CH_4 is a classic example of sp³ hybridization. Each hydrogen has one valence electron existing in a 1s orbital, while carbon has four valence electrons, two existing in a 2s orbital, and two in two lobes of a 2p orbital. Carbon's orbital diagram would convert as shown in Figure 8.3.14 (notice the 1s electrons are not affected).

$C \ 1s^2 2s^2 2p^2$

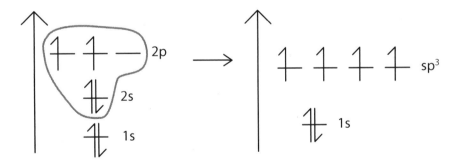

Figure 8.3.14 *Conversion of carbon's orbital diagram*

The s and p orbitals combine to form four *identical* bonding orbitals, designated sp³. Each of these can share their electron with one hydrogen atom. This is called sp³ hybridization. *One* spherical s orbital and *three* figure-8-shaped p orbitals (one p_x, one p_y and one p_z) combine to form *four* identical sp³ hybrid orbitals. An sp³ hybrid orbital resembles a p orbital with an enlarged end (Figure 8.3.15).

There are *four* of these that overlap about a central point to make a methane molecule, CH_4 (or any AX_4 species). This is typical of a *tetrahedral* arrangement with all bond angles approximately 109.5° (Figure 8.3.16).

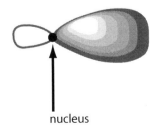

nucleus

Figure 8.3.15 *An sp³ hybrid orbital*

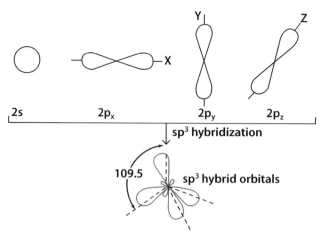

2s   2p_x   2p_y   2p_z

sp³ hybridization

109.5   sp³ hybrid orbitals

Figure 8.3.16 *A methane molecule*

- Hybridized orbitals can hold lone pairs or bonding pairs.
- The region in space occupied by a pair of bonding or lone electrons, regions of high electron density, is a "domain".
- Lone electrons exert greater repulsive forces than bonding electrons.

Sample Problem — Deducing Molecular Shape and Hybridization

Determine the shape and the hybridization for a molecule of water.

What to Think About	How To Do It
1. Determine the Lewis structure for the molecule.	$\overset{\cdot\cdot}{\underset{H \quad H}{O}}$
2. Determine the number of electron "domains" around the central oxygen atom.	The four electron domains are arranged in a tetrahedron. Two of the domains contain lone pairs of electrons.
	Four sp³ hybrid orbitals are oriented in a tetrahedral array. Two of the sp³ orbitals are occupied by bonding electron pairs and two are occupied by non-bonding electron pairs leading to an **angular** or **bent (v-shaped)** arrangement.
3. Four electron domains will be most likely to exist as four sp³ hybrid orbitals.	Due to the large interelectron repulsion of the lone-paired electrons, the usual 109.5° bond angle found in a tetrahedron will be reduced and closer to 104.5° between the hydrogen atoms. 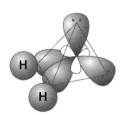

sp³d and sp³d² Hybridization

Elements in the third row of the periodic table (or below) are able to form bonding arrangements involving *expanded octets*. In third period elements such as phosphorus, sulfur, and chlorine, the 3d orbitals are so close in energy to the 3s and 3p orbitals that the hybridization of one s, three p, and one d orbital results in a *trigonal bipyramid* geometry. Sp³d hybridization is particularly common for molecules whose central atoms have five valence electrons.

Elements with six, seven, or eight valence electrons can accommodate an expanded octet to produce up to six bonds. The formation of sp³d² hybrid orbitals in an *octahedral* (or *square bipyramid*) array can be accomplished by the hybridizing of one s, three p, and two d orbitals. (See Figure 8.3.17)

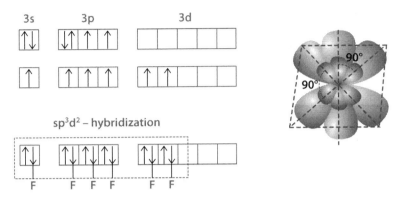

Figure 8.3.17 *As shown, sp³d² hybridization creates six degenerate orbitals in an octahedral array. Six single bonds all 90° apart extend from a central atom as in sulfur hexafluoride, SF₆, for example.*

Note: While the use of electron geometry to predict hybridization is largely successful, there are cases where it fails. H₂S for example is predicted to have tetrahedral *electron* geometry and a bent shape with about a bond angle of about 104°. In fact, the bond angle is closer to 90°, indicating that this molecule is largely unhybridized. Recently, complex computer-based calculations indicate that the sp³d and sp³d² hybrids are the most difficult to accurately predict. For this reason, these two types of hybridization are not being assessed on the AP Chemistry examination at the moment.

Sigma (σ) and Pi (π) Bonding

A sigma (σ) bond occurs when two atomic orbitals combine to form a covalent bond that lies along an axis connecting the nuclei of the two atoms. The simplest example of a sigma bond would be the overlap of two 1s orbitals in the formation of diatomic hydrogen, H₂. Sigma bonds are also formed by the overlap of two hybridized orbitals. In double bond formation, there is overlap between two hybridized orbitals, called a sigma bond overlap, and the overlap of two unhybridized p orbitals, which is called a pi (π) bond overlap. A double bond consists of one sigma and one pi bond overlap.

A pi bond occurs due to p_y or p_z orbital overlap in a sausage-shaped region above and below (in the case of p_y overlap) or in front and behind (in the case of p_z overlap) the nuclei of bonded atoms (Figure 8.3.18).

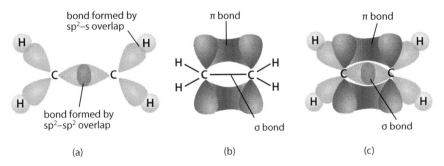

(a) (b) (c)

Figure 8.3.18 *(a) shows overlap of p_x hybridized orbitals along an axis between the carbon atoms to form a σ bond; (b) shows overlap of p_y orbitals above and below an axis between the carbon atoms to form a π bond; (c) shows double-bonded C₂H₄ with one σ and one π bond between the two carbon atoms in the molecule.*

sp and sp² Hybridization

Double and triple bonds are commonly associated with carbon atoms and always consist of one sigma (σ) and one or two pi (π) bonds. In terms of hybridization, the entire region of orbital overlap is considered one hybrid orbital, even though it may be a double or triple bond. For this reason, multiple bonds are often associated with sp or sp² hybridization.

> In the determination of molecular shape and/or hybridization, it is important to think of a double or triple covalent bond as occupying one domain only.

Other examples of compounds that exhibit sp and sp² hybridization are those with beryllium or boron as these may form stable compounds with less than an octet of electrons around their central atoms.

Sample Problem — Deducing Molecular Shape, Hybridization, and Presence of Sigma (σ) and Pi (π) Bonds

Determine the shape and hybridization for a molecule of methanal, CH_2O. Determine the number of sigma and pi bonds in the molecule. The common name for methanal is formaldehyde.

What To Think About	How To Do It

1. Refer to the steps listed in Section 6.4 to determine the Lewis structure for the molecule.	H
	  \
	   C = O:
	  /
	 H

2. Determine the number of electron "domains" existing around the central atom (the double bond is one domain).	There are a total of 12 valence electrons with carbon occupying the central position in the molecule. This means a double bond is needed between the carbon and the oxygen atoms.
3. The total number of orbitals is conserved.	There are **three** electron domains. This indicates three hybrid orbitals. The orbitals should be **sp²** hybridized.
4. Maximize the inter-domain distance to predict the shape of the molecule and the bond angles.	The molecule should have 120.5° bond angles and should be **trigonal planar**.
5. All single bonds are σ and all multiple bonds consist of first σ and then π bonds.	There should be 3 σ bonds (between C and each H and C and O) and 1 π bond (between C and O).

Practice Problems—Deducing Molecular Shape, Hybridization, and Presence of Sigma (σ) and Pi (π) Bonds

1. Draw Lewis structures for each of the following species.

   a) CH_4 b) H_3O^+ c) OF_2 d) HCN   e) SF_6 f) SOF_4

2. State the shape and the central atom hybridization for each of the structures.

3. Label each molecule as polar or non-polar.

Table 8.3.5 *Summary Table Including Hybridization, Bond Type, and Shape*

Hybridization	# Of Bonds	# Lone Pairs	Molecular Shape		Bond Angle	Example
sp	2	0		Linear	180°	CO_2
sp^2	3	0		Trigonal planar	120°	SO_3
sp^2	2	1		Angular	< 120°	SO_2
sp^3	4	0		Tetrahedral	109.5°	CH_4
sp^3	3	1		Trigonal pyramidal	< 109.5°	NH_3
sp^3	2	2		Bent (angular)	< 109.5°	H_2O
sp^3d	5	0		Trigonal bipyramidal	120°, 90°	PCl_5
sp^3d	4	1		Seesaw or irregular tetrahedron	< 120°, < 90°	SF_4
sp^3d	3	2	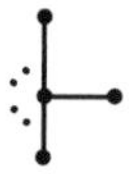	T-shaped	< 90°	CF_3
sp^3d	2	3		Linear	180°	XeF_2
sp^3d^2	6	0		Octahedron	90°	SF_8
sp^3d^2	5	1		Square pyramidal	< 90°	IF_5
sp^3d^2	4	2		Square planar	90°	XeF_4

Formal Charge

Formal charge is an entirely fictitious charge that is used to defend the most probable Lewis structure of a molecule when several different Lewis structure arrangements are possible. The formal charge on an atom in a molecule is the charge each atom would have *if all bonding electrons were shared equally between the bonded atoms*. There are a couple of ways to calculate the formal charge of each atom.

formal charge of an atom = the number of valence electrons [the number of lone electrons + the number of bonding electron pairs]

This method for calculating formal charge can be simplified if the Lewis structure is drawn using lines for each bonding pair of electrons. In that case:

formal charge = valence electrons – (dots + lines)

© Edvantage Interactive 2016

While not particularly scientific sounding, this is a very easy way to calculate formal charge. Formal charges are generally shown next to each atom in a structure with a *circle* drawn around the charge.

It is important to remember that formal charges are *not* actual charges. They do *not* produce electronegativity or polarity in a molecule. They simply assist us in determining which is the most likely structure from among a selection of Lewis structures. The following general rules apply to formal charges.

1. The *sum* of all formal charges in a *neutral molecule* is equal to *zero*.
2. The *sum* of all formal charges in an *ion* is equal to the *ion's charge*.
3. *Small* or *zero* formal charges on atoms are preferred.*
4. For structures with atoms with a non-zero formal charge, the preferred structure will be the one with a negative charge on the more electronegative element.

* Statement 3 has been questioned by bonding theorists lately — in fact a structure that satisfies the octet rule may be more likely than one in which formal charges are minimized.

Sample Problem — Deduction of a Preferred Structure Using Formal Charge

Hydrocyanic acid is produced by bubbling gaseous hydrogen cyanide through water to produce an aqueous solution. Draw two possible structures for the molecule with a triple bond between the C and the N and assign formal charges to all atoms. Which structure is preferred based on minimizing formal charge?

What to Think About	How to Do It
1. Determine the Lewis structure for the molecule.	There are a total of 10 valence electrons. The structure may be drawn with the carbon in the centre or the nitrogen. Either way, the C-N bond must be triple (as indicated in the question) and the H bond single.
2. If there is more than one possible resonance structure or isomer, repeat the steps and produce any alternate structures. Note: there are several resonance structures possible, but the question limits us to the two involving a triple C-N bond.	Possible structures include:
	$H-C\equiv N\colon$ and $H-C\equiv C\colon$
3. Calculate formal charges using the formula: valence electrons – (dots + dashes) for each atom in the first structure.	H: $1 - (0 + 1) = 0$ C: $4 - (0 + 4) = 0$ N: $5 - (2 + 3) = 0$
4. Repeat for the second structure.	H: $1 - (0 + 1) = 0$ N: $5 - (0 + 4) = +1$ C: $4 - (2 + 3) = -1$
5. Place the "charges" on the appropriate atoms in a circle.	⓪ ⓪ ⓪ ⓪ ⊕ ⊖ $H-C\equiv \ddot{N}$ and $H-N\equiv \ddot{C}$
6. Predict the preferred structure.	The first structure (with the central carbon) is preferred.

Practice Problems—Assigning and Using Formal Charges

1. Assign formal charges to each atom in each of the following two structures for CO_2. Predict which structure is favoured.

   (a) $\ddot{O} = C = \ddot{O}$ (b) $:\ddot{O} - C \equiv O:$

2. Assign formal charges to each atom in each of the following six structures for SCO. Predict which structure is favoured. Which is least likely to form?

   (a)
   $:\ddot{O} = C = \ddot{S}:$

   (b)
   $:\ddot{O} - C \equiv S:$

   (c)
   $:O \equiv C - \ddot{S}:$

   (d)
   $:\ddot{C} = O = \ddot{S}:$

   (e)
   $:\ddot{C} - O \equiv S:$

   (f)
   $:C \equiv O - \ddot{S}:$

3. Draw two structures for SO_3, one with an expanded octet and one without. You do not need to show resonance structures for the non-expanded form. Use formal charges to predict which structure is favoured. Check the Internet to see whether you can find any information indicating that the other structure might, in fact, be favoured.

8.3 Activity: Modeling the AX_mE_n Molecules

Question

How can building the various AX_mE_n shapes help us to determine molecular polarities?

Build each of the shapes listed in the table below, but before you take each apart, look at each structure and ask yourself the following question: If each of the bonds in these molecules were polar and all of the peripheral atoms were the same, would the *molecule* be polar or non-polar?

Complete the following table below as you construct each shape:

AX_mE_n Notation	Sample Molecule	Name of Shape	Polar Molecule? Yes/No
AX_2	CO_2		
AX_3	BF_3		
AX_2E	SO_2		
AX_4	CH_4		
AX_3E	NH_3		
AX_2E_2	H_2O		
AX_5	PCl_5		
AX_4E	SF_4		
AX_3E_2	BrF_3		
AX_2E_3	XeF_2		
AX_6	SF_6		
AX_5E	BrF_5		
AX_4E_2	XeF_4		

Results and Discussion

1. Note that an electronegativity value is not listed for xenon in the table shown earlier in this section. In spite of this, you are still able to determine if the two molecules above containing Xe as the central atom are polar or not. Why?

8.3 Review Questions

1. (a) What do the letters: V S E P and R in the term "VSEPR theory" stand for?

   (b) What does the theory allow us to do?

2. Why do non-bonding or lone-pair electrons attached to a central atom occupy more space than bonding electron pairs?

3. Consider the following Lewis structures. Would you expect these molecules to have the same shape or a different shape? Explain.

$$:\overset{..}{F} - B - \overset{..}{F}:$$
$$|$$
$$:\overset{..}{F}:$$

$$\overset{H}{\underset{|}{H - C = \overset{..}{O}:}}$$

4. For each pair of columns, draw lines to connect the AX_mE_n notation on the left to the correct shape listed on the right. (The first one is done for you.)

AX_mE_n Notation	Molecular Shape	AX_mE_n Notation	Molecular Shape
AX_3	angular	AX_4E	T-shaped
AX_2E_3	trigonal bipyramidal	AX_2E	octahedral
AX_4	trigonal pyramidal	AX_3E_2	square pyramidal
AX_3E	trigonal planar	AX_6	square planar
AX_2E_2	tetrahedral	AX_5E	angular
AX_5	linear	AX_4E_2	seesaw

5. Consider the Lewis structures for methane and ammonia.
   (a) Which molecule will have the smaller X–A–X bond angle and why?

$$H - \overset{\overset{H}{|}}{\underset{\underset{H}{|}}{C}} - H \qquad H - \overset{\overset{..}{N}}{\underset{\underset{H}{|}}{N}} - H$$

   (b) Identify the main intermolecular force acting between the molecules of methane and between the molecules of ammonia in pure samples of each compound.

6. Assume that all of the peripheral atoms are the same for each AX_mE_n category listed below and complete the following table. (Note that two different bond angles exist in an AX_5 molecule.)

AX_mE_n Category	AX_2	AX_3	AX_4	AX_5		AX_2E_3	AX_6	AX_4E_2
X–A–X Bond Angle								

7. Consider the following group 17 binary hydrides: HI, HBr, HCl, and HF. Which should have the highest boiling point and why?

8. The industrial production of ammonia, NH_3, from H_2 and N_2 is called the Haber process, named for Fritz Haber, the German chemist who developed it just before World War I. During the process, in a gaseous mixture of all three substances, NH_3 must be separated from H_2 and N_2. This is done by cooling the gaseous mixture so as to condense only the NH_3. This leaves the elemental nitrogen and hydrogen as gases to be recycled and produce more ammonia. Why does only the ammonia liquefy upon cooling, but not the H_2 or N_2?

9. Identify two examples of how hydrogen bonding between molecules makes life on Earth possible.

10. Iodine is a non-polar diatomic molecule, yet its molecules have enough attraction for each other that the element exists as a solid at room temperature. Identify the attractive force and explain why it is strong enough to keep the molecules of I_2 attached to each other even at room temperature.

11. Ionic compounds such as NaCl have very high melting points because a great deal of energy is required to overcome the many attractive forces between the oppositely charged ions in an ionic crystal lattice. NaCl melts at 801°C, yet its ions will readily separate from each other at room temperature when the solid is added to water. Explain this by discussing the predominant force that allows an ionic compound to dissolve in water.

12. Complete the following table:

Lewis Structure	AX$_m$E$_n$ Notation	Shape of Molecule (Name and Diagram)	Type of Intermolecular Force Acting Between Molecules
(a) dichloromethane			
(b) phosgene			
(c) sulfur hexafluoride			
(d) iodine pentafluoride			

© Edvantage Interactive 2016

13. (a) Draw Lewis structures for each of the species below in the space provided.

(b) State the shape and the central atom hybridization for each.

(c) Consider the polarity of the bonds in each molecule and then determine whether there is a molecular dipole.

(d) Indicate the number of sigma and/or pi bonds in each molecule or ion.

(e) Assign formal charges to each atom in each of the species.

SCl_2 TeF_5^-

XeF_4 CO_3^{-2}

IOF_5 IF_4^+

8.4 Applying Quantum Mechanics to Electrons in Atoms

Warm Up

1. What part of Bohr's theory remains as part of the quantum mechanical view of the atom?

   _____

2. Quantum mechanics replaces the concept of an electron orbit with an orbital. What is an electron orbital?

   _____

3. The laws of probability are a necessary part of describing electron behaviour. Why?

   _____

Starting with Hydrogen — One on One

In this section, we will apply the quantum mechanical model of the atom to describing electrons in the atoms of the elements. We will begin with hydrogen and then use that information to expand our discussion to include multi-electron atoms.

An analogy of a guitar string can help to explain the requirement of standing waves for the allowed energy states of electrons in atoms. If we solve Schrdinger's wave equation for the allowed energy states for hydrogen, we see that each energy state results in different numbers and types of orbitals. The equation shows us that the higher the energy, the greater the number and types of orbitals present.

Quantum Numbers

In an atom, these three-dimensional electron waves or orbitals are more complicated than a standing wave on a guitar string. To describe them, quantum mechanics employs the use of special numbers called **quantum numbers** Each quantum number specifies something different about the orbitals and electrons. We will discuss these numbers as we investigate the orbitals associated with each of allowed energy states for hydrogen.

The Principal Quantum Number (*n*)

The first quantum number is called the **principal quantum number** (*n*). It indicates the relative size of the atomic orbital.

We have already been introduced to this number because it also represents the allowed energy states for the electron. We know that the value of *n* can be a positive integer (1, 2, 3, and so on).

When hydrogen's electron is in the lowest allowed energy state or ground state, then *n* = 1. Schrödinger's equation shows us where an electron possessing that amount of energy will most likely be found. When we represent this pictorially, we see an electron "probability density diagram" resembling a spherical cloud. The cloud is what you might see if you could take many snapshots of the hydrogen electron around the nucleus and then superimpose all of them onto one picture. At the centre of this cloud is the hydrogen nucleus. The cloud's density is not uniform throughout, but is greater near the nucleus and decreases as we move away. This tells us that the probability of locating the electron is higher closer to the nucleus and lower further away from the nucleus.

As we move out from the nucleus, we find that hydrogen's electron in its ground state is likely to spend most of its time a slight distance from the nucleus, rather than at the nucleus itself. This is called the "radial probability." It's interesting to note that the electron's distance from the nucleus to the region of highest probability corresponds exactly to the orbit for this electron that Bohr calculated. Remember, however, that Bohr assumed the electron followed a circular path and would always be found at that distance from the nucleus. Quantum mechanics describes this as the most probable distance from the nucleus for the electron.

When we enclose the cloud in a volume representing about a 90% probability of finding the electron, we call this the 1s orbital. The number "1" represents the principal quantum number, telling us the size of the orbital, and the letter "s" refers to the type or "shape" of the orbital. Figure 8.4.1(a) shows an artistic representation of what a spherical 1s orbital might look like if viewed from the outside. Figure 8.4.1(b) is a cross-sectional view showing radial probability (indicated by greater dot density a slight distance from nucleus).

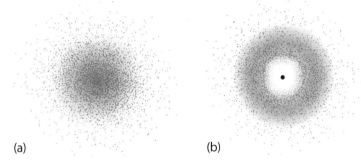

(a)   (b)

Figure 8.4.1 *(a) A view of a spherical 1s orbital from the outside; (b) A cross-sectional view of a spherical 1s orbital*

The Second Quantum Number (ℓ)

The second quantum number is called the **angular momentum quantum number** (ℓ). It is related to the shape of an atomic orbital.

The different values of ℓ at each energy level represent the number of orbital shapes or sublevels that exist in that energy level. That number equals the energy level itself. So for $n = 1$, there is only one orbital type or shape, namely the s orbital.

Each new energy level has one new orbital shape in addition to those existing in the previous level. So if hydrogen's electron is "excited" and absorbs enough energy to reach the second allowed energy state, then $n = 2$ and two orbital shapes or sublevels exist. There is an s orbital with a shape identical to the 1s, except larger, called the 2s orbital. This means that the electron with this greater amount of energy will spend more of its time farther from the nucleus. There is also a new shape: a p orbital. As $n = 2$, we call it a 2p orbital and it resembles a dumbbell or long balloon pinched in the middle (where the nucleus is located).

The Third Quantum Number (m_ℓ)

> The third quantum number, called the **magnetic quantum number** (m_ℓ) tells us the orientation in space of a given atomic orbital.

The number of possible different orientations in space for any orbital shape also represents the number of individual orbitals of that particular shape or sublevel.

Only a single s orbital exists in any given energy level because a spherical cloud can only have one orientation in 3D space. However, this new p sublevel includes three separate orbitals, each with a different spatial orientation. If we consider a 3D set of Cartesian coordinates, one is oriented along an imaginary x-axis (with the nucleus at the origin) called a $2p_x$ orbital. The other two are oriented along the y- and z-axes and are called the $2p_y$ and $2p_z$ orbitals respectively. Each of these 2p orbitals is identical in energy to the others. For hydrogen, they are also identical in energy to the 2s orbital. Chemists call orbitals of equal energy "degenerate" orbitals.

In Figure 8.4.2, note that the lobes of each p orbital in the first three diagrams disappear at the origin where the nucleus is located. This means that the amplitude of the electron wave at the nucleus is zero. A wave amplitude of zero is called a node, and it tells us that there is a zero probability of locating the electron here. In the far left diagram in Figure 8.4.2, all three 2p orbitals are shown together. Once again, the nucleus is at the centre or origin.

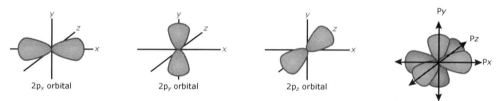

2p$_x$ orbital   2p$_y$ orbital   2p$_z$ orbital

Figure 8.4.2 *The p orbitals are each shown individually in the first three diagrams. The last diagram shows them all together.*

We noted earlier that the number of different sublevels in any energy level equals the value of *n*. We also see here that a total of four orbitals exists in the second energy level. So the value n^2 tells us the number of orbitals existing in the nth energy level. In this case, there are $2^2 = 4$ orbitals: one 2s and three 2p orbitals.

The three quantum numbers, taken together, will always specify a particular atomic orbital because they tell us all we need to know about that orbital: its size, shape, and orientation in space.

If hydrogen's electron absorbs enough energy to reach the third allowed energy state, then $n = 3$ and three different orbital shapes or sublevels exist. As expected, we see one spherical 3s orbital and three dumbbell-shaped 3p orbitals. But we also discover a third sublevel whose orbitals have a more complicated shape. This is called the 3d sublevel and it contains five different orbitals, each with a different spatial orientation. Orbitals in a given sublevel are equal in energy to each other, and in hydrogen's case, are also equal in energy to all of the other orbitals in the energy level. This means that in a given energy level, hydrogen's electron has an equal likelihood of occupying any of them.

Although the d orbitals are shown in Figure 2.4.3, you may not be required to remember either their shapes or their names. You should, however, know that there are five of them.

                                    © Edvantage Interactive 2016

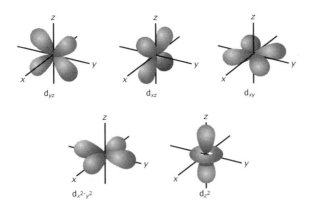

Figure 8.4.3 *The d orbitals*

Notice that as $n = 3$, there are three sublevels: 3s, 3p, and 3d. Also, there are a total of nine orbitals: one 3s orbital, three 3p orbitals, and five 3d orbitals corresponding to 3^2.

Finally, let's elevate hydrogen's electron to the fourth energy level, where $n = 4$. A higher energy level means that the electron will spend more of its time farther from the nucleus than when it possesses energy equal to $n = 1, 2,$ or 3. Therefore, the orbitals or "charge clouds" are larger.

In the fourth energy level, we see the expected 4s, three 4p, and five 4d orbitals. As well, because $n = 4$, we also see a fourth shape called the 4f sublevel. Each higher energy level introduces another sublevel with a greater number (by two) of more complicated orbitals than the previous ones, and so there are seven 4f orbitals, each with a more complicated shape than the d orbitals. You should remember the number of f orbitals as well. The fourth energy level results in $4^2 = 16$ orbitals: one 4s, three 4p, five 4d, and seven 4f orbitals, all of which are equal in energy in the case of hydrogen.

Let's summarize what we have learned about energy levels and orbitals using a table and a diagram. Table 8.4.1 shows the sublevels and orbitals for the first four energy levels. Figure 8.4.4 is the energy diagram for hydrogen showing the sublevels and orbitals present from $n = 1$ through $n = 4$. Each circle represents an orbital. Note that all the sublevels are of equal energy in each allowed energy state.

Table 8.4.1 *Sublevels and orbitals for the first four energy levels*

Principal Quantum Number or Energy Level (*n*)	Number of Orbital Shapes or Sublevels per Energy Level (*n*)	Total Number of Orbitals per Energy Level (*n²*)
1	**1** – 1s sublevel	**1** – the 1s orbital
2	**2** – 2s sublevel 2p sublevel	**4** – one 2s orbital three 2p orbitals
3	**3** – 3s sublevel 3p sublevel 3d sublevel	**9** – one 3s orbital three 3p orbitals five 3d orbitals
4	**4** – 4s sublevel 4p sublevel 4d sublevel 4f sublevel	**16** – one 4s orbital three 4p orbitals five 4d orbitals seven 4f orbitals

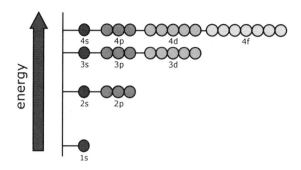

Figure 8.4.4 *Energy diagram for hydrogen. Each circle represents an orbital*

Quick Check

1. State what each of the three quantum numbers described above tells us about atomic orbitals.

   _____

   _____

2. (a) What is the difference between a 1s and a 2s orbital?

   _____

   (b) What is the difference between a $2p_x$ orbital and a $2p_y$ orbital?

   _____

3. How many different orbitals are available to an excited hydrogen electron in the fourth energy level?

   _____

The Orbitals of Multi-Electron Atoms

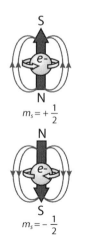

Figure 8.4.5 *The spin quantum number (m_s) identifies which possible spin an electron has.*

Hydrogen is the simplest atom with one proton in the nucleus surrounded by one electron in a 1s orbital in its ground state. There are no electron-electron interactions, and in any excited state, all of the atomic orbitals available to that single electron are of equal energy.

We might expect a different situation, however, for multi-electron atoms. Electrons are charged particle-waves. It seems reasonable to conclude that they will affect each other when two or more of them occupy the same region of space around an atom's nucleus — and they do.

To describe those electrons in multi-electron atoms, we must introduce several additional considerations.

Experiments have shown that the single electron in hydrogen generates a tiny magnetic field as if the electron were a spinning charge. Also, in any sample of hydrogen, analyzing the many atoms present shows two opposing magnetic fields. This tells us that in half of the atoms, the electrons seem to spin in one direction and, in the remainder of the atoms, in the other direction. An electron's spin is as fundamental a part of its nature as its charge.

The fourth quantum number is called the **spin quantum number** (m_s). It tells us the two possible electron spins, either +½ or −½.

© Edvantage Interactive 2016

We already know that we can identify any orbital in an atom by the use of the first three quantum numbers, but we must use all four quantum numbers mentioned to specify any electron in an atom.

This is based on the fact that any atomic orbital can hold a maximum of two electrons. When two electrons are in the same orbital, their spins must be opposite. Originally proposed in 1925 by the Austrian physicist Wolfgang Pauli, this can be viewed as the first rule governing electrons in multi-electron atoms.

1. The **Pauli exclusion principle**: No two electrons in the same atom can be described by the same set of four quantum numbers.

If two electrons are in the same atomic orbital, they therefore have the same first three quantum numbers. Because they then must have opposite spins, their fourth quantum numbers are different.

We noted earlier that the total number of orbitals existing in any level n equals n^2.

If two electrons can occupy each orbital, the maximum number of electrons that can exist in any energy level n is given by $2n^2$.

A further consideration for multi-electron atoms is the effect of electron-electron repulsions on the relative energies of the sublevels in a given energy level. For hydrogen, where no repulsive forces exist, all of the sublevels in any energy level have identical energies. This is not the case for atoms of other elements. Although the same types of orbitals exist in multi-electron atoms, their relative energies are different. Repulsive forces cause a sublevel with a greater number of orbitals to have a greater energy. Therefore the order of sublevel energies is:

s < p < d < f.

Consider Figure 8.4.6. Compare this energy diagram for a multi-electron atom with Figure 8.4.4 for hydrogen. Note that in several cases energies get closer together as n increases. In these cases, repulsive forces are such that some sublevels containing smaller orbitals actually have higher energies than some larger orbitals. For example, observe the relative energy of the 3d compared to the 4s sublevel.

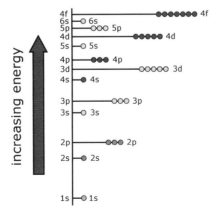

Figure 8.4.6 *Energy diagram for multi-electron atoms*

Quick Check

1. What does the fourth quantum number tell us about electrons?

   _____

2. Why can't two electrons in the same atom have the same four quantum numbers?

   _____

3. What is the maximum number of electrons that can exist in the energy levels $n = 1$ through $n = 4$?

   _____

Electron Configurations and Orbital Diagrams

We are now in a position to organize electrons into orbitals for the atoms of the elements. Understanding this organization will prove to be a powerful tool as we discuss the periodic table and bonding in the next chapter. In beginnning this process, we introduce the second rule associated with describing electrons in multi-electron atoms.

> 2. The **Aufbau principle**: When filling orbitals, the lowest energy orbitals available are always filled first. ("Aufbau" means a building or a construction in German.)

The order for filling orbitals is given above in Figure 8.4.6, showing sublevel energies. We start at the lowest energy orbitals and move up.

Let's begin with hydrogen. In its lowest energy or ground state, hydrogen's electron exists in the 1s orbital. We can represent this in two ways:

1. We can use a shorthand notation called an **electron configuration,** which is written in the format $n\ell$ $^{\#number\ of\ electrons}$ showing the energy level, sublevel, and number of electrons respectively. Hydrogen's electron configuration is therefore written as: $1s^1$. Read as "one s one," this tells us that hydrogen's one electron resides in the 1s orbital in its ground state.

2. We can construct an **orbital diagram**, which depicts electrons and their spin using arrows facing up and down. The arrows are placed inside boxes or over lines representing individual orbitals in sublevels. Hydrogen's orbital diagram is shown as:

1s

The configuration for the next element, helium, is $1s^2$. This is read "one s two" rather than "one s squared." Following the Pauli exclusion principle, the orbital diagram shows the two electrons with opposite spins in the now full 1s orbital:

1s

To indicate increasing sublevel energy, the boxes can be written vertically or also left to right to save space on a page. Let's continue below by moving past helium to the elements in period 2 of the periodic table using horizontally written orbital diagrams.

Note that period 2 corresponds to the second energy level, $n = 2$. Following the Aufbau principle:

<table>
<tr><td></td><td>**Electron Configuration**</td><td colspan="4">**Orbital Diagram**
 INCREASING ENERGY →</td></tr>
<tr><td></td><td></td><td>**1s**</td><td>**2s**</td><td colspan="2">**2p**</td></tr>
<tr><td>lithium</td><td>$1s^2 2s^1$</td><td>↑↓</td><td>↑</td><td colspan="2"></td></tr>
<tr><td>beryllium</td><td>$1s^2 2s^2$</td><td>↑↓</td><td>↑↓</td><td colspan="2"></td></tr>
</table>

For the 2p sublevel:

<table>
<tr><td>boron</td><td>$1s^2 2s^2 2p^1$</td><td>↑↓</td><td>↑↓</td><td>↑</td><td></td><td></td></tr>
</table>

Note that the sum of the superscript numbers equals the total number of electrons present.

We must now use the third rule governing orbitals in multi-electron atoms:

3. **Hund's rule:** When orbitals of equal energy are being filled, the most stable configuration is the one with the maximum number of unpaired electrons with the same spin.

So carbon and nitrogen's orbital diagrams are:

<table>
<tr><td>carbon</td><td>$1s^2 2s^2 2p^2$</td><td>↑↓</td><td>↑↓</td><td>↑</td><td>↑</td><td></td></tr>
<tr><td>nitrogen</td><td>$1s^2 2s^2 2p^3$</td><td>↑↓</td><td>↑↓</td><td>↑</td><td>↑</td><td>↑</td></tr>
</table>

After nitrogen, we must again begin to pair electrons:

<table>
<tr><td>oxygen</td><td>$1s^2 2s^2 2p^4$</td><td>↑↓</td><td>↑↓</td><td>↑↓</td><td>↑</td><td>↑</td></tr>
<tr><td>fluorine</td><td>$1s^2 2s^2 2p^5$</td><td>↑↓</td><td>↑↓</td><td>↑↓</td><td>↑↓</td><td>↑</td></tr>
<tr><td>neon</td><td>$1s^2 2s^2 2p^6$</td><td>↑↓</td><td>↑↓</td><td>↑↓</td><td>↑↓</td><td>↑↓</td></tr>
</table>

After a noble gas, a new period begins in the periodic table and so too, a new energy level. As we begin period 3, let's represent the elements up to scandium in Table 8.4.2 using electron configurations only. We can condense electron configurations using **core notation**, in which the configuration of the previous noble gas is represented by that noble gas symbol in square brackets as shown in the table. Outer electrons are indicated in **bold** type.

Table 8.4.2 *Electron Configurations of Period 3 Elements up to Scandium*

Element	Full Electron Configuration	Core Notation
sodium	$1s^2\,2s^2\,2p^6\,\mathbf{3s^1}$	[Ne] $\mathbf{3s^1}$
magnesium	$1s^2\,2s^2\,2p^6\,\mathbf{3s^2}$	[Ne] $\mathbf{3s^2}$
aluminum	$1s^2\,2s^2\,2p^6\,\mathbf{3s^2\,3p^1}$	[Ne] $\mathbf{3s^2\,3p^1}$
silicon	$1s^2\,2s^2\,2p^6\,\mathbf{3s^2\,3p^2}$	[Ne] $\mathbf{3s^2\,3p^2}$
phosphorus	$1s^2\,2s^2\,2p^6\,\mathbf{3s^2\,3p^3}$	[Ne] $\mathbf{3s^2\,3p^3}$
sulfur	$1s^2\,2s^2\,2p^6\,\mathbf{3s^2\,3p^4}$	[Ne] $\mathbf{3s^2\,3p^4}$
chlorine	$1s^2\,2s^2\,2p^6\,\mathbf{3s^2\,3p^5}$	[Ne] $\mathbf{3s^2\,3p^5}$
argon	$1s^2\,2s^2\,2p^6\,\mathbf{3s^2\,3p^6}$	[Ne] $\mathbf{3s^2\,3p^6}$
potassium	$1s^2\,2s^2\,2p^6\,3s^2\,3p^6\,\mathbf{4s^1}$	[Ar] $\mathbf{4s^1}$
calcium	$1s^2\,2s^2\,2p^6\,3s^2\,3p^6\,\mathbf{4s^2}$	[Ar] $\mathbf{4s^2}$
scandium	$1s^2\,2s^2\,2p^6\,3s^2\,3p^6\,\mathbf{4s^2\,3d^1}$	[Ar] $\mathbf{4s^2\,3d^1}$

Notice in the table that, as we move from argon to potassium, the 4s sublevel starts to fill before the 3d sublevel. After the 4s sublevel, the 3d sublevel starts to fill, reaching the first transition metal, scandium. Although the 3d sublevel fills after the 4s sublevel, the 3d sublevel still contains electrons that spend most of their time nearer the nucleus and so is inside the 4s sublevel. Some periodic tables indicate the electron configurations in order of sublevel size and so will show scandium's configuration as [Ar] $3d^1\,4s^2$.

Figure 8.4.7 is a simple way of remembering the order for filling sublevels. We begin at the top with the 1s and fill that sublevel. After reaching the end of each arrow, we then start at the top of the next arrow below it. When using this diagram, you must remember how many electrons each sublevel can hold.

Figure 8.4.7 *This diagram indicates the order for filling sublevels.*

© Edvantage Interactive 2016

Sample Problem — Drawing an Orbital Diagram

Draw the orbital diagram and write the full electron configuration and the core notation for an atom of cobalt in its ground state.

What to Think about

1. Cobalt's atomic number is 27 and so the orbital diagram must account for 27 electrons. Cobalt is a transition metal in period 4 in the periodic table. We should expect the highest energy electrons to be in the 3d subshell.
2. Remember how many electrons are placed in each subshell as you fill the orbitals and employ Hund's rule as necessary.
3. Sketch the diagonal diagram to help you remember the order that subshells fill.
4. Represent each electron in an orbital using an arrow as in the notation described above.

How to Do It

Orbital diagram for cobalt:

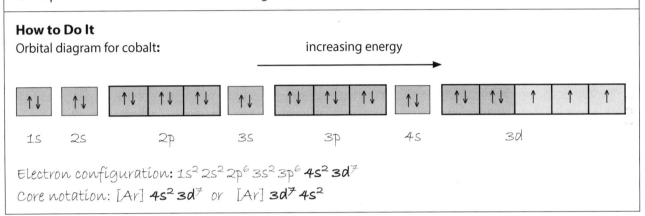

Electron configuration: $1s^2\,2s^2\,2p^6\,3s^2\,3p^6\,4s^2\,3d^7$

Core notation: $[Ar]\,4s^2\,3d^7$ or $[Ar]\,3d^7\,4s^2$

Practice Problem — Drawing an Orbital Diagram

1. Write the full electron configuration and draw the orbital diagram for an atom of titanium in its ground state.

Recall that a cation has fewer electrons than the original neutral atom and an anion has more. This means that the electron configurations for ions will be different than those for neutral atoms.

The process is easily shown using examples. To write the electron configuration for the S^{2-} anion, we simply need to add two more electrons to the last unfilled sublevel. Thus the configuration: $1s^2 2s^2 2p^6 3s^2 3p^4$ for the S atom becomes: $1s^2 2s^2 2p^6 3s^2 3p^6$ for the S^{2-} anion. Notice that the sulfide anion now has the same electron configuration as the nearest noble gas argon. The sulfide ion is therefore considered to be **isoelectronic** with argon because the two species have the same number and configuration of electrons.

To write cation configurations, electrons are always removed *from the outermost orbitals with the highest energy first*. Therefore, it is sometimes worthwhile to first write the neutral atom's configuration in core notation with the final orbitals listed from smallest to largest, rather than in the order the orbitals fill. Then remove the appropriate electrons from the outer orbitals first.

For example, if asked to write the configuration for the Sn^{4+} ion, first write the configuration for a neutral Sn atom as $[Kr] 4d^{10} \mathbf{5s^2 5p^2}$ rather than writing $[Kr] \mathbf{5s^2} 4d^{10} \mathbf{5p^2}$.

Now remove the four *outermost* electrons to give the configuration for Sn^{4+}: $[Kr] 4d^{10}$. This avoids the error of removing two 4d electrons to give $[Kr] \mathbf{5s^2} 4d^8$. Note that an Sn^{2+} ion would form by losing the two 5p electrons, as they are at higher energy than the 5s.

As a final note, there are several exceptions to the orbital filling order discussed here. The elements Cr, Cu, Mo, Ag, and Au are examples of such exceptions. Your teacher may choose to discuss these and others and the possible reasons.

We shouldn't be surprised that irregularities exist. We have already seen ample evidence that the quantum world is full of surprises!

© Edvantage Interactive 2016

8.4 Activity: A Post-it® Periodic Table

Question

Can we organize a series of Post-it® notes on a standard periodic table to represent the order that orbitals are filled according the Aufbau principle?

Materials

- a small pad of each of four different colors of Post-it® or other sticky notes
- transparent tape

Procedure

Refer to the diagonal diagram in Figure 8.4.7 showing the order for filling sublevels.

1.. Obtain a pad of small Post-it® or other sticky notes. Choose a separate color for each of the four shapes, s, p, d, and f, and write the symbol for each of the 19 sublevels (1s, 2s, 2p, etc....) on a separate note.

2. Place the notes from left to right on a flat surface in the correct order that each sublevel fills.

3. Obtain a copy of the periodic table from your teacher. Number each horizontal period of the table, beginning with 1 for the top period containing H and He, down to 7 for Fr.

4. Now "read" the periods left-to-right like words on a page, moving down at the end of each. Trim the bottom portion of each Post-it® note to fit, and stick the appropriate sublevel symbol onto each section of each period as you read it.

Results and Discussion

1. Once you're finished, confirm the correct location of each Post-it® note sublevel symbol with your teacher. Then place transparent tape over each to permanently attach it to the periodic table. Save this completed table for the discussion coming up in the next chapter.

8.4 Review Questions

1. If hydrogen's electron exists in a spherical orbital, why doesn't this mean that the electron moves around the nucleus in a circle?

2. What is the difference between a 1s orbital and a 2s orbital? What does that difference indicate about an electron possessing energy equal to $n = 2$ as compared to $n = 1$?

3. Describe the two differences between a $2p_x$ orbital and a $3p_y$ orbital.

4. The lobes of a p orbital disappear at the nucleus. What does this tell us about electrons in p orbitals?

5. You may have heard in previous science classes that the maximum numbers of electrons that can exist in the first four energy levels are 2, 8, 8, and 18 respectively. Do you agree with those numbers and if not, what should they be?

6. The electron configuration for phosphorus, written in core notation, is [Ne] $3s^2\,3p^3$.
    What two things does Hund's rule tell us about the three electrons in the 3p sublevel?

7. Use the periodic table to complete the following table:

Atom or Ion	Full Electron Configuration	Core Notation
Ge		
Zn^{2+}		
Sr		
Br^-		
Sn		
In^{3+}		

8. (a) Use the periodic table to identify the neutral atoms having the following electron configurations:

Electron Configuration	Element Name
[Ne] $3s^2$	
[Ar] $4s^2\, 3d^5$	
[Kr] $5s^2\, 4d^{10}\, 5p^3$	
[Xe] $6s^2\, 4f^7$	

(b) Notice where each of these elements is located on the periodic table. Look at the highest energy sublevel being filled (**bold type**) in each of the atoms in the table, and identify the four different sections of the periodic table associated with each of these four sublevels.

9. Consider the following six stable ions: N^{3-}, O^{2-}, F^-, Na^+, Mg^{2+}, and Al^{3+}.
   (a) How many electrons are present in each ion?

   (b) Write a single electron configuration representing all of the ions.

   (c) Which neutral atom possesses this electron configuration? What does this suggest about a possible reason for some ion formation?

10. (a) Complete the following table for some elements in two families of the periodic table.

Alkali Metals	Core Notation	# Outer Electrons	Halogens	Core Notation	# Outer Electrons
lithium			fluorine		
sodium			chlorine		
potassium			bromine		
rubidium			iodine		

(b) Consider the numbers of outer electrons present and suggest a reason why elements belonging to the same chemical family demonstrate similar chemical behaviour.

(c) What change occurs in the atoms as we move down each chemical family?

11. (a) On a separate sheet of paper, draw an orbital diagram for an atom of iron with sublevel energy increasing vertically. Arrange equal energy orbitals in each sublevel horizontally.

   (b) Use a highlighter to label the electrons that would be lost when the Fe^{3+} cation forms.

8.5 Quantum Theory and the Bohr Model of the Atom

The Bohr Model

One of the scientists who paid particular attention to the work of Planck and Einstein was a young Danish physicist named Niels Bohr. As a young grad student, Bohr had met Ernest Rutherford at the Cavendish Laboratory in Cambridge and then worked with Rutherford at the University of Manchester. Bohr believed in the nuclear atomic model and started to see a way to "save" it using the quantum theory. If energy was indeed quantized and so could be seen to have only certain values and not others, perhaps the energies associated with electrons orbiting the nucleus had similar restrictions.

Bohr was working on this idea at Rutherford's laboratory in Manchester in 1912. In the middle of his experiments and calculations, he returned to Copenhagen to get married. He was so excited about his work that he managed to convince his new bride to cancel their honeymoon and return to England with him. Soon thereafter, Niels Bohr completed one of the most brilliant papers on atomic structure ever written. In doing so, he managed to rescue Rutherford's nuclear model of the atom.

Scientific theories are carefully constructed on a firm foundation of data gathered from a multitude of meticulously documented, rigorously controlled, and perpetually repeatable experiments. Bohr's theory was no exception. In Grade 11, we discussed the conduction of charges through gases in glass discharge tubes. Those experiments in the later years of the 1800s not only led to Thomson's discovery of the electron, but also provided Bohr with valuable data for his ideas about the nature of those electrons in atoms.

Quantum Theory Rescues the Nuclear Model

Bohr knew that when high voltage was applied across the electrodes of a sealed glass tube containing a gas such as hydrogen, the gas was heated and emitted light. As part of his investigations, Bohr looked at this light through a spectroscope. A spectroscope is a device similar to a prism, which separates the light into its component wavelengths. When Bohr viewed the light from the heated hydrogen through the spectroscope, he saw only a series of coloured lines against a black background, rather than a continuous rainbow of colour. For hydrogen, the same pattern of four coloured lines was always seen: a red, blue-green, blue, and violet line (Figure 8.5.1). For each gaseous element used, a bright-line pattern unique to that element called a **bright-line spectrum** always appeared (much like a bar code on a modern grocery item).

The phenomenon had mystified scientists. None could explain why only certain colours of light, each corresponding to specific wavelength, frequency, and energy, were emitted by the heated gases — until Bohr. Bohr realized that by applying quantum principles to the behaviour of hydrogen's lone electron, he could not only account for the existence of the bright-line spectrum, but also save Rutherford's nuclear model of the atom.

410.1   433.9   486.0   656.1

Wavelength (nm)

Figure 8.5.1 *Hydrogen's bright-line spectrum*

Bohr's Postulates

Bohr's postulates for hydrogen are summarized below:

1. The hydrogen atom had only certain **allowed energy levels** or **stationary states.** Each of these states corresponded to a circular electron orbit of a fixed size. The larger the allowed orbit, the greater the energy associated with it. No other orbits existed in the atom. Each allowed energy state was given an integer number "n" that Bohr called a **quantum number** with allowed values that ranged from 1 to ∞ (i.e., n could equal 1, 2, 3…etc). The lowest energy (smallest) orbit corresponded to the lowest allowed energy state called the **ground state** and was designated as $n = 1$. The larger orbits of greater energy were designated as $n = 2$, $n = 3$, $n = 4$, etc. and were said to be **excited states**.

2. As long as an electron moved in an allowed orbit or stationary state, the electron (and therefore the atom) did not radiate or absorb energy.

3. The electron could only move from one allowed orbit to another if it absorbed or emitted an amount of energy exactly equal to the energy difference between the two orbits, ΔE. This meant that the hydrogen atom could only change from one stationary energy state to another.

Bohr's Postulates — Another Look

Postulate 1 employed Planck's theory by quantizing the energies allowed for the hydrogen atom (and thus the electron). Because only certain-sized orbits were allowed, the atom was restricted to existing in only certain energy states and not others. Think of the electron as a ball on a staircase. Just as the ball can only rest on any particular stair and so have only certain amounts of potential energy and not others, so too is the electron restricted to only specific energies.

Postulate 2 meant that the nuclear model of the atom proposed by Rutherford would not collapse as predicted. Although the postulate violated the laws of classical physics, Bohr insisted that it must be true, even though he didn't know why.

Postulates 1 and 3 explained the origin and nature of hydrogen's bright-line spectrum. An atomic spectrum could not be continuous (i.e., a complete rainbow of colours) because an atom's energy states could only be certain values and not others. When a sample of hydrogen gas is heated in a discharge tube, the electrons in the hydrogen atoms absorb sufficient amounts of energy to "jump" to larger orbits. (In any one hydrogen atom, only one electron is involved, but in a sample of the gas, the electrons of many hydrogen atoms are undergoing many transitions). Once in a higher energy orbit, any electron could then return to a lower energy orbit by emitting a specific amount of energy corresponding exactly to the difference between the higher and lower energy orbits (Figure 8.5.2). If the frequency of that emitted energy corresponds to any part of the visible spectrum, then a bright line of that specific colour would be seen. Four of hydrogen's electron transitions emitted energy in the visible spectrum.

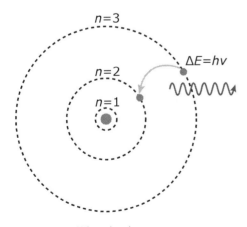

Figure 8.5.2 *When the electron moves to an inner energy level, it emits energy.*

If an excited electron emits energy and drops to $n = 2$ from a higher energy orbit, the wavelength of the emitted energy corresponds to a particular colour of visible light. If an electron drops from $n = 3$ to $n = 2$, the energy difference between the two orbits (and therefore the energy emitted) corresponds to that of red light. Hence the red line appears in the emission spectrum. The blue-green line results from an electron transition from $n = 4$ to $n = 2$, the blue line from an electron transition from $n = 5$ to $n = 2$, and the violet line from an electron transition from $n = 6$ to $n = 2$. This series of four bright lines in the visible spectrum is called the Balmer series, named after the Swiss schoolteacher who first derived a mathematical relationship between the lines in hydrogen's visible emission spectrum (Figure 8.5.3).

Bohr's model of the hydrogen atom was successful in explaining the mystery of bright line spectra. His calculations and predictions worked for hydrogen and he even calculated the radius of the orbit for hydrogen's electron in its ground state. In 1922, Niels Bohr was awarded the Nobel Prize in physics.

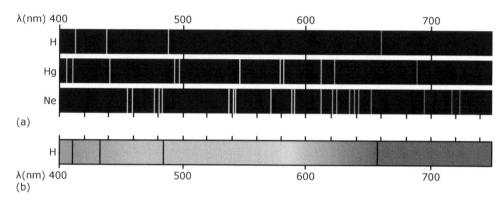

Figure 8.5.3 *(a) The emission spectra of hydrogen, mercury, and neon; (b) The absorption spectrum of hydrogen*

The Emission Spectrum of Hydrogen — Two Views

The diagram on the left in Figure 8.5.4 shows the circular orbits Bohr envisioned for the hydrogen electron and the transitions associated with the Lyman, Balmer, and Paschen emission spectra. The diagram on the right shows that the energy *differences* between various stationary states (*n*) decrease as the energies of those states increase. The arrows pointing down represent electrons falling to lower energy states and thus emitting energy. Electrons absorbing energy could be indicated by arrows pointing up and would represent absorption spectra.

Any electron transitions from an excited state down to $n = 1$ result in the emission of energy in the ultraviolet region of the electromagnetic spectrum (the Lyman series). Any transitions from excited states down to the third and fourth orbits result in energies in the infrared region being emitted (the Paschen and Brackett series respectively).

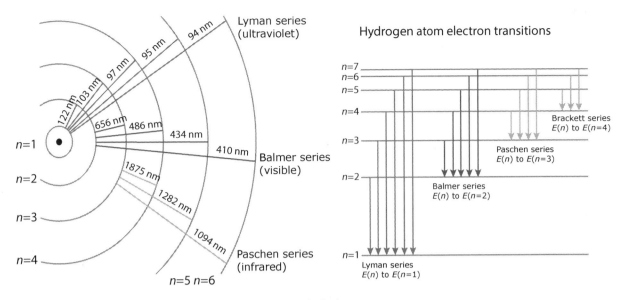

Figure 8.5.4 *The Lyman, Balmer, and Paschen emission series for hydrogen*

Quick Check

1. Describe the appearance of hydrogen's "bright-line" spectrum.

   _____

2. Briefly indicate how electrons generate each visible line in hydrogen's emission spectrum.

   _____

   _____

3. Which electron transitions in the emission spectrum generate lines in the UV region of the electromagnetic spectrum?

   _____

Using Some Simple Equations

In 1885, a Swiss schoolteacher named Johann Balmer found an equation that was able to determine the wavelengths of the lines in the visible portion of hydrogen's emission spectrum. Three years later, the Swedish physicist Johannes Rydberg derived an equation that could be used to calculate the wavelengths of all of hydrogen's spectral lines. This is worth mentioning because if a mathematical relationship exists for a natural phenomenon, it usually means there's a theoretical foundation waiting to be discovered. Both Balmer's and Rydberg's equations were based on data, rather than theory. Neither equation had any physical meaning in terms of atomic structure, but both worked.

The physical meaning was supplied by Niels Bohr. Bohr derived an equation for the energy associated with the electron in each allowed orbit. He correctly predicted the visible, ultraviolet, and infrared spectral lines in hydrogen's emission spectrum by calculating the energy differences between those stationary states.

Although a rigorous mathematical treatment of this material is not intended here, we will present two equations that are quite straightforward. The first equation gives the

---

change in energy ΔE (energy of photon released) when an electron initially in a higher energy orbit (with a higher quantum number n_h) drops to a lower energy orbit (and so with a lower quantum number n_l).

$$\Delta E = R\left(1/n_l^2 - 1/n_h^2\right)$$

where b is a constant with value of 2.18×10^{-18} J.

The second equation arises from the fact that, according to Planck's equation, the energy of this photon, $\Delta E = hv$. Because $v = c/\lambda$, we can replace ΔE with hc/λ. Now dividing both sides of the equation by hc yields:

$$1/\lambda = R/hc\left(1/n_l^2 - 1/n_h^2\right)$$

This equation allows us to solve for the wavelength λ of the spectral line we would observe when the electron lost energy as it made the above transition.

The combination of the constants, R/hc, is itself a constant. Remembering that Planck's constant, $h = 6.626 \times 10^{-34}$ J·s and that the speed of light, $c = 3.00 \times 10^8$ m/s, we can combine these three constants to give $R/hc = 1.097\ 30 \times 10^7$ m^{-1}. Let's use this to calculate the wavelength of the spectral line we would see when hydrogen's electron made the transition from $n = 4$ down to $n = 2$.

Sample Problem — Calculating the Wavelength of Emission Spectral Lines

Calculate the wavelength λ (in nm) of the spectral line seen in hydrogen's emission spectrum when hydrogen's electron falls from the fourth allowed orbit ($n = 4$) to the second allowed orbit ($n = 2$).

What to Think about

1. Consider the equation:
$$1/\lambda = (1.097\ 30 \times 10^7\ \text{m}^{-1})\left(1/n_l^2 - 1/n_h^2\right)$$
The values of n_l and n_h are given in the question:
$n = 4$ and $n = 2$.

2. Convert this to nanometers.
This value corresponds exactly to the green line seen in hydrogen's emission spectrum.

How to Do It

$$
\begin{aligned}
1/\lambda &= (1.097\ 30 \times 10^7\ \text{m}^{-1})\left(1/n_l^2 - 1/n_h^2\right) \\
&= (1.097\ 30 \times 10^7\ \text{m}^{-1})\left(1/2^2 - 1/4^2\right) \\
&= (1.097\ 30 \times 10^7\ \text{m}^{-1})(0.1875) \\
&= 2.0574 \times 10^6\ \text{m}^{-1}
\end{aligned}
$$

$$\lambda = \frac{1}{2.0574 \times 10^6\ \text{m}^{-1}} = 4.8604 \times 10^{-7}\ \text{m}$$

$$4.860 \times 10^{-7}\ \text{m} \times \frac{1.0 \times 10^9\ \text{nm}}{\text{m}} = 486.04\ \text{nm}$$

Practice Problem

1. Use equation $\Delta E = R\left(1/n_l^2 - 1/n_h^2\right)$ and the value for b given above to calculate the energy released when an excited hydrogen electron drops from the fourth allowed orbit ($n = 4$) to the second allowed orbit ($n = 2$).

© Edvantage Interactive 2016

Quick Check

1. (a) List three properties of waves such as water waves or visible light.

   _____

   (b) What would you expect to happen when two water waves moving in opposite directions met each other?

   _____

2. (a) List three properties of solid objects or particles such as the marbles in a bag.

   _____

   (b) What would you expect to happen when two marbles moving in opposite directions met each other?

   _____

3. Are any of your answers to question 1 identical to question 2? (Stay tuned...)

   _____

Waves Particle Duality

A serious challenge to Rutherford's atomic model arose almost immediately. A very secure prediction of the physics available at the end of the 1800s was that accelerating charges should radiate energy. Because orbiting electrons are accelerating charges, electrons in atoms should lose energy. That prediction was catastrophic for Rutherford's model. It meant that all atoms, and so also all matter, should collapse in a fraction of a second as their electrons lost energy and spiraled into the nucleus! Obviously, a significant piece of the atomic puzzle was missing and even Rutherford himself was ready to abandon his view of the atom. Yet, his conclusions and his nuclear model were correct. The real problem was that the physics of the day needed to be re-written to explain the behaviour of electrons in atoms.

To begin to understand how the solution came about, we must consider the work of German physicist Max Planck. In 1900, this conservative professor began nothing short of a revolution in physics. He proposed that energy, long considered to be strictly a wave phenomenon, could be shown to behave like particles in the form of very tiny, discreet energy packets or bundles he called quanta (plural for quantum). Planck called this the quantum theory and arrived at his conclusions (reluctantly) by studying the energy radiated from heated solids. Planck developed the following equation for the energy associated with each packet or quantum:

$$E = h\nu$$

where E = energy, ν = frequency, h = a very tiny proportionality constant ($h = 6.626 \times 10^{-34}$ J·s) called Planck's constant. According to Planck, energy could only be absorbed or emitted in whole numbers of quanta, that is, one quantum of energy ($E = h\nu$), two quanta ($E = 2h\nu$), three quanta ($E = 3h\nu$) and so on, but nowhere in between. Think of each energy quantum as a glass marble in a bag of identical marbles (Figure 8.5.6). In the same way that you could only ever add or remove a specific amount of glass from the bag in the form of a whole number of marbles, so too could amounts of energy only be absorbed or emitted in the form of whole numbers of quanta.

Figure 8.5.6 *Quanta of energy are like marbles in bag. The marbles can only be removed as whole units.*

At the end of the 1800s, the behaviour of waves and the behaviour of particles were seen as very different and mutually exclusive. Waves were disturbances that moved through space, could pass through and interfere with each other, and could have any value within a range. Particles were objects with definite boundaries that bounced off each other when they collided and could only exist in certain whole-number quantities. A firm experimental and mathematical foundation supported the idea that waves were fundamentally different from particles. To now suggest that waves could behave like particles was almost sacrilegious! Planck himself wrote about his work: "By nature, I am peacefully inclined and reject all doubtful adventures. …However, a theoretical interpretation had to be found at any cost….I was ready to sacrifice every one of my previous convictions about physical laws."

Planck's theory wasn't taken very seriously at first. But in 1905, a 26-year-old clerk in a Swiss patent office named Albert Einstein wrote five papers that changed the scientific world forever. One of those papers used the quantum theory to explain a phenomenon involving light called the "photoelectric effect" that had baffled physicists until then. According to Einstein, the only way to make sense of the photoelectric effect was to consider light as being composed of tiny discreet packets of energy. (These were later called "photons" by American chemist Gilbert Lewis.) Einstein's paper was the first practical application of the quantum theory and as a result, the theory soon began to gain widespread acceptance. In 1921, Einstein was awarded the Nobel Prize in physics for his explanation of the photoelectric effect.

Quick Check

1. Briefly state what it means for something to be a "quantized."

   _____

2. Give three common examples of things considered to be "quantized."

   _____

   _____

3. According to Planck, could an amount of energy equal to $2.5hv$ be absorbed or emitted by an object? Explain.

   _____

   _____

© Edvantage Interactive 2016

Practice Problems

I) The Lyman series in the emission spectrum of the hydrogen atom consists of transitions from higher levels to n = 1 level.

    a) Calculate the maximum and minimum wavelengths lines, nm, of this series, noting the n values of the higher levels involved in each.

    b) The series limit of the Balmer series, transitions to n = 2 occurs at about 365 nm, corresponding an energy of 5.49×10^{-19} J. Compare this energy to the lowest energy transition in the Lyman series and explain what this implies about the spacing between the energy levels in the H atom.

II) When light with a wavelength of 300 nm falls on sodium, electrons with a KE of 1.68×10^5 J/mol are emitted. What is the minimum energy needed to remove an electron from sodium? What is the maximum wavelength of light that will cause an electron to be emitted?

III) The energy needed to dissociate a chlorine molecule into chlorine atoms is 243 kJ/mol. What is the maximum wavelength of light that will initiate the substitution reaction of chlorine with an alkane?

IV) a) Calculate the frequency of the radiation released by the transitions of an electron in a hydrogen atom from the n= 5 to the n= 3 level. Show all of your work.

b) Is this part of the Lyman, Balmer or Paschen series? In what range of electromagnetic radiation is the photon that is released?

© Edvantage Interactive 2016

8.5 Review Questions

1. Explain the serious problem initially associated with Rutherford's atomic model.

2. State Planck's quantum theory in your own words.

3. Why was this theory not accepted by most physicists at first?

4. What finally convinced the scientific community that Planck's theory was credible?

5. Explain how the work of Planck and Einstein contributed to Bohr's theory about electron behaviour.

6. State how Bohr's theory "saved" Rutherford's nuclear atomic model.

7. Briefly explain why hydrogen's visible emission spectrum does not resemble a continuous spectrum or rainbow

8. Describe what you would expect to see if hydrogen's visible emission and absorption spectra were superimposed upon each other.

10. Calculate the energy released when an excited hydrogen electron returns from $n = 5$ to $n = 2$.

9. Explain why, when hydrogen's electron transitions occur from excited states down to $n = 1$ or to $n = 3$, no visible spectral lines are observed.

11. Calculate the wavelength of the spectral line seen when the electron transition described in 10 above occurs, and use the wavelength to identify the colour of this line.

© Edvantage Interactive 2016

9 Oxidation-Reduction and Its Applications

By the end of this chapter, you should be able to do the following:

- Describe oxidation and reduction processes
- Analyze the relative strengths of reducing and oxidizing agents
- Balance equations for redox reactions
- Determine the concentration of a species by performing a redox titration
- Analyze an electrochemical cell in terms of its components and their functions
- Describe how electrochemical concepts can be used in various practical applications
- Analyze the process of metal corrosion in electrochemical terms
- Analyze an electrolytic cell in terms of its components and their functions
- Describe how electrolytic concepts can be used in various practical applications

By the end of this chapter, you should know the meaning of these **key terms**:

- cathodic protection
- corrosion
- electrochemical cell
- electrode
- electrolysis
- electrolytic cell
- electroplating
- electrorefining
- Faraday's law
- half-cell
- half-reaction
- oxidation
- oxidation number
- oxidizing agent
- redox reaction
- redox titration
- reducing agent
- reduction
- volt

An old ship undergoing a redox reaction — rusting

9.1 Oxidation-Reduction

Warm Up

1. Complete the following table of compounds of multivalent metals.

Name	Formula	Metal Ion Charge
	$FeCl_3$	
	$Fe(CH_3COO)_2$	
	$Mn(BrO_3)_2$	
	MnO_2	
	$KMnO_4$	

2. How did you determine the ion charge of the metal in each case?

_____

_____

Electrochemistry

You have learned about the importance of chemistry to our everyday lives. We use conversions of chemical energy to other energy forms to do work for us, such as heating our homes and moving our vehicles. The heat or enthalpy stored in chemical bonds is being used at this very moment to sustain every living cell in your body.

There is another form of chemical conversion that is critical to life. This is the conversion of chemical to electrical energy. This conversion and the reverse change of electrical to chemical energy make up the study of **electrochemistry.**

Electrochemistry is the study of the interchange of chemical and electrical energy.

All electrochemical reactions have one thing in common. They involve the transfer of electrons from one reacting species to another. Most of the major types of chemical reactions you learned about in previous years involve electron transfer.

Synthesis and decomposition reactions involving species in elemental form always involve electron transfer. Single displacement and combustion reactions also fall into this category.

Reactions that involve electron transfer are commonly called **oxidation-reduction reactions.** Such reactions are often referred to as **redox reactions** for short.

Double displacement reactions are the major group of reactions that do not involve electron transfer. Synthesis and decomposition reactions involving oxides are a smaller group. Reactions that *do not* involve electron transfer are referred to as **metathesis reactions.**

© Edvantage Interactive 2016

Oxidation Numbers: A System for Tracking Electrons

The easiest way to determine whether electrons have been transferred between elements during a chemical reaction is to keep track of each atom's **oxidation number** (also referred to as the **oxidation state**).

> The **oxidation number** is the real or apparent charge of an atom or ion when all bonds in the species containing the atom or ion are considered to be ionic.

You probably referred to the oxidation number as the *combining capacity*. Multivalent metals such as iron, for example, may combine with chlorine to form $FeCl_2$ or $FeCl_3$, depending on the oxidation number of the iron ion involved. The compound containing iron with an oxidation number of +2 has the formula $FeCl_2$ and is called iron(II) chloride. This distinguishes it from $FeCl_3$ or iron(III) chloride, which contains iron with an oxidation number of +3. Notice that the charge is indicated before the number in an oxidation number.

Oxidation numbers (states) may be assigned to any atom in any aggregation, whether the atom exists in an element, a monatomic ion, or as part of a polyatomic ion or compound. The aggregation is simply the arrangement of atoms the element is in. As we're assuming all species are ionic in order to assign oxidation numbers, we should remember that the more electronegative elements gain electrons, so all electrons in an ionic bond should be assumed to belong to the more electronegative element. The easiest way to assign oxidation numbers to atoms is to follow the simple set of rules given in Table 9.1.1.

Table 9.1.1 *Rules for Assigning Oxidation numbers*

Rule	Statement about Oxidation Number	Examples
1.	Atoms in elemental form = 0	Na, O_2, P_4, As, Zn
2.	Monatomic ions = the ion's charge	K^+, Ca^{2+}, Fe^{2+}, Fe^{3+}, Cl^-
3.	Oxygen = 2– except in peroxides (O_2^{2-}) = – and OF_2 = 2+	Na_2O_2, OF_2
4.	Hydrogen = + except in **metal** hydrides = –	CaH_2, LiH
5.	Oxidation numbers in compounds must sum to zero.	CuCl, $CuCl_2$ contain copper(I) and copper(II)
6.	Oxidation numbers in polyatomic ions must sum to the ion charge.	ClO_4^-, ClO_3^- contain chlorine = 7+ and 5+
7.	Always assign the more electronegative element a negative oxidation number.	PF_5 contains F = – and thus P = 5+
8.	In a compound or ion containing more than two elements, the element written furthest to the right takes its most common oxidation number.	SCN^- contains N = 3– (most common), S = 2– (negative value), thus C = 4+.

If the species contains oxygen and/or hydrogen, it is usually a good idea to assign their oxidation numbers first. For a species containing multiple types of atoms, assign the more electronegative element first. If the more electronegative element can have more than one oxidation number, use its most common oxidation number.

It is important to note that we always calculate the oxidation number of *one* atom of a particular element. While they are useful in the *calculation* of oxidation numbers, the subscripts that may be assigned to a particular atom have *no effect* on the oxidation number of that atom.

Practice Problems — Assigning Oxidation Numbers

Assign the oxidation number of each atom in the following species:

1. H_2O

2. Cs_2O_2

3. CO_3^{2-}

4. $Na_2Cr_2O_7$

5. BaH_2

6. NH_4^+

7. S_8

8. $Al_2(SO_4)_3$

Oxidation and Reduction

When an atom gains electrons during a reaction, its oxidation number becomes less positive or more negative. This is logical as the electrons being gained are negative particles. A substance whose oxidation number becomes smaller is being reduced.

A *decrease in oxidation number* is called **reduction**.

On the other hand, when an atom loses electrons during a reaction, its oxidation number becomes more positive. This is because the number of protons (positive charges) does not change, but there are fewer electrons. Consequently, the atom now has more positive protons than negative electrons and hence the net charge is greater. The substance whose oxidation number increases is being oxidized.

An *increase in oxidation number* is called **oxidation**.

In the equation shown below, the oxidation number of the iron increases by two, while the oxidation number of the Cu^{2+} ion decreases by two. Hence, iron metal is oxidized and copper(II) ion is reduced.

It is important to realize that reduction and oxidation always occur together in a reaction. If one atom has its oxidation number increase due to a loss of electrons, another substance must have its oxidation number decrease due to a gain of electrons. This is why reactions that involve electron transfer are called oxidation-reduction reactions or redox reactions for short. These reactions are always *coupled* and the oxidation number changes are entirely due to the transfer of electrons.

Remember that we always state the oxidation number for just *one* atom of a particular element, *no matter what subscript or coefficient* may be associated with the atom. Figure 9.1.1 shows a handy mnemonic device to help you remember what happens to electrons during the redox process.

oxidation

$$Fe(s) + Cu^{2+}(aq) \longrightarrow Fe^{2+}(aq) + Cu(s)$$

reduction

A *gain of electrons* is **REDUCTION**, while a *loss of electrons* is **OXIDATION**.

LEO goes GER

lose electrons = oxidation   gain electrons = reduction

Figure 9.1.1 *Leo can help you remember the redox process.*

Quick Check

Study the following reaction:

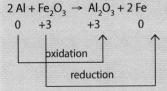

$2\,Al + Fe_2O_3 \rightarrow Al_2O_3 + 2\,Fe$

1. (a) Are electrons gained or lost by each iron(III) ion? _____

     How many? _____

    (b) Are electrons are gained or lost by each Al atom? _____

     How many? _____

2. How many electrons were transferred in total during the reaction? _____

3. What happened to the oxide ion, O^{2-}, during the reaction?

     _____

Agents Cause Electron Transfer

Examination of the Quick Check above indicates that the number of electrons lost by the species being oxidized must always equal the number of electrons gained by the species being reduced.

So far we have examined electron transfer in terms of the species that lost or gained the electrons. Another approach is to view the event from the perspective of the species that cause the electron loss or gain. In this sense, the species that gets oxidized causes another species to gain electrons and be reduced. For this reason, the species that gets oxidized is called a reducing agent. A similar argument describes the chemical that takes electrons from another species and is consequently reduced, as an oxidizing agent (Figure 9.1.2).

> A substance that is *reduced* acts as an **oxidizing agent**, while a substance that is *oxidized* acts as a **reducing agent**.

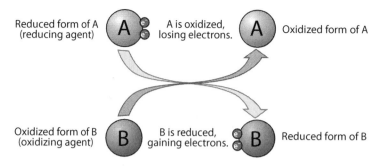

Figure 9.1.2 *Species being oxidized and reduced act as reducing and oxidizing agents.*

Solving Problems with Redox Reactions

In the sample problem below, the second example may not appear to fit any of the traditional five categories of classification from our past chemistry studies. (It is the combustion of ammonia.) Often redox reactions do not fit our classic categories. You will encounter many more of these in the rest of this chapter.

© Edvantage Interactive 2016

Sample Problem — Recognizing Oxidizing and Reducing Agents

Indicate the oxidizing and reducing agent in each of the following reactions:

(a) $Mg(s) + 2 HCl(aq) \rightarrow MgCl_2(aq) + H_2(g)$ (b) $4 NH_3(g) + 7 O_2(g) \rightarrow 4 NO_2(g) + 6 H_2O(l)$

What to Think About	How to Do It
(a) $Mg(s) + 2 HCl(aq) \rightarrow MgCl_2(aq) + H_2(g)$ 1. Assign oxidation numbers to all atoms in the equation. (You may wish to write these values above each atom to help keep track.) 2. Indicate the increase in oxidation number as an oxidation and the decrease in oxidation number as a reduction. 3. The species that was oxidized is the reducing agent. The one that was reduced is the oxidizing agent. This is a classic single displacement reaction.	Mg: $0 \rightarrow +2$ H: $+1 \rightarrow 0$ Cl: $1 \rightarrow -1$ Magnesium atom was oxidized. Hydrogen ion was reduced. Reducing agent: magnesium atom (Mg) Oxidizing agent: hydrogen ion (H^+) Notice that the Mg atom lost two electrons, while each H^+ ion gained one.
(b) $4 NH_3(g) + 7 O_2(g) \rightarrow 4 NO_2(g) + 6 H_2O(l)$ 1. Assign oxidation numbers to all elements in the equation. Notice that even though hydrogen is written second in the formula for ammonia, ammonia is not a *metal* hydride so hydrogen is assigned its usual oxidation number of +1. 2. Indicate the increase in oxidation number as an oxidation and the decrease in oxidation number as a reduction. 3. The species that was oxidized is the reducing agent. The one that was reduced is the oxidizing agent.	H: $+1 \rightarrow +1$ O: $0 \rightarrow -2$ (in both products) N: $-3 \rightarrow +4$ Oxygen gas was reduced. N in ammonia was oxidized. Oxidizing agent: oxygen gas (O_2) Reducing agent: ammonia (NH_3) NOTE: When the atom that is oxidized or reduced belongs to a covalent compound, we indicate the *entire species* as the agent.

Practice Problems — Recognizing Oxidizing and Reducing Agents

Determine the oxidizing and reducing agent in each of the following reactions. Write the appropriate formula for each agent. Begin by clearly indicating the oxidation numbers of all elements in each equation. Question 1 is done as an example. Hint: Always show the agent as it would appear in a *net ionic equation*. (See H^+ in Sample Problem 1.1.1 above, as HCl is a strong acid.)

1. $\overset{0}{C}(s) + 2 \overset{0}{H_2}(g) \rightarrow \overset{-4\,+1}{CH_4}(g)$ O.A. = C(s)   R.A. = $H_2(g)$

2. $3 Sr(s) + 2 FeBr_3(aq) \rightarrow 2 Fe(s) + 3 SrBr_2(aq)$

3. $5 CO(g) + Cl_2O_5(s) \rightarrow 5 CO_2(g) + Cl_2(g)$

4. $4 PH_3(g) \rightarrow P_4(g) + 6 H_2(g)$

5. $Ba(s) + 2 H_2O(l) \rightarrow Ba(OH)_2(s) + H_2(g)$

9.1 Review Questions

1. Elements that get oxidized (act as reducing agents) form (a)_____ ions when they react. This means reducing agents are generally (b)_____. Reducing agents may also be (c)_____ charged ions. The most active reducing agents likely belong to the (d)_____ family on the periodic table. The most active oxidizing agents must belong to the (e)_____ family.

2. Give the oxidation number for the underlined element in each of the following species:

   (a) $\underline{Ca}I_2$ (b) $\underline{O}F_2$ (c) $\underline{C}_6H_{12}O_6$ (d) $Rb_2\underline{O}_2$ (e) $\underline{S}_2O_3{}^{2-}$ (f) $Be\underline{H}_2$ (g) $\underline{Br}O^-$ (h) $\underline{Cl}_2$

3. (a) What is an oxidizing agent?

   (b) What is a reducing agent?

   (c) How would you expect electronegativity to be related to the strength of each?

4. For each of the following reactions, indicate the species being oxidized and reduced and show the oxidation numbers above their symbols.

   (a) $2\ KBrO_3(s)\ \rightarrow\ 2\ KBr(s) + 3\ O_2(g)$ Oxidized: Reduced:

   (b) $Sr(s) + 2\ CuNO_3(aq)\ \rightarrow\ Sr(NO_3)_2(aq) + 2\ Cu(s)$ Oxidized: Reduced:

   (c) $2\ F_2(g) + O_2(g)\ \rightarrow\ 2\ OF_2(g)$ Oxidized: Reduced:

   (d) $NH_4NO_3(s)\ \rightarrow\ N_2O(g) + 2\ H_2O(l)$ Oxidized: Reduced:

© Edvantage Interactive 2016

5. Determine the oxidizing and reducing agent in each of the following reactions. Then indicate the number of electrons transferred by one atom of the reducing agent.

(a) $2 Sn(s) + O_2(g) \rightarrow 2 SnO(s)$ OA: RA: No. e⁻:

(b) $2 V(s) + 5 I_2(g) \rightarrow 2 VI_5(s)$ OA: RA: No. e⁻:

(c) $Sr(s) + 2 HCl(aq) \rightarrow SrCl_2(aq) + H_2(g)$ OA: RA: No. e⁻:

(d) $C_3H_8(g) + 5 O_2(g) \rightarrow 3 CO_2(g) + 4 H_2O(g)$ OA: RA: No. e⁻:

6. The pictures indicate the same reacting system following a 12 h period.

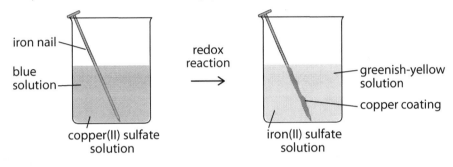

(a) Write a balanced redox equation (in net ionic form) to show what has occurred in the beaker over time.

(b) Which substance is the oxidizing agent?   The reducing agent?

(c) How many electrons were transferred in the equation?

7. Give the oxidation number of the underlined element in each species:

(a) P̲³⁻   (b) $(NH_4)_2\underline{Zr}(SO_4)_3$ (c) $Na_2\underline{C}_2O_4$ (d) $\underline{N}_2H_5Cl$ (e) $\underline{Mn}O_4{}^{2-}$

8.

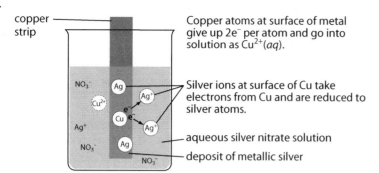

copper strip

Copper atoms at surface of metal give up $2e^-$ per atom and go into solution as $Cu^{2+}(aq)$.

Silver ions at surface of Cu take electrons from Cu and are reduced to silver atoms.

aqueous silver nitrate solution

deposit of metallic silver

(a) Write a balanced net ionic equation to represent the redox reaction occurring in the beaker.

(b) Which substance is getting oxidized?   Reduced?

(c) Which substance is the reducing agent?   The oxidizing agent?

(d) How many electrons are transferred in each reaction?

9. What family on the periodic table would likely contain:

(a) The strongest reducing agents?

(b) The strongest oxidizing agents?

10. (a) Which of the following substances could be formed by the oxidation of ClO^-: ClO_4^-, Cl_2, ClO_2^-, Cl^-, ClO_3^-?

(b) The reduction of ClO^-?

© Edvantage Interactive 2016

9.2 Balancing Oxidation-Reduction Equations

Warm Up

Examine the following equation: $Zn(s) + Cu^+(aq) \rightarrow Zn^{2+}(aq) + Cu(s)$

1. Which species acts as a reducing agent and consequently is oxidized? _____

2. Which species acts as an oxidizing agent and consequently is reduced? _____

3. How many electrons are lost by each atom of the reducing agent as it is oxidized? _____

4. A Cu^+ ion accepts only one electron to become a neutral Cu atom. How many Cu^+ ions does it take to accept two electrons?

    _____

5. Add coefficients to the equation so that the number of electrons donated by the reducing agent equals the number of electrons received by the oxidizing agent.

6. Does the net charge of the reactants now equal the net charge of the products? _____

The Conservation of Mass *and* Charge

For the past several years, you've been applying Antoine Lavoisier's Law of Conservation of Mass to every chemical reaction you've encountered. This law states that the mass of the products equals the mass of the reactants in any chemical reaction. This is because no atoms are gained or lost during a chemical reaction. In previous science classes, you learned to place coefficients in front of various chemical species to make sure that the total number of atoms of each type on the reactant side would equal the total number of atoms of the same type on the product side of the equation.

You have learned to write net ionic equations for a variety of reaction types. In these equations, it was necessary to balance the charge as well as the number of each type of each atom. In oxidation-reduction reactions, charge is balanced by making certain that the number of electrons lost equals the number gained. This is sometimes done by simple inspection. An example is the reduction of copper(I) ion by zinc metal in the Warm Up question above. Examination reveals that two Cu^+ ions are reduced for every Zn atom oxidized, so the balanced equation is:

$$Zn(s) + 2\,Cu^+(aq) \rightarrow Zn^{2+}(aq) + 2\,Cu(s)$$

There are many oxidation-reduction reactions that are considerably more complex than this simple example. For these more complicated cases, we require a system to help us determine the number of electrons lost and gained so we can balance not only the number of atoms of each type, but also the number of electrons transferred.

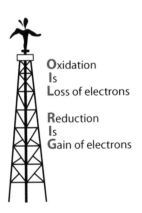

Oxidation
Is
Loss of electrons

Reduction
Is
Gain of electrons

Figure 9.2.1 *Remember the OIL RIG.*

Half-Reactions

It is possible to separate the reduction and oxidation portions of a redox reaction and to represent them as two separate **half-reactions**. For example, the sample reaction from the Warm Up may be broken into the following half-reactions:

$$Zn \rightarrow Zn^{2+} + 2e^- \text{ (oxidation) } and \text{ } Cu^+ + e^- \rightarrow Cu \text{ (reduction)}$$

Notice that the half-reactions include the number of electrons lost, in the case of oxidation, or gained, in the case of reduction.

> A **half-reaction** is an equation representing either an oxidation or a reduction, including the number of electrons lost or gained.

Balancing questions usually specify whether the reaction is occurring under acidic or basic conditions. Sometimes this will be readily apparent from the chemical reactants. If this isn't obvious or isn't stated, the conditions are likely acidic. It is possible, however, that it is occurring under neutral conditions. This means that when you balance it, you find that any H^+ or OH^- ions will cancel out and not appear in the final reaction statement.

Balancing Half-Reactions

Balancing a half-reaction requires the application of the following steps:

OTHER atoms — Balance atoms other than H and O.

All atoms *except* oxygen and hydrogen should be balanced first. This is not always necessary, so people tend to forget to balance the "other" atoms. Do *not* forget this step and watch the way coefficients affect charges.

OXYGEN atoms — Balance oxygen atoms by adding H_2O.

Redox reactions occur in aqueous solution. Consequently, you may add as many water molecules as required to balance the number of oxygen atoms.

HYDROGEN atoms — Balance hydrogen atoms by adding H^+ ions.

As most reactions occur in an acidic environment, you may add as many hydrogen ions, H^+, as are needed.

CHARGE — Balance the charge by adding electrons.

Always add the electrons to the *more positive* (or less negative) side. Add the number of electrons needed to ensure that the charge is the *same* on both sides of the equation. This is a good time to *check* that the total number of atoms of each type is in fact the same on both sides, so the equation is indeed balanced in terms of mass and charge.

Sample Problem — Balancing Half-Reactions in Acidic Conditions

Balance the following half-reaction occurring under acidic conditions: $ClO_4^- \rightarrow Cl_2$

Does this represent an oxidation or a reduction?

What to Think About	How to Do It
1. Balance atoms *other than* O and H. This requires a coefficient 2 in front of the perchlorate ion, ClO_4^-. Because the "other" atoms are often already balanced, students frequently do not need to balance them and as a result they tend to forget to apply the first step. *Always* check the "other" atoms first.	$2\ ClO_4^- \rightarrow Cl_2$
2. Balance *oxygen atoms* by adding H_2O *molecules*. As there are now 8 oxygen atoms on the reactant side, add 8 water molecules to the products.	$2\ ClO_4^- \rightarrow Cl_2 + 8\ H_2O$
3. Balance *hydrogen atoms* by adding H^+ *ions*. As there are now 16 hydrogen atoms on the product side, add 16 H^+ ions on the reactant side.	$16\ H^+ + 2\ ClO_4^- \rightarrow Cl_2 + 8\ H_2O$
4. Balance the charge by adding the e^- to the *more positive side*. As the total charge on the reactant side is +14 and there is no charge on the product side, add 14 electrons on the reactant side. Electrons are gained (they are "reactants").	$14\ e^- + 16\ H^+ + 2\ ClO_4^- \rightarrow Cl_2 + 8\ H_2O$ An **oxidation number check** is helpful to perform on half-reactions. Note that the number of electrons gained matches the oxidation number change. $\overset{+7}{2\ ClO_4^-} \rightarrow \overset{0}{Cl_2}$ ✓ [Gain of 7e^- (×2) = 14e^- gained.] This is a **reduction**.

While all redox reactions occur in aqueous solution, some occur in basic, rather than acidic conditions. When balancing a reaction that is occurring under basic conditions, chemists simply add a step to our sequence to convert from an acidic to a basic environment. When a redox reaction is to be balanced in base, *the hydrogen ions must be neutralized*. This is accomplished by adding hydroxide ions, OH^-, to cancel any H^+ ions. If hydroxide ions are added to one side of the equation, the same number must be added to the other side.

Thus, complete the first four steps and then…

BASE — Add OH^- ions to both sides to neutralize all H^+ Ions.

The number of OH^- ions added to neutralize the H^+ must be balanced by adding the same number of OH^- ions to the other side of the reaction. Free H^+ and OH^- ions on the same side of the equation should be combined to form the corresponding number of H_2O molecules. This step may result in water molecules showing up on both sides of the equation. Be sure to cancel so that H_2O appears on one side of the equation only.

It is critically important to pay close attention to all charges during the balancing process. Dropping the charge from an ion or inadvertently changing a charge will lead to a wrong answer every time!

Sample Problem — Balancing Half-Reactions in Basic Conditions

Balance the following half-reaction: $I_2 \rightarrow IO_4^-$ in base.
Does this represent an oxidation or a reduction?

What to Think About	How to Do It
1. Balance atoms *other than* O and H. A coefficient 2 is needed in front of IO_4^-.	$I_2 \rightarrow 2\,IO_4^-$
2. Balance *oxygen atoms* by adding H_2O *molecules*. As there are 8 oxygen atoms on the product side, add 8 H_2O molecules as reactants.	$8\,H_2O + I_2 \rightarrow 2\,IO_4^-$
3. Balance *hydrogen atoms* by adding H^+*ions* to the product side. As there are now 16 hydrogen atoms on the reactant side, add 16 H^+ to the product side.	$8\,H_2O + I_2 \rightarrow 2\,IO_4^- + 16\,H^+$
4. Add the e^- to the *more positive side*. As the total charge on the product side is +14 and there is no charge on the reactant side, add 14 electrons on the product side.	$8\,H_2O + I_2 \rightarrow 2\,IO_4^- + 16\,H^+ + 14e^-$
5. The objective for balancing a reaction in base is to *neutralize the H⁺ions*. As there are 16 H^+ ions on the product side, add 16 OH^- ions to both sides. Each combination of H^+ with OH^- forms an H_2O molecule. Water molecules present on both sides of the equation algebraically cancel. *NEVER leave H_2O molecules on both sides.* Electrons are produced-hence they are lost.	$\cancel{8\,H_2O} + I_2 \rightarrow 2\,IO_4^- + \cancel{16\,H^+} + 14e^-$ 16 OH⁻ .... 16 OH⁻ _____ $16\,OH^- + I_2 \rightarrow 2\,IO_4^- + 8\,H_2O + 14\,e^-$ Oxidation number check: $\quad 0 \qquad +7 \qquad\qquad\qquad\qquad\qquad ✓$ $I_2 \rightarrow 2\,IO_4^- \qquad$ [Loss of $7e^-$ (×2) = $14e^-$ lost] This process is an **oxidation**.

Practice Problems — Balancing Half-Reactions in Acidic and Basic Conditions

Balance the following half-reactions. Assume the reactions occur in acid unless specified otherwise. In each case, indicate whether the half-reaction is an oxidation or a reduction.

1. $Sm \rightarrow Sm^{3+}$

2. $NO_3^- \rightarrow NH_4^+$

3. $IO_4^- \rightarrow IO_3^-$ (basic)

4. $S_2O_3^{2-} \rightarrow SO_4^{2-}$

5. $BrO_3^- \rightarrow Br_2$ (basic)

© Edvantage Interactive 2016

Redox Reactions

The equation for an oxidation-reduction reaction is a combination of two of the half-reactions we have just finished balancing (an oxidation and a reduction). When a reducing agent is oxidized, the electrons are not actually *lost* in the usual sense of the word. In fact, chemists know exactly where those electrons go. They are, of course, gained by an oxidizing agent that will become reduced. The goal of balancing a redox reaction is to ensure the number of electrons lost by a reducing agent (as it becomes oxidized) exactly equals the number of electrons gained by the oxidizing agent (as it becomes reduced).

> Oxidation-reduction (redox) reactions are characterized by a balanced loss and gain of electrons.

There are two common methods for balancing redox reactions. We will begin by focusing on the method that involves balancing two half-reactions. This method is appropriately called the *half-reaction method*. It consists of the following steps:

SEPARATE the redox equation into its half-reactions.

In most cases, it is easy to identify the two half-reactions by noting species in the reactants that contain atoms in common with species in the products.

BALANCE each half-reaction.

Give yourself plenty of room and don't forget to compare the change in oxidation numbers with the electron gain or loss.

MULTIPLY each half-reaction by an integer to balance the transfer of electrons.

Take the time and space to rewrite each reaction and take care as you transcribe the formulas and coefficients to avoid errors.

ADD the half-reactions together.

Algebraically cancel those species that appear on both sides of the equation. Again: be care*ful* — not care*less*! No common species should remain on both sides of the equation.

If the equation is basic, ADD OH⁻ to *both sides* to neutralize the H⁺ ions *only after* recombining the equations.

Balancing redox equations can seem tedious at times, as there are many steps involved. Errors made early will lead to a series of mistakes but even one late error will result in the wrong answer. Taking care in transcribing steps and checking each process as you go will lead to consistent success.

Sample Problem — Balancing Redox Reactions: Acidic

Balance the following redox reaction: $IO_3^- + HSO_3^- \rightarrow SO_4^{2-} + I_2$

What to Think About	How to Do It
1. Separate the redox equation Into its two half-reactions. Look for common atoms to assist you. IO_3^- and I_2 both contain iodine. HSO_3^- and SO_4^{2-} both contain sulfur.	$IO_3^- \rightarrow I_2$ $HSO_3^- \rightarrow SO_4^{2-}$
2. Balance each half-reaction. Note: There must be an electron *gain* on one side and *loss* on the other. If not, you have made an error!	$10e^- + 12 H^+ + 2 IO_3^- \rightarrow I_2 + 6 H_2O$ $H_2O + HSO_3^- \rightarrow SO_4^{2-} + 3 H^+ + 2e^-$ Don't forget to do a quick check of oxidation numbers at this point. $\overset{+5}{2 IO_3^-} \rightarrow \overset{0}{I_2}$ $\qquad$ $\overset{+4}{HSO_3^-} \rightarrow \overset{+6}{SO_4^{2-}}$ $(-5 \times 2 = 10e^- \text{ gain})$ $\quad (+2 = 2e^- \text{ lost})$ ✓
3. Balance the electron loss and gain. Look for the *lowest common multiple*. Multiply the second half-reaction by 5 and rewrite both equations.	$1(10e^- + 12 H^+ + 2 IO_3^- \rightarrow I_2 + 6 H_2O)$ $5(H_2O + HSO_3^- \rightarrow SO_4^{2-} + 3 H^+ + 2e^-)$
4. Add the balanced half-reactions together, cancelling where appropriate.	$\cancel{10e^-} + 12 H^+ + 2 IO_3^- \rightarrow I_2 + 6 H_2O$ $5 H_2O + 5 HSO_3^- \rightarrow 5 SO_4^{2-} + 15 H^+ + \cancel{10e^-}$ ——————————————————————— $5 HSO_3^- + 2 IO_3^- \rightarrow 5 SO_4^{2-} + 3 H^+ + I_2 + H_2O$

Once you have balanced a full redox reaction, it is worth taking the time to do a full balancing check. You may have performed similar checks when balancing standard equations at some point in your chemistry past. A table is a helpful tool:

Species	Reactants	Products
Hydrogen	5	5
Sulfur	5	5
Oxygen	21	21
Iodine	2	2
Charge	–7	–7

✔

Be sure to take care in how you assign charges, do not drop or change ion charges during transcription. More than one student has done a wonderful job of correctly balancing an equation that wasn't assigned to them because they changed one of the species.

 © Edvantage Interactive 2016

Practice Problems — Balancing Redox Reactions in Acid

Balance each of the following equations in acidic solution. Perform a check for each.

1. $H_3AsO_4 + Zn \longrightarrow AsH_3 + Zn^{2+}$

2. $C_2H_5OH + NO_3^- \longrightarrow CH_3COOH + N_2O_4$

Disproportionation Reactions

Some redox reactions can be rather difficult to break into half-reactions. One of the most troublesome almost appears, at first glance, to be a half-reaction. Take the reaction,

$$Sn^{2+} \longrightarrow Sn^{4+} + Sn$$

The tin(II) ion is both oxidized (to form the tin(IV) ion) and reduced (to form tin metal). A reaction such as this is called a disproportionation reaction.

> A **disproportionation** reaction is a redox reaction in which the same species is both oxidized and reduced.

Occasionally, multiple reactants form only one product. A chemical change of this sort is called a **comproportionation** reaction. This may be the reverse of a disproportionation in which one species is reduced to form a product and a different species is oxidized to give the same product.

Sample Problem — Balancing Disproportionation Reactions: Basic

Balance the following in base: $IAsO_4 \rightarrow AsO_4^{3-} + I_2 + IO_3^-$

What to Think About	**How to Do It**
1. Separate the half-reactions. Both half-reactions must contain the same reactant, so this is a disproportionation reaction. Arsenic must be a product in both half-reactions. Hence the remaining two iodine-containing species must be split between the two half-reactions.	$IAsO_4 \rightarrow AsO_4^{3-} + I_2$ $IAsO_4 \rightarrow AsO_4^{3-} + IO_3^-$
2. Balance each half-reaction and check the oxidation numbers with the electron loss and gain.	$6e^- + 2\,IAsO_4 \rightarrow 2\,AsO_4^{3-} + I_2$ $3\,H_2O + IAsO_4 \rightarrow AsO_4^{3-} + IO_3^- + 6\,H^+ + 2e^-$ $\overset{+3}{2\,IAsO_4} \rightarrow AsO_4^{3-} + \overset{0}{I_2} \quad (-3 \times 2 = \text{gain } 6e^-)$ $\overset{+3}{IAsO_4} \rightarrow AsO_4^{3-} + \overset{+5}{IO_3^-} \quad (+2 = \text{loss of } 2e^-) \; \checkmark$
3. Multiply the second half-reaction by 3.	$6e^- + 2\,IAsO_4 \rightarrow 2\,AsO_4^{3-} + I_2$ $9\,H_2O + 3\,IAsO_4 \rightarrow 3\,AsO_4^{3-} + 3\,IO_3^- + 18\,H^+ + 6e^-$
4. Sum the two halves with appropriate cancelling.	$\overline{9\,H_2O + 5\,IAsO_4 \rightarrow 5\,AsO_4^{3-} + 3\,IO_3^- + I_2 + 18\,H^+}$ $\quad (+18\,OH^-) \qquad\qquad\qquad (+18\,OH^-)$
5. To balance in base, add 18 OH⁻ ions to each side; then cancel 9 H₂O's. A final check is always a good idea.	$\overline{18\,OH^- + 5\,IAsO_4 \rightarrow 5\,AsO_4^{3-} + 3\,IO_3^- + I_2 + 9\,H_2O}$

Species	Products	Reactants
Hydrogen	18	18
Arsenic	5	5
Oxygen	38	38
Iodine	5	5
Charge	−18	−18

© Edvantage Interactive 2016

Practice Problems — Balancing Disproportionation Reactions

Balance the following reactions in a basic environment. Perform a check for each.

1. $HXeO_4^- \longrightarrow XeO_6^{4-} + Xe + O_2$

2. $BrO_3^- + Br^- \longrightarrow Br_2$ (a comproportionation)

3. $CH_3COO^- \longrightarrow CH_4 + CO_2$

An acronym you may find helpful in remembering how to balance redox reactions is OOHe as described below
OOHe — Other atoms, **O**xygen (with H_2O), **H**ydrogen (with H^+), **e**lectrons

9.2 Review Questions

1. Electrons can be used to cancel positive charges or to increase negative charge. Complete the following table by indicating how many electrons must be added to the reactants or the products to balance the electrical charge.

	Reactants	Products	Add
e.g.	2+	3+	$1e^-$ to the products
(a)	3+	2–	
(b)	1–	3–	
(c)	2–	4+	
(d)	1+	5+	

Examine your answers. Are you following the suggestion to *always add electrons to the more positive side?*

2. Balance the electrical charge of each of the following half-reactions by adding the appropriate number of electrons to either the reactants or products. Indicate whether the half-reaction is an *oxidation* or a *reduction*.

   (a) $2\,NO_3^- + 2\,H_2O \rightarrow N_2O_4 + 4\,OH^-$

   (b) $2\,Cr^{3+} + 7\,H_2O \rightarrow Cr_2O_7^{2-} + 14\,H^+$

   (c) $ClO_4^- + 4\,H_2O \rightarrow Cl^- + 8\,OH^-$

   (d) $S_2O_5^{2-} + 3\,H_2O \rightarrow 2\,SO_4^{2-} + 6\,H^+$

© **Edvantage Interactive 2016**

3. Balance the following half-reactions under acidic conditions. Indicate whether each is an *oxidation* or a *reduction*.

(a) $ClO_4^- \longrightarrow Cl_2$

(b) $FeO \longrightarrow Fe_2O_3$

(c) $N_2O_4 \longrightarrow NO_3^-$

4. Balance the following half-reactions under basic conditions. Indicate whether each is an *oxidation* or a *reduction*.

(a) $CrO_4^{2-} \longrightarrow Cr(OH)_2$

(b) $S_2O_3^{2-} \longrightarrow S_4O_6^{2-}$

(c) $IO_3^- + Cl^- \longrightarrow ICl_2^-$

5. Balance the following reactions using the half-reaction method. Assume acidic conditions unless stated otherwise.

(a) $Sn^{2+} + MnO_4^- \rightarrow Sn^{4+} + MnO_2$ (basic)

(b) $V^{2+} + H_2SO_3 \rightarrow V^{3+} + S_2O_3^{2-}$

(c) $IO_3^- + I^- \rightarrow I_2$ (basic)

(d) $ClO_3^- + N_2H_4 \rightarrow NO + Cl^-$

(e) $NO_3^- + Zn \rightarrow Zn^{2+} + NO$ (basic)

(f) $ClO_3^- \rightarrow ClO_4^- + Cl^- + Cl_2$

Use the ΔON values to help you determine how to break this into two half-reactions.

(g) $SnS_2O_3 + MnO_4^- \rightarrow MnO_2 + SO_4^{2-} + Sn^{4+}$ (basic)

(h) $Mg_3(AsO_4)_2 + SiO_2 + C \rightarrow As_4 + MgSiO_3 + CO$

6. **Extension:** Use the half-reaction method to balance the following reactions occurring in aqueous solution:

(a) $K_2Cr_2O_7 + CH_3CH_2OH + HCl \rightarrow CH_3COOH + KCl + CrCl_3 + H_2O$

You must first convert the equation into net ionic form, balance the net ionic equation, and then convert it back into the original formula equation. This is the reaction performed in the prototype BAT (Breath Alcohol Testing) mobiles.

(b) C.W. Scheele prepared chlorine gas in 1774 using the following reaction:

$NaCl + H_2SO_4 + MnO_2 \rightarrow Na_2SO_4 + MnCl_2 + H_2O + Cl_2$

9.3 Using the Standard Reduction Potential (SRP) Table to Predict Redox Reactions

Warm Up

1. Compare a table Standard Reduction Potentials of Half-Cells with a table Relative Strengths of Brønsted-Lowry Acids and Bases at the back of the book. List four similarities between the tables.

   (a) _____   (c) _____

   (b) _____   (d) _____

2. The half-reactions in the SRP table are written as _____.

   This means the reactant species are all _____ agents.

3. Find the strongest reducing agents on the SRP table. What family do these reducing agents belong to?

   _____

4. What element is the strongest oxidizing agent? _____ What family does this element belong to?

   _____

Using the Standard Reduction Potential (SRP) Table

Chemists use the standard reduction potential (SRP) table to predict whether a chemical species will spontaneously give electrons to or take electrons from another species. The oxidizing agents, which are the species that take electrons, are on the left side of the SRP table. The reducing agents, which are the species that give electrons, are on the right side of the SRP table.

> Chemical species in the left column of the SRP table will only take electrons spontaneously from species *below them* in the right column.

In chemical terms, oxidizing agents only spontaneously oxidize the reducing agents below them in the SRP table. For example, Br_2 spontaneously oxidizes Ag but not Cl^- (Figure 9.3.1).

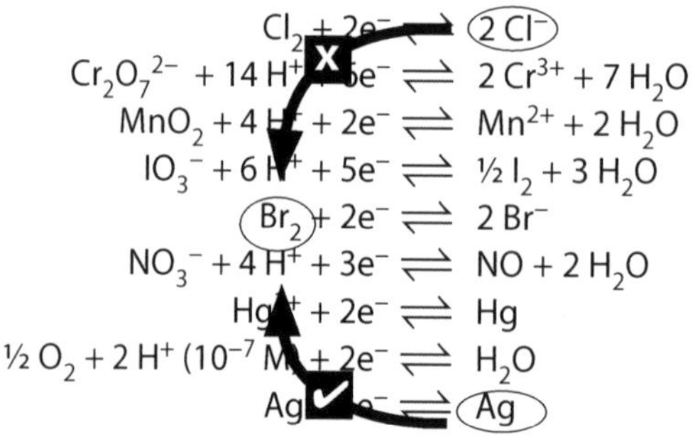

$$Cl_2 + 2e^- \rightleftharpoons 2\,Cl^-$$
$$Cr_2O_7^{2-} + 14\,H^+ + 6e^- \rightleftharpoons 2\,Cr^{3+} + 7\,H_2O$$
$$MnO_2 + 4\,H^+ + 2e^- \rightleftharpoons Mn^{2+} + 2\,H_2O$$
$$IO_3^- + 6\,H^+ + 5e^- \rightleftharpoons \tfrac{1}{2}\,I_2 + 3\,H_2O$$
$$Br_2 + 2e^- \rightleftharpoons 2\,Br^-$$
$$NO_3^- + 4\,H^+ + 3e^- \rightleftharpoons NO + 2\,H_2O$$
$$Hg^{2+} + 2e^- \rightleftharpoons Hg$$
$$\tfrac{1}{2}\,O_2 + 2\,H^+\,(10^{-7}\,M) + 2e^- \rightleftharpoons H_2O$$
$$Ag^+ + e^- \rightleftharpoons Ag$$

Figure 9.3.1 *You can tell that Br_2 spontaneously oxidizes Ag because Ag is below Br_2 in the SRP table.*

Of course, the event can also be described from the reducing agent's point of view.

Chemical species in the right column only give electrons spontaneously to chemicals *above* them in the left column.

In chemical terms, reducing agents only spontaneously reduce the oxidizing agents above them in the SRP table. For example, Ag reduces Br_2 but Cl^- doesn't. Thus, spontaneous redox reactions occur with the oxidation half-reaction below the reduction half-reaction on the SRP table. Electrons are passed in a clockwise direction. Remember that the oxidizing agent (Br_2) gets reduced and the reducing agent (Ag) gets oxidized.

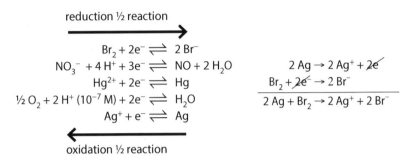

reduction ½ reaction

$$Br_2 + 2e^- \rightleftharpoons 2\ Br^-$$
$$NO_3^- + 4\ H^+ + 3e^- \rightleftharpoons NO + 2\ H_2O$$
$$Hg^{2+} + 2e^- \rightleftharpoons Hg$$
$$\tfrac{1}{2}\ O_2 + 2\ H^+\ (10^{-7}\ M) + 2e^- \rightleftharpoons H_2O$$
$$Ag^+ + e^- \rightleftharpoons Ag$$

oxidation ½ reaction

$$2\ Ag \rightarrow 2\ Ag^+ + 2e^-$$
$$\underline{Br_2 + 2e^- \rightarrow 2\ Br^-}$$
$$2\ Ag + Br_2 \rightarrow 2\ Ag^+ + 2\ Br^-$$

Sample Problem — Determining Whether a Spontaneous Redox Reaction Will Occur

For each of the following, state whether a reaction will spontaneously occur. If so, write the balanced equation for the reaction.
(a) $Fe^{3+} + Cl^-$ (b) $Ca + Zn^{2+}$ (c) $I^- + Al$

What to Think About	How to Do It
(a) $Fe^{3+} + Cl^-$ 1. Identify the oxidizing agent and the reducing agent. 2. Oxidizing agents only take electrons spontaneously from reducing agents below them in the SRP table.	Fe^{3+} is an oxidizing agent. Cl^- is a reducing agent. Cl^- is not below Fe^{3+} in the SRP table so Fe^{3+} will not oxidize it. <u>No reaction</u>.
(b) $Ca + Zn^{2+}$ 1. Identify the oxidizing agent and the reducing agent. 2. Oxidizing agents can only take electrons spontaneously from reducing agents below them in the SRP table. 3. Write the two half-reactions, balance the transfer of electrons if necessary and then add the half-reactions together.	Ca is a reducing agent. Zn^{2+} is an oxidizing agent. Ca is below Zn^{2+} in the SRP table so Zn^{2+} will oxidize it. $$Ca \rightarrow Ca^{2+} + 2e^-$$ $$\underline{Zn^{2+} + 2e^- \rightarrow Zn}$$ $$Zn^{2+} + Ca \rightarrow Ca^{2+} + Zn$$
(c) $I^- + Al$ 1. Identify the oxidizing agent and the reducing agent.	I^- and Al are both reducing agents so no reaction occurs.

Practice Problems — Determining Whether a Spontaneous Redox Reaction Will Occur

For each of the following, state whether a spontaneous reaction will occur and if so, write the balanced equation for the reaction.

1. $I^- + Br_2$

2. $F_2 + Al^{3+}$

3. $Ag^+ + Sn$

4. $I_2 + Cl^-$

Single Displacement Reactions

Recall that both metals and non-metals are more stable as ions because as ions they have complete valence shells. Non-metals have high electron affinities, needing only one, two, or three electrons to complete their valence shells. Non-metals, as strong oxidizing agents, are found at the top left side of the SRP table, where they are shown being reduced to form anions (negatively charged ions). Non-metals can also be oxidized to form non-metallic oxides and oxyanions. For example, chlorine can be oxidized to chlorine dioxide (ClO_2), the hypochlorite ion (ClO^-), the chlorite ion (ClO_2^-), the chlorate ion (ClO_3^-), or the perchlorate ion (ClO_4^-). Metals, on the other hand, can only be oxidized. A metal empties its valence shell and the complete shell beneath it becomes its new valence shell. Most metals, as strong reducing agents, are found at the bottom, right side of the SRP table, where they are shown being oxidized to form cations (positively charged ions).

Recall that one chemical species passes or loses one or more electrons to another species in redox reactions. In the synthesis of ionic compounds, metals give electrons to non-metals and both form ions that are more stable than their neutral atoms. In the SRP table, this is reflected by most of the non-metals being above most of the metals. Single displacement reactions are also a type of redox reaction. In single displacement reactions, a non-metal oxidizes a different non-metal's anion, or a metal reduces a different metal's cation. Think of a non-metal displacement reaction as an electron tug-of-war between two non-metals for the "extra" electron(s) that one of them already possesses. A metal displacement reaction can be viewed as a metal atom trying to force its valence electron(s) onto a different metal's stable ion. In both cases, we use the SRP table to determine which chemical species wins.

Sample Problem — Determining the Outcome of a Single Displacement Reaction

Will chlorine and sodium bromide spontaneously react to produce bromine and sodium chloride? If so, write the balanced net ionic equation for the reaction.

What to Think About	How to Do It
1. Write the balanced formula equation.	$Cl_2 + 2\,NaBr \rightarrow Br_2 + 2\,NaCl$
2. Write the complete ionic equation.	$Cl_2 + 2\,Na^+ + 2\,Br^- \rightarrow Br_2 + 2\,Na^+ + 2\,Cl^-$
3. Write the net ionic equation.	$Cl_2 + 2\,Br^- \rightarrow Br_2 + 2\,Cl^-$
4. Identify the oxidizing agent and the reducing agent.	Cl_2 is an oxidizing agent. Br^- is a reducing agent.
5. Oxidizing agents only spontaneously take electrons from reducing agents below them in the SRP table.	Br^- is below Cl_2 in the SRP table so Cl_2 can oxidize it as shown in part 3 above.

The chlorine atoms won the electron tug-of-war with the bromide ions in the sample problem above. The chlorine atoms that were sharing a pair of valence electrons to complete their valence shells now each have an electron of their own and the bromine atoms are forced to share valence electrons (Br_2). The sodium ions were spectator ions because they were unchanged by the reaction. We began with chlorine dissolved in a solution of sodium bromide and finished with bromine dissolved in a solution of sodium chloride.

Practice Problems — Determining the Outcome of a Single Displacement Reaction

For each of the following, determine whether a reaction will occur and if so, write the balanced net ionic equation for the reaction.

1. $I_2 + CaF_2$

2. $Al + CuSO_4$

3. $Cl_2 + NaCl$

4. $Sn + Al(NO_2)_3$

The Strength of Oxidizing and Reducing Agents

Have you noticed that oxidizing and reducing agents closely parallel Brønsted-Lowry acids and bases? Brønsted-Lowry acids and bases pass protons back and forth. Oxidizing and reducing agents pass electrons back and forth. An acid and its conjugate base are the same chemical species with and without the proton. A reducing agent and its complementary oxidizing agent are the same chemical species with and without the electron. In the Warm Up exercise you identified similarities between a SRP table and a table of acid strengths.

Recall that the weaker an acid, the stronger its conjugate base because the less an acid's tendency to give its proton away, the greater its conjugate base's tendency to take it back. Although the term *conjugate* is not used by chemists to describe the reduced and oxidized forms of a chemical species, the same inverse relationship exists between their strengths.

> The stronger a reducing agent (A^-) is, the weaker its complementary oxidizing agent (A) is.

In other words, if a chemical species has a strong tendency to give an electron away then it will have a weak tendency to take it back.

Oxidizing Agents		**Reducing Agents**
STRONG	$F_2 + 2e^- \rightarrow 2\,F^-$	WEAK
	$2\,H^+ + 2e^- \rightarrow H_2$	
WEAK	$Li^+ + e^- \rightarrow Li$	STRONG

Just as there are amphiprotic species that can act as both proton donors and acceptors, there are also some chemical species that can act as both reducing agents and oxidizing agents. Multivalent transition metals have ions such as Cu^+, Sn^{2+}, and Fe^{2+} that can be further oxidized or reduced back to the metal. H_2O_2 can also be an oxidizing agent or a reducing agent. Can you find it in both columns of the SRP table?

The halogens are a little difficult to spot in the SRP table. An element's oxidizing strength corresponds with its electronegativity. Its ability to oxidize various chemical species corresponds with how strongly it attracts the shared pair of electrons in a covalent bond. Electronegativity increases as you move up a group in the periodic table and thus the relative positions of the halogens in the SRP table are the same as they are in the periodic table (Table 9.3.1). Fluorine can therefore oxidize any of the other halide ions. Chlorine can oxidize any halide ion other than fluoride, etc.

Table 9.3.1 *The Position of the Halogens in the SRP Table*

$$F_2 + 2e^- \rightleftharpoons 2\,F^-$$

$$S_2O_8{}^{2-} + 2e^- \rightleftharpoons 2\,SO_4{}^{2-}$$
$$H_2O_2 + 2\,H^+ + 2e^- \rightleftharpoons 2\,H_2O$$
$$MnO_4{}^- + 8\,H^+ + 5e^- \rightleftharpoons Mn^{2+} + 4\,H_2O$$
$$Au^{3+} + 3e^- \rightleftharpoons Au$$
$$BrO_3{}^- + 6\,H^+ + 5e^- \rightleftharpoons \tfrac{1}{2}\,Br_2 + 3\,H_2O$$
$$ClO_4{}^- + 8\,H^+ + 8e^- \rightleftharpoons Cl^- + 4\,H_2O$$

$$Cl_2 + 2e^- \rightleftharpoons 2\,Cl-$$

$$Cr_2O_7{}^{2-} + 14\,H^+ + 6e^- \rightleftharpoons 2\,Cr^{3+} + 7\,H_2O$$
$$\tfrac{1}{2}\,O_2 + 2\,H^+ + 2e^- \rightleftharpoons H_2O$$
$$MnO_2 + 4\,H^+ + 2e^- \rightleftharpoons Mn^{2+} + 2\,H_2O$$
$$IO_3{}^- + 6\,H^+ + 5e^- \rightleftharpoons \tfrac{1}{2}\,I_2 + 3\,H_2O$$

$$Br_2 + 2e^- \rightleftharpoons 2Br^-$$

$$AuCl_4{}^- + 3e^- \rightleftharpoons Au + 4\,Cl^-$$
$$NO_3{}^- + 4\,H^+ + 3e^- \rightleftharpoons NO + 2\,H_2O$$
$$Hg^{2+} + 2e^- \rightleftharpoons Hg$$
$$\tfrac{1}{2}\,O_2 + 2\,H^+ (10^{-7}\,M) + 2e^- \rightleftharpoons H_2O$$
$$2\,NO_3{}^- + 4\,H^+ + 2e^- \rightleftharpoons N_2O_4 + 2\,H_2O$$
$$Ag^+ + e^- \rightleftharpoons Ag$$
$$\tfrac{1}{2}\,Hg_2{}^{2+} + e^- \rightleftharpoons Hg$$
$$Fe^{3+} + e^- \rightleftharpoons Fe^{2+}$$
$$O_2 + 2\,H^+ + 2e^- \rightleftharpoons H_2O_2$$

$$I_2 + 2e^- \rightleftharpoons 2\,I^-$$

Some redox terminology is counter-intuitive. For instance, the strength of an oxidizing agent is called its **reduction potential** ($E°$). *Reduction potential* means *potential to be reduced*, not *potential to reduce*. Oxidizing agents get reduced and therefore have a reduction potential. Reduction and oxidation potentials are measured in volts. This will be explained in section 1.4. $F_2(g)$ is the strongest oxidizing agent shown in the SRP table, with a reduction potential of 2.87 V. Note that the *-ates* ions (e.g., bromate, permanganate, chlorate, dichromate) are strong oxidizing agents.

Likewise, **oxidation potentials** measure the strength of reducing agents since reducing agents become oxidized when they give up electrons. When the reduction half-reactions are read backwards, from right to left, they are oxidation half-reactions. Oxidation potentials of reducing agents are simply the opposite of the reduction potentials of their complementary oxidizing agents. For example, Al^{3+} has a reduction potential of –1.66 V while Al has an oxidation potential of +1.66 V. Li(*s*) is the strongest reducing agent shown in the SRP table we are using, with an oxidation potential of 3.04 V.

To change your standard reduction potential (SRP) table into a standard oxidation potential (SOP) table, you would turn it around 180° so it reads upside down and backwards, and you would reverse the E° signs (+ to − and − to +).

Quick Check

1. Which is the stronger reducing agent, Co or Sr? _____

2. Which is the stronger oxidizing agent, Fe^{3+} or Al^{3+}? _____

3. Which has the greater oxidation potential, Br^- or I^-? _____

4. Which has the greater reduction potential, Cr^{3+} or Sn^{2+}? _____

5. A and B are hypothetical elements. A^{2+} is a stronger oxidizing agent than B. Which has the greater oxidation potential, A or B^-? _____

6. What is the reduction potential of Ag^+? _____

7. What is the oxidation potential of Ca? _____

Determining the Predominant Redox Reaction

In chemical mixtures, there are sometimes more than two chemical species available to react. We use the SRP table to predict which species will react.

The predominant redox reaction between the chemicals in a mixture will be between the strongest available oxidizing agent and the strongest available reducing agent.

Sample Problem — Determining the Predominant Redox Reaction Write

the predominant redox reaction that will occur in a mixture of Cl_2, Ag^+, Sn^{2+}, and I^-.

What to Think About	How to Do It
1. Identify the oxidizing agent(s) and the reducing agent(s).	Cl_2, Ag^+, and Sn^{2+} are oxidizing agents. Sn^{2+} and I^- are reducing agents.

2. Use the SRP table to determine which species is the strongest oxidizing agent and which species is the strongest reducing agent.

Increasing Strength (left arrow) | **Increasing Strength** (right arrow)

Oxidizing Agents		Reducing Agents
$ClO_4^- + 8\,H^+ + 8e^-$	$\rightleftharpoons$	$Cl^- + 4\,H_2O$
$\boxed{Cl_2} + 2e^-$	$\rightleftharpoons$	$2\,Cl^-$
$Cr_2O_7^{2-} + 14\,H^+ + 6e^-$	$\rightleftharpoons$	$2\,Cr^{3+} + 7\,H_2O$
$Br_2 + 2e^-$	$\rightleftharpoons$	$2\,Br^-$
$NO_3^- + 4\,H^+ + 3e^-$	$\rightleftharpoons$	$NO + 2\,H_2O$
$Hg^{2+} + 2e^-$	$\rightleftharpoons$	Hg
$\frac{1}{2}\,O_2(g) + 2\,H^+\,(10^{-7}\,M) + 2e^-$	$\rightleftharpoons$	H_2O
$I_2 + 2e^-$	$\rightleftharpoons$	$\boxed{2\,I^-}$
$\boxed{Ag^+} + e^-$	$\rightleftharpoons$	Ag
$H_2SO_3 + 4\,H^+ + 4e^-$	$\rightleftharpoons$	$S + 3\,H_2O$
$Cu^{2+} + 2e^-$	$\rightleftharpoons$	Cu
$SO_4^{2-} + 4\,H^+ + 2e^-$	$\rightleftharpoons$	$H_2SO_3 + H_2O$
$Sn^{4+} + 2e^-$	$\rightleftharpoons$	$\boxed{Sn^{2+}}$
$S + 2\,H^+ + 2e^-$	$\rightleftharpoons$	H_2S
$2\,H^+ + 2e^-$	$\rightleftharpoons$	H_2
$Pb^{2+} + 2e^-$	$\rightleftharpoons$	Pb
$\boxed{Sn^{2+}} + 2e^-$	$\rightleftharpoons$	Sn
$Ni^{2+} + 2e^-$	$\rightleftharpoons$	Ni

Cl_2 is a stronger oxidizing agent than Ag^+ or Sn^{2+}. Sn^{2+} is a stronger reducing agent than I^-.

3. The strongest oxidizing agent will oxidize the strongest reducing agent.

Cl_2 will oxidize Sn^{2+}.

4. Write the two half-reactions and balance the transfer of electrons if necessary. Then add the half-reactions together.

$$Sn^{2+} \rightarrow Sn^{4+} + 2e^-$$
$$Cl_2 + 2e^- \rightarrow 2\,Cl^-$$
$$\overline{Cl_2 + Sn^{2+} \rightarrow Sn^{4+} + 2\,Cl^-}$$

In the sample problem above, there are many other reactions that would occur but in every case the products can be oxidized by Cl_2 or reduced by Sn^{2+}. For example, Ag^+ can also oxidize I^- forming Ag and I_2 but this I_2 would then be reduced back to I^- by Sn^{2+} and the Ag would be oxidized back to Ag^+ by Cl_2. In every instance, the products would ultimately end up being those shown in the solution to the sample problem. Also keep in mind that if one species runs out, then the strongest remaining agent is "next up to bat."

© Edvantage Interactive 2016

Practice Problems — Determining the Predominant Redox Reaction

Write the predominant redox reaction that will occur in each of the following mixtures:

1. Sn^{4+}, Br^-, Zn^{2+}, and Ni

2. $CuBr_2(aq)$ and $Al(s)$

3. Na^+, Cu^+, and F^-

4. Copper and bromine in a solution of iron(III) chloride

Redox Titrations

All the general principles of titrations apply to redox titrations. A chemist titrates an acid with a base or vice versa. Similarly, a chemist titrates an oxidizing agent with a reducing agent or vice versa. The chemist must choose a titrant that is a strong enough oxidizing agent to react with the reducing agent or a strong enough reducing agent to react with the oxidizing agent.

The indicator of an acid-base titration is itself a weak acid with a different color in its base form. Similarly, the indicator of a redox titration is itself a reducing agent with a different color in its oxidized form. Otherwise, redox indicators operate in a much simpler way than acid-base indicators. A chemist chooses a redox indicator that is a weaker oxidizing or reducing agent than the analyte (the chemical being analyzed) so that the indicator's reaction indicates that the analyte has been completely consumed.

In redox titrations it is not uncommon for the titrant to act as its own indicator. The purple permanganate ion is sometimes used as an oxidizing agent to titrate a chemical species. The permanganate ion is reduced to the very faint pink Mn^{2+} under acidic conditions. When the permanganate solution is slowly added to a reducing agent of unknown molarity, the permanganate ion is reduced, and the purple color disappears. Eventually a drop is added and the purple color remains. At this point, the chemist knows that the chemical species that was reducing the permanganate ion has been totally consumed, and the equivalence point has been reached.

Sample Problem — Determining a Chemical's Concentration via Redox Titration

To titrate a 25.0 mL solution of Fe^{2+} to the equivalence point, 16.7 mL of 0.0152 MnO_4^- in acidic solution was needed. What was the [Fe^{2+}]?

What to Think About	How to Do It
1. Write the balanced net ionic equation for the titration reaction.	$5\,Fe^{2+} + MnO_4^- + 8\,H^+ \rightarrow 5\,Fe^{3+} + Mn^{2+} + 4\,H_2O$
2. Calculate the moles of MnO_4^- reacted.	$0.0167\ L \times 0.0152\ \frac{mol}{L} = 2.54 \times 10^{-4}\ mol\ MnO_4^-$
3. Calculate the moles of Fe^{2+} reacted.	$2.54 \times 10^{-4}\ mol\ MnO_4^- \times \frac{5\ mol\ Fe^{2+}}{1\ mol\ MnO_4^-}$ $= 1.27 \times 10^{-3}\ mol\ Fe^{2+}$
4. Calculate the [Fe^{2+}] in the original sample.	$[Fe^{2+}] = \frac{1.27 \times 10^{-3}\ mol}{0.0250\ L} = 0.0508\ M\ Fe^{2+}$

Note: Under basic conditions the permanganate ion is reduced to $MnO_2(s)$, as shown on the SRP table (+.60 V).

Practice Problems — Determining a Chemical's Concentration via Redox Titration

1. Potassium dichromate is used to titrate a solution of iron(II) chloride. The dichromate ion acts as its own indicator. As the $Cr_2O_7^{2-}$ solution is added to the Fe^{2+} solution, the orange dichromate ion is reduced to green Cr^{3+} as it oxidizes the Fe^{2+} to Fe^{3+}. The equivalence point is evident when the orange color remains indicating that all the Fe^{2+} has reacted. An amount of 15.0 mL of 0.0200 M $Cr_2O_7^{2-}$ solution was required to titrate 20.0 mL of acidified $FeCl_2$.

   (a) Balance the redox equation for this titration: $Cr_2O_7^{2-} + Fe^{2+} \rightarrow Cr^{3+} + Fe^{3+}$

   (b) What was the $[FeCl_2]$?

2. A student uses 16.3 mL of an acidified $KMnO_4$ solution to titrate 1.00 g $Na_2C_2O_4$ to the equivalence point. The balanced equation is:

   $$5\,C_2O_4^{2-} + 2\,MnO_4^- + 16\,H^+ \rightarrow 10\,CO_2 + 2\,Mn^{2+} + 8\,H_2O$$

   Calculate the $[KMnO_4]$.

3. The following redox reaction occurs between the dichromate ion and ethanol:

   $$3\,CH_3CH_2OH + 2\,Cr_2O_7^{2-} + 16\,H^+ \rightarrow 3\,CH_3COOH + 4\,Cr^{3+} + 11\,H_2O$$
   ethanol   orange   ethanoic   green
                                     acid

   A chemist uses 26.25 mL of 0.500 M $Cr_2O_7^{2-}$ to titrate a 10.0 mL sample of wine to the equivalence point.

   (a) What is the $[CH_3CH_2OH]$ in the wine?

   (b) The concentration of ethanol in alcoholic beverages is expressed as percent by volume. If a wine is 10% alcohol, it means that there are 10 mL of ethanol for every 100 mL of the beverage. The density of ethanol is 0.789 g/mL. Convert your answer in part (a) into percent by volume.

© Edvantage Interactive 2016

9.3 Activity: Making an SRP Table

Question
How can you make a standard reduction potential table from a set of experimental data?

Background
Each redox reaction allows you to determine the relative position of its two half-reactions in the table. For example, from the following reaction in which L reduces M^{2+} you can infer that M^{2+} is a stronger oxidizing agent than L^+. M^+ is therefore above L^+ in the SRP table.

$$L + M^{2+} \rightarrow 2\,L^+ + M$$

reduction ½ reaction

$\xrightarrow{\hspace{4cm}}$

$$M^{2+} + 2e^- \rightarrow M$$

$$L^+ + e^- \leftarrow L$$

$\xleftarrow{\hspace{4cm}}$

oxidation ½ reaction

Procedure
Use the following information to produce an SRP table with six half-reactions.

1. $L + M^{2+} \rightarrow 2\,L^+ + M$
2. P^- reduces D^{3+} to D^{2+}.
3. Element Q is the strongest oxidizing agent. $(Q + e^- \rightarrow Q^-)$
4. $M + 2\,P \rightarrow M^{2+} + 2\,P^-$
5. L^+ oxidizes C to C^{2+}.

Results and Discussion
1. Fill in the SRP table below:

Oxidizing Agents   **Reducing Agents**

_____ $\rightleftarrows$ _____

_____ $\rightleftarrows$ _____

_____ $\rightleftarrows$ _____

_____ $\rightleftarrows$ _____

_____ $\rightleftarrows$ _____

_____ $\rightleftarrows$ _____

2. Which chemical species is the weakest reducing agent? _____

3. Which chemical species has the lowest reduction potential? _____

9.3 Review Questions

1. Will iodine spontaneously oxidize: (a) Fe^{2+}?   (b) Sn?

2. Identify a metal ion that will spontaneously oxidize I^- but not Cl^-.

3. For each of the following, state whether a spontaneous reaction will occur and if so, write the balanced equation for the reaction.
    (a) $Mg + Al^{3+} \rightarrow$

    (b) $Cl^- + I_2 \rightarrow$

    (c) $Hg^{2+} + Ag \rightarrow$

4. Complete the following table:

Metals	Non-metals
bottom right of SRP table	
	tend to take electrons
give e⁻ to chemicals above them on the left	

5. For each of the following, state whether a spontaneous reaction will occur and if so, write the balanced net ionic equation for the reaction.
    (a) $Fe + Sn(NO_3)_2 \rightarrow$

    (b) $F_2 + KBr \rightarrow$

    (c) $Cu + NaI \rightarrow$

6. (a) Write the net ionic equation for the reaction between KI and $FeCl_3$.

    (b) Write the net ionic equation for the reaction between Br_2 and $FeCl_2$.

7. When tin(II) nitrate dissolves in acid the two dissociated ions react with each other. Write the net ionic equation for this reaction.

8. Would it be practical to store a 0.5 M $FeCl_3$ solution in an aluminum container? Explain.

9. State whether the forward or the reverse reaction is spontaneous.
   (a) $Sn^{4+} + 2\,Fe^{2+} \leftarrow ? \rightarrow 2\,Fe^{3+} + Sn^{2+}$

   (b) $Cr_2O_7{}^{2-} + 14\,H^+ + 3\,Cu \leftarrow ? \rightarrow 2\,Cr^{3+} + 7\,H_2O + 3\,Cu^{2+}$

10. One characteristic of acids is that they react with magnesium, liberating hydrogen gas. Write the balanced redox equation for this reaction.

11. Explain why silver oxidizes and then dissolves in 1 M nitric acid but not in 1 M hydrochloric acid.

12. A few drops of phenolphthalein are added to a petri dish of water. A small piece of sodium reacts violently when placed in the water, leaving pink tracks as it skips across the water's surface. The air ignites above the sodium producing a small flame. Write the redox reaction that occurs and briefly explain the pink tracks and the flame.

13. (a) Which has the greatest reduction potential, I_2, Ag^+, or Mg^{2+}?

    (b) Which has the greatest oxidation potential, I^-, Ag, or Mg?

14. The surface of a sheet of aluminum is observed to darken after being placed in a solution of gallium nitrate. From this observation, determine which has the greater reduction potential, Al^{3+} or Ga^{3+}.

15. (a) What is the reduction potential of $Br_2(l)$?

    (b) What is the oxidation potential of $Zn(s)$?

16. Write the predominant redox reaction that will occur in each of the following mixtures:
    (a) Co^{2+}, Cu, Mn^{2+}, and Fe

    (b) Cu, Hg, Cu^+, and Cr^{2+}

    (c) $CuCl_2(aq) + SnI_2(aq)$

17. If a zinc sheet were placed into a solution of $Cu^{2+}(aq)$ and $Fe^{3+}(aq)$ what would the predominant reaction be?

18. Each of the following redox reactions is spontaneous in the forward direction:

$A^{2+} + B \rightarrow B^{2+} + A$ $\qquad$ $2\,C^{3+} + A \rightarrow 2\,C^{2+} + A^{2+}$ $\qquad$ $B^{2+} + 2\,D \rightarrow 2\,D^+ + B$

Which of the chemical species involved in these reactions is:

(a) the strongest oxidizing agent

(b) the strongest reducing agent

19. A chemist titrates 15.0 mL of $KI(aq)$ to the equivalence point with 32.8 mL of 0.200 M $Na_2Cr_2O_7$. What is the $[KI]$?

$Cr_2O_7{}^{2-} + 14\,H^+ + 6\,I^- \rightarrow 2\,Cr^{3+} + 3\,I_2 + 7\,H_2O$

20. A $KMnO_4$ solution is standardized with oxalic acid. The equation for the redox reaction is:

$5\,H_2C_2O_4 + 2\,MnO_4{}^- + 6\,H^+ \rightarrow 10\,CO_2 + 2\,Mn^{2+} + 8\,H_2O$

What is the molar concentration of the $KMnO_4$ solution if 18.6 mL of the solution was required to titrate 0.105 g $H_2C_2O_4 \cdot 2H_2O$?

21. The legal limit for intoxication while driving in British Columbia had been a blood alcohol content (BAC) of 0.08% by mass for many years until it was reduced to 0.05% in September 2010. A 5.00 g sample of blood is titrated with 10.15 mL of 0.0150 M $K_2Cr_2O_7$. The dichromate ion acts as an oxidizing agent in the reaction of ethanol, C_2H_5OH, to form carbon dioxide and the Cr^{3+} ion.

(a) Balance the equation for the reaction that occurs during the titration.

(b) Calculate the percent alcohol by mass in the blood sample. Would this driver be considered legally impaired before September 2010? Now?

9.4 The Electrochemical Cell

Warm Up

1. A charged atom or group of atoms is called a(n) _____.

2. The charged subatomic particle that travels around the nucleus is called a(n) _____.

3. Current electricity is a steady flow of electric charge. A current of 1 amp means that one coulomb of charge is flowing past the point of measurement each second. The charge of a single electron is only 1.60×10^{-19} C. How many electrons does it take to make up one coulomb of charge?

The Standard Electrochemical Cell

Electrons are transferred from one chemical species to another in all redox reactions. An **electrochemical cell** is a portable source of electricity, in which the electricity is produced by a spontaneous redox reaction within the cell. Electrochemical cells are also referred to as voltaic cells and galvanic cells. The electrochemical cell is the most common application of redox reactions and is also the best tool for measuring the tendency of redox reactions to occur.

The basic design of an electrochemical cell isolates an oxidation half-reaction from a reduction half-reaction within the device. Electrons can travel only from the reducing agent to the oxidizing agent when the two agents are connected through an external circuit. The basic components of an electrochemical cell are two different conductive materials (electrodes immersed in the same or different electrolyte solutions. If each electrode is immersed in a separate solution then two half-cells are created. The two half-cells must be connected in some manner that allows ion migration between them. For example, a salt bridge is a U-tube filled with an electrolyte solution or gel that allows ion migration (Figure 9.4.1).

How does an electrochemical cell work? The chemical species in the two half-cells exert forces on each other's electrons through the wire that connects the two half-cells. Electrons spontaneously flow through the wire from the strongest available reducing agent to the strongest available oxidizing agent.

One type of half-cell consists of a metal electrode immersed in a solution containing ions of the same metal. Either the metal electrode gives electrons to the other half-cell or the metal ions receive electrons from the other half-cell. Let's consider a cell with two metal | metal ion half-cells. The cell in Figure 9.4.1 has one half-cell with a magnesium electrode immersed in a solution containing magnesium ions and another half-cell with a copper electrode immersed in a solution containing copper(II) ions. Although the metals are not in physical contact with the other half-cell's ions, they are electrically connected through the wire connecting the two half-cells.

The predominant redox reaction will be between the strongest available oxidizing agent and the strongest available reducing agent, just as though the chemicals were all in the same container. In fact, a SRP table specifically provides the tendency of redox reactions to occur between standard half-cells. A standard cell has ion concentrations of 1 M at 25°C as shown just below the heading of the SRP table. The SRP table thus allows us to predict the resulting direction of electron flow under standard conditions:

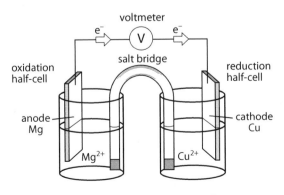

Figure 9.4.1 *A standard electrochemical cell*

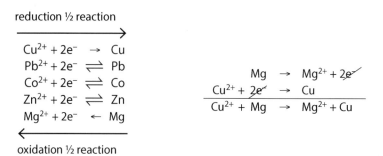

reduction ½ reaction

$$
\begin{array}{rcl}
Cu^{2+} + 2e^- & \rightarrow & Cu \\
Pb^{2+} + 2e^- & \rightleftharpoons & Pb \\
Co^{2+} + 2e^- & \rightleftharpoons & Co \\
Zn^{2+} + 2e^- & \rightleftharpoons & Zn \\
Mg^{2+} + 2e^- & \leftarrow & Mg
\end{array}
$$

oxidation ½ reaction

$$
\begin{array}{rcl}
Mg & \rightarrow & Mg^{2+} + 2e^- \\
Cu^{2+} + 2e^- & \rightarrow & Cu \\
\hline
Cu^{2+} + Mg & \rightarrow & Mg^{2+} + Cu
\end{array}
$$

The **anode** is defined as the electrode where oxidation occurs. The **cathode** is defined as the electrode where reduction occurs.

> Oxidation occurs at the anode.
> Reduction occurs at the cathode.

Thus in the cells in Figure 9.4.1, the magnesium electrode is the anode and the copper electrode is the cathode. Note that although reduction occurs at the cathode, it isn't the cathode itself that is being reduced. In our example, it is the copper(II) ions (Cu^{2+}) that are being reduced and plating out as copper metal (Cu) at the cathode. In any cell where plating occurs, it will be at the cathode. While the cathode thus increases in mass, the anode decreases in mass as metal atoms donate electrons and become ions, which dissolve into solution.

A conductor doesn't increase in mass or become charged when an electric current flows through it. When electrons move into a copper wire, they displace or push the wire's free moving valence electrons ahead. Magnesium's two electrons need only move one atom toward the copper half-cell to displace electrons all the way through the wire and pop two electrons out the other end to the waiting Cu^{2+} ions. This is similar to what happens when water flows from a tap into a hose that is already full of water, immediately pushing some water out the other end of the hose.

The Salt Bridge

A salt bridge or a porous barrier allows ion migration that completes the circuit. In effect, the ion migration electrically counterbalances the electron flow. Without this ion migration, a charge build-up would occur: the reduction half-cell would become negative and the oxidation half-cell would become positive. This would create a polarization that would stop the electron flow. The natural ion migration prevents such a charge build-up. Consider a cell and its external circuit as one continuous loop with the negatively charged particles (electrons and anions) flowing in a continuous clockwise or counter-clockwise direction. In Figure 9.4.2, the negatively charged particles flow in a clockwise direction.

> Anions migrate toward the anode.
> Cations migrate toward the cathode.

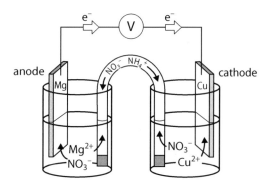

Figure 9.4.2 *Ion migration in an electrochemical cell*

The oxidation half-cell above consists of a Mg electrode in $Mg(NO_3)_2(aq)$. The reduction half-cell consists of a Cu electrode in $Cu(NO_3)_2(aq)$. The salt bridge contains $NH_4NO_3(aq)$. The anion (NO_3^-) moves toward the anode while the cations (NH_4^+, Cu^{2+}, and Mg^{2+}) move toward the cathode.

Students sometimes ask whether the anode is the positive or the negative electrode. It is neither. The electrodes do not have any significant charge. Why then do commercial cells have a (–) label and a (+) label on them? The anode and the cathode each have a (–) and a (+) terminal or end, just as a magnet has a north and a south pole. Electrons flow externally from the (–) terminal of the anode to the (+) terminal of the cathode while internally anions migrate from the (–) terminal of the cathode to the (+) terminal of the anode (Figure 9.4.3).

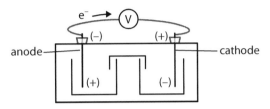

Figure 9.4.3 *Electrons move the through the wire connecting the electrodes while ions move through the salt bridge.*

Non-metal | Non-metal Ion Half-Cells

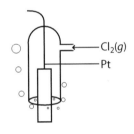

Figure 9.4.4 *A chlorine electrode*

Another type of half-cell consists of a non-metal electrode immersed in a solution containing ions of the same non-metal. What does a non-metal electrode such as a chlorine electrode look like? Obviously, a gas or a liquid electrode can't simply be a piece of the substance. They are essentially an inverted test tube filled with the liquid or gas (Figure 1.4.4). A platinum (inert metal) wire runs through the liquid or gas and connects at the bottom, open end of the tube to a piece of porous platinum foil where most of the electron transfer occurs. The gas is fed into the tube at 1 atm pressure through a side arm at the closed, top end of the tube. There are several variations on this design. Sometimes, an inert electrode is simply suspended above the open end of a tube that feeds gas bubbles into the solution. Many of the bubbles make contact with and even adhere to the electrode as they rise up through the solution.

A chlorine electrode immersed in a solution containing chloride ions is an example of a non-metal | non-metal ion half-cell. Either the non-metal electrode receives electrons from the other half-cell or the non-metal ions give electrons to the other half-cell when the electrochemical cell is operating. Hydrogen cells are an exception. Either the hydrogen electrode gives electrons to the other half-cell or the hydrogen ions receive electrons from the other half-cell. If a hydrogen | hydrogen ion half-cell were connected to a chlorine | chloride ion half-cell then electrons would flow from the hydrogen half-cell to the chlorine half-cell. The hydrogen gas would be oxidized and the chlorine gas would be reduced.

reduction ½ reaction →

$$Cl_2 + 2e^- \rightarrow 2\,Cl^-$$
$$Br_2 + 2e^- \rightleftharpoons 2\,Br^-$$
$$I_2 + 2e^- \rightleftharpoons 2\,I^-$$
$$Cu^{2+} + 2e^- \rightleftharpoons Cu$$
$$2\,H^+ + 2e^- \leftarrow H_2$$

← oxidation ½ reaction

$$H_2 \rightarrow 2\,H^+ + 2e^-$$
$$Cl_2 + 2e^- \rightarrow 2\,Cl^-$$
$$\overline{Cl_2 + H_2 \rightarrow 2\,H^+ + 2\,Cl^-}$$

Predicting Standard Cell Potentials (Voltages)

The simple design of the standard electrochemical cell makes it ideal for measuring redox potentials. The redox potential is the tendency of a redox reaction to occur. Standard cell potentials are measured in volts. Voltage can be thought of as the difference in electrical pressure that causes the flow of electrons in much the same way that a difference in air pressure causes a flow of air (wind). Cell voltages measure the net tendency for electron transfer between one redox tandem (oxidizing agent–reducing agent) and another. Cell voltages do not apply outside the context of standard

Quick Check

For the cell shown on the right:

1. Which electrode is the anode? _____

2. In which direction do the electrons flow through the wire?

   _____

3. In which direction do the cations flow through the salt bridge?

   _____

4. Which electrode gains in mass? _____

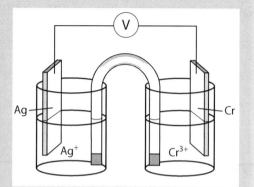

electrochemical cells. However, they can still be useful for predicting the spontaneity of a reaction between these species in other circumstances.

By now you are discovering that answering redox questions is all about knowing how to use a SRP table. The SRP table not only allows us to predict the direction of electron flow in standard cells, it also allows us to predict the tendency of electron flow. All E° values in this table are reported relative to the $H_2(g)$ half-cell. The hydrogen electrode is thus referred to as a *reference* electrode. The result of any other "competition" can be determined by a third-party comparison against what might be considered their common enemy, H^+. This is like predicting the result of a football game by comparing how the two teams did against a common opponent. If Team A defeats Team B by 14 points and Team B defeats Team C by 10 points then we would predict that Team A would defeat Team C by 24 points. Third party comparisons are not always valid in sports, but they do work for predicting the voltages of half-cell combinations in electrochemical cells.

The half-reactions highlighted below show that, under standard conditions, a Ni | Ni^{2+} half-cell would lose to a hydrogen half-cell by 0.26 V. However an I_2 | I^- half-cell would win against a hydrogen half-cell by 0.54 V. It's predictable that, when a Ni | Ni^{2+} half-cell and a I_2 | I^- half-cell are connected, the result would be a 0.80 V victory for the I_2 | I^- half-cell.

reduction ½ reaction	$I_2 + 2e^- \rightarrow 2I^-$ .... +0.54 V
	$Cu^+ + e^- \rightleftharpoons Cu$ .... +0.52 V
	$H_2SO_3 + 4H^+ + 2e^- \rightleftharpoons S + 3H_2O$ .... +0.45 V
	$Cu^{2+} + 2e^- \rightleftharpoons Cu$ .... +0.34 V
	$SO_4^{2-} + 4H^+ + 2e^- \rightleftharpoons H_2SO_3 + H_2O$ .... +0.17 V
	$Cu^{2+} + e^- \rightleftharpoons Cu^+$ .... +0.15 V
	$Sn^{4+} + 2e^- \rightleftharpoons Sn^{2+}$ .... +0.15 V
	$S + 2H^+ + 2e^- \rightleftharpoons H_2S$ .... +0.14 V
	$2H^+ + 2e^- \rightleftharpoons H_2$ .... 0.00 V
	$Pb^{2+} + 2e^- \rightleftharpoons Pb$ .... –0.13 V
	$Sn^{2+} + 2e^- \rightleftharpoons Sn$ .... –0.14 V
oxidation ½ reaction	$Ni^{2+} + 2e^- \leftarrow Ni$ .... –0.26 V

Voltage is also called *potential difference* because it measures the difference in electrical potential energy between two points in a circuit. The difference between the reduction potentials of Ni^{2+} and I_2 is 0.54 V – (–0.26 V) = 0.80 V. Perhaps the easiest way to determine standard cell voltages is to write each half-reaction the way it occurs and then add the half-cell potentials together. When a half-reaction is written in the opposite direction as that shown in the SRP table then its half-cell potential is also changed from (+) to (–) or vice versa.

Sometimes it is necessary to multiply one or both of the half-reactions by an integer in order to balance the transfer of electrons. A half-cell potential ($E°$) doesn't change when its half-reaction is multiplied by an integer. One volt is one joule of energy per coulomb of charge. One coulomb of charge represents 6.2×10^{18} electrons. Tripling the half-reaction does not affect the half-cell potential since the energy *per electron* (voltage) is unchanged. Changing the size of metal electrodes does not affect the cell voltage.

Sample Problem — Determining Standard Cell Potentials (Voltages)

Determine the voltage of a standard cell consisting of a Ni | Ni^{2+} half-cell and an I_2 | I^- half-cell.

What to Think About	How to Do It
1. Write each half-reaction and its standard potential. The oxidation potential of Ni is +0.26 V because it is the reverse of the reduction potential of Ni^{2+} provided in a SRP table.	$Ni \rightarrow Ni^{2+} + 2e^- \qquad E° = 0.26\ V$ $I_2 + 2e^- \rightarrow 2I^- \qquad E° = 0.54\ V$ $I_2 + Ni \rightarrow Ni^{2+} + 2I^- \qquad E° = 0.80\ V$
2. Add the reduction potential to the oxidation potential.	

A positive $E°$ indicates that the reaction is spontaneous. A negative $E°$ indicates that the reverse reaction is spontaneous. In the context of an electrochemical cell, a negative $E°$ means that you wrote the half-reactions backwards. The beauty of the SRP table is that it displays the strength of oxidizing and reducing agents, while also allowing you to quickly calculate the standard cell voltage of hundreds of half-cell combinations. A two-dimensional table could also be used to directly display the standard cell voltages of a limited number of half-cell combinations. Table 9.4.1 shows an example.

Table 9.4.1 *Example of Table to Display Half-cell Combinations*

		Reduction Half-cell		
		$2H^+ + 2e^- \rightarrow H_2$	$Ni^{2+} + 2e^- \rightarrow Ni$	$I_2 + 2e^- \rightarrow 2I^-$
Oxidation Half-cell	$H_2 \rightarrow 2H^+ + 2e^-$		–0.26 V	0.54 V
	$Ni \rightarrow Ni^{2+} + 2e^-$	0.26 V		0.80 V
	$2I^- \rightarrow I_2 + 2e^-$	–0.54 V	–0.80 V	

Practice Problems — Determining Standard Cell Potentials (Voltages)

Determine the standard cell potential of each of the following combinations of half-cells. Show the oxidation and reduction half-reactions as well as the overall redox reaction occurring in each cell.

1. $Ni \mid Ni^{2+}$ and $Br_2 \mid Br^-$

2. $Cu \mid Cu^{2+}$ and $Al \mid Al^{3+}$

3. $Au \mid Au^{3+}$ and $I_2 \mid I^-$

Non-Standard Conditions

A cell's conditions usually change as it operates. The voltages predicted using the SRP table are cell voltages under standard conditions (1 M, 25°C). As a cell operates, its voltage drops. Recall the $Cu \mid Cu^{2+} \parallel Mg \mid Mg^{2+}$ cell from the original examples in this section.

$$Cu^{2+} + Mg \rightarrow Mg^{2+} + Cu$$

For the purposes of this discussion let's consider Cu^{2+} to be having an electron tug-of-war with Mg^{2+} in this cell. Both Cu^{2+} and Mg^{2+} are, after all, oxidizing agents. The Cu^{2+} pulls Mg's valence electrons toward the $Cu \mid Cu^{2+}$ half-cell while Mg^{2+} pulls Cu's valence electrons toward the $Mg \mid Mg^{2+}$ half-cell. These are opposing forces even though they are pulling on different electrons because electrons cannot simultaneously flow in two directions through a wire. Just as water can, at any given time, flow only in one direction through a hose, electrons can at any given time flow only in one direction through a wire. If you connected two taps with a hose, the water would flow from the tap with the greatest pressure to that with the least pressure. The tap with the greatest pressure would win the "push-of-war," but the water pressure in the opposite direction would act as a resistance to that flow. Similarly, electrons flow from the $Mg \mid Mg^{2+}$ half-cell to the $Cu \mid Cu^{2+}$ half-cell and the electrical pressure in the opposite direction acts as a resistance. In other words, Cu^{2+} wins the electron tug-of-war against Mg^{2+}.

Now let's consider how the cell's conditions change as it operates and how those changes affect the cell's voltage. As the cell operates, Mg transfers electrons to Cu^{2+}, thereby decreasing the $[Cu^{2+}]$ and increasing the $[Mg^{2+}]$. The increased $[Mg^{2+}]$ increases its pulling force while the decreasing $[Cu^{2+}]$ decreases its pulling force. Eventually the pulling forces of the Mg^{2+} and Cu^{2+} become equal and the cell now has 0 V so it is "dead." As an analogy, consider a tug-of-war between 20 grade 12s and 20 grade 8s. Naturally the grade 12s would win. But what would happen if every time the rope moved one foot, the grade 12s lost one of their pullers and the grade 8s gained another puller? Eventually the grade 8s' pulling force and the grade 12s' pulling force would be equal and the contest would come to a draw.

Cell Equilibrium

A "dead" cell is often said to be at equilibrium. The equilibrium referred to in the context of an electrochemical cell is a static equilibrium of forces. It is **not** a dynamic chemical equilibrium because electrons cannot travel simultaneously in two directions through the same wire. This same redox reaction could develop a chemical equilibrium if the reactants were both present in the same solution. Just as protons (H^+) are passed back and forth in Brønsted-Lowry acid-base equilibria, electrons are passed back and forth in redox equilibria. A reaction's E° indicates essentially the same thing as its K_{eq}. A formula called the *Nernst equation* converts E°s into K_{eqs}. Even small cell voltages generally correspond to large equilibrium constants. The reactions go almost to completion before establishing equilibrium. Small negative cell voltages therefore correspond to small equilibrium constants for reactions that establish equilibrium with little product. Chemists use cell voltages and the Nernst equation to determine equilibrium constants that would be virtually impossible to determine by direct chemical analysis.

We have seen that changes to a cell's conditions will affect its voltage. If the reactant concentrations are greater than 1 M or the product concentrations are less than 1 M then the cell's potential will be greater than the standard cell potential because the forward reaction has to proceed further to achieve the equilibrium of forces. Conversely if the reactant concentrations are less than 1 M or the product concentrations are greater than 1 M, the cell's potential will be less than the standard cell potential. This is because the forward reaction has less reactant to consume before achieving the equilibrium of forces. The concentration of an ion may be lowered in a half-cell by precipitating some ions out of solution. For example, if some sodium sulfide were added to a $Cu \mid Cu^{2+}$ half-cell then some Cu^{2+} ions would precipitate out with S^{2-} ions. This would cause the voltage in our $Cu \mid Cu^{2+} \parallel Mg \mid Mg^{2+}$ cell to drop.

Common Cells and Batteries

With the proliferation of handheld electronic devices, worldwide battery sales now top $7 billion annually. You obviously cannot put a standard electrochemical cell into a portable electronic device. The cells used in electronic devices are called *dry* cells because their electrolytes are in gels or pastes rather than ordinary aqueous solutions that would be more likely to leak. Most commercial cells have only one electrolyte and thus need no barrier at all between the locations of the two half-reactions.

Alkaline Dry Cell

A **battery** is a group or battery of cells. The common household 1.5 V battery that we use to power portable electronics is actually an individual alkaline dry cell. Two or more of them connected end to end are a battery. The modern alkaline cell was invented by Canadian engineer Lewis Urry in the 1950's. Over 500 million alkaline cells are purchased annually in Canada.

An alkaline cell's anode consists of zinc powder packed around a brass pin in the middle of the cell (Figure 9.4.6). Its cathode is a paste of solid manganese dioxide (MnO_2) and powdered carbon. The two electrodes are separated by a fibrous fabric. The alkaline cell is so named because its electrolyte is a moist paste of the base KOH.

The alkaline dry cell lasts longer and generates a steadier voltage than its predecessor, the Leclanch cell, which instead had a moist paste of the acidic salt, ammonium chloride (NH_4Cl) and zinc chloride ($ZnCl_2$). The alkaline cell's half-reactions are:

Anode	$Zn + 2\,OH^- \rightarrow ZnO(s) + H_2O + 2e^-$
Cathode	$2\,MnO_2 + H_2O + 2e^- \rightarrow Mn_2O_3(s) + 2\,OH^-$

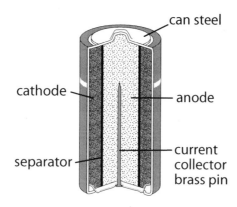

Figure 9.4.6 *An alkaline dry cell*

Other related cells include the button batteries used in calculators and watches, nickel-cadmium (Ni-Cad batteries, and lithium ion batteries. Lithium ion batteries are a type of rechargeable battery used in everything from cellphones to electric vehicles.

Lead-Acid Storage Battery

A 12 V lead storage battery consists of six cells connected in series (Figure 9.4.7). This type of battery is most commonly used in cars. The anodes are lead alloy grids packed with spongy lead. The cathodes are lead alloy grids packed with lead oxide (PbO_2. The lead storage battery consists of true "wet" cells

because its electrolyte is an aqueous solution of sulfuric acid. The cell doesn't have separate anode and cathode compartments because the oxidizing and reducing agents are both solids (PbO_2 and Pb and both are immersed in the same electrolyte (HSO_4^-)

Anode	$Pb(s) + HSO_4^{-2} \rightarrow PbSO_4(s) + H^+ + 2e^-$
Cathode	$PbO_2(s) + 3\,H^+ + HSO_4^- + 2e^- \rightarrow PbSO_4(s) + 2\,H_2O$

The product $PbSO_4(s)$ adheres to the electrodes' surfaces. When a car's engine is running, an alternator continuously recharges the battery. The alternator supplies an electric current to the battery, operating it "backwards" as an electrolytic cell (section 1.5) to restore the original reactants.

© Edvantage Interactive 2016

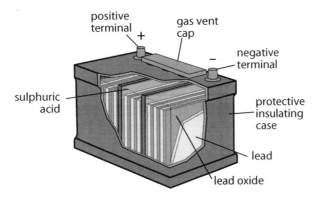

Figure 9.4.7 *A lead-acid storage battery*

For a cell to be classified as rechargeable, the redox reaction that occurs during the cell's operation must be "efficiently reversed" when the opposite electric potential is applied across the cell so that hundreds of recharging cycles are possible. Standard alkaline batteries are non-rechargeable cells because, in addition to the required reverse reactions, other reactions occur when the opposite electric potential is applied across the cell. Since not all of the original reactants are reformed during the reverse operation, the number of recharging cycles is very limited, with the cell lasting for a shorter period of time with each successive recharge. More importantly, recharging a standard alkaline battery is not safe because one of the side-products formed during the reverse operation is hydrogen gas, which can ignite and cause the battery to explode. (Non-rechargeable cells are also called primary cells.)

Fuel Cells

A **fuel cell** is a cell that has its reactants continuously resupplied from an external source as they are consumed. Fuel cells are used to power electric cars and buses as well as provide electricity for vehicles used in space travel. Fuel cells are also being used to provide backup, supplemental, and even mainstream power for industrial complexes and isolated communities. The most common fuel cell is the hydrogen-oxygen fuel cell (Figure 9.4.8). Hydrogen (the fuel) is oxidized at the anode while oxygen (the oxidizer) is reduced at the cathode. Both electrodes are composed of a porous carbon material.

Ballard Power Systems of Burnaby, Canada, is a world leader in fuel cell technology. In Ballard's current cell, the electrodes are bonded to a "cellophane-like" proton exchange membrane (PEM) that is coated with a very thin layer of platinum. The platinum catalyzes the half-reaction at the anode. The proton exchange membrane acts as an electrolyte medium conducting the hydrogen ions (protons) from the anode to the cathode.

Anode $\qquad\qquad 2\,H_2(g) \rightarrow 4\,H^+ + 4e^-$

Cathode $\qquad O_2(g) + 4\,H^+ + 4e^- \rightarrow 2\,H_2O$

The overall reaction is: $2\,H_2 + O_2 \rightarrow 2\,H_2O$. The water produced at the cathode is vented out the bottom half of the cell as steam. The same reaction occurs when hydrogen burns or explodes in oxygen. The heat released from burning hydrogen could be converted into electricity in a variety of ways but the vast majority of that energy would be lost during the conversion from heat to electrical energy. By contrast, fuel cells' conversions of chemical energy directly into electrical energy are 40% to 60% efficient.

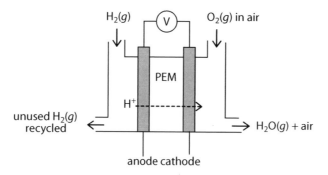

$H_2(g)$ (V) $O_2(g)$ in air

PEM

H^+ - - - - - - - >

unused $H_2(g)$ recycled   <—   —> $H_2O(g)$ + air

anode cathode

Figure 9.4.8 *A hydrogen fuel cell*

Quick Check

1. Complete the following table:

Type	Anode Material	Cathode Material	Electrolyte Medium	Use
Alkaline cell				
Lead-acid storage battery				
Fuel cell				

Corrosion

Corrosion is a term people use for *unwanted oxidation*, much like we use the term *weed* for an unwanted plant. **Rusting**, the corrosion of iron, is the most familiar and commercially important type of corrosion. Repairing rust damage to buildings, bridges, ships, cars, etc. costs billions of dollars each year.

Let's look at a simplified description of the rusting process. Droplets of water act as an electrolyte to create tiny voltaic cells on iron surfaces (Figure 9.4.9). Iron is more readily oxidized in some surface regions than others due to factors such as impurities and physical stresses such as being bent. When a water droplet forms over one of these "anode" regions, a pit forms as the iron is oxidized to Fe^{2+}:

Anode $Fe(s) \rightarrow Fe^{2+} + 2e^-$

The lost electrons are passed through the iron itself to oxygen molecules at the edge of the droplet:

Cathode $\frac{1}{2}O_2(g) + 2H^+ + 2e^- \rightarrow H_2O$ and/or
             $\frac{1}{2}O_2(g) + H_2O + 2e^- \rightarrow 2OH^-$

Migrating Fe^{2+} ions are further oxidized to Fe^{3+} as they react with dissolved O_2 near the droplet's edge. The Fe^{3+} then readily reacts with water to form rust (hydrated iron (III) oxide), which, having low solubility, deposits on the iron's surface:

     $2Fe^{3+}(aq) + 4H_2O(l) \rightarrow Fe_2O_3 \cdot H_2O(s) + 6H^+(aq)$
                     (rust)

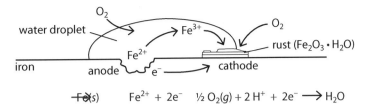

$$Fe(s) \qquad Fe^{2+} + 2e^- \qquad \tfrac{1}{2} O_2(g) + 2\,H^+ + 2e^- \longrightarrow H_2O$$

Figure 9.4.9 *Voltaic mechanism for rusting*

Dissolved salts in the water droplet increase its conductivity, thus increasing the corrosion rate. This is why cars generally rust faster in eastern Canada where more road salt is used in the winter than in western Canada.

The tarnishing of silver is another example of corrosion. The black color typical of tarnishing results from silver reacting with sulfur compounds in the air or in materials that it touches.

Oxygen is capable of oxidizing most metals but most other metal oxides such as aluminum oxide, chromium oxide, and zinc oxide form hard, impenetrable coatings that protect their metals from further corrosion. By contrast, rust is porous and flaky and unable to shield the underlying metal from further oxidation.

The Prevention of Corrosion

Iron can be protected from rusting by coating it with paint or grease, by cathodic protection, or by galvanizing it.

One way to prevent a reaction from occurring is to prevent the reactants from coming into contact (collision theory). Rusting is commonly prevented by painting the iron's surface so that it is not directly exposed to water or air. To prevent a redox reaction from occurring, the paint must electrically insulate the iron as well as coat it. If the paint can conduct electrons to the oxidizing agent then its physical coating offers no protection from rusting.

Cathodic protection is another way to prevent rusting. In one form of cathodic protection, a metal is protected from corrosion by attaching a metal to it that is a stronger reducing agent. The attached metal gets oxidized instead of the metal you are protecting. The oxidizing agent draws electrons from the sacrificial metal through the metal being protected. As electrons from the oxidized metal move into the conductor, they displace or push the conductor's valence electrons through to the oxidizing agent. The exposed metal thus remains intact, acting only as a conductor for the electrons. Because the metal that is protected acts as a cathode, this process is called *cathodic protection*.

Cathodic protection is used to protect structures such as underground pipelines, steel reinforcing bars in concrete, deep-sea oil rigs, and ship hulls. Steel is an alloy consisting primarily of iron. Without protection, the steel hulls of ships would be quickly corroded by ocean water because of its salt content. Zinc bars are welded to ships' hulls. The cations in the ocean water preferentially oxidize the zinc through the steel hull and leave the steel alone. The zinc saves the iron from corrosion but the combination of the two metals causes the zinc to be oxidized much more quickly than if it had been exposed to the oxidizing agent alone. This is due to the increased surface area exposed to the oxidizing agent via conduction of its electrons through the iron. In a well-documented example of this phenomenon, the Statue of Liberty's internal support structure of iron ribs was corroded quickly by the moist sea air through the statue's copper skin.

Some iron materials are coated with zinc in a process known as **galvanizing**. Any chemical mixture that can oxidize iron can more easily oxidize zinc so how does the zinc coating offer the iron any protection? If the zinc is oxidized it forms zinc oxide. Zinc oxide forms a hard, impenetrable coating. Should the zinc or the zinc oxide coating be scratched off in some areas, the remaining zinc coating still provides cathodic protection.

Quick Check

1. What is the chemical name for rust? _____

2. Identify the reduction half-reaction responsible for rusting.

3. List three factors that influence the corrosion rate of iron.

   (a) _____

   (b) _____

   (c) _____

4. What are two methods that could be used to reduce the corrosion rate of iron?

   (a) _____

   (b) _____

© Edvantage Interactive 2016

9.4 Review Questions

1. Complete the following table for an electrochemical (metal electrode/metallic ions) cell.

Anode	Cathode
	reduction occurs
mass decreases	
	attracts cations
electrons flow away	

2. The electrochemical cell below consists of a strip of iron in 1.0 M $Fe(NO_3)_2$ and a strip of nickel in 1.0 M $Ni(NO_3)_2$. A salt bridge containing 1.0 M NH_4NO_3 connects these half-cells. A voltmeter connects the two electrodes. (Make sure your answers to the following questions refer specifically to the cell below. Generic responses that are true for any cell, such as "oxidation occurs at the anode," will not be marked correct.)

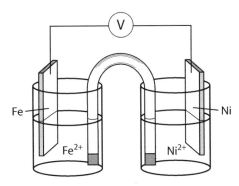

(a) Show the direction of electron flow on the diagram.
(b) In which half-cell does oxidation occur?

(c) Write the half-cell reactions involved.

(d) Label the anode and the cathode.
(e) What is the expected initial voltage?

(f) Describe the flow of the NH_4^+ and NO_3^- ions within the cell.

(g) Describe how the mass of each electrode changes as the cell operates.

3. Elemental bromine does not exist in nature. Bromine is a corrosive, red-brown liquid at room temperature. Draw and label a bromine half-cell.

Use the following diagram for questions 4 and 5.

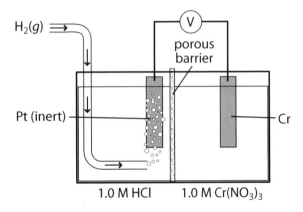

$H_2(g) \Rightarrow$

porous barrier

Pt (inert)

Cr

1.0 M HCl   1.0 M Cr(NO$_3$)$_3$

4. (a)   Show the direction of electron flow on the above diagram.
    (b)   In which half-cell does reduction occur?
    (c)   Write the half-cell reactions involved.

5. (a) Label the anode and the cathode.

    (b) What is the expected initial voltage?

    (c) Describe the flow of ions within the cell.

    (d) Describe how the mass of each electrode changes as the cell operates.

6. (a) Draw a Zn | Zn^{2+} || F$_2$ | F$^-$ electrochemical cell with the following labels:
    •   electrodes (Zn, F$_2$)
    •   solutions (1 M ZnCl$_2$, 1 M NaF)
    •   anode and the cathode

    (b) Show the direction of electron flow on your diagram.
    (c) Show the direction of anion and cation flow on your diagram.
    (d) Write the cell's two half-reactions and overall redox reaction.

    (e) Calculate the cell's initial voltage.

7. What is the purpose of a salt bridge in an electrochemical cell?

8. Calculate the standard cell potential for the reaction: $Br_2 + 2\,Fe^{2+} \rightarrow 2\,Br^- + 2\,Fe^{3+}$

9. Suppose that the silver-silver ion electrode were used as the reference for E° values, instead of the hydrogen electrode. What would be the standard reduction potentials, E°, for these half-cell reactions?
    (a) $F_2(g) + 2e^- \rightleftharpoons 2\,F^-$

    (b) $Mg^{2+} + 2e^- \rightleftharpoons Mg(s)$

10. The standard cell potential for the following reaction is 2.33 V.
$$Sr + Cr^{2+} \rightarrow Sr^{2+} + Cr$$
    Write the reduction half-reaction and determine its standard reduction potential (E°).

11. Given:

$$Pd^{2+} + Cu \rightarrow Pd + Cu^{2+} \qquad E° = 0.49\ V$$
$$2\,Np + 3\,Pd^{2+} \rightarrow 2\,Np^{3+} + 3\,Pd \qquad E° = 2.73\ V$$

    (a) What is the standard reduction potential (E°) of Pd^{2+}?

    (b) What is the standard reduction potential (E°) of Np^{3+}?

12. In the table below, fill in the missing cell voltages by using the voltages provided for other combinations of half-cells.

		Reduction Half-Cell	
		$Cd^{2+} + 2e^- \rightarrow Cd$	$Pt^{2+} + 2e^- \rightarrow Pt$
Oxidation Half-cell	$Pt \rightarrow Pt^{2+} + 2e^-$		0 V
	$Ni \rightarrow Ni^{2+} + 2e^-$	– 0.17 V	+ 1.43 V
	$Ce \rightarrow Ce^{3+} + 3e^-$	+ 1.93 V	

13. In an Fe | Fe^{2+} || Pb | Pb^{2+} standard cell, electrons are transferred from the Fe half-cell to the Pb half-cell.
    (a) What would be the effect on the voltage if Pb(NO$_3$)$_2$ were added to the lead half-cell?

    (b) What is the voltmeter reading when the cell reaches "equilibrium"?

    (c) What would be the effect on the voltage if sulfide ions (S^{2-}) were added to the Fe^{2+} ion compartment?

    (d) What would be the effect on the voltage if the size of the Fe electrode were doubled?

14. Sony demonstrated a paper cell at the Eco-Products 2011 Exhibition in Tokyo. Sony's bio-cell uses cellulase enzymes to hydrolyze paper into glucose, which is then oxidized. What features of this cell make it eco-friendly when compared to current commercial cells?

15. Describe how cathodic protection could be used to protect a steel stairway exposed to an ocean spray. Explain how this works.

16. Some steel nails are galvanized. Zinc is easier to oxidize than iron so how can coating a steel nail with zinc prevent it from corroding?

17. What adaptation to collision theory is necessary for redox reactions occurring in electrochemical cells?

Appendix — Reference Tables

© **Edvantage Interactive 2017**

Table A1 Atomic Masses of the Elements

Based on mass of carbon-12 at 12.00.

For elements that do not occur naturally, the atomic mass of the most stable or best known isotope is shown in parentheses.

Element	Symbol	Atomic Number	Atomic Mass
Actinium	Ac	89	(227)
Aluminum	Al	13	27.0
Americium	Am	95	(243)
Antimony	Sb	51	121.8
Argon	Ar	18	39.9
Arsenic	As	33	74.9
Astatine	At	85	(210)
Barium	Ba	56	137.3
Berkelium	Bk	97	(247)
Beryllium	Be	4	9.0
Bismuth	Bi	83	209.0
Boron	B	5	10.8
Bromine	Br	35	79.9
Cadmium	Cd	48	112.4
Calcium	Ca	20	40.1
Californium	Cf	98	(251)
Carbon	C	6	12.0
Cerium	Ce	58	140.1
Cesium	Cs	55	132.9
Chlorine	Cl	17	35.5
Chromium	Cr	24	52.0
Cobalt	Co	27	58.9
Copper	Cu	29	63.5
Curium	Cm	96	(247)
Dubnium	Db	105	(262)
Dysprosium	Dy	66	162.5
Einsteinium	Es	99	(252)
Erbium	Er	68	167.3
Europium	Eu	63	152.0
Fermium	Fm	100	(257)
Fluorine	F	9	19.0
Francium	Fr	87	(223)
Gadolinium	Gd	64	157.3
Gallium	Ga	31	69.7
Germanium	Ge	32	72.6
Gold	Au	79	197.0
Hafnium	Hf	72	178.5
Helium	He	2	4.0
Holmium	Ho	67	164.9
Hydrogen	H	1	1.0
Indium	In	49	114.8
Iodine	I	53	126.9
Iridium	Ir	77	192.2
Iron	Fe	26	55.8
Krypton	Kr	36	83.8
Lanthanum	La	57	138.9
Lawrencium	Lr	103	(262)
Lead	Pb	82	207.2
Lithium	Li	3	6.9
Lutetium	Lu	71	175.0
Magnesium	Mg	12	24.3
Manganese	Mn	25	54.9
Mendelevium	Md	101	(258)
Mercury	Hg	80	200.6
Molybdenum	Mo	42	95.9
Neodymium	Nd	60	144.2
Neon	Ne	10	20.2
Neptunium	Np	93	(237)
Nickel	Ni	28	58.7
Niobium	Nb	41	92.9
Nitrogen	N	7	14.0
Nobelium	No	102	(259)
Osmium	Os	76	190.2
Oxygen	O	8	16.0
Palladium	Pd	46	106.4
Phosphorus	P	15	31.0
Platinum	Pt	78	195.1
Plutonium	Pu	94	(244)
Polonium	Po	84	(209)
Potassium	K	19	39.1
Praseodymium	Pr	59	140.9
Promethium	Pm	61	(145)
Protactinium	Pa	91	231.0
Radium	Ra	88	(226)
Radon	Rn	86	(222)
Rhenium	Re	75	186.2
Rhodium	Rh	45	102.9
Rubidium	Rb	37	85.5
Ruthenium	Ru	44	101.1
Rutherfordium	Rf	104	(261)
Samarium	Sm	62	150.4
Scandium	Sc	21	45.0
Selenium	Se	34	79.0
Silicon	Si	14	28.1
Silver	Ag	47	107.9
Sodium	Na	11	23.0
Strontium	Sr	38	87.6
Sulfur	S	16	32.1
Tantalum	Ta	73	180.9
Technetium	Tc	43	(98)
Tellurium	Te	52	127.6
Terbium	Tb	65	158.9
Thallium	Tl	81	204.4
Thorium	Th	90	232.0
Thulium	Tm	69	168.9
Tin	Sn	50	118.7
Titanium	Ti	22	47.9
Tungsten	W	74	183.8
Uranium	U	92	238.0
Vanadium	V	23	50.9
Xenon	Xe	54	131.3
Ytterbium	Yb	70	173.0
Yttrium	Y	39	88.9
Zinc	Zn	30	65.4
Zirconium	Zr	40	91.2

Table A2 Names, Formulas, and Charges of Some Common Ions

* Aqueous solutions readily oxidized by air
** Not stable in aqueous solutions

Positive Ions (Cations)

Al^{3+}	Aluminum	Pb^{4+}	Lead(IV), plumbic
NH_4^+	Ammonium	Li^+	Lithium
Ba^{2+}	Barium	Mg^{2+}	Magnesium
Ca^{2+}	Calcium	Mn^{2+}	Manganese(II), manganous
Cr^{2+}	Chromium(II), chromous	Mn^{4+}	Manganese(IV)
Cr^{3+}	Chromium(III), chromic	Hg_2^{2+}	Mercury(I)*, mercurous
Cu^+	Copper(I)*, cuprous	Hg^{2+}	Mercury(II), mercuric
Cu^{2+}	Copper(II), cupric	K^+	Potassium
H^+	Hydrogen	Ag^+	Silver
H_3O^+	Hydronium	Na^+	Sodium
Fe^{2+}	Iron(II)*, ferrous	Sn^{2+}	Tin(II)*, stannous
Fe^{3+}	Iron(III), ferric	Sn^{4+}	Tin(IV), stannic
Pb^{2+}	Lead(II), plumbous	Zn^{2+}	Zinc

Negative Ions (Anions)

Br^-	Bromide	OH^-	Hydroxide
CO_3^{2-}	Carbonate	ClO^-	Hypochlorite
ClO_3^-	Chlorate	I^-	Iodide
Cl^-	Chloride	HPO_4^{2-}	Monohydrogen phosphate
ClO_2^-	Chlorite	NO_3^-	Nitrate
CrO_4^{2-}	Chromate	NO_2^-	Nitrite
CN^-	Cyanide	$C_2O_4^{2-}$	Oxalate
$Cr_2O_7^{2-}$	Dichromate	O^{2-}	Oxide**
$H_2PO_4^-$	Dihydrogen phosphate	ClO_4^-	Perchlorate
CH_3COO^-	Ethanoate, acetate	MnO_4^-	Permanganate
F^-	Fluoride	$PO_4^{?-}$	Phosphate
HCO_3^-	Hydrogen carbonate, bicarbonate	SO_4^{2-}	Sulfate
$HC_2O_4^-$	Hydrogen oxalate, binoxalate	S^{2-}	Sulfide
HSO_4^-	Hydrogen sulfate, bisulfate	SO_3^{2-}	Sulfite
HS^-	Hydrogen sulfide, bisulfide	SCN^-	Thiocyanate
HSO_3^-	Hydrogen sulfite, bisulfite		

© Edvantage Interactive 2017

Table A3 Solubility of Common Compounds in Water

"Soluble" means > 0.1 mol/L at 25°C.

Negative Ions (Anions)	Positive Ions (Cations)	Solubility of Compounds
All	Alkali ions: Li^+, Na^+, K^+, Rb^+, Cs^+, Fr^+	Soluble
All	Hydrogen ion: H^+	Soluble
All	Ammonium ion: NH_4^+	Soluble
Nitrate, NO_3^-	All	Soluble
Chloride, Cl^- or Bromide, Br^- or Iodide, I^-	All others	Soluble
	Ag^+, Pb^{2+}, Cu^+	Low Solubility
Sulfate, SO_4^{2-}	All others	Soluble
	Ag^+, Ca^{2+}, Sr^{2+}, Ba^{2+}, Pb^{2+}	Low Solubility
Sulfide, S^{2-}	Alkali ions, H^+, NH_4^+, Be^{2+}, Mg^{2+}, Ca^{2+}, Sr^{2+}, Ba^{2+}	Soluble
	All others	Low Solubility
Hydroxide, OH^-	Alkali ions, H^+, NH_4^+, Sr^{2+}	Soluble
	All others	Low Solubility
Phosphate, PO_4^{3-} or Carbonate, CO_3^{2-} or Sulfite, SO_3^{2-}	Alkali ions, H^+, NH_4^+	Soluble
	All others	Low Solubility

Table A4 Solubility Product Constants at 25°C

Name	Formula	K_{sp}
Barium carbonate	$BaCO_3$	2.6×10^{-9}
Barium chromate	$BaCrO_4$	1.2×10^{-10}
Barium sulfate	$BaSO_4$	1.1×10^{-10}
Calcium carbonate	$CaCO_3$	5.0×10^{-9}
Calcium oxalate	CaC_2O_4	2.3×10^{-9}
Calcium sulfate	$CaSO_4$	7.1×10^{-5}
Copper(I) iodide	CuI	1.3×10^{-12}
Copper(II) iodate	$Cu(IO_3)_2$	6.9×10^{-8}
Copper(II) sulfide	CuS	6.0×10^{-37}
Iron(II) hydroxide	$Fe(OH)_2$	4.9×10^{-17}
Iron(II) sulfide	FeS	6.0×10^{-19}
Iron(III) hydroxide	$Fe(OH)_3$	2.6×10^{-39}
Lead(II) bromide	$PbBr_2$	6.6×10^{-6}
Lead(II) chloride	$PbCl_2$	1.2×10^{-5}
Lead(II) iodate	$Pb(IO_3)_2$	3.7×10^{-13}
Lead(II) iodide	PbI_2	8.5×10^{-9}
Lead(II) sulfate	$PbSO_4$	1.8×10^{-8}
Magnesium carbonate	$MgCO_3$	6.8×10^{-6}
Magnesium hydroxide	$Mg(OH)_2$	5.6×10^{-12}
Silver bromate	$AgBrO_3$	5.3×10^{-5}
Silver bromide	$AgBr$	5.4×10^{-13}
Silver carbonate	Ag_2CO_3	8.5×10^{-12}
Silver chloride	$AgCl$	1.8×10^{-10}
Silver chromate	Ag_2CrO_4	1.1×10^{-12}
Silver iodate	$AgIO_3$	3.2×10^{-8}
Silver iodide	AgI	8.5×10^{-17}
Strontium carbonate	$SrCO_3$	5.6×10^{-10}
Strontium fluoride	SrF_2	4.3×10^{-9}
Strontium sulfate	$SrSO_4$	3.4×10^{-7}
Zinc sulfide	ZnS	2.0×10^{-25}

© Edvantage Interactive 2017

Table A5 Relative Strengths of Brønsted-Lowry Acids and Bases

In aqueous solution at room temperature

Name of Acid	Acid		Base	K_a
Perchloric	$HClO_4$	$\rightarrow$	$H^+ + ClO_4^-$	very large
Hydriodic	HI	$\rightarrow$	$H^+ + I^-$	very large
Hydrobromic	HBr	$\rightarrow$	$H^+ + Br^-$	very large
Hydrochloric	HCl	$\rightarrow$	$H^+ + Cl^-$	very large
Nitric	HNO_3	$\rightarrow$	$H^+ + NO_3^-$	very large
Sulfuric	H_2SO_4	$\rightarrow$	$H^+ + HSO_4^-$	very large
Hydronium Ion	H_3O^+	$\rightleftarrows$	$H^+ + H_2O$	1.0
Iodic	HIO_3	$\rightleftarrows$	$H^+ + IO_3^-$	1.7×10^{-1}
Oxalic	$H_2C_2O_4$	$\rightleftarrows$	$H^+ + HC_2O_4^-$	5.9×10^{-2}
Sulfurous ($SO_2 + H_2O$)	H_2SO_3	$\rightleftarrows$	$H^+ + HSO_3^-$	1.5×10^{-2}
Hydrogen sulfate ion	HSO_4^-	$\rightleftarrows$	$H^+ + SO_4^{2-}$	1.2×10^{-2}
Phosphoric	H_3PO_4	$\rightleftarrows$	$H^+ + H_2PO_4^-$	7.5×10^{-3}
Hexaaquoiron ion, iron(III) ion	$Fe(H_2O)_6^{3+}$	$\rightleftarrows$	$H^+ + Fe(H_2O)_5(OH)^{2+}$	6.0×10^{-3}
Citric	$H_3C_6H_5O_7$	$\rightleftarrows$	$H^+ + H_2C_6H_5O_7^-$	7.1×10^{-4}
Nitrous	HNO_2	$\rightleftarrows$	$H^+ + NO_2^-$	4.6×10^{-4}
Hydrofluoric	HF	$\rightleftarrows$	$H^+ + F^-$	3.5×10^{-4}
Methanoic, formic	$HCOOH$	$\rightleftarrows$	$H^+ + HCOO^-$	1.8×10^{-4}
Hexaaquochromium ion, chromium(III) ion	$Cr(H_2O)_6^{3+}$	$\rightleftarrows$	$H^+ + Cr(H_2O)_5(OH)^{2+}$	1.5×10^{-4}
Benzoic	C_6H_5COOH	$\rightleftarrows$	$H^+ + C_6H_5COO^-$	6.5×10^{-5}
Hydrogen oxalate ion	$HC_2O_4^-$	$\rightleftarrows$	$H^+ + C_2O_4^{2-}$	6.4×10^{-5}
Ethanoic, acetic	CH_3COOH	$\rightleftarrows$	$H^+ + CH_3COO^-$	1.8×10^{-5}
Dihydrogen citrate ion	$H_2C_6H_5O_7^-$	$\rightleftarrows$	$H^+ + HC_6H_5O_7^{2-}$	1.7×10^{-5}
Hexaaquoaluminum ion, aluminum ion	$Al(H_2O)_6^{3+}$	$\rightleftarrows$	$H^+ + Al(H_2O)_5(OH)^{2+}$	1.4×10^{-5}
Carbonic ($CO_2 + H_2O$)	H_2CO_3	$\rightleftarrows$	$H^+ + HCO_3^-$	4.3×10^{-7}
Monohydrogen citrate ion	$HC_6H_5O_7^{2-}$	$\rightleftarrows$	$H^+ + C_6H_5O_7^{3-}$	4.1×10^{-7}
Hydrogen sulfite ion	HSO_3^-	$\rightleftarrows$	$H^+ + SO_3^{2-}$	1.0×10^{-7}
Hydrogen sulfide	H_2S	$\rightleftarrows$	$H^+ + HS^-$	9.1×10^{-8}
Dihydrogen phosphate ion	$H_2PO_4^-$	$\rightleftarrows$	$H^+ + HPO_4^{2-}$	6.2×10^{-8}
Boric	H_3BO_3	$\rightleftarrows$	$H^+ + H_2BO_3^-$	7.3×10^{-10}
Ammonium ion	NH_4^+	$\rightleftarrows$	$H^+ + NH_3$	5.6×10^{-10}
Hydrocyanic	HCN	$\rightleftarrows$	$H^+ + CN^-$	4.9×10^{-10}
Phenol	C_6H_5OH	$\rightleftarrows$	$H^+ + C_6H_5O^-$	1.3×10^{-10}
Hydrogen carbonate ion	HCO_3^-	$\rightleftarrows$	$H^+ + CO_3^{2-}$	5.6×10^{-11}
Hydrogen peroxide	H_2O_2	$\rightleftarrows$	$H^+ + HO_2^-$	2.4×10^{-12}
Monohydrogen phosphate ion	HPO_4^{2-}	$\rightleftarrows$	$H^+ + PO_4^{3-}$	2.2×10^{-13}
Water	H_2O	$\rightleftarrows$	$H^+ + OH^-$	1.0×10^{-14}
Hydroxide ion	OH^-	$\leftarrow$	$H^+ + O^{2-}$	very small
Ammonia	NH_3	$\leftarrow$	$H^+ + NH_2^-$	very small

STRONG ... WEAK (STRENGTH OF ACID) — WEAK ... STRONG (STRENGTH OF BASE)

Table A6 Acid-Base Indicators

Indicator	pH Range in Which Colour Change Occurs	Colour Change as pH Increases
Methyl violet	0.0 – 1.6	yellow to blue
Thymol blue	1.2 – 2.8	red to yellow
Orange IV	1.4 – 2.8	red to yellow
Methyl orange	3.2 – 4.4	red to yellow
Bromcresol green	3.8 – 5.4	yellow to blue
Methyl red	4.8 – 6.0	red to yellow
Chlorophenol red	5.2 – 6.8	yellow to red
Bromthymol blue	6.0 – 7.6	yellow to blue
Phenol red	6.6 – 8.0	yellow to red
Neutral red	6.8 – 8.0	red to amber
Thymol blue	8.0 – 9.6	yellow to blue
Phenolphthalein	8.2 – 10.0	colourless to pink
Thymolphthalein	9.4 – 10.6	colourless to blue
Alizarin yellow	10.1 – 12.0	yellow to red
Indigo carmine	11.4 – 13.0	blue to yellow

© Edvantage Interactive 2017

Table A7 Standard Reduction Potentials of Half-Cells

Ionic concentrations are at 1 M in water at 25°C.

Oxidizing Agents		Reducing Agents	$E°$ (Volts)
$F_2(g) + 2e^-$	⇌	$2F^-$	+2.87
$S_2O_8{}^{2-} + 2e^-$	⇌	$2SO_4{}^{2-}$	+2.01
$H_2O_2 + 2H^+ + 2e^-$	⇌	$2H_2O$	+1.78
$MnO_4{}^- + 8H^+ + 5e^-$	⇌	$Mn^{2+} + 4H_2O$	+1.51
$Au^{3+} + 3e^-$	⇌	$Au(s)$	+1.50
$BrO_3{}^- + 6H^+ + 5e^-$	⇌	$\frac{1}{2}Br_2(\ell) + 3H_2O$	+1.48
$ClO_4{}^- + 8H^+ + 8e^-$	⇌	$Cl^- + 4H_2O$	+1.39
$Cl_2(g) + 2e^-$	⇌	$2Cl^-$	+1.36
$Cr_2O_7{}^{2-} + 14H^+ + 6e^-$	⇌	$2Cr^{3+} + 7H_2O$	+1.23
$\frac{1}{2}O_2(g) + 2H^+ + 2e^-$	⇌	H_2O	+1.23
$MnO_2(s) + 4H^+ + 2e^-$	⇌	$Mn^{2+} + 2H_2O$	+1.22
$IO_3{}^- + 6H^+ + 5e^-$	⇌	$\frac{1}{2}I_2(s) + 3H_2O$	+1.20
$Br_2(\ell) + 2e^-$	⇌	$2Br^-$	+1.09
$AuCl_4{}^- + 3e^-$	⇌	$Au(s) + 4Cl^-$	+1.00
$NO_3{}^- + 4H^+ + 3e^-$	⇌	$NO(g) + 2H_2O$	+0.96
$Hg^{2+} + 2e^-$	⇌	$Hg(\ell)$	+0.85
$\frac{1}{2}O_2(g) + 2H^+ (10^{-7}\,M) + 2e^-$	⇌	H_2O	+0.82
$2NO_3{}^- + 4H^+ + 2e^-$	⇌	$N_2O_4 + 2H_2O$	+0.80
$Ag^+ + e^-$	⇌	$Ag(s)$	+0.80
$\frac{1}{2}Hg_2{}^{2+} + e^-$	⇌	$Hg(\ell)$	+0.80
$Fe^{3+} + e^-$	⇌	Fe^{2+}	+0.77
$O_2(g) + 2H^+ + 2e^-$	⇌	H_2O_2	+0.70
$MnO_4{}^- + 2H_2O + 3e^-$	⇌	$MnO_2(s) + 4OH^-$	+0.60
$I_2(s) + 2e^-$	⇌	$2I^-$	+0.54
$Cu^+ + e^-$	⇌	$Cu(s)$	+0.52
$H_2SO_3 + 4H^+ + 4e^-$	⇌	$S(s) + 3H_2O$	+0.45
$Cu^{2+} + 2e^-$	⇌	$Cu(s)$	+0.34
$SO_4{}^{2-} + 4H^+ + 2e^-$	⇌	$H_2SO_3 + H_2O$	+0.17
$Cu^{2+} + e^-$	⇌	Cu^+	+0.15
$Sn^{4+} + 2e^-$	⇌	Sn^{2+}	+0.15
$S(s) + 2H^+ + 2e^-$	⇌	$H_2S(g)$	+0.14
$2H^+ + 2e^-$	⇌	$H_2(g)$	+0.00
$Pb^{2+} + 2e^-$	⇌	$Pb(s)$	−0.13
$Sn^{2+} + 2e^-$	⇌	$Sn(s)$	−0.14
$Ni^{2+} + 2e^-$	⇌	$Ni(s)$	−0.26
$H_3PO_4 + 2H^+ + 2e^-$	⇌	$H_3PO_3 + H_2O$	−0.28
$Co^{2+} + 2e^-$	⇌	$Co(s)$	−0.28
$Se(s) + 2H^+ + 2e^-$	⇌	H_2Se	−0.40
$Cr^{3+} + e^-$	⇌	Cr^{2+}	−0.41
$2H_2O + 2e^-$	⇌	$H_2 + 2OH^- (10^{-7}\,M)$	−0.41
$Fe^{2+} + 2e^-$	⇌	$Fe(s)$	−0.45
$Ag_2S(s) + 2e^-$	⇌	$2Ag(s) + S^{2-}$	−0.69
$Cr^{3+} + 3e^-$	⇌	$Cr(s)$	−0.74
$Zn^{2+} + 2e^-$	⇌	$Zn(s)$	−0.76
$Te(s) + 2H^+ + 2e^-$	⇌	H_2Te	−0.79
$2H_2O + 2e^-$	⇌	$H_2(g) + 2OH^-$	−0.83
$Mn^{2+} + 2e^-$	⇌	$Mn(s)$	−1.19
$Al^{3+} + 3e^-$	⇌	$Al(s)$	−1.66
$Mg^{2+} + 2e^-$	⇌	$Mg(s)$	−2.37
$Na^+ + e^-$	⇌	$Na(s)$	−2.71
$Ca^{2+} + 2e^-$	⇌	$Ca(s)$	−2.87
$Sr^{2+} + 2e^-$	⇌	$Sr(s)$	−2.89
$Ba^{2+} + 2e^-$	⇌	$Ba(s)$	−2.91
$K^+ + e^-$	⇌	$K(s)$	−2.93
$Rb^+ + e^-$	⇌	$Rb(s)$	−2.98
$Cs^+ + e^-$	⇌	$Cs(s)$	−3.03
$Li^+ + e^-$	⇌	$Li(s)$	−3.04

STRONG — STRENGTH OF OXIDIZING AGENT — WEAK (left axis)

WEAK — STRENGTH OF REDUCING AGENT — STRONG (right axis)

Overpotential Effect

Overpotential Effect

Table A8 Thermodynamic Data at 25°C for Assorted Substances

Table A8-Inorganic *Thermodynamic data at 25°C for assorted inorganic substances.*

Substance	Enthalpy of formation ΔH_f^0, kJ/mol	Free energy of formation ΔG_f^0, kJ/mol	Entropy S^0, J/(K·mol)
Aluminum			
Al(*s*)	0	0	28.33
Al^{3+}(*aq*)	-524.7	-481.2	-321.7
Al$_2$O$_3$(*s*)	-1675.7	-1582.3	50.92
Al(OH)$_3$(*s*)	-1276	---	---
AlCl$_3$(*s*)	-704.2	-628.8	110.67
Antimony			
SbH$_3$(*g*)	145.11	147.75	232.78
SbCl$_3$(*g*)	-313.8	-301.2	337.80
SbCl$_5$(*g*)	-394.34	-334.29	401.94
Arsenic			
As(*s, gray*)	0	0	35.1
As$_2$S$_3$(*s*)	-169.0	-168.6	163.6
AsO$_4^{3-}$(*aq*)	-888.14	-648.41	-162.8
Barium			
Ba(*s*)	0	0	62.8
Ba^{2+}(*aq*)	-537.64	-560.77	9.6
BaO(*s*)	-553.5	-525.1	70.42
BaCO$_3$(*s*)	-1216.3	-1137.6	112.1
BaCO$_3$(*aq*)	-1214.78	-1088.59	-47.3
Boron			
B(*s*)	0	0	5.86
B$_2$O$_3$(*s*)	-1272.8	-1193.7	53.97
BF$_3$(*g*)	-1137.0	-1120.3	254.12
Bromine			
Br$_2$(*l*)	0	0	152.23
Br$_2$(*g*)	30.91	3.11	245.46
Br(*g*)	111.88	82.40	175.02
Br$^-$(*aq*)	-121.55	-103.96	82.4
HBr(*g*)	-36.40	-53.45	198.70
Calcium			
Ca(*s*)	0	0	41.42
Ca(*g*)	178.2	144.3	154.88
Ca^{2+}(*aq*)	-542.83	-553.58	-53.1
CaO(*s*)	-635.09	-604.03	39.79
Ca(OH)$_2$(*s*)	-986.09	-898.49	83.39
Ca(OH)$_2$(*aq*)	-1002.82	-868.07	-74.5

© Edvantage Interactive 2017

Table A8-Inorganic *Thermodynamic data at 25°C for assorted inorganic substances (continued).*

Substance	Enthalpy of formation ΔH_f^0, kJ/mol	Free energy of formation ΔG_f^0, kJ/mol	Entropy S^0, J/(K·mol)
$CaCO_3(s, \text{calcite})$	-1206.9	-1128.8	92.9
$CaCO_3(s, \text{aragonite})$	-1207.1	-1127.8	88.7
$CaCO_3(aq)$	-1219.97	-1081.39	-110.0
$CaF_2(s)$	-1219.6	-1167.3	68.87
$CaF_2(aq)$	-1208.09	-1111.15	-80.8
$CaCl_2(s)$	-795.8	-748.1	104.6
$CaCl_2(aq)$	-877.1	-816.0	59.8
$CaBr_2(s)$	-682.8	-663.6	130
$CaC_2(s)$	-59.8	-64.9	69.96
$CaSO_4(s)$	-1434.11	-1321.79	106.7
$CaSO_4(aq)$	-1452.10	-1298.10	-33.1
Carbon			
$C(s, \text{graphite})$	0	0	5.740
$C(s, \text{diamond})$	1.895	2.900	2.377
$C(g)$	716.68	671.26	158.10
$CO(g)$	-110.53	-137.17	197.67
$CO_2(g)$	-393.51	-394.36	213.74
$CO_3^{2-}(aq)$	-677.14	-527.81	-56.9
$CCl_4(l)$	-135.44	-65.21	216.40
$CS_2(l)$	89.70	65.27	153.34
$HCN(g)$	135.1	124.7	201.78
$HCN(l)$	108.87	124.97	112.84
Cerium			
$Ce(s)$	0	0	72.0
$Ce^{3+}(aq)$	-696.2	-672.0	-205
$Ce^{4+}(aq)$	-537.2	-503.8	-301
Chlorine			
$Cl_2(g)$	0	0	223.07
$Cl(g)$	121.68	105.68	165.20
$Cl^-(aq)$	-167.16	-131.23	56.5
$HCl(g)$	-92.31	-95.30	186.91
$HCl(aq)$	-167.16	-131.23	56.5
Copper			
$Cu(s)$	0	0	33.15
$Cu^+(aq)$	71.67	49.98	40.6
$Cu^{2+}(aq)$	64.77	65.49	-99.6
$Cu_2O(s)$	-168.6	-146.0	93.14
$CuO(s)$	-157.3	-129.7	42.63
$CuSO_4(s)$	-771.36	-661.8	109

Table A8-Inorganic *Thermodynamic data at 25°C for assorted inorganic substances (continued).*

Substance	Enthalpy of formation ΔH_f^0, kJ/mol	Free energy of formation ΔG_f^0, kJ/mol	Entropy S^0, J/(K·mol)
Fluorine			
$F_2(g)$	0	0	202.78
$F^-(aq)$	-332.63	-278.79	-13.8
$HF(g)$	-271.1	-273.2	173.78
$HF(aq)$	-332.36	-278.79	-13.8
Hydrogen			
$H_2(g)$	0	0	130.68
$H(g)$	217.97	203.25	114.71
$H^+(aq)$	0	0	0
$H_2O(l)$	-285.83	-237.13	69.91
$H_2O(g)$	-241.82	-228.57	188.83
$H_2O_2(l)$	-187.78	-120.35	109.6
$H_2O_2(aq)$	-191.17	-134.03	143.9
$D_2(g)$	0	0	144.96
$D_2O(l)$	-294.60	-243.44	75.94
$D_2O(g)$	-249.20	-234.54	198.34
Iodine			
$I_2(s)$	0	0	116.14
$I_2(g)$	62.44	19.33	260.69
$I^-(aq)$	-55.19	-51.57	111.3
$HI(g)$	26.48	1.70	206.59
Iron			
$Fe(s)$	0	0	27.28
$Fe^{2+}(aq)$	-89.1	-78.90	-137.7
$Fe^{3+}(aq)$	-48.5	-4.7	-315.9
$Fe_3O_4(s, \text{ magnetite})$	-1118.4	-1015.4	146.4
$Fe_2O_3(s, \text{ hematite})$	-824.2	-742.2	87.40
$FeS(s, \alpha)$	-100.0	-100.4	60.29
$FeS(aq)$	---	6.9	---
$FeS_2(s)$	-178.2	-166.9	52.93
Lead			
$Pb(s)$	0	0	64.81
$Pb^{2+}(aq)$	-1.7	-24.43	10.5
$PbO_2(s)$	-277.4	-217.33	68.6
$PbSO_4(s)$	-919.94	-813.14	148.57
$PbBr_2(s)$	-278.7	-261.92	161.5
$PbBr_2(aq)$	-244.8	-232.34	175.3
Magnesium			
$Mg(s)$	0	0	32.68

© Edvantage Interactive 2017

Substance	Enthalpy of formation ΔH_f^0, kJ/mol	Free energy of formation ΔG_f^0, kJ/mol	Entropy S^0, J/(K·mol)
Mg(g)	147.70	113.10	148.65
Mg^{2+}(aq)	-466.85	-454.8	-138.1
MgO(s)	-601.70	-569.43	26.94
$MgCO_3$(s)	-1095.8	-1012.1	65.7
$MgBr_2$(s)	-524.3	-503.8	117.2
Mercury			
Hg(l)	0	0	76.02
Hg(g)	61.32	31.82	174.96
HgO(s)	-90.83	-58.54	70.29
Hg_2Cl_2(s)	-265.22	-210.75	192.5
Nitrogen			
N_2(g)	0	0	191.61
NO(g)	90.25	86.55	210.76
N_2O(g)	82.05	104.20	219.85
NO_2(g)	33.18	51.31	240.06
N_2O_4(g)	9.16	97.89	304.29
HNO_3(l)	-174.10	-80.71	155.60
HNO_3(aq)	-207.36	-111.22	146.4
NO_3^-(aq)	-205.0	-108.74	146.4
NH_3(g)	-46.11	-16.45	192.45
NH_3(aq)	-80.29	-26.50	111.3
NH_4^+(aq)	-132.51	-79.31	113.4
NH_2OH(s)	-114.2	---	---
HN_3(g)	294.1	328.1	238.97
N_2H_4(l)	50.63	149.34	121.21
NH_4NO_3(s)	-365.56	-183.87	151.08
NH_4Cl(s)	-314.43	-202.87	94.6
NH_4ClO_4(s)	-295.31	-88.75	186.2
Oxygen			
O_2(g)	0	0	205.14
O_3(g)	142.7	163.2	238.93
OH^-(aq)	-229.99	-157.24	-10.75
Phosphorus			
P(s, white)	0	0	41.09
P_4(g)	58.91	24.44	279.98
PH_3(g)	5.4	13.4	210.23
P_4O_{10}(s)	-2984.0	-2697.0	228.86
H_3PO_3(aq)	-964.0	---	---
H_3PO_4(l)	-1266.9	-1111.69	---

Table A8-Inorganic *Thermodynamic data at 25°C for assorted inorganic substances (continued).*

Substance	Enthalpy of formation ΔH_f^0, kJ/mol	Free energy of formation ΔG_f^0, kJ/mol	Entropy S^0, J/(K·mol)
$H_3PO_4(aq)$	-277.4	-1018.7	---
$PCl_3(l)$	-319.7	-272.3	217.18
$PCl_3(g)$	-287.0	-267.8	311.78
$PCl_5(g)$	-374.9	-305.0	364.6
$PCl_5(s)$	-443.5	---	---
Potassium			
$K(s)$	0	0	64.18
$K(g)$	89.24	60.59	160.34
$K^+(aq)$	-252.38	-283.27	102.5
$KOH(s)$	-424.76	-379.08	78.9
$KOH(aq)$	-482.37	-440.50	91.6
$KF(s)$	-567.27	-537.75	66.57
$KCl(s)$	-436.75	-409.14	82.59
$KBr(s)$	-393.80	-380.66	95.90
$KI(s)$	-327.90	-324.89	106.32
$KClO_3(s)$	-397.73	-296.25	143.1
$KClO_4(s)$	-432.75	-303.09	151.0
$K_2S(s)$	-380.7	-364.0	105
$K_2S(aq)$	-471.5	-480.7	190.4
Silicon			
$Si(s)$	0	0	18.83
$SiO_2(s, \alpha)$	-910.94	-856.64	41.84
Silver			
$Ag(s)$	0	0	42.55
$Ag^+(aq)$	105.58	77.11	72.68
$Ag_2O(s)$	-31.05	-11.20	121.3
$AgBr(s)$	-100.37	-96.90	107.1
$AgBr(aq)$	-15.98	-26.86	155.2
$AgCl(s)$	-127.7	-109.79	96.2
$AgCl(aq)$	-61.58	-54.12	129.3
$AgI(s)$	-61.84	-66.19	115.5
$AgI(aq)$	50.38	25.52	184.1
$AgNO_3(s)$	-124.39	-33.41	140.92
Sodium			
$Na(s)$	0	0	51.21
$Na(g)$	107.32	76.76	153.71
$Na^+(aq)$	-240.12	-261.91	59.0
$NaOH(s)$	-425.61	-379.49	64.46
$NaOH(aq)$	-470.11	-419.15	48.1

© Edvantage Interactive 2017

Substance	Enthalpy of formation ΔH_f^0, kJ/mol	Free energy of formation ΔG_f^0, kJ/mol	Entropy S^0, J/(K·mol)
NaCl(s)	-411.15	-384.12	72.13
NaBr(s)	-361.06	-348.98	86.82
NaI(s)	-287.78	-286.06	98.53
Sulfur			
S(s, rhombic)	0	0	31.80
S(s, monoclinic)	0.33	0.1	32.6
S^{2-}(aq)	33.1	85.8	-14.6
SO_2(g)	-296.83	-300.19	248.22
SO_3(g)	-395.72	-371.06	256.76
H_2SO_4(l)	-813.99	-690.00	156.90
H_2SO_4(aq)	-909.27	-744.53	20.1
SO_4^{2-}(aq)	-909.27	-744.53	20.1
H_2S(g)	-20.63	-33.56	205.79
H_2S(aq)	-39.7	-27.83	121
SF_6(g)	-1209	-1105.3	291.82
Tin			
Sn(s, white)	0	0	51.55
Sn(s, gray)	-2.09	0.13	44.14
SnO(s)	-285.8	-256.9	56.5
SnO_2(s)	-580.7	-519.6	52.3
Zinc			
Zn(s)	0	0	41.63
Zn^{2+}(aq)	-153.89	-147.06	-112.1
ZnO(s)	-348.28	-318.30	43.64

Table A8-Organic *Thermodynamic data at 25°C for assorted organic substances.*

Substance	Enthalpy of combustion ΔH_c^0, kJ/mol	Enthalpy of formation ΔH_f^0, kJ/mol	Free energy of formation ΔG_f^0, kJ/mol	Entropy S^0, J/(K·mol)
Hydrocarbons				
$CH_4(g)$, methane	-890	-74.81	-50.72	186.26
$C_2H_2(g)$, acethylene	-1300	226.73	209.20	200.94
$C_2H_4(g)$, ethylene	-1411	52.26	68.15	219.56
$C_2H_6(g)$, ethane	-1560	-84.68	-32.82	229.60
$C_3H_6(g)$, propylene	-2058	20.42	62.78	266.6
$C_3H_6(g)$, cyclopropane	-2091	53.30	104.45	237.4
$C_3H_8(g)$, propane	-2220	-103.85	-23.49	270.2
$C_4H_{10}(g)$, butane	-2878	-126.15	-17.03	310.1
$C_5H_{12}(g)$, pentane	-3537	-146.44	-8.20	349
$C_6H_6(l)$, benzene	-3268	49.0	124.3	173.3
$C_6H_6(g)$	-3302	---	---	---
$C_7H_8(l)$, toluene	-3910	12.0	113.8	221.0
$C_7H_8(g)$	-3953	---	---	---
$C_6H_{12}(l)$, cyclohexane	-3920	-156.4	26.7	204.4
$C_6H_{12}(g)$	-3953	---	---	---
$C_8H_{18}(l)$, octane	-5471	-249.9	6.4	358
Alcohols, phenols				
$CH_3OH(l)$, methanol	-726	-238.86	-166.27	126.8
$CH_3OH(g)$	-764	-200.66	-161.96	239.81
$C_2H_5OH(l)$, ethanol	-1368	-277.69	-174.78	160.7
$C_2H_5OH(g)$	-1409	-235.10	-168.49	282.70
$C_6H_5OH(s)$, phenol	-3054	-164.6	-50.42	144.0

© Edvantage Interactive 2017

Table A8-Inorganic *Thermodynamic data at 25°C for assorted organic substances (continued).*

Substance	Enthalpy of combustion ΔH_c^0, kJ/mol	Enthalpy of formation ΔH_f^0, kJ/mol	Free energy of formation ΔG_f^0, kJ/mol	Entropy S^0, J/(K·mol)
Aldehydes, ketones				
HCHO (g), *formaldehyde*	-571	-108.57	-102.53	218.77
CH_3CHO (l), *acetaldehyde*	-1166	-192.30	-128.12	160.2
CH_3CHO (g)	-1192	-166.19	-128.86	250.3
CH_3COCH_3 (l), *acetone*	-1790	-248.1	-155.4	200
Carboxylic acids				
HCOOH (l), *formic acid*	-255	-424.72	-361.35	128.95
CH_3COOH (l), *acetic acid*	-875	-484.5	-389.9	159.8
CH_3COOH (aq)	---	-485.76	-396.46	86.6
$(COOH)_2$ (s), *oxalic acid*	-254	-827.2	-697.9	120
C_6H_5COOH (s), *benzoic acid*	-3227	-385.1	-245.3	167.6
Sugars				
$C_6H_{12}O_6$ (s), *glucose*	-2808	-1268	-910	212
$C_6H_{12}O_6$ (aq)	---	---	-917	---
$C_6H_{12}O_6$ (s), *fructose*	-2810	-1266	---	---
$C_{12}H_{22}O_{11}$ (s), *sucrose*	-5645	-2222	-1545	360
Nitrogen compounds				
$CO(NH_2)_2$ (s), *urea*	-632	-333.51	-197.33	104.60
$C_6H_5NH_2$ (l), *aniline*	-3395	31.6	149.1	191.3
NH_2CH_2COOH(s), *glycine*	-969	-532.9	-373.4	103.51
CH_3NH_2 (g), *methylamine*	-1085	-22.97	32.16	243.41

Answer Key

Chapter 1

Chapter 2

Chapter 3

Chapter 4

Chapter 5

Chapter 6

Chapter 7

Chapter 8

Chapter 9

24044092R00315

Made in the USA
Columbia, SC
21 August 2018